Student Solutions Manual

Karen Schwitters/Jesse Turner

INTRODUCTORY and INTERMEDIATE ALGEBRA

K. Elayn Martin-Gay

Pearson Education
PRENTICE HALL Upper Saddle River, NJ 07458

Contents

Printed in the United States of America

10 9 8 7

ISBN 0-13-380908-X

Prentice-Hall International (UK) Limited, *London*
Prentice-Hall of Australia Pty. Limited, *Sydney*
Prentice-Hall Canada, Inc., *Toronto*
Prentice-Hall Hispanoamericana, S.A., *Mexico*
Prentice-Hall of India Private Limited, *New Delhi*
Prentice-Hall of Japan, Inc., *Tokyo*
Simon & Schuster Asia Pte. Ltd., *Singapore*
Editora Prentice-Hall do Brasil, Ltda., *Rio de Janeiro*

Exercise Set 1.1

1. $4 < 10$
3. $7 > 3$
5. $18 = 18$
7. $0 < 7$
9. $11 \leq 11$ True
11. $10 > 11$ False
13. $3 + 8 \geq 3(8)$ False
15. $7 > 0$ True
17. $8 < 12$
19. $5 \geq 4$
21. $2 + 3 < 6$
23. $\frac{10}{2} = 5$
25. $4 \leq (3)(5)$
27. $5 < 7$
29. $7 > 5$
31. $3 \bullet 8 < 25$
33. $15 - 9 = 6$
35. $15 - 9 > 5$
37. $5 - 0 = 5$ True
39. $5(0) = 5$ False
41. $0 \leq 7$ True
43. $25 \leq 25$
45. $6 > 0$
47. $b \geq a$
49. $y < x$
51. $4 > 2.5$
53. $8 \leq 12$
55. $5 \leq 6$
57. $5 + 6 > 10$
59. $(3)(5) > 12$
61. $\frac{12}{6} > 1$
63. $3 > 2$
65. $4 = 4 + 0$
67. $a \leq 5$
69. $c < d$
71. $150 > 57$
73. $32 < 212$
75. $30 \leq 45$
77. 90
79. Grades are increasing.

Exercise Set 1.2

1. 0; whole, integers, rational, real
3. -2; integers, rational, real
5. 6; natural, whole, integers, rational, real
7. $\frac{2}{3}$; rational, real
9. $10 < 20$
11. $0 > -2$
13. $0.01 = 0.01$
15. $-1.5 < 2.8$
17. $|20| = 20$
19. $-7 > -12$
21. $-500 < |-50|$

23. -9; integers, rational, real

25. π; irrational, real

27. 2; natural, whole, integers, rational, real

29. $5 < 6$ True

31. $-5 < -6$ False

33. $|-5| < |-6|$ True

35. $|-5| \geq |5|$ True

37. $-3 > 2$ False

39. $|8| = |-8|$ True

41. $|0| > |-4|$ False

43. $-10 > -100$

45. $32 > 5.2$

47. $\frac{18}{3} < \frac{24}{3}$

49. $-51 < -50$

51. $|-5| > -4$

53. $|-1| = |1|$

55. False

57. True

59. False

61. False

63. $0 > -26.7$

65. The Sun

67. The Sun

69. Tuesday

71. 7°

Exercise Set 1.3

1. $\frac{3}{8}$

3. $\frac{5}{7}$

5. $20 = 2 \bullet 2 \bullet 5$

7. $75 = 3 \bullet 5 \bullet 5$

9. $45 = 3 \bullet 3 \bullet 5$

11. $\frac{2}{4} = \frac{2}{2 \bullet 2} = \frac{1}{2}$

13. $\frac{10}{15} = \frac{2 \bullet 5}{3 \bullet 5} = \frac{2}{3}$

15. $\frac{3}{7}$ is in lowest terms.

17. $\frac{18}{30} = \frac{2 \bullet 3 \bullet 3}{2 \bullet 3 \bullet 5} = \frac{3}{5}$

19. $\frac{1}{2} \bullet \frac{3}{4} = \frac{3}{8}$

21. $\frac{2}{3} \bullet \frac{3}{4} = \frac{2 \bullet 3}{3 \bullet 2 \bullet 2} = \frac{1}{2}$

23. $\frac{1}{2} \div \frac{7}{12} = \frac{1}{2} \bullet \frac{12}{7} = \frac{1 \bullet 2 \bullet 2 \bullet 3}{2 \bullet 7} = \frac{6}{7}$

25. $\frac{3}{4} \div \frac{1}{20} = \frac{3}{4} \bullet \frac{20}{1} = \frac{3 \bullet 2 \bullet 2 \bullet 5}{2 \bullet 2} = 15$

27. $\frac{7}{10} \bullet \frac{5}{21} = \frac{7 \bullet 5}{2 \bullet 5 \bullet 3 \bullet 7} = \frac{1}{6}$

29. $2\frac{7}{9} \bullet \frac{1}{3} = \frac{25}{9} \bullet \frac{1}{3} = \frac{5 \bullet 5 \bullet 1}{3 \bullet 3 \bullet 3} = \frac{25}{27}$

31. $\frac{4}{5} - \frac{1}{5} = \frac{4-1}{5} = \frac{3}{5}$

33. $\frac{4}{5} + \frac{1}{5} = \frac{4+1}{5} = \frac{5}{5} = 1$

35. $\frac{17}{21} - \frac{10}{21} = \frac{17-10}{21} = \frac{7}{21} = \frac{7}{7 \bullet 3} = \frac{1}{3}$

37. $\frac{23}{105} + \frac{4}{105} = \frac{23+4}{105} = \frac{27}{105} = \frac{3 \bullet 3 \bullet 3}{3 \bullet 5 \bullet 7} = \frac{9}{35}$

39. $\frac{7}{10} \bullet \frac{\boldsymbol{3}}{\boldsymbol{3}} = \frac{21}{30}$

41. $\frac{2}{9} \bullet \frac{\boldsymbol{2}}{\boldsymbol{2}} = \frac{4}{18}$

43. $\frac{4}{5} \bullet \frac{\boldsymbol{4}}{\boldsymbol{4}} = \frac{16}{20}$

45. $\frac{2}{3}+\frac{3}{7}$ LCD = 21

$\frac{2}{3}\bullet\frac{7}{7}=\frac{14}{21}$

$\frac{3}{7}\bullet\frac{3}{3}=\frac{9}{21}$

$\frac{14}{21}+\frac{9}{21}=\frac{14+9}{21}=\frac{23}{21}$

47. $\frac{13}{15}-\frac{1}{5}$ LCD = 15

$\frac{1}{5}\bullet\frac{3}{3}=\frac{3}{15}$

$\frac{13}{15}-\frac{3}{15}=\frac{10}{15}=\frac{2\bullet 5}{3\bullet 5}=\frac{2}{3}$

49. $\frac{5}{22}-\frac{5}{33}$ LCD = 66

$\frac{5}{22}\bullet\frac{3}{3}=\frac{15}{66}$

$\frac{5}{33}\bullet\frac{2}{2}=\frac{10}{66}$

$\frac{15}{66}-\frac{10}{66}=\frac{5}{66}$

51. $\frac{12}{5}-1$ LCD = 5

$1\bullet\frac{5}{5}=\frac{5}{5}$

$\frac{12}{5}-\frac{5}{5}=\frac{7}{5}$

53. $\frac{10}{21}+\frac{5}{21}=\frac{10+5}{21}=\frac{15}{21}$

$\frac{15}{21}=\frac{3\bullet 5}{3\bullet 7}=\frac{5}{7}$

55. $\frac{10}{3}-\frac{5}{21}$ LCD = 21

$\frac{10}{3}\bullet\frac{7}{7}=\frac{70}{21}$

$\frac{70}{21}-\frac{5}{21}=\frac{65}{21}$

57. $\frac{2}{3}\bullet\frac{3}{5}=\frac{2\bullet 3}{3\bullet 5}=\frac{2}{5}$

59. $\frac{3}{4}\div\frac{7}{12}=\frac{3}{4}\bullet\frac{12}{7}=\frac{3\bullet 2\bullet 2\bullet 3}{2\bullet 2\bullet 7}=\frac{9}{7}$

61. $\frac{5}{12}+\frac{4}{12}=\frac{4+5}{12}=\frac{9}{12}=\frac{3\bullet 3}{2\bullet 2\bullet 3}=\frac{3}{4}$

63. $5+\frac{2}{3}$ LCD = 3

$\frac{5}{1}\bullet\frac{3}{3}=\frac{15}{3}$

$\frac{15}{3}+\frac{2}{3}=\frac{17}{3}$

65. $\frac{7}{8}\div 3\frac{1}{4}=\frac{7}{8}\div\frac{13}{4}=$

$\frac{7}{8}\bullet\frac{4}{13}=\frac{7\bullet 2\bullet 2}{2\bullet 2\bullet 2\bullet 13}=\frac{7}{26}$

67. $\frac{7}{18}\div\frac{14}{36}=\frac{7}{18}\bullet\frac{36}{14}=$

$\frac{7\bullet 2\bullet 2\bullet 3\bullet 3}{2\bullet 3\bullet 3\bullet 2\bullet 7}=1$

69. $\frac{23}{105}-\frac{2}{105}=\frac{23-2}{105}=\frac{21}{105}$

$\frac{21}{105}=\frac{3\bullet 7}{3\bullet 5\bullet 7}=\frac{1}{5}$

71. $1\frac{1}{2}+3\frac{2}{3}=\frac{3}{2}+\frac{11}{3}$ LCD = 6

$\frac{3}{2}\bullet\frac{3}{3}=\frac{9}{6}$

$\frac{11}{3}\bullet\frac{2}{2}=\frac{22}{6}$

$\frac{9}{6}+\frac{22}{6}=\frac{31}{6}$

73. $\frac{2}{3}-\frac{5}{9}+\frac{5}{6}$ LCD = 18

$\frac{2}{3}\bullet\frac{6}{6}=\frac{12}{18}$

$\frac{5}{9}\bullet\frac{2}{2}=\frac{10}{18}$

$\frac{5}{6}\bullet\frac{3}{3}=\frac{15}{18}$

$\frac{12}{18}-\frac{10}{18}+\frac{15}{18}=\frac{12-10+15}{18}=\frac{17}{18}$

75. $1-\left(\frac{3}{10}+\frac{5}{10}\right)$

$1-\frac{8}{10}$

$\frac{2}{10}=\frac{1}{5}$

77. $1-\left(\frac{1}{4}+\frac{3}{8}\right)$

$1-\left(\frac{2}{8}+\frac{3}{8}\right)$

$1-\frac{5}{8}$

$\frac{3}{8}$

79. $20-11\frac{1}{2}$

$19\frac{2}{2} - 11\frac{1}{2}$

$8\frac{1}{2}$

81. $100\% - (11\% + 14\% + 15\%)$

$100\% - 40\%$

60%

83. $\frac{3}{4} + 2 + 1\frac{1}{2}$

$\frac{3}{4} + 2 + 1\frac{2}{4}$

$3\frac{5}{4}$

$4\frac{1}{4}$ inches

Exercise Set 1.4

1. $3^5 = 3 \bullet 3 \bullet 3 \bullet 3 \bullet 3 = 243$

3. $3^3 = 3 \bullet 3 \bullet 3 = 27$

5. $1^5 = 1 \bullet 1 \bullet 1 \bullet 1 \bullet 1 = 1$

7. $5^1 = 5$

9. $\left(\frac{1}{5}\right)^3 = \frac{1}{5} \bullet \frac{1}{5} \bullet \frac{1}{5} = \frac{1}{125}$

11. $\left(\frac{2}{3}\right)^4 = \frac{2}{3} \bullet \frac{2}{3} \bullet \frac{2}{3} \bullet \frac{2}{3} = \frac{16}{81}$

13. $\sqrt{49}$

7

15. $\sqrt{\frac{1}{9}}$

$\frac{1}{3}$

17. $\sqrt[3]{64}$

4

19. $\sqrt[4]{81}$

3

21. $5 + 6 \bullet 2$

Multiply $5 + 12$

Add 17

23. $4 \bullet 8 - 6 \bullet 2$

Multiply $32 - 12$

Subtract 20

25. $2(8 - 3)$

Parentheses $2(5)$

Multiply 10

27. $2 + (5 - 2) + 4^2$

Parentheses $2 + 3 + 4^2$

Exponent $2 + 3 + 16$

Add 21

29. $2 \bullet 5^2$

Exponent $2 \bullet 25$

Multiply 50

31. $\frac{3}{4} \bullet \frac{1}{2} + \frac{2}{3}$

Multiply $\frac{3}{8} + \frac{2}{3}$

Add LCD=24 $\frac{3}{8} \bullet \frac{\mathbf{3}}{\mathbf{3}} = \frac{9}{24}$

$\frac{2}{3} \bullet \frac{\mathbf{8}}{\mathbf{8}} = \frac{16}{24}$

$\frac{9}{24} + \frac{16}{24} = \frac{25}{24}$

33. $\frac{|6 - 2| + 3}{8 + 2 \bullet 5}$

Simplify inside absolute value $\frac{|4| + 3}{8 + 2 \bullet 5}$

Absolute Value $\frac{4 + 3}{8 + 2 \bullet 5}$

Multiply $\frac{4 + 3}{8 + 10}$

Add $\frac{7}{18}$

35. $\frac{3(2 + 5)}{6 + 2}$

Parentheses $\frac{3(7)}{6 + 2}$

Multiply $\frac{21}{6 + 2}$

Add $\frac{21}{8}$

37. $\frac{4 \bullet 3 + 2}{4 + 3 \bullet 2}$

Multiply $\frac{12 + 2}{4 + 6}$

Add $\frac{14}{10}$

Reduce $\frac{14}{10}=\frac{2\bullet 7}{2\bullet 5}=\frac{7}{5}$

39. $4[5(2+4)-8]$

Parentheses $4[5(6)-8]$

Multiply inside square brackets $4[30-8]$

Subtract $4[22]$

Multiply 88

41. $|-18|-|-7|$

$18-7$

11

43. $2\bullet 5^2$

$2\bullet 25$

50

45. $45-6^2\div 3^2+\sqrt{1}$

$45-36\div 9+1$

$45-4+1$

$41+1$

42

47. $\frac{|-6|^2}{|-8|-2^2}$

$\frac{6^2}{8-2^2}$

$\frac{36}{8-4}$

$\frac{36}{4}$

9

49. $6+3(7-2)$

Parentheses $6+3(5)$

Multiply $6+15$

Add 21

51. $3+(7-3)+3^2$

Parentheses $3+4+3^2$

Exponent $3+4+9$

Add 16

53. $\frac{8-5}{24-20}$

Subtract $\frac{3}{4}$

55. $2[5+2(8-3)]$

Parentheses $2[5+2(5)]$

Multiply inside square brackets $2[5+10]$

Add inside square brackets $2[15]$

Multiply 30

57. $(5\bullet 3)^2$

Parentheses $(15)^2$

Exponent 225

59. $\sqrt[3]{8}+24\div 3\bullet 2-6$

Root $2+24\div 3\bullet 2-6$

Divide $2+8\bullet 2-6$

Multiply $2+16-6$

Add $18-6$

Subtract 12

61. $\frac{3+2\bullet 3^2}{3+2^2}$

Exponents $\frac{3+2\bullet 9}{3+4}$

Multiply $\frac{3+18}{3+4}$

Add $\frac{21}{7}$

Reduce $\frac{21}{7}=\frac{3\bullet 7}{7}=3$

63. $9+16\div 8\bullet 2-4$

Divide $9+2\bullet 2-4$

Multiply $9+4-4$

Add $13-4$

Subtract 9

65. $\frac{3}{4}\bullet\frac{1}{2}+\frac{1}{3}$

Multiply $\frac{3}{8}+\frac{1}{3}$

Add LCD $=24$ $\frac{3}{8}\bullet\boldsymbol{\frac{3}{3}}=\frac{9}{24}$

$\frac{1}{3}\bullet\boldsymbol{\frac{8}{8}}=\frac{8}{24}$

$\frac{9}{24}+\frac{8}{24}=\frac{17}{24}$

67. $\dfrac{3+6(8-5)}{4^2+2}$

Parentheses $\dfrac{3+6(3)}{4^2+2}$

Exponents $\dfrac{3+6(3)}{16+2}$

Multiply $\dfrac{3+18}{16+2}$

Add $\dfrac{21}{18}$

Reduce $\dfrac{21}{18}=\dfrac{3\bullet 7}{2\bullet 3\bullet 3}=\dfrac{7}{6}$

69. $6(12\div 4+2)-3(10\div 2+3)$

Divide inside parentheses $6(3+2)-3(5+3)$

Add inside parentheses $6(5)-3(8)$

Multiply $30-24$

Subtract 6

71. $\dfrac{6+|8-2|+3^2}{18-3}$

Simplify inside absolute value $\dfrac{6+|6|+3^2}{18-3}$

Absolute Value $\dfrac{6+6+3^2}{18-3}$

Exponent $\dfrac{6+6+9}{18-3}$

Add and Subtract $\dfrac{21}{15}$

Reduce $\dfrac{21}{15}=\dfrac{3\bullet 7}{3\bullet 5}=\dfrac{7}{5}$

73. $\dfrac{3\bullet 6+3^2}{12\bullet 5-5}$

Exponent $\dfrac{3\bullet 6+9}{12\bullet 5-5}$

Multiply $\dfrac{18+9}{60-5}$

Add and Subtract $\dfrac{27}{55}$

75. $2.6[1.3(4+3)-8]$

Parentheses $2.6[1.3(7)-8]$

Multiply inside square brackets $2.6[9.1-8]$

Subtract inside square brackets $2.6[1.1]$

Multiply 2.86

77. $\sqrt{\frac{25}{9}}-\sqrt{\frac{1}{9}}$

$\frac{5}{3}-\frac{1}{3}$

$\frac{4}{3}$

$1\frac{1}{3}$

79. $\sqrt[3]{27}+\sqrt{64}$

$3+8$

11

81. $(7+3)(35-2)$

$(10)(33)$

330

83. $2\bullet\sqrt{121}-100\div 20$

$2\bullet 11-100\div 20$

$22-5$

17

85. $\dfrac{6+2(1.3)^2}{0.55+3(0.65)}$

$\dfrac{6+2(1.69)}{0.55+3(0.65)}$

$\dfrac{6+3.38}{0.55+1.95}$

$\dfrac{9.38}{2.5}$

3.752

87. $\sqrt{3^2+4^2}$

$\sqrt{9+16}$

$\sqrt{25}$

5

Exercise Set 1.5

1. $3x-2$

$3(1)-2$

$3-2$

1

3. $|2x+3y|$

$|2(1)+3(3)|$

$|2+9|$

$|11|$

11

5. $xy+z$

$(1)(3)+5$

$3+5$

8

7. x^2+y^2

$(1)^2+(3)^2$

$1+9$

10

9. $|10y-3z|$

$|10(3)-3(5)|$

$|30-15|$

$|15|$

15

11. $\frac{1}{2}x$

13. $\frac{x}{9}$

15. $8x$

17. $2x+7=3x$

$2(6)+7\stackrel{?}{=}3(6)$

$12+7\stackrel{?}{=}18$

$19\neq 18$

6 is not a solution.

19. $4x+2=x+8$

$4(2)+2\stackrel{?}{=}2+8$

$8+2\stackrel{?}{=}2+8$

$10=10$

2 is a solution.

21. $x^2+2x-35=0$

$(5)^2+2(5)-35\stackrel{?}{=}0$

$25+10-35\stackrel{?}{=}0$

$0=0$

5 is a solution.

23. $2x=17$

25. $x-7=0$

27. $8+2x=42$

29. $|4z-2y|$

$|4(3)-2(6)|$

$|12-12|$

$|0|$

0

31. $\frac{6z}{5x}$

$\frac{6(3)}{5(2)}$

$\frac{18}{10}=\frac{2\bullet 3\bullet 3}{2\bullet 5}=\frac{9}{5}$

33. $\frac{9}{z}+\frac{4z}{y}$

$\frac{9}{3}+\frac{4(3)}{6}$

$3+\frac{12}{6}$

$3+2$

5

35. $y+4z^2$

$6+4(3)^2$

$6+4(9)$

$6+36$

42

37. $z+xy$

$3+(2)(6)$

$3+12$

15

39. $\frac{y}{\sqrt{z}}+8x$

$\frac{8}{\sqrt{4}}+8(12)$

$\frac{8}{2}+96$

$4+96$

100

41. $7y+y^2$

$7(8)+(8)^2$

$56+64$

120

43. y^2-3x+y

$(8)^2-3(12)+8$

$64-36+8$

$28+8$

36

45. $\dfrac{3x-\sqrt[3]{y}}{4z+x}$

$\dfrac{3(12)-\sqrt[3]{8}}{4(4)+12}$

$\dfrac{36-2}{16+12}$

$\dfrac{34}{28}=\dfrac{17}{14}$

47. $\dfrac{y^2+x}{x^2+3y}$

$\dfrac{(8)^2+12}{(12)^2+3(8)}$

$\dfrac{64+12}{144+24}$

$\dfrac{76}{168}=\dfrac{2\bullet 2\bullet 19}{2\bullet 2\bullet 2\bullet 3\bullet 7}=\dfrac{19}{42}$

49. $3x-10=8$

$3(6)-10\stackrel{?}{=}8$

$18-10\stackrel{?}{=}8$

$8=8$

6 is a solution.

51. $x+6=x+6$

$10+6\stackrel{?}{=}10+6$

$16=16$

10 is a solution.

53. $4=1-x$

$4\stackrel{?}{=}1-1$

$4\neq 0$

1 is not a solution.

55. Let $x=$ number
$7(x+19)$

57. Let $x=$ number
$4x-x=75.6$

59. Let $x=$ number
$12-x$

61. Let $x=$ number

$\frac{3}{4}(x+1)=9$

63. Let $x=$ number

$1\frac{11}{12}+3x=x+2$

65. $P=a+b+c$

$P=\frac{1}{7}+\frac{2}{7}+\frac{5}{14}$

$P=\frac{1}{7}\bullet\frac{2}{2}+\frac{2}{7}\bullet\frac{2}{2}+\frac{5}{14}$

$P=\frac{2}{14}+\frac{4}{14}+\frac{5}{14}$

$P=\frac{11}{14}$ yd.

67. $A=\dfrac{(B+b)h}{2}$

$A=\dfrac{(15+7)5}{2}$

$A=\dfrac{(22)(5)}{2}$

$A=\dfrac{110}{2}=55$ sq. in.

69. $r=\frac{d}{t}$

$r=\dfrac{432 \text{ miles}}{8.5 \text{ hours}}$

$r=50.8235$ mph

rounded off
$r=51$ mph

Exercise Set 1.6

1. $6+3$

   9

3. $-6+(-8)$

   -14

5. $-8+(-7)$

   -15

7. $-52+36$

   -16

9. $6+(-4)+9$

   $2+9$

   11

11. $2\frac{3}{4}+\left(-\frac{1}{8}\right)$

    $\frac{11}{4}+\left(-\frac{1}{8}\right)$

    $\frac{11}{4}\bullet\frac{2}{2}+\left(-\frac{1}{8}\right)$

    $\frac{22}{8}+\left(-\frac{1}{8}\right)$

    $\frac{21}{8}=2\frac{5}{8}$

13. 6

    The additive inverse is -6.

15. -2

    The additive inverse is 2.

17. 0

    The additive inverse is 0.

19. $|-6|$

    $|-6|=6$

    The additive inverse is -6.

21. $-|-2|$

    $-(+2)$ The absolute value of -2 is 2.

    -2

23. $-|0|$

    -0 The absolute value of 0 is 0.

    0

25. $-\left|-\frac{2}{3}\right|$

    $-\left(+\frac{2}{3}\right)$ The absolute value of $-\frac{2}{3}$ is $\frac{2}{3}$.

    $-\frac{2}{3}$

27. $-6-4$

    $-6+(-4)$

    -10

29. $4-9$

    $4+(-9)$

    -5

31. $16-(-3)$

    $16+(+3)$

    19

33. $18-33$

    $18+(-33)$

    -15

35. $-16-18$

    $-16+(-18)$

    -34

37. $-2-3$

    $-2+(-3)$

    -5

39. $-6-(2-11)$

    $-6-[2+(-11)]$

    $-6-[-9]$

    $-6+(+9)$

    3

41. $3^3-8\bullet9$

    $27-72$

    $27+(-72)$

    -45

43. $2-3(8-6)$

$2-3[8+(-6)]$

$2-3[2]$

$2-6$

$2+(-6)$

-4

45. $|-3|+2^2+[-4-(-6)]$

$3+2^2+[-4+(+6)]$

$3+2^2+[2]$

$3+4+2$

9

47. $x-y$

$-6-(-3)$

$-6+(+3)$

-3

49. $x+t-12$

$-6+(2)-12$

$-6+2-12$

$-4-12$

$-4+(-12)$

-16

51. $\frac{x-(-12)}{y+6}$

$\frac{-6-(-12)}{(-3)+6}$

$\frac{-6+(+12)}{-3+6}$

$\frac{6}{3}=2$

53. $x-t^2$

$-6-(2)^2$

$-6-(4)$

$-6+(-4)$

-10

55. $\frac{4t-y}{3t}$

$\frac{4(2)-(-3)}{3(2)}$

$\frac{8-(-3)}{6}$

$\frac{8+(+3)}{6}$

$\frac{11}{6}$

57. $-56^\circ-(44^\circ)$

$-56^\circ+(-44^\circ)$

-100°

The negative sign indicates a drop in temperature.

Therefore the temperature fell 100°.

59. $15-24$

-9

61. $-6-5$

$-6+(-5)$

-11

63. $7-(-4)$

$7+(+4)$

11

65. $-6-(-11)$

$-6+(+11)$

5

67. $-\frac{3}{5}-\frac{5}{6}$

$-\frac{18}{30}-\frac{25}{30}=-\frac{43}{30}$

69. $-6.1-(-5.3)=-0.8$

71. $6-11+(-8)$

$-5+(-8)=-13$

73. $-6-14-(-3)$

$-6+(-14)+(3)$

$-20+3=-17$

75. $-13+27=14$

77. $15-(-33)$

$15+33=48$

79. $-36-(-51)$

$-36+51=15$

81. $-\frac{1}{6}-\left(-\frac{3}{4}\right)$

$-\frac{1}{6}+\frac{3}{4}$

$-\frac{2}{12}+\frac{9}{12}=\frac{7}{12}$

83. $8.3-11.2=-2.9$

85. $3-(6[3-(-2)]-8)$

$3-(6[3+2]-8)$

$3-(6[5]-8)$

$3-(30-8)$

$3-22=-19$

87. $3-6\bullet 4^2$

$3-6\bullet 16$

$3-96=-93$

89. $(3-6)\bullet 4^2$

$(-3)\bullet 16=-48$

91. $3-(6\bullet 4)^2$

$3-(24)^2$

$3-576=-573$

93. $7-8=-1$

95. $-8-15=-23$

97. $x-y$

$-5-4$

-9

99. $|x|+2t-8y$

$|-5|+2(10)-8(4)$

$5+20-32$

$25-32=-7$

101. $\frac{9-x}{y+6}$

$\frac{9-(-5)}{4+6}$

$\frac{14}{10}=\frac{7}{5}$

103. y^2+x

$4^2+(-5)$

$16+(-5)=11$

105.

Day	Daily increase or decrease
Monday	$3-(-4)=7^\circ$
Tuesday	$7-3=4^\circ$
Wednesday	$-2-7=-9^\circ$
Thursday	$1-(-2)=3^\circ$
Friday	$-5-1=-6^\circ$
Saturday	$1-(-5)=6^\circ$

107. Wednesday

109. $x-10=-7$

$3-10\stackrel{?}{=}-7$

$-7=-7$

3 is a solution.

111. $-x+6=-x-1$

$-(-10)+6\stackrel{?}{=}-(-10)-1$

$10+6\stackrel{?}{=}10-1$

$16\neq 9$

-10 is not a solution.

113. $4=1-x$

$4\stackrel{?}{=}1-5$

$4\neq -4$

5 is not a solution.

115. $-250+120-178$

-308 feet

117. $-512+658$

146 feet

119. $-1\frac{5}{8}+\left(-2\frac{1}{2}\right)$

$-1\frac{5}{8}+\left(-2\frac{4}{8}\right)$

$-3\frac{9}{8}$

$-4\frac{1}{8}$

Exercise Set 1.7

1. $(-3)(+4)$

-12

3. $-6(-7)$

42

5. $(-2)(-5)(0)$

$10(0)$

0

7. $2(-9)$

-18

9. $\left(-\frac{3}{4}\right)\left(\frac{8}{9}\right)$

$-\frac{\overset{1}{\cancel{3}}}{\underset{1}{\cancel{2}}\bullet\underset{1}{\cancel{2}}}\bullet\frac{\overset{1}{\cancel{2}}\bullet\overset{1}{\cancel{2}}\bullet 2}{\underset{1}{\cancel{3}}\bullet 3}$

$-\frac{2}{3}$

11. $\left(-1\frac{1}{5}\right)\left(-1\frac{2}{3}\right)$

$-\frac{6}{5}\bullet-\frac{5}{3}$

$-\frac{2\bullet\overset{1}{\cancel{3}}}{\underset{1}{\cancel{5}}}\bullet-\frac{\overset{1}{\cancel{5}}}{\underset{1}{\cancel{3}}}$

$+2$

13. $(-1)(2)(-3)(-5)$

$(-2)(-3)(-5)$

$(+6)(-5)$

-30

15. $(2)(-1)(-3)(5)(3)$

$(-2)(-3)(5)(3)$

$(+6)(5)(3)$

$(30)(3)$

90

17. $(-4)^2$

$(-4)^2=(-4)(-4)$

16

19. $\frac{18}{-2}$

-9

21. $\frac{-12}{-4}$

3

23. $\frac{-45}{-9}$

5

25. $\frac{0}{-3}=0$

27. $-\frac{3}{0}$

undefined – division by zero is not defined

29. $\frac{-6^2+4}{-2}$

$\frac{-(6)^2+4}{-2}$

$\frac{-(36)+4}{-2}$

$\frac{-36+4}{-2}$

$\frac{-32}{-2}$

16

31. $\frac{8+(-4)^2}{4-12}$

$\frac{8+(16)}{4+(-12)}$

$\frac{24}{-8}$

-3

33. $\frac{22+(3)(-2)}{-5-2}$

$\frac{22+(-6)}{-5+(-2)}$

$\frac{16}{-7}=-\frac{16}{7}$

35. $3x+2y$

$3(-5)+2(-3)$

$-15+(-6)$

-21

37. $2x^2-y^2$

$2(-5)^2-(-3)^2$

$2(25)-(9)$

$50+(-9)$

41

39. x^3+3y

$(-5)^3+3(-3)$

$-125+(-9)$

-134

41. $\frac{2x-5}{y-2}$

$\frac{2(-5)-5}{-3-2}$

$\frac{-10+(-5)}{-3-2}$

$\frac{-15}{-5}$

3

43. $\frac{6-y}{x-4}$

$\frac{6-(-3)}{-5-4}$

$\frac{6+(+3)}{-5+(-4)}$

$\frac{9}{-9}$

-1

45. $(-6)(-2)$

12

47. $(-7)(2)$

-14

49. $\frac{18}{-3}$

-6

51. $\frac{-6}{0}$

undefined – division by zero is not defined

53. $-\frac{15}{-3}$

$-(-5)$

5

55. $\frac{0}{-7}$

0

57. $(-6)(3)(-2)(-1)$

$(-18)(-2)(-1)$

$(36)(-1)$

-36

59. $(-5)^3=(-5)(-5)(-5)$

-125

61. $(-4)^2=(-4)(-4)$

16

63. $-4^2=-(4)(4)$

$-(16)$

-16

65. $\frac{-3-5^2}{2(-7)}$

$\frac{-3-25}{-14}$

$\frac{-3+(-25)}{-14}$

$\frac{-28}{-14}$

2

67. $\frac{6-2(-3)}{4-3(-2)}$

$\frac{6-(-6)}{4-(-6)}$

$\frac{6+(+6)}{4+(+6)}$

$\frac{12}{10}=\frac{\overset{1}{\cancel{2}}\bullet 2\bullet 3}{\underset{1}{\cancel{2}}\bullet 5}=\frac{6}{5}$

69. $\frac{-3-2(-9)}{-15-3(-4)}$

$\frac{-3-(-18)}{-15-(-12)}$

$\frac{-3+(+18)}{-15+(+12)}$

$\frac{15}{-3}$

-5

71. $-3(2-8)$

$-3[2+(-8)]$

$-3[-6]$

18

73. $6(3-8)$

$6[3+(-8)]$

$6[-5]$

-30

75. $-3[(2-8)-(-6-8)]$

$-3[(2+(-8))-(-6+(-8))]$

$-3[(-6)-(-14)]$

$-3[-6+(+14)]$

$-3[8]$

-24

77. $\left(\frac{2}{5}\right)\left(-1\frac{1}{4}\right)$

$\left(\frac{2}{5}\right)\left(-\frac{5}{4}\right)$

$\frac{\overset{1}{\cancel{2}}}{\underset{1}{\cancel{5}}}\bullet -\frac{\overset{1}{\cancel{5}}}{\underset{1}{\cancel{2}}\bullet 2}$

$-\frac{1}{2}$

79. $-4\frac{1}{6}+\left(-\frac{1}{30}\right)$

$-\frac{25}{6}+\left(-\frac{1}{30}\right)$

$-\frac{25}{6}\bullet\frac{\mathbf{5}}{\mathbf{5}}+\left(-\frac{1}{30}\right)$

$-\frac{125}{30}+\left(-\frac{1}{30}\right)$

$-\frac{126}{30}=-4\frac{6}{30}=-4\frac{1}{5}$

81. $(1.82)(-4.6)$

-8.372

83. $-22.4\div(-1.6)$

14

85. $2x-3y$

$2(2)-3(-6)$

$4-(-18)$

$4+(+18)$

22

87. $2x^2+y$

$2(2)^2+(-6)$

$2(4)+(-6)$

$8+(-6)$

2

89. $\frac{xy}{-4}$

$\frac{2(-6)}{-4}$

$\frac{-12}{-4}$

3

91. $\frac{2x+8}{y+2}$

$\frac{2(2)+8}{-6+2}$

$\frac{4+8}{-6+2}$

$\frac{12}{-4}$

-3

93. $\frac{x-y}{3x+6}$

$\frac{2-(-6)}{3(2)+6}$

$\frac{2+(+6)}{6+6}$

$\frac{8}{12}=\frac{\cancel{2}\bullet\cancel{2}\bullet 2}{\cancel{2}\bullet\cancel{2}\bullet 3}=\frac{2}{3}$

95. $\frac{-15}{3}+(-2)$

$-5+(-2)$

-7

97. $2[-5+(-3)]$

$2[-8]$

-16

99. $-5x=-35$

$-5(7)\stackrel{?}{=}-35$

$-35=-35$

7 is a solution.

101. $\frac{x}{-10}=2$

$\frac{-20}{-10}\stackrel{?}{=}2$

$2=2$

-20 is a solution.

103. $-3x-5=-20$

$-3(5)-5\stackrel{?}{=}-20$

$-15-5\stackrel{?}{=}-20$

$-20=-20$

5 is a solution.

105. $\frac{(33.50-20)}{1.50}$

$\frac{13.50}{1.50}$

9

In 9 more trading days, (excluding Saturday and Sunday); so on Wednesday Oct. 6 the stock will be worth $20.00.

Exercise Set 1.8

1. $3\bullet 5=5\bullet 3$
commutative property of multiplication

3. $2+(8+5)=(2+8)+5$
associative property of addition

5. $9(3+7)=9(3)+9(7)$
distributive property

7. $3(6+x)$

$3(6)+3(x)$

$18+3x$

9. $-2(y-z)$

$-2(y)+(-2)(-z)$

$-2y+2z$

11. $-7(3y-5)$

$-7(3y)+(-7)(-5)$

$-21y+35$

13. 16
The additive inverse is -16.

15. -8
The additive inverse is 8.

17. $|-9|=9$
The additive inverse is -9.

19. $\frac{2}{3}$
The multiplicative inverse is $\frac{3}{2}$.

21. $-\frac{5}{6}$
The multiplicative inverse is $-\frac{6}{5}$.

23. 6
The multiplicative inverse is $\frac{1}{6}$.

25. -2
The multiplicative inverse is $-\frac{1}{2}$.

27. $\frac{2}{3}\bullet\frac{3}{2}$; multiplicative inverse property

$\frac{2}{3} \bullet \frac{3}{2} = 1$

29. $(-4)(-3)$; commutative property of multiplication
    $(-3)(-4)$

31. $3+(8+9)$; associative property of addition
    $(3+8)+9$

33. $(4 \bullet 8) \bullet 9 = 4 \bullet (8 \bullet 9)$
    associative property of multiplication

35. $0+6=6$
    identity property of addition

37. $-4(3+7) = -4 \bullet 3 + (-4) \bullet 7$
    distributive property

39. $-4 \bullet (8 \bullet 3) = (-4 \bullet 8) \bullet 3$
    associative property of multiplication

41. $5(x+4m+2)$
    $5(x)+5(4m)+5(2)$
    $5x+20m+10$

43. $-4(1-2m+n)$
    $-4(1)+(-4)(-2m)+(-4)(n)$
    $-4+8m-4n$

45. $-(5x+2)$
    $-1(5x+2)$
    $-1(5x)+(-1)(2)$
    $-5x-2$

47. $-(r-3-7p)$
    $-1(r-3-7p)$
    $-1(r)+(-1)(-3)+(-1)(-7p)$
    $-r+3+7p$

49. 0
    The additive inverse is 0.

51. $|2| = 2$
    The additive inverse is -2.

53. $|8| = 8$
    The additive inverse is -8.

55. $-(-3) = 3$
    The additive inverse is -3.

57. $-|-2| = -(2) = -2$
    The additive inverse is 2.

59. $\frac{1}{5}$
    The multiplicative inverse is 5.

61. $\frac{3}{9} = \frac{1}{3}$
    The multiplicative inverse is 3.

63. -1
    The multiplicative inverse is -1.

65. $0 = \frac{0}{1}$
    There is no multiplicative inverse. Division by zero is undefined.

67. $-\left|-\frac{3}{5}\right| = -\left(\frac{3}{5}\right) = -\frac{3}{5}$
    The multiplicative inverse is $-\frac{5}{3}$.

69. $3\frac{5}{6} = \frac{23}{6}$
    The multiplicative inverse is $\frac{6}{23}$.

71. $y+0$; additive identity property
    $y+0=y$

73. $x(a+b)$; distributive property
    $xa+xb$

75. $a(b+c)$; commutative property of multiplication
    $(b+c)a$

77. Yes

79. No

Chapter 1 - Review

1. $2 < 6$

3. $10.6 = 10.6$

5. $4 \geq 3$

7. $8 + 4 \leq 12$

9. $7 = 3 + 4$

11. $50 > 40$

13a. Natural numbers
{2, 5}

b. Whole numbers
{2, 5}

c. Integers
{−3, 2, 5}

d. Rational numbers
$\{-3, -1.6, 2, 5, \frac{11}{2}, 15.1\}$

e. Irrational numbers
$\{\sqrt{5}, 2\pi\}$

f. Real numbers
$\{-3, -1.6, 2, 5, \frac{11}{2}, 15.1, \sqrt{5}, 2\pi\}$

15. $6 > -8$

17. $-\frac{3}{2} < -\frac{3}{4}$

19. Wednesday

21. $120 = 2 \bullet 2 \bullet 2 \bullet 3 \bullet 5$

23. $\frac{7}{8} \div \frac{21}{32} = \frac{7}{8} \bullet \frac{32}{21} = \frac{1}{1} \bullet \frac{4}{3} = \frac{4}{3}$

25. $\frac{3}{4} - \frac{3}{20} = \frac{15}{20} - \frac{3}{20} = \frac{12}{20} = \frac{3}{5}$

27. $7\frac{1}{6} - 2\frac{2}{3} = \frac{43}{6} - \frac{8}{3} =$
$\frac{43}{6} - \frac{16}{6} = \frac{27}{6} = \frac{9}{2} = 4\frac{1}{2}$

29. $6 \bullet 3^2 + 2 \bullet 8$
$6 \bullet 9 + 2 \bullet 8$
$54 + 16$
70

31. $3(1 + 2 \bullet 5) + 4$
$3(1 + 10) + 4$
$3(11) + 4$
$33 + 4$
37

33. $\frac{\sqrt{4} + |6 - 2| + 8^2}{4 + 6 \bullet 4}$
$\frac{2 + 4 + 64}{4 + 24}$
$\frac{70}{28} = \frac{\overset{1}{\cancel{2}} \bullet 5 \bullet \overset{1}{\cancel{7}}}{\underset{1}{\cancel{2}} \bullet 2 \bullet \underset{1}{\cancel{7}}} = \frac{5}{2}$

35. $2x + 3y$
$2(6) + 3(2)$
$12 + 6$
18

37. $\frac{x}{y} + \frac{z}{2y}$
$\frac{6}{2} + \frac{8}{2(2)}$
$3 + \frac{8}{4}$
$3 + 2$
5

39. $180 - a - b$
$180 - 37 - 80$
$143 - 80$
63°

41. The additive inverse of −3 is 3.

43. $-6 + (-11) = -17$

45. $-8 + |-3|$
$-8 + 3$
-5

47. $-2.8 + 6.7 = 3.9$

49. $-3 - 8 = -11$

51. $4 - 15 = -11$

53. $\frac{11-(-9)+6(8-2)}{2+3\bullet 4}$

$\frac{11+9+6(6)}{2+12}$

$\frac{11+9+36}{14}$

$\frac{56}{14}=4$

55. $\frac{y-x+5x}{2x}$

$\frac{-6-3+5(3)}{2(3)}$

$\frac{-6-3+15}{6}$

$\frac{6}{6}=1$

57. $6(-8)$

-48

59. $\frac{-18}{-6}$

3

61. $-3(-6)(-2)$

$+18(-2)$

-36

63. $\frac{4\bullet(-3)+(-8)}{2+(-2)}$

$\frac{-12+(-8)}{2+(-2)}$

$\frac{-20}{0}$

undefined – division by zero is not defined.

65. -6
The additive inverse is 6.

67. -6
The multiplicative inverse is $-\frac{1}{6}$.

69. $-6+5=5+(-6)$
commutative property of addition

71. $3(8-5)=3(8)+3(-5)$
distributive property

73. $2+(3+9)=(2+3)+9$
associative property of addition

75. $6(8+5)=6(8)+6(5)$
distributive property

77. $4\bullet\frac{1}{4}=1$
multiplicative inverse

79. $4(8+3)=4(3+8)$
commutative property of addition

Chapter 1 - Test

1. $|-7|>5$

2. $(9+5)\geq 4$

3. $-13+8$

-5

4. $-13-(-2)$

$-13+(+2)$

-11

5. $6\bullet 3-8\bullet 4$

$18-32$

$18+(-32)$

-14

6. $(13)(-3)$

-39

7. $(-6)(-2)$

12

8. $\frac{|-16|}{-8}$

$\frac{16}{-8}$

-2

9. $\frac{-8}{0}$

undefined – division by zero is not defined.

10. $\frac{-6+2}{5-6}$

$\frac{-4}{5+(-6)}$

$\frac{-4}{-1}$

4

11. $\frac{1}{2}-\frac{5}{6}$

$\frac{1}{2}+\left(-\frac{5}{6}\right)$

$\frac{1}{2}\bullet\frac{3}{3}+\left(-\frac{5}{6}\right)$

$\frac{3}{6}+\left(-\frac{5}{6}\right)$

$-\frac{2}{6}=-\frac{\overset{1}{\cancel{2}}}{\underset{1}{\cancel{2}}\bullet 3}=-\frac{1}{3}$

12. $-1\frac{1}{8}+5\frac{3}{4}$

$-\frac{9}{8}+\frac{23}{4}$

$-\frac{9}{8}+\frac{23}{4}\bullet\frac{2}{2}$

$-\frac{9}{8}+\frac{46}{8}$

$\frac{37}{8}$

13. $-\frac{3}{5}+\frac{15}{8}$

$-\frac{3}{5}\bullet\frac{8}{8}+\frac{15}{8}\bullet\frac{5}{5}$

$-\frac{24}{40}+\frac{75}{40}$

$\frac{51}{40}$

14. $3(-4)^2-80$

$3(16)-80$

$48-80$

$48+(-80)$

-32

15. $6[5+2(3-8)-3]$

$6[5+2(3+(-8))-3]$

$6[5+2(-5)-3]$

$6[5+(-10)-3]$

$6[5+(-10)+(-3)]$

$6[-5+(-3)]$

$6[-8]$

-48

16. $\frac{-12+3\bullet 8}{4}$

$\frac{-12+24}{4}$

$\frac{12}{4}$

3

17. $\frac{(-2)(0)(-3)}{-6}$

$\frac{0}{-6}$

0

18. $-3>-7$

19. $4>-8$

20. $|-3|\ ?\ 2$

$3\ ?\ 2$

$3>2$

$|-3|>2$

21. $|-2|\ ?\ -1-(-3)$

$2\ ?\ -1+(+3)$

$2\ ?\ 2$

$2=2$

$|-2|=-1-(-3)$

22a. $\{1,\ 7\}$

b. $\{0,\ 1,\ 7\}$

c. $\{-5,\ -1,\ 0,\ 1,\ 7\}$

d. $\{-5,\ -1,\ 0,\ \frac{1}{4},\ 1,\ 7,\ 11.6\}$

e. $\{\sqrt{7},\ 3\pi\}$

f. $\{-5,\ -1,\ 0,\ \frac{1}{4},\ 1,\ \sqrt{7},\ 7,\ 3\pi,\ 11.6\}$

23. x^2+y^2

$(6)^2+(-2)^2$

$36+4$

40

24. $x+yz$

$6+(-2)(-3)$

$6+6$

12

25. $2+3x-y$

$2+3(6)-(-2)$

$2+18+(+2)$

22

26. $\frac{y+z-1}{x}$

$\frac{-2+(-3)-1}{6}$

$\frac{-2+(-3)+(-1)}{6}$

$\frac{-6}{6}$

-1

27. $8+(9+3)=(8+9)+3$
associative property of addition

28. $6\bullet 8=8\bullet 6$
commutative property
of multiplication

29. $-6(2+4)=-6(2)+(-6)(4)$
distributive property

30. $\frac{1}{6}(6)=1$
multiplicative inverse

31. 9
The opposite of -9 is 9.

32. -3
The reciprocal of $-\frac{1}{3}$ is -3.

33. Second down

34. First down $22-5=17$
Second down $17+10=27$
Third down $27+2=29$
Fourth down $29-29=0$
Yes

35. $-14+31$

17°

36. $280(-\$1.50)$

$-\$420$

Exercise Set 2.1

1. $7y+8y=$

$(7+8)y=$

$15y$

3. $8w-w+6w=$

$(8-1+6)w=$

$13w$

5. $3b-5-10b-4=$

$3b-10b-5-4=$

$(3-10)b+(-5-4)=$

$-7b-9$

7. $m-4m+2m-6=$

$(1-4+2)m-6=$

$-m-6$

9. $5(y-4)=5y-20$

11. $7(d-3)+10=$

$7d-21+10=$

$7d-11$

13. $-(3x-2y+1)=-3x+2y-1$

15. $5(x+2)-(3x-4)=$

$5x+10-3x+4=$

$5x-3x+10+4=$

$2x+14$

17. $(6x+7)+(4x-10)=$

$6x+7+4x-10=$

$6x+4x+7-10=$

$10x-3$

19. $(3x-8)-(7x+1)=$

$3x-8-7x-1=$

$3x-7x-8-1=$

$-4x-9$

21. $2x-4$;

Let x represent the unknown number

Twice a number	decreased	four
↓	↓	↓
$2x$	$-$	4

23. $\frac{3}{4}x+12$;

Let x represent the unknown number

Three-fourth of a number	increased	twelve
↓	↓	↓
$\frac{3}{4}x$	$+$	12

25. $-2+5x+7x$

Let x represent the unknown number

Negative 2	sum	5 times a number	added to	7 times a number
↓	↓	↓	↓	↓
-2	$+$	$5x$	$+$	$7x$

$-2+12x$

27. $7x^2+8x^2-10x^2=5x^2$

29. $6x-5x+x-3+2x=$

$6x-5x+x+2x-3=$

$4x-3$

31. $-5+8(x-6)=$

$-5+8x-48=$

$8x-5-48=$

$8x-53$

33. $5g-3-5-5g=$

$5g-5g-3-5=$

-8

35. $6.2x-4+x-1.2=$

$6.2x+x-4-1.2=$

$7.2x-5.2$

37. $2k-k-6=k-6$

39. $0.5(m+2)+0.4m=$

$0.5m+1.0+0.4m=$

$0.5m+0.4m+1.0=$

$0.9m+1.0$

41. $-4(3y-4)=-12y+16$

43. $3(2x-5)-5(x-4)=$

$6x-15-5x+20=$

$6x-5x-15+20=$

$x+5$

45. $3.4m-4-3.4m-7=$

$3.4m-3.4m-4-7=$

-11

47. $6x+0.5-4.3x-0.4x+3=$

$6x-4.3x-0.4x+0.5+3=$

$6.0x-4.3x-0.4x+0.5+3.0=$

$1.3x+3.5$

49. $-2(3x-4)+7x-6=$

$-6x+8+7x-6=$

$-6x+7x+8-6=$

$x+2$

51. $-9x+4x+18-10x$

$-5x+18-10x$

$-15x+18$

53. $5k-(3k-10)$

$5k-3k+10$

$2k+10$

55. $(3x+4)-(6x-1)$

$3x+4-6x+1$

$-3x+5$

57. $(m-9)-(5m-6)=$

$m-9-5m+6=$

$m-5m-9+6=$

$-4m-3$

59. $8x+48$;

Let x represent the unknown number

Eight	times	Sum of a number and six
↓	↓	↓
8	•	(x+6)

$8(x+6)=8x+48$

61. $x-10$;

Let x represent the unknown number

Double	Number	minus	Sum of the number and ten
↓	↓	↓	↓
2 •	x	−	(x+10)

$2x-(x+10)=2x-x-10=x-10$

63. $\text{Perimeter}=5x+(4x-1)+5x+(4x-1)$

$=5x+4x-1+5x+4x-1$

$=5x+4x+5x+4x-1-1$

$=(18x-2)$ feet

65. $\frac{7x}{6}$;

Let x represent the number

seven	multiply	quotient of a number and six
↓	↓	↓
7	•	$\left(\frac{x}{6}\right)$

$7\left(\frac{x}{6}\right)=\frac{7}{1}\bullet\left(\frac{x}{6}\right)=\frac{7x}{6}$

67. $y-x^2$ when $x=-1$ and $y=3$

$3-(-1)^2$

$3-(+1)$

$3-1$

2

69. $yz-y^2$ when $y=-5$ and $z=0$

$(-5)(0)-(-5)^2$

$0-(+25)$

$0-25$

-25

71. x^3-x^2+4 when $x=-3$

$(-3)^3-(-3)^2+4$

$-27-(+9)+4$

$-27+(-9)+4$

-32

73. 5 hours

75. 2 hours

77. Between hours 6 and 7

79. $4m^4p^2+m^4p^2-5m^2p^4$

$5m^4p^2-5m^2p^4$

81. $9y^2-(6xy^2-5y^2)-8xy^2$

$9y^2-6xy^2+5y^2-8xy^2$

$14y^2-14xy^2$

83. $-(7c^3d-8c)-5c-4c^3d$

$-7c^3d+8c-5c-4c^3d$

$-11c^3d+3c$

Exercise Set 2.2

1. $x+11=-2$

$x+11+(-11)=-2+(-11)$

$x=-13$

$\{-13\}$

3. $5y+14=4y$

$5y+14+(-4y)=4y+(-4y)$

$y+14=0$

$y+14+(-14)=0+(-14)$

$y=-14$

$\{-14\}$

5. $8x=7x-8$

$8x+(-7x)=7x-8+(-7x)$

$x=-8$

$\{-8\}$

7. $3x - 6 = 2x + 5$

$3x - 6 - 2x = 2x + 5 - 2x$

$x - 6 = 5$

$x - 6 + 6 = 5 + 6$

$x = 11$

$\{11\}$

9. $3t - t - 7 = t - 7$

$2t - 7 = t - 7$

$2t - 7 - t = t - 7 - t$

$t - 7 = -7$

$t - 7 + 7 = -7 + 7$

$t = 0$

$\{0\}$

11. $7x + 2x = 8x - 3$

$9x = 8x - 3$

$9x - 8x = 8x - 8x - 3$

$x = -3$

$\{-3\}$

13. $-2(x + 1) + 3x = 14$

$-2x - 2 + 3x = 14$

$x - 2 = 14$

$x - 2 + 2 = 14 + 2$

$x = 16$

$\{16\}$

15. $-5x = 20$

$\frac{-5x}{-5} = \frac{20}{-5}$

$x = -4$

$\{-4\}$

17. $3x = 0$

$\frac{3x}{3} = \frac{0}{3}$

$x = 0$

$\{0\}$

19. $-x = -12$

$\frac{-x}{-1} = \frac{-12}{-1}$

$x = 12$

$\{12\}$

21. $3x + 2x = 50$

$\frac{5x}{5} = \frac{50}{5}$

$x = 10$

$\{10\}$

23. $\frac{2}{3}x = -8$

$\frac{3}{2} \bullet \frac{2}{3}x = \frac{3}{2} \bullet -8$

$x = -12$

$\{-12\}$

25. $\frac{1}{6}d = \frac{1}{2}$

$6 \bullet \frac{1}{6}d = 6 \bullet \frac{1}{2}$

$d = 3$

$\{3\}$

27. $\frac{a}{-2} = 1$

$-2 \bullet \frac{a}{-2} = -2 \bullet 1$

$a = -2$

$\{-2\}$

29. $\frac{k}{7} = 0$

$7 \bullet \frac{k}{7} = 7 \bullet 0$

$k = 0$

$\{0\}$

31. $2(x - 4) = x + 3$

$2x - 8 = x + 3$

$2x - x - 8 = x - x + 3$

$x - 8 = 3$

$x - 8 + 8 = 3 + 8$

$x = 11$

$\{11\}$

33. $7(6 + w) = 6(2 + w)$

$42 + 7w = 12 + 6w$

$42+7w-6w=12+6w-6w$

$42+w=12$

$42-42+w=12-42$

$w=-30$

$\{-30\}$

35. $10-(2x-4)=7-3x$

$10-2x+4=7-3x$

$14-2x=7-3x$

$14-2x+3x=7-3x+3x$

$14+x=7$

$14-14+x=7-14$

$x=-7$

$\{-7\}$

37. Let x represent the number

$2x+7=x+6$

$2x+7-x=x-x+6$

$x+7=6$

$x+7-7=6-7$

$x=-1$

39. Let x represent the number

$\frac{1}{2}x=-5$

$2\bullet\frac{1}{2}x=2\bullet -5$

$x=-10$

41. $x-2=-4$

$x=-2$

$\{-2\}$

43. $2y+10=y$

$2y-y+10=y-y$

$y+10=0$

$y+10-10=0-10$

$y=-10$

$\{-10\}$

45. $y+0.8=9.7$

$y+0.8-0.8=9.7-0.8$

$y=8.9$

$\{8.9\}$

47. $-3w=18$

$\frac{-3w}{-3}=\frac{18}{-3}$

$w=-6$

$\{-6\}$

49. $-0.2z=-0.8$

$\frac{-0.2z}{-0.2}=\frac{-0.8}{-0.2}$

$z=4$

$\{4\}$

51. $-h=-\frac{3}{4}$

$(-1)(-h)=-\frac{3}{4}(-1)$

$h=\frac{3}{4}$

$\left\{\frac{3}{4}\right\}$

53. $5b-0.7=6b$

$5b-5b-0.7=6b-5b$

$-0.7=b$

$\{-0.7\}$

55. $5x-6=6x-5$

$5x-5x-6=6x-5x-5$

$-6=x-5$

$-6+5=x-5+5$

$-1=x$

$\{-1\}$

57. $7t-12=6t$

$7t-6t-12=6t-6t$

$t-12=0$

$t-12+12=0+12$

$t=12$

$\{12\}$

59. $-5(n-2)=8-4n$

$-5n+10=8-4n$

$-5n+5n+10=8-4n+5n$

$10=8+n$

$10-8=8-8+n$

$2=n$

$\{2\}$

61. $y-5y+0.6=0.8-5y$

$-4y+0.6=0.8-5y$

$-4y+5y+0.6=0.8-5y+5y$

$y+0.6=0.8$

$y+0.6-0.6=0.8-0.6$

$y=0.2$

$\{0.2\}$

63. $-3(x-4)=-4x$

$-3x+12=-4x$

$-3x+4x+12=-4x+4x$

$x+12=0$

$x+12-12=0-12$

$x=-12$

$\{-12\}$

65. $5x-7x+8x=-6$

$6x=-6$

$x=\frac{-6}{6}$

$x=-1$

$\{-1\}$

67. $x+6x-10x=0$

$-3x=0$

$x=\frac{0}{-3}$

$x=0$

$\{0\}$

69. $4x+(-2)=5x+(-2)$

$4x+(-2)+2=5x+(-2)+2$

$4x=5x$

$4x-4x=5x-4x$

$0=x$

$\{0\}$

71. $5(x-1)=6x$

$5x-5=6x$

$-5=x$

$\{-5\}$

73. $6x=3x$

$6x-3x=3x-3x$

$3x=0$

$x=\frac{0}{3}$

$x=0$

$\{0\}$

75. $x+2x+1+3x-2=35$

$6x-1=35$

$\frac{6x}{6}=\frac{36}{6}$

$x=6$ meters

$2x+1=13$ meters

$3x-2=16$ meters

77. $\frac{7}{8}\bullet\frac{24}{29}=\frac{21}{29}$

79. $\frac{9}{10}\div\frac{4}{3}=\frac{9}{10}\bullet\frac{3}{4}=\frac{27}{40}$

81. $\frac{6}{15}\bullet\frac{45}{18}\bullet\frac{4}{5}=\frac{4}{5}$

83. $(-2)^4 \ ? \ -2^2$

$(-2)^4 \ ? \ -(2^4)$

$(-2)(-2)(-2)(-2) \ ? \ -(2)(2)(2)(2)$

$16>-16$

85. $(-4)^3 \ ? \ -4^3$

$(-4)^3 \ ? \ -(4^3)$

$(-4)(-4)(-4) \ ? \ -(4)(4)(4)$

$-64=-64$

87. $-|-0.7| \ ? \ -0.7$

$-(0.7) \ ? \ -0.7$

$-0.7=-0.7$

89. $-|2|-|-7| \ ? \ |2-7|$

$-2-(+7) \ ? \ |2+(-7)|$

$-2+(-7) \ ? \ |-5|$

$-9<5$

Exercise Set 2.3

1. $\frac{3}{4}x-\frac{1}{2}=1$

$4\left(\frac{3}{4}x-\frac{1}{2}\right)=4\bullet 1$

$4\left(\frac{3}{4}x\right)-4\left(\frac{1}{2}\right)=4$

$3x-2=4$

$3x-2+2=4+2$

$3x=6$

$\frac{3x}{3}=\frac{6}{3}$

$x=2$

$\{2\}$

3. $x+\frac{5}{4}=\frac{3}{4}x$

$4\left(x+\frac{5}{4}\right)=4\left(\frac{3}{4}x\right)$

$4(x)+4\left(\frac{5}{4}\right)=4\left(\frac{3}{4}x\right)$

$4x+5=3x$

$4x-3x+5=3x-3x$

$x+5=0$

$x+5-5=0-5$

$x=-5$

$\{-5\}$

5. $\frac{x}{2}-1=\frac{x}{5}+2$

$10\left(\frac{x}{2}-1\right)=10\left(\frac{x}{5}+2\right)$

$10\left(\frac{x}{2}\right)-10\bullet 1=10\left(\frac{x}{5}\right)+10\bullet 2$

$5x-10=2x+20$

$5x-2x-10=2x-2x+20$

$3x-10=20$

$3x-10+10=20+10$

$3x=30$

$\frac{3x}{3}=\frac{30}{3}$

$x=10$

$\{10\}$

7. $5x+12=2(2x+7)$

$5x+12=4x+14$

$5x+12-12=4x+14-12$

$5x=4x+2$

$5x-4x=4x-4x+2$

$x=2$

$\{2\}$

9. $3(x-6)=5x$

$3x-18=5x$

$-18=2x$

$x=-9$

$\{-9\}$

11. $-2(5y-1)-y=-4(y-3)$

$-10y+2-y=-4y+12$

$-11y+2=-4y+12$

$-7y=10$

$y=-\frac{10}{7}$

$\left\{-\frac{10}{7}\right\}$

13. $\frac{x}{2}+\frac{2}{3}=\frac{3}{4}$

$6x+8=9$

$6x=1$

$x=\frac{1}{6}$

$\left\{\frac{1}{6}\right\}$

15. $\frac{n-3}{4}+\frac{n+5}{7}=\frac{5}{14}$

$7(n-3)+4(n+5)=10$

$7n-21+4n+20=10$

$11n-1=10$

$11n=11$

$n = 1$

$\{1\}$

17. $5x - 5 = 2(x + 1) + 3x - 7$

$5x - 5 = 2x + 2 + 3x - 7$

$5x - 5 = 5x - 5$

$5x - 5x - 5 = 5x - 5x - 5$

$-5 = -5$

$-5 + 5 = -5 + 5$

$0 = 0$

$\{x | x \text{ is a real number}\}$

19. $\frac{x}{4} + 1 = \frac{x}{4}$

$4\left(\frac{x}{4} + 1\right) = 4\left(\frac{x}{4}\right)$

$4\left(\frac{x}{4}\right) + 4(1) = 4\left(\frac{x}{4}\right)$

$x + 4 = x$

$x - x + 4 = x - x$

$4 = 0$

No Solution

$\{\ \}$

21. $3x - 7 = 3(x + 1)$

$3x - 7 = 3x + 3$

$3x - 3x - 7 = 3x - 3x + 3$

$-7 = 3$

No Solution

$\{\ \}$

23. Let $x =$ the number

$2(x + 6) = 3(x + 4)$

$2x + 12 = 3x + 12$

$2x + 12 - 12 = 3x + 12 - 12$

$2x = 3x$

$2x - 2x = 3x - 2x$

$0 = x$

25. $(180 - x)°$;

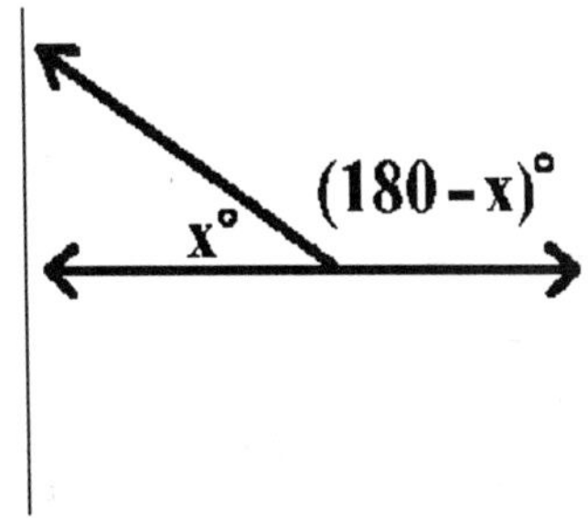

27. one number $= z$

other number $= 12 - z$

29. $-5x + 1 = -19$

$-5x + 1 - 1 = -19 - 1$

$-5x = -20$

$x = \frac{-20}{-5}$

$x = 4$

$\{4\}$

31. $4x + 3 = 2x + 11$

$4x - 2x + 3 = 2x - 2x + 11$

$2x + 3 = 11$

$2x + 3 - 3 = 11 - 3$

$2x = 8$

$\frac{2x}{2} = \frac{8}{2}$

$x = 4$

$\{4\}$

33. $-2y - 10 = 5y + 18$

$-2y + 2y - 10 = 5y + 2y + 18$

$-10 = 7y + 18$

$-10 - 18 = 7y + 18 - 18$

$-28 = 7y$

$\frac{-28}{7} = \frac{7y}{7}$

$-4 = y$

$\{-4\}$

35. $6x - 1 = 5x + 2$

$6x - 5x - 1 = 5x - 5x + 2$

$x - 1 = 2$

$x - 1 + 1 = 2 + 1$

$x = 3$

$\{3\}$

37. $2y + 2 = y$

$2y - 2y + 2 = y - 2y$

$2 = -y$

$\frac{2}{-1} = \frac{-y}{-1}$

$-2 = y$

$\{-2\}$

39. $3(5c - 1) - 2 = 13c + 3$

$15c - 3 - 2 = 13c + 3$

$15c - 5 = 13c + 3$

$15c - 13c - 5 = 13c - 13c + 3$

$2c - 5 = 3$

$2c - 5 + 5 = 3 + 5$

$2c = 8$

$\frac{2c}{2} = \frac{8}{2}$

$c = 4$

$\{4\}$

41. $x + \frac{7}{6} = 2x - \frac{7}{6}$

$6\left(x + \frac{7}{6}\right) = 6\left(2x - \frac{7}{6}\right)$

$6(x) + 6\left(\frac{7}{6}\right) = 6(2x) + 6\left(-\frac{7}{6}\right)$

$6x + 7 = 12x - 7$

$6x - 12x + 7 = 12x - 12x - 7$

$-6x + 7 = -7$

$-6x + 7 - 7 = -7 - 7$

$-6x = -14$

$\frac{-6x}{-6} = \frac{-14}{-6}$

$x = \frac{14}{6}$

$x = \frac{7}{3}$

$\left\{\frac{7}{3}\right\}$

43. $2(x - 5) = 7 + 2x$

$2x - 10 = 7 + 2x$

$2x - 2x - 10 = 7 + 2x - 2x$

$-10 = 7$

No Solution

$\{\ \}$

45. $\frac{2(z+3)}{3} = 5 - z$

$3 \bullet \frac{2(z+3)}{3} = 3(5 - z)$

$\overset{1}{\cancel{3}} \bullet \frac{2(z+3)}{\cancel{3}} = 3(5 - z)$

$2(z + 3) = 3(5 - z)$

$2z + 6 = 15 - 3z$

$2z + 3z + 6 = 15 - 3z + 3z$

$5z + 6 = 15$

$5z + 6 - 6 = 15 - 6$

$5z = 9$

$\frac{5z}{5} = \frac{9}{5}$

$z = \frac{9}{5}$

$\left\{\frac{9}{5}\right\}$

47. $\frac{4(y-1)}{5} = -3y$

$5 \bullet \frac{4(y-1)}{5} = 5(-3y)$

$\overset{1}{\cancel{5}} \bullet \frac{4(y-1)}{\cancel{5}} = 5(-3y)$

$4(y - 1) = 5(-3y)$

$4y - 4 = -15y$

$4y - 4y - 4 = -15y - 4y$

$-4 = -19y$

$\frac{-4}{-19} = \frac{-19y}{-19}$

$\frac{4}{19} = y$

$\left\{\frac{4}{19}\right\}$

49. $8 - 2(a - 1) = 7 + a$

$8 - 2a + 2 = 7 + a$

$-2a+10=7+a$

$-2a-a+10=7+a-a$

$-3a+10=7$

$-3a+10-10=7-10$

$-3a=-3$

$\frac{-3a}{-3}=\frac{-3}{-3}$

$a=1$

$\{1\}$

51. $2(x+3)-5=5x-3(1+x)$

$2x+6-5=5x-3-3x$

$2x+1=2x-3$

$2x-2x+1=2x-2x-3$

$1=-3$

No Solution

$\{\ \}$

53. $\frac{5x-7}{3}=x$

$3\bullet\frac{5x-7}{3}=3(x)$

$\cancel{3}^{1}\bullet\frac{5x-7}{\cancel{3}}=3(x)$

$5x-7=3x$

$5x-5x-7=3x-5x$

$-7=-2x$

$\frac{-7}{-2}=\frac{-2x}{-2}$

$\frac{7}{2}=x$

$\left\{\frac{7}{2}\right\}$

55. $\frac{9+5v}{2}=2v-4$

$2\bullet\frac{9+5v}{2}=2(2v-4)$

$\cancel{2}^{1}\bullet\frac{9+5v}{\cancel{2}}=2(2v-4)$

$9+5v=4v-8$

$9+5v-4v=4v-4v-8$

$9+v=-8$

$9-9+v=-8-9$

$v=-17$

$\{-17\}$

57. $-3(t-5)+2t=5t-4$

$-3t+15+2t=5t-4$

$-t+15=5t-4$

$-t+t+15=5t+t-4$

$15=6t-4$

$15+4=6t-4+4$

$19=6t$

$\frac{19}{6}=\frac{6t}{6}$

$\frac{19}{6}=t$

$\left\{\frac{19}{6}\right\}$

59. $6-(x+1)=-2(2-x)$

$6-x-1=-4+2x$

$-x+5=-4+2x$

$-x+x+5=-4+2x+x$

$5=-4+3x$

$5+4=-4+4+3x$

$9=3x$

$\frac{9}{3}=\frac{3x}{3}$

$3=x$

$\{3\}$

61. $\frac{3(x-5)}{2}=\frac{2(x+5)}{3}$

$6\bullet\frac{3(x-5)}{2}=6\bullet\frac{2(x+5)}{3}$

$\cancel{6}^{3}\bullet\frac{3(x-5)}{\cancel{2}_{1}}=\cancel{6}^{2}\bullet\frac{2(x+5)}{\cancel{3}_{1}}$

$9(x-5)=4(x+5)$

$9x-45=4x+20$

$9x-4x-45=4x-4x+20$

$5x-45=20$

$5x-45+45=20+45$

$5x=65$

$\frac{5x}{5}=\frac{65}{5}$

$x = 13$

$\{13\}$

63. $\frac{m-4}{3} - \frac{3m-1}{5} = 1$

$15 \bullet \frac{m-4}{3} = 15 \bullet \frac{3m-1}{5} = 15 \bullet 1$

$5(m-4) - 3(3m-1) = 15$

$5m - 20 - 9m + 3 = 15$

$-4m - 17 = 15$

$-4m - 17 + 17 = 15 + 17$

$\frac{-4m}{-4} = \frac{32}{-4}$

$m = -8$

$\{-8\}$

65. $\frac{5x-1}{6} - 3x = \frac{1}{3} + \frac{4x-3}{9}$

$\frac{18(5x-1)}{6} - 18(3x) = 18\left(\frac{1}{3}\right) + \frac{18(4x-3)}{9}$

$3(5x-1) - 18(3x) = 6 + 2(4x-3)$

$15x - 3 - 54x = 6 + 8x - 6$

$-39x - 3 = 8x$

$-39x + 39x - 3 = 8x + 39x$

$-3 = 47x$

$-\frac{3}{47} = x$

$\left\{-\frac{3}{47}\right\}$

67. $3x - 1 = 2x$

$3x - 3x - 1 = 2x - 3x$

$-1 = -1x$

$\frac{-1}{-1} = x$

$1 = x$

$\{1\}$

69. $30 - x$

71. $8 - x$

73. $x + 55 = 2x - 90$

$x + 55 - 55 = 2x - 90 - 55$

$x = 2x - 145$

$x - 2x = 2x - 2x - 145$

$-x = -145$

$x = \frac{-145}{-1} = 145$; Yes

75. Midway

77. $|2^3 - 3^2| - |5 - 7|$

$|8 - 9| - |-2|$

$|-1| - |-2|$

$1 - 2$

-1

79. $\frac{\sqrt{25}}{4 + 3 \bullet 7}$

$\frac{5}{4 + 21}$

$\frac{5}{25} = \frac{1}{5}$

81. $x + 2x - 3 + 3x - 5$

$(6x - 8)$ meters

Exercise Set 2.4

1. $A = bh$

$45 = 15h$

$\frac{45}{15} = \frac{15h}{15}$

$3 = h$

3. $I = PRT$

$I = 5000(0.08)(2)$

$I = 800$

5. $C = 2\pi r$

$94.2 = 2(3.14)r$

$94.2 = 6.28r$

$\frac{94.2}{6.28} = \frac{6.28r}{6.28}$

$15 \approx r$

7. $d = rt$

$93,000,000 = 186,000t$

$\frac{93,000,000}{186,000} = t$

$500 \text{ seconds} = t$

9. $d = rt$

$d = 470(5.5)$

$d = 2585$ miles

Frequent flyer miles are 3000 miles.

11. $d = 2r$

$d = 2(4000)$

$d = 8000$

$C = \pi d$

$C = 3.14(8000)$

$C = 25{,}120$ miles

13. $F = \frac{9}{5}C + 32$

$F = \frac{9}{5}(-78.5) + 32$

$F = -141.3 + 32$

$F = -109.3^\circ$

15. $C = \frac{5}{9}(F - 32)$

$C = \frac{5}{9}(14 - 32)$

$C = \frac{5}{9}(-18)$

$C = -10^\circ$

17. $I = Prt$

$40{,}000 = P(0.08)(1)$

$40{,}000 = 0.08P$

$\frac{40{,}000}{0.08} = P$

$\$500{,}000 = P$

19. $f = 5gh$

$\frac{f}{5g} = \frac{5gh}{5g}$

$\frac{f}{5g} = h$

21. $V = LWH$

$\frac{V}{LH} = \frac{LWH}{LH}$

$\frac{V}{LH} = W$

23. $3x + y = 7$

$3x - 3x + y = 7 - 3x$

$y = 7 - 3x$

25. $A = p + PRT$

$A - p = p - p + PRT$

$A - p = PRT$

$\frac{A - p}{PT} = \frac{PRT}{PT}$

$\frac{A - p}{PT} = R$

27. $V = \frac{1}{3}Ah$

$3(V) = 3\left(\frac{1}{3}Ah\right)$

$3V = Ah$

$\frac{3V}{h} = \frac{Ah}{h}$

$\frac{3V}{h} = A$

29. Let $x = 1^{st}$ integer
$x + 1 = 2^{nd}$ integer
$x + 2 = 3^{rd}$ integer

$x + x + 2$

$2x + 2$

31. $360 - (3x + 5x + x)$

$360 - 9x$

33. $y = mx + b$

$2 = 3(-1) + b$

$2 = -3 + b$

$2 + 3 = -3 + 3 + b$

$5 = b$

35. $A = 0.5h(b_1 + b_2)$

$40 = 0.5h(11 + 9)$

$40 = 0.5(11 + 9)h$

$40 = 0.5(20)h$

$40 = 10h$

$\frac{40}{10} = \frac{40h}{10}$

$4 = h$

37. $V = \frac{1}{3}\pi r^2 h$

$565.2 = \frac{1}{3}(3.14)(6)^2 h$

$565.2 = \frac{1}{3}(3.14)(36)h$

$565.2 = 37.68h$

$\frac{565.2}{37.68} = \frac{37.68h}{37.68}$

$15 = h$

39. $d = rt$

$3000 = r\left(\frac{3}{2}\right)$

$\left(\frac{2}{3}\right)3000 = r\left(\frac{3}{2}\right)\left(\frac{2}{3}\right)$

$2000 \text{ mph} = r$

41. $P = 2l + 2w$

$140 = 2(40) + 2w$

$140 = 80 + 2w$

$140 - 80 = 80 - 80 + 2w$

$60 = 2w$

$\frac{60}{2} = w$

$30 \text{ feet} = w$

43. $I = PRT$

$35{,}000 = P(0.07)$

$3{,}500{,}000 = 7P$

$\frac{3{,}500{,}000}{7} = \frac{7P}{7}$

$\$500{,}000 = P$

45. $V = lwh$

$V = 10(8)(10)$

$V = 800$ cubic feet

47. $V = lwh$

$V = 8(3)(6)$

$V = 144$ cubic feet

$\frac{144}{1.5} = 96$

Ninety-six piranhas can live in this tank.

49. $d = rt$

$\frac{d}{r} = t$

$\frac{135}{60} = t$

$2.25 \text{ hrs.} = t$

51. $F = \frac{9}{5}C + 32$

If $F = C$, then $F = \frac{9}{5}F + 32$

$-\frac{4}{5}F = 32$

$F = \frac{-5}{4}(32) = -40^\circ$

53. Let $x =$ the number of times to travel around the earth.

$\frac{25{,}000x}{25{,}000} = \frac{270{,}000}{25{,}000}$

$x = 10.8$

55. $V = \frac{4}{3}\pi r^3$

$V = \frac{4}{3}(3.14)(2000)^3$

$V = 33{,}493{,}333{,}333$ cubic miles

57. $V = \pi r^2 h$

$d = 2 \text{ inches} = \frac{2}{12} \text{ feet} = 0.167 \text{ feet}$

$r = 0.083$ ft.

$V = 3.14(0.083)^2(15)$

$V = 0.324$ cubic feet

59. $C = \frac{5}{9}(F - 32)$

$C = \frac{5}{9}(78 - 32)$

$C = \frac{5}{9}(46)$

$C = 25.6^\circ$

61. $d = rt$

$25{,}000 = 4000t$

$\frac{25{,}000}{4{,}000} = t$

$6.25 \text{ hours} = t$

63. $D = rt$

$\frac{D}{r} = t$

65. $I = PRT$

$\frac{I}{PT} = R$

67. $9x - 4y = 16$

$9x - 16 = 4y$

$\frac{9x - 16}{4} = y$

69. $P = a + b + c$

$P - b - c = a$

71. $T = C(2 + AB)$

$T = 2C + ABC$

$\frac{T - 2C}{AC} = B$

73. $C = 2\pi r$

$\frac{C}{2\pi} = r$

75. $\frac{1}{u} - \frac{1}{v} = \frac{1}{w}$

$uvw\left(\frac{1}{u} - \frac{1}{v}\right) = uvw\left(\frac{1}{w}\right)$

$vw - uw = uv$

$w(v - u) = uv$

$w = \frac{uv}{v - u}$

77. $n + 284$

79. $x + 2$

81. $x + 2$

83. $x + x + 2 + x + 4$

$3x + 6$

85. $5x + 10(5x) + 25(30x - 1)$

$5x + 50x + 750x - 25$

$805x - 25$

87. Let $x = \text{number}$

$\frac{9}{x + 5}$

89. Let $x = \text{number}$

$3(x + 4)$

91. Let $x = \text{number}$

$2(10 + 4x)$

93. Let $x = \text{number}$

$3(x - 12)$

Exercise Set 2.5

1. Let $x = \text{length}$

then $\frac{2}{3}x = \text{width}$

$P = 2L + 2W$

$260 = 2(x) + 2\left(\frac{2}{3}x\right)$

$260 = 2x + \frac{4}{3}x$

$260 = \frac{6}{3}x + \frac{4}{3}x$

$260 = \frac{10}{3}x$

$\frac{3}{10}(260) = \frac{3}{10} \bullet \frac{10}{3}x$

78 ft. $= x$

length $= 78$ ft.

width $= \frac{2}{3}(78 \text{ ft.}) = 52$ ft.

3. shortest side $= x - 2$
2nd side $= x$
3rd side $= x$

$22 = x + x + x - 2$

$22 = 3x - 2$

$\frac{24}{3} = \frac{3x}{3}$

$8 = x$

shortest side $= x - 2$
$= 8 - 2$
shortest side $= 6$ feet

5. Let $x =$ number of US gold medals
$x + 8 =$ number of Soviet gold

$x + x + 8 = 82$

$2x + 8 = 82$

$2x + 8 - 8 = 82 - 8$

$2x = 74$

$x = \frac{74}{2} = 37$

US won 37 gold medals.
Soviets won 45 gold medals.

7. Let $x = \text{number of hours}$

$404 = 27x + 80$

$404 - 80 = 27x + 80 - 80$

$324 = 27x$

$\frac{324}{27} = x$

$12 \text{ hours} = x$

The job is expected to take 12 hours.

9. 1st angle $= x$
2nd angle $= 2x - 15$

$x + 2x - 15 + x + 2x - 15 = 360$

$6x - 30 = 360$

$6x - 30 + 30 = 360 + 30$

$6x = 390$

$x = \frac{390}{6}$

$x = 65^\circ$

1st angle is 65°.
2nd angle is 115°.

11. Let $x = \text{side of square}$
$x + 5 = \text{side of triangle}$
Perimeter of square $= 4x$
Perimeter of triangle $= 3(x + 5)$

$3(x + 5) = 4x + 7$

$3x + 15 = 4x + 7$

$3x - 3x + 15 = 4x - 3x + 7$

$15 = x + 7$

$15 - 7 = x + 7 - 7$

$8 \text{ inches} = x$

The side of the triangle is 13 inches.

13. 1st integer $= x$
2nd integer $= x + 1$

$x + x + 1 = 197$

$2x + 1 = 197$

$2x + 1 - 1 = 197 - 1$

$2x = 196$

$x = \frac{196}{2}$

$x = 98$

The score was 98 points to 99 points.

15. 1st integer $= x$
2nd integer $= x + 2$

$7x = 5(x + 2) + 54$

$7x = 5x + 10 + 54$

$7x = 5x + 64$

$7x - 5x = 5x - 5x + 64$

$2x = 64$

$x = \frac{64}{2}$

$x = 32$

No, the integers would be even numbers.

17. Let $x = \text{width}$
$1.6x = \text{length}$

$P = 2l + 2w$

$78 = 2(1.6x) + 2x$

$78 = 3.2x + 2x$

$78 = 5.2x$

$15 \text{ feet} = x$

The dimensions are 15 feet by 24 feet.

19. Let $x = \text{the angle}$
$90 - x = \text{complementary angle}$

$x = 2(90 - x) + 30$

$x = 180 - 2x + 30$

$x = -2x + 210$

$x + 2x = -2x + 2x + 210$

$3x = 210$

$x = \frac{210}{3}$

$x = 70^\circ$

The angles are 70° and 20°.

21. Let $x = \text{height}$
$2x - 19 = \text{diameter}$

$x + 2x - 19 = 83$

$3x - 19 = 83$

$3x - 19 + 19 = 83 + 19$

$3x = 102$

$x = \frac{102}{3}$

$x = 34$ inches

The height is 34 inches and the diameter is 49 inches.

23. 1st integer $= x$
2nd integer $= x + 2$
3rd integer $= x + 4$

$x + 3(x + 4) = 64 + x + 2$

$x + 3x + 12 = x + 66$

$4x + 12 = x + 66$

$4x = x + 54$

$4x - x = x - x + 54$

$3x = 54$

$x = \frac{54}{3}$

$x = 18$

The integers are 18, 20, and 22.

25. Shortest side $= x$
Second side $= 2x$
Third side $= x + 30$

$x + 2x + x + 30 = 102$

$4x + 30 = 102$

$4x + 30 - 30 = 102 - 30$

$4x = 72$

$x = \frac{72}{4}$

$x = 18$

The sides are 18 feet, 36 feet, and 48 feet.

27. 1st integer $= x$
2nd integer $= x + 1$
3rd integer $= x + 2$

$x + 2(x + 1) = x + 2 + 54$

$x + 2x + 2 = x + 56$

$3x + 2 = x + 56$

$3x + 2 - 2 = x + 56 - 2$

$3x = x + 54$

$3x - x = x - x + 54$

$2x = 54$

$x = \frac{54}{2}$

$x = 27$

The integers are 27, 28, and 29.

29. 1st angle $= x$
2nd angle $= x$
3rd angle $= 3x - 10$

$x + x + 3x - 10 = 180$

$5x - 10 = 180$

$5x - 10 + 10 = 180 + 10$

$5x = 190$

$x = \frac{190}{5}$

$x = 38^\circ$

The angles are 38°, 38°, and 104°.

31. Shorter piece $= x$
Longer piece $= 21 - x$

$21 - x = 3x + 1$

$21 - x - 21 = 3x + 1 - 21$

$-x = 3x - 20$

$-x - 3x = 3x - 3x - 20$

$-4x = -20$

$x = \frac{-20}{-4}$

$x = 5$ feet

The pieces are 5 ft. and 16 ft.

33. $x =$ money son receives
$2x =$ money husband receives

$x + 2x = 15,000$

$3x = 15,000$

$x = \frac{15,000}{3}$

$x = 5,000$

Son receives \$5,000.
Husband receives \$10,000.

35. $3 + (-7)$

-4

37. $4 - 10$

-6

39. $-5 - (-1)$

$-5 + (+1)$

-4

41. Let $x = \text{number}$

$\frac{1}{2}(x - 1) = 37$

43. Let $x = \text{number}$

$\frac{3(x+2)}{5} = 0$

Exercise Set 2.6

1. 5.1¢

3. Alaska Village and Southern Cal. Edison

5. $110 million

7. Snow White and the Seven Dwarfs

9. 58 beats per minute

11. $85 - 58$
27 beats per minute

13.

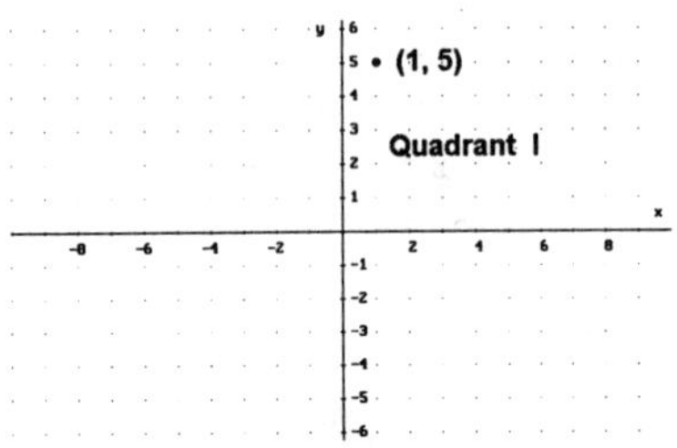

15.

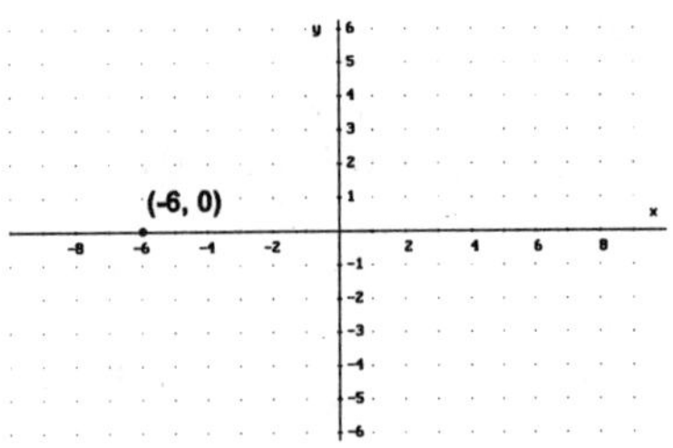

17.

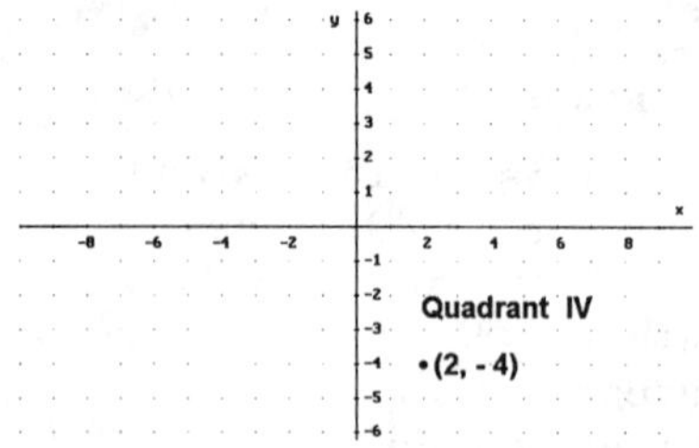

19.

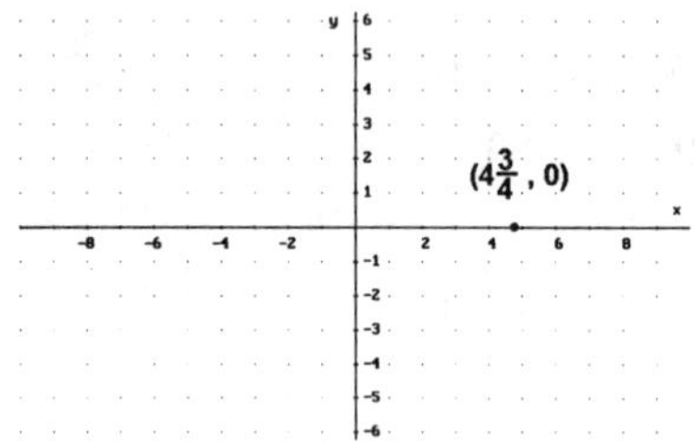

21. Cleveland Indians

23. They have both gone the same amount of time without being in a playoff.

25. $11 - 8$

3 years

27. A $(0, 0)$

B $\left(3\frac{1}{2}, 0\right)$

C $(3, 2)$

D $(-1, 3)$

E $(-2, -2)$

F $(0, -1)$

G $(2, -1)$

29. 1975

31. 37 pounds

33. $80 - 29$

51 pounds

35. From 1975 to 1980

37. Beef consumption decreased. Chicken consumption increased.

39. The point $(2, -1)$ lies in the fourth quadrant.

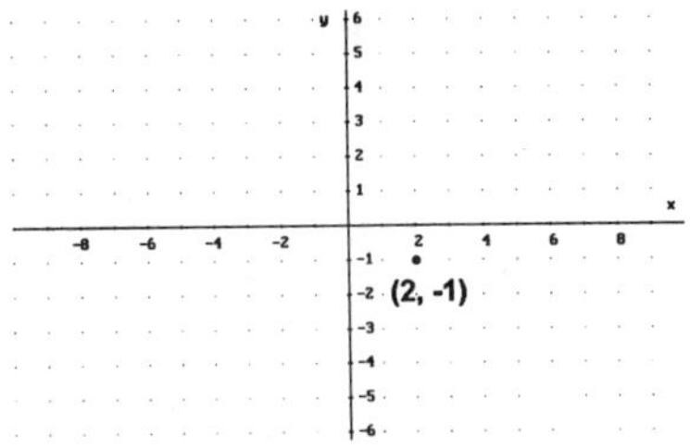

41. The point $(-3, -1)$ lies in the third quadrant.

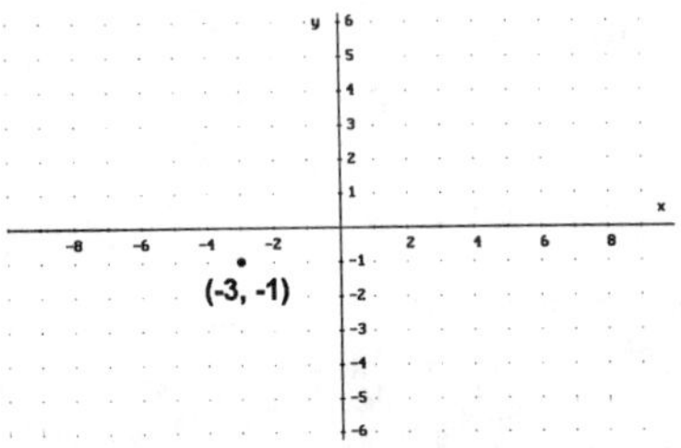

43. The point $(2, 3)$ lies in the first quadrant.

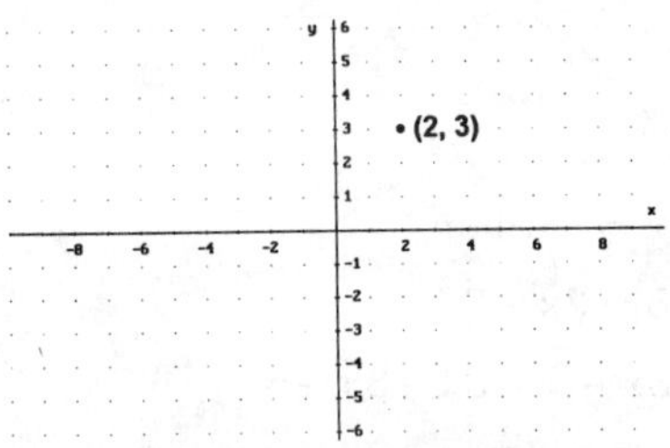

45. The point $(-2, 4)$ lies in the second quadrant.

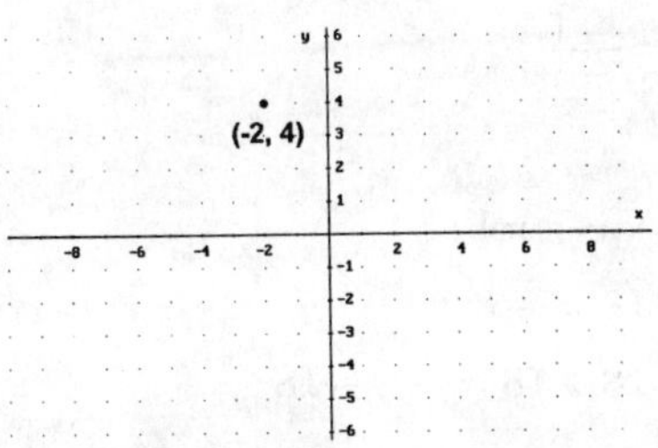

47. The point $(5, 0)$ lies on the x-axis.

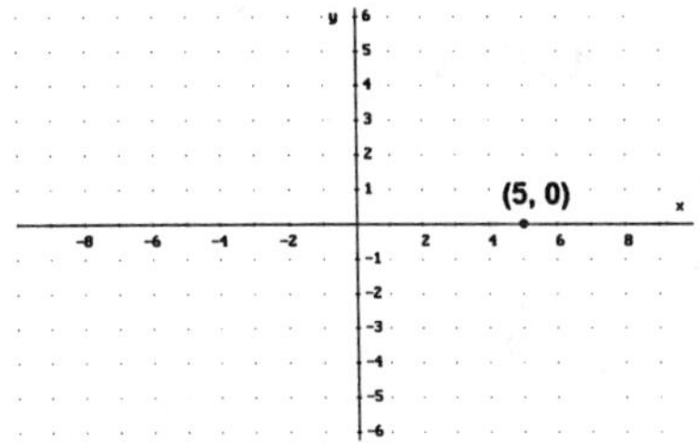

49. x-coordinate > 0 in Quadrant I and IV. The overlap where x-coordinate > 0 and y-coordinate < 0 is Quadrant IV.

51. The x-coordinate are positive in Quadrant I and IV.

53.
$$3(x-2)+5x=6x-16$$
$$3x-6+5x=6x-16$$
$$8x-6=6x-16$$
$$8x-6+6=6x-16+6$$
$$8x=6x-10$$
$$8x-6x=6x-6x-10$$
$$2x=-10$$
$$x=\frac{-10}{2}$$
$$x=-5$$
$$\{-5\}$$

55.
$$3x+\frac{2}{5}=\frac{1}{10}$$
$$3x+\frac{2}{5}-\frac{2}{5}=\frac{1}{10}-\frac{2}{5}$$
$$3x=\frac{1}{10}-\frac{4}{10}$$
$$3x=-\frac{3}{10}$$
$$\frac{1}{3}(3x)=\frac{1}{3}\left(-\frac{3}{10}\right)$$
$$x=-\frac{1}{10}$$
$$\left\{-\frac{1}{10}\right\}$$

57. $\frac{7}{35}=\frac{7\bullet 1}{7\bullet 5}=\frac{1}{5}$

59. $-\frac{15}{50} = -\frac{5 \bullet 3}{5 \bullet 10} = -\frac{3}{10}$

Chapter 2 - Review

1. $5x - x + 2x$

$4x + 2x$

$6x$

3. $\frac{1}{2}x + 3 + \frac{7}{2}x - 5$

$\frac{8}{2}x - 2$

$4x - 2$

5. $2(n-4) + n - 10$

$2n - 8 + n - 10$

$3n - 18$

7. $x + 5 - (7x - 2)$

$x + 5 - 7x + 2$

$-6x + 7$

9. Let $x =$ number
$3x - 7$

11. Let $x =$ number
$10 - x =$ other number

13. $8x + 4 = 9x$

$8x - 8x + 4 = 9x - 8x$

$4 = x$

$\{4\}$

15. $3x - 5 = 4x + 1$

$3x - 3x - 5 = 4x - 3x + 1$

$-5 = x + 1$

$-5 - 1 = x + 1 - 1$

$-6 = x$

$\{-6\}$

17. $4(x+3) = 3(1+x)$

$4x + 12 = 3 + 3x$

$4x - 3x + 12 = 3 + 3x - 3x$

$x + 12 = 3$

$x + 12 - 12 = 3 - 12$

$x = -9$

$\{-9\}$

19. $\frac{3}{4}x = -9$

$\frac{4}{3}\left(\frac{3}{4}x\right) = \frac{4}{3}(-9)$

$x = -12$

$\{-12\}$

21. $-3x + x = 19$

$\frac{-2x}{-2} = \frac{19}{-2}$

$x = -\frac{19}{2}$

$\left\{-\frac{19}{2}\right\}$

23. $5x - 6 - x = 9 + 3x - 1$

$4x - 6 = 3x + 8$

$4x - 6 + 6 = 3x + 8 + 6$

$4x = 3x + 14$

$4x - 3x = 3x - 3x + 14$

$x = 14$

$\{14\}$

25. Let $x =$ number

$2x - 5 = 3x - 6$

$2x - 3x - 5 = 3x - 3x - 6$

$-x - 5 = -6$

$-x - 5 + 5 = -6 + 5$

$-x = -1$

$\frac{-x}{-1} = \frac{-1}{-1}$

$x = 1$

27. Let $x =$ number

$5x - 18 = -3$

$5x - 18 + 18 = -3 + 18$

$5x = 15$

$\frac{5x}{5} = \frac{15}{5}$

$x = 3$

29. Let $x = \text{number}$

$2(x+6) = -x$

$2x+12 = -x$

$2x-2x+12 = -x-2x$

$12 = -3x$

$\frac{12}{-3} = \frac{-3x}{-3}$

$-4 = x$

31. $\frac{5}{3}x+4 = \frac{2}{3}x$

$\frac{5}{3}x-\frac{5}{3}x+4 = \frac{2}{3}x-\frac{5}{3}x$

$4 = -\frac{3}{3}x$

$4 = -x$

$\frac{4}{-1} = \frac{-x}{-1}$

$-4 = x$

$\{-4\}$

33. $-4(2x+1) = -5x+5$

$-8x-4 = -5x+5$

$-8x+5x-4 = -5x+5x+5$

$-3x-4 = 5$

$-3x-4+4 = 5+4$

$-3x = 9$

$\frac{-3x}{-3} = \frac{9}{-3}$

$x = -3$

$\{-3\}$

35. $3(8y-1) = 6(5+4y)$

$24y-3 = 30+24y$

$24y-24y-3 = 30+24y-24y$

$-3 = 30$

No Solution

$\{\ \}$

37. $\frac{4(n+2)}{5} = -n$

$5\left[\frac{4(n+2)}{5}\right] = 5(-n)$

$4(n+2) = -5n$

$4n+8 = -5n$

$4n-4n+8 = -5n-4n$

$8 = -9n$

$\frac{8}{-9} = \frac{-9n}{-9}$

$\frac{8}{-9} = n$

$\left\{-\frac{8}{9}\right\}$

39. $-2(4y-3)+4 = 3(5-y)$

$-8y+6+4 = 15-3y$

$-8y+10 = 15-3y$

$-8y+3y+10 = 15-3y+3y$

$-5y+10 = 15$

$-5y+10-10 = 15-10$

$-5y = 5$

$\frac{-5y}{-5} = \frac{5}{-5}$

$y = -1$

$\{-1\}$

41. $5t-3-t = 3(t+4)-15$

$4t-3 = 3t+12-15$

$4t-3 = 3t-3$

$4t-3t-3 = 3t-3t-3$

$t-3 = -3$

$t-3+3 = -3+3$

$t = 0$

$\{0\}$

43. $-9-5a = 3(6a-1)$

$-9-5a = 18a-3$

$-9-5a+5a = 18a+5a-3$

$-9 = 23a-3$

$-9+3 = 23a-3+3$

$-6 = 23a$

$\frac{-6}{23} = \frac{23a}{23}$

$\frac{-6}{23} = a$

$\left\{-\frac{6}{23}\right\}$

45. $\frac{2(8-a)}{3}=4-4a$

$3\left[\frac{2(8-a)}{3}\right]=3(4-4a)$

$2(8-a)=12-12a$

$16-2a=12-12a$

$16-2a+12a=12-12a+12a$

$16+10a=12$

$16-16+10a=12-16$

$10a=-4$

$\frac{10a}{10}=\frac{-4}{10}$

$a=-\frac{4}{10}=-\frac{2}{5}$

$\left\{-\frac{2}{5}\right\}$

47. $y-0.4y=0.42$

$1.0y-0.4y=0.42$

$0.6y=0.42$

$\frac{0.6y}{0.6}=\frac{0.42}{0.6}$

$y=0.7$

$\{0.7\}$

49. Let $x=$ number

$\frac{x+5}{4}=2x$

$4\left[\frac{x+5}{4}\right]=4(2x)$

$x+5=8x$

$x-x+5=8x-x$

$5=7x$

$\frac{5}{7}=\frac{7x}{7}$

$\frac{5}{7}=x$

51. 1st integer $=x$
2nd integer $=x+2$
3rd integer $=x+4$

$3x=(x+2)+(x+4)-1$

$3x=x+2+x+4-1$

$3x=2x+5$

$3x-2x=2x-2x+5$

$x=5$

The integers are 5, 7, and 9.

53. $r=vst-5$

$r+5=vst-5+5$

$r+5=vst$

$\frac{r+5}{vt}=\frac{vst}{vt}$

$\frac{r+5}{vt}=s$

55. $3x-6y=-2$

$3x-3x-6y=-2-3x$

$-6y=-2-3x$

$\frac{-6y}{-6}=\frac{-2-3x}{-6}$

$y=\frac{-2-3x}{-6}$

$y=\frac{-1(-2-3x)}{-1(-6)}$

$y=\frac{2+3x}{6}$

57. $C=2\pi r$

$\frac{C}{2r}=\frac{2\pi r}{2r}$

$\frac{C}{2r}=\pi$

59. $C=\frac{5}{9}(F-32)$

$C=\frac{5}{9}(90-32)$

$C=\frac{5}{9}(58)$

$C=\frac{290}{9}=32\frac{2}{9}^{\circ}$

61. Let $x=$ width
$2x=$ length

$P=2L+2W$

$90=2(2x)+2(x)$

$90=4x+2x$

$90=6x$

$\frac{90}{6}=\frac{6x}{6}$

$15=x$

The length is $2(15m)=30m$.

63. 1st integer $=x$
2nd integer $=x+2$
3rd integer $=x+4$

$x+x+2+x+4=-114$

$3x+6=-114$

$3x+6-6=-114-6$

$3x=-120$

$x=\frac{-120}{3}$

$x=-40$

The integers are $-40, -38$, and -36.

65. Point A (5, 2)

67. Point C (3, −1)

69. Point E (−5, −2)

71. Point G (−1, 0)

73.

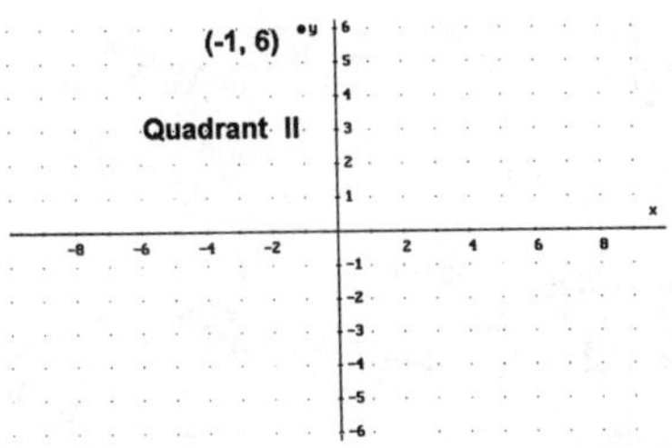

75.

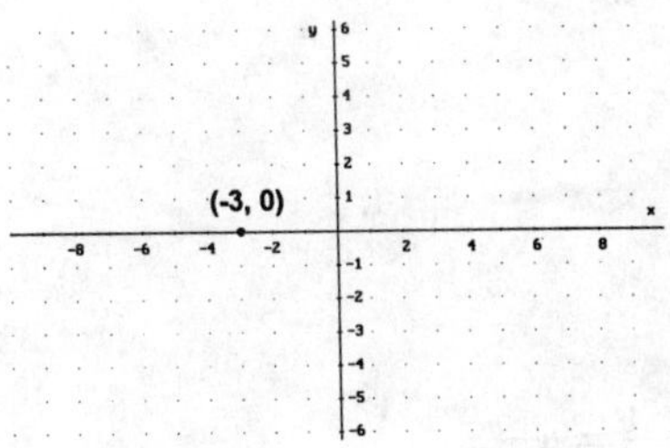

77.

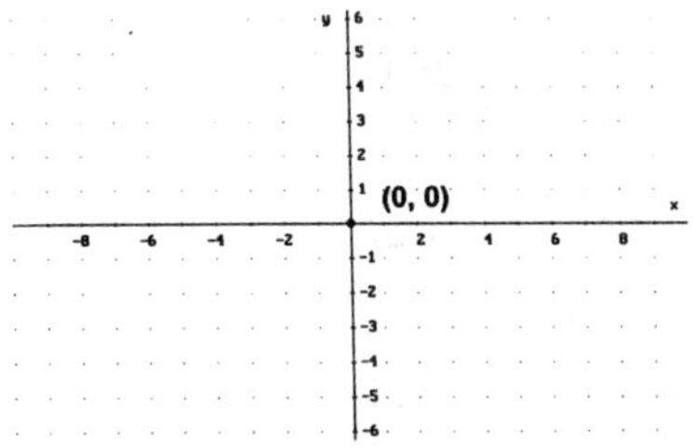

79.

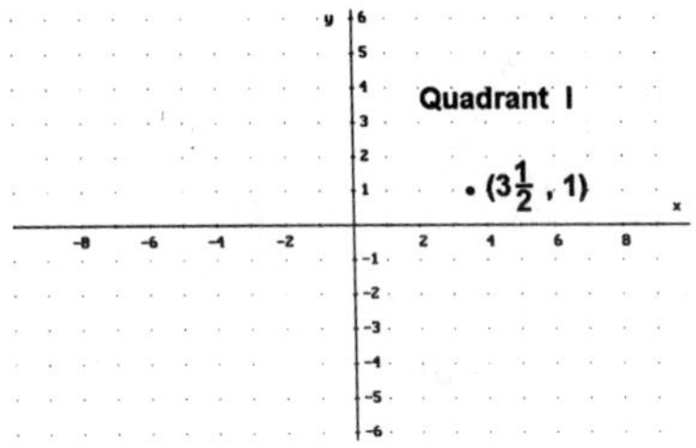

81. 20 mpg

83. $21.7-18.2$
3.5 mpg

85. From 1986 to 1987.

Chapter 2 - Test

1. $2y-6-y-4$

$y-10$

2. $x+7+x-16$

$2x-9$

3. $4(x-2)-3(2x-6)$

$4x-8-6x+18$

$-2x+10$

4. $-5(y+1)+2(3-5y)$

$-5y-5+6-10y$

$-15y+1$

5. $-\frac{4}{5}x=4$

$-\frac{5}{4}\left(-\frac{4}{5}x\right)=-\frac{5}{4}(4)$

$x=-5$

$\{-5\}$

6. $4(n-5) = -(4-2n)$

$4n-20 = -4+2n$

$4n-2n-20 = -4+2n-2n$

$2n-20 = -4$

$2n-20+20 = -4+20$

$2n = 16$

$\frac{2n}{2} = \frac{16}{2}$

$n = 8$

$\{8\}$

7. $5y-7+y = -(y+3y)$

$5y-7+y = -y-3y$

$6y-7 = -4y$

$6y-6y-7 = -4y-6y$

$-7 = -10y$

$\frac{-7}{-10} = \frac{-10y}{-10}$

$\frac{-7}{-10} = y$

$\frac{7}{10} = y$

$\left\{\frac{7}{10}\right\}$

8. $4z+1-z = 1+z$

$3z+1 = 1+z$

$3z-z+1 = 1+z-z$

$2z+1 = 1$

$2z+1-1 = 1-1$

$2z = 0$

$\frac{2z}{2} = \frac{0}{2}$

$z = 0$

$\{0\}$

9. $\frac{2(x+6)}{3} = x-5$

$3\left[\frac{2(x+6)}{3}\right] = 3(x-5)$

$2(x+6) = 3(x-5)$

$2x+12 = 3x-15$

$2x-2x+12 = 3x-2x-15$

$12 = x-15$

$12+15 = x-15+15$

$27 = x$

$\{27\}$

10. $\frac{4(y-1)}{5} = 2y+3$

$5\left[\frac{4(y-1)}{5}\right] = 5(2y+3)$

$4(y-1) = 5(2y+3)$

$4y-4 = 10y+15$

$4y-10y-4 = 10y-10y+15$

$-6y-4 = 15$

$-6y-4+4 = 15+4$

$-6y = 19$

$\frac{-6y}{-6} = \frac{19}{-6}$

$y = -\frac{19}{6}$

$\left\{-\frac{19}{6}\right\}$

11. $\frac{1}{2}-x+\frac{3}{2} = x-4$

$-x+\frac{4}{2} = x-4$

$-x+2 = x-4$

$-x+x+2 = x+x-4$

$2 = 2x-4$

$2+4 = 2x-4+4$

$6 = 2x$

$\frac{6}{2} = \frac{2x}{2}$

$3 = x$

$\{3\}$

12. $\frac{2}{3}+n+\frac{1}{3} = n+2$

$n+\frac{3}{3} = n+2$

$n+1 = n+2$

$n-n+1 = n-n+2$

$1 = 2$

No Solution

$\{\ \}$

13. $\frac{1}{3}(y+3) = 4y$

$3\left[\frac{1}{3}(y+3)\right] = 3(4y)$

$y+3 = 12y$

$y - y + 3 = 12y - y$

$3 = 11y$

$\frac{3}{11} = \frac{11y}{11}$

$\frac{3}{11} = y$

$\left\{\frac{3}{11}\right\}$

14. $\frac{2}{3}(1-c) = 5c$

$3\left[\frac{2}{3}(1-c)\right] = 3(5c)$

$2(1-c) = 15c$

$2 - 2c = 15c$

$2 - 2c + 2c = 15c + 2c$

$2 = 17c$

$\frac{2}{17} = \frac{17c}{17}$

$\frac{2}{17} = c$

$\left\{\frac{2}{17}\right\}$

15. $-3(x-4) + x = 5(3-x)$

$-3x + 12 + x = 15 - 5x$

$-2x + 12 = 15 - 5x$

$-2x + 5x + 12 = 15 - 5x + 5x$

$3x + 12 = 15$

$3x + 12 - 12 = 15 - 12$

$3x = 3$

$\frac{3x}{3} = \frac{3}{3}$

$x = 1$

$\{1\}$

16. $-4(a+1) - 3a = -7(2a-3)$

$-4a - 4 - 3a = -14a + 21$

$-7a - 4 = -14a + 21$

$-7a + 14a - 4 = -14a + 14a + 21$

$7a - 4 = 21$

$7a - 4 + 4 = 21 + 4$

$7a = 25$

$\frac{7a}{7} = \frac{25}{7}$

$a = \frac{25}{7}$

$\left\{\frac{25}{7}\right\}$

17. Let $x =$ number

$x + \frac{2}{3}x = 35$

$\frac{3}{3}x + \frac{2}{3}x = 35$

$\frac{5}{3}x = 35$

$\frac{3}{5}\left(\frac{5}{3}x\right) = \frac{3}{5}(35)$

$x = 21$

18. Area of deck

$A = lw$

$A = (20\text{ ft.})(35\text{ ft.})$

$A = 700$ sq. ft.

Two coats are needed.
Twice the Area $= 2(700$ sq. ft.$)$
Twice the Area $= 1400$ sq. ft.

$\frac{1400\text{ sq. ft}}{200\text{ sq. ft./gal}}$

7 gallons

19. 1st integer $= x$
2nd integer $= x + 2$

$2(x+2) = 3x + 15$

$2x + 4 = 3x + 15$

$2x - 3x + 4 = 3x - 3x + 15$

$-x + 4 = 15$

$-x + 4 - 4 = 15 - 4$

$-x = 11$

$x = \frac{11}{-1}$

$x = -11$

The integers are -11 and -9.

20. Let $x =$ height of Winter's jump.
$x + 14 =$ height of Sotomayor's jump.

$x + x + 14 = 170$

$2x + 14 = 170$

$2x + 14 - 14 = 170 - 14$

$2x = 156$

$x = \frac{156}{2}$

$x = 78$ inches

Winter jumped 78 inches.
Sotomayor jumped 92 inches.

21. $V = \pi r^2 h$

$\frac{V}{\pi r^2} = \frac{\pi r^2 h}{\pi r^2}$

$\frac{V}{\pi r^2} = h$

22. $W = 6bt$

$\frac{W}{6b} = \frac{6bt}{6b}$

$\frac{W}{6b} = t$

23. $5g - 2h = p$

$5g - 5g - 2h = p - 5g$

$-2h = p - 5g$

$\frac{-2h}{-2} = \frac{p - 5g}{-2}$

$h = \frac{p - 5g}{-2}$

$h = \frac{-1(p - 5g)}{-1(-2)}$

$h = \frac{-p + 5g}{2}$

$h = \frac{5g - p}{2}$

24. $3x - 4y = 10$

$3x - 3x - 4y = 10 - 3x$

$-4y = 10 - 3x$

$\frac{-4y}{-4} = \frac{10 - 3x}{-4}$

$y = \frac{10 - 3x}{-4}$

$y = \frac{-1(10 - 3x)}{-1(-4)}$

$y = \frac{-10 + 3x}{4}$

$y = \frac{3x - 10}{4}$

25.

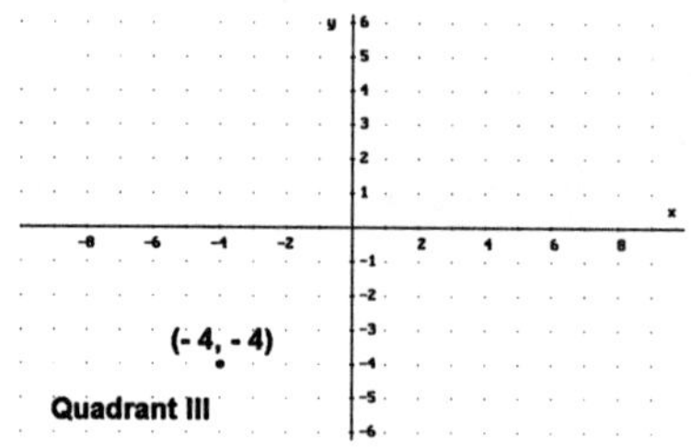

26.

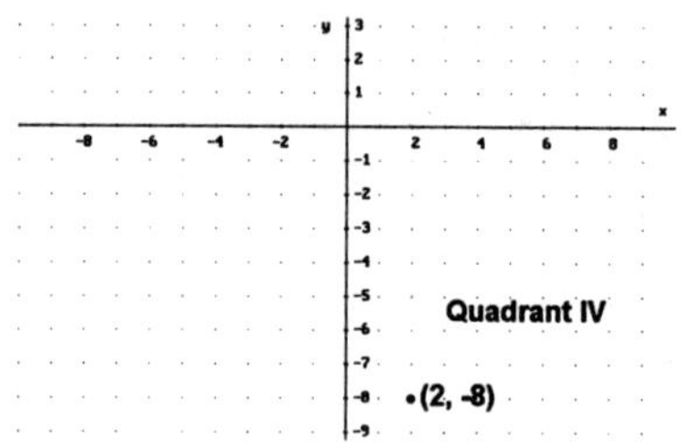

27.

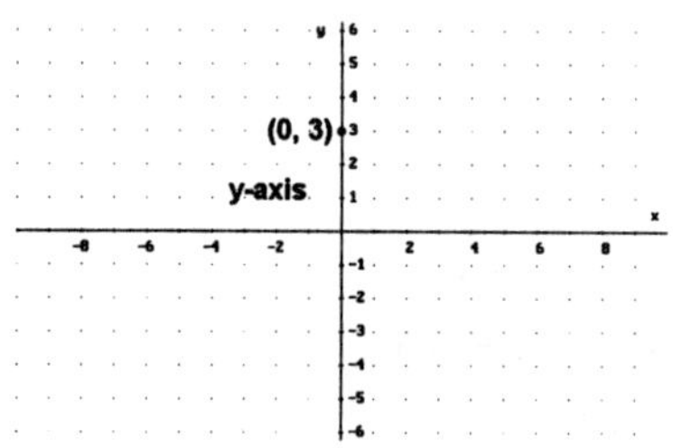

28.

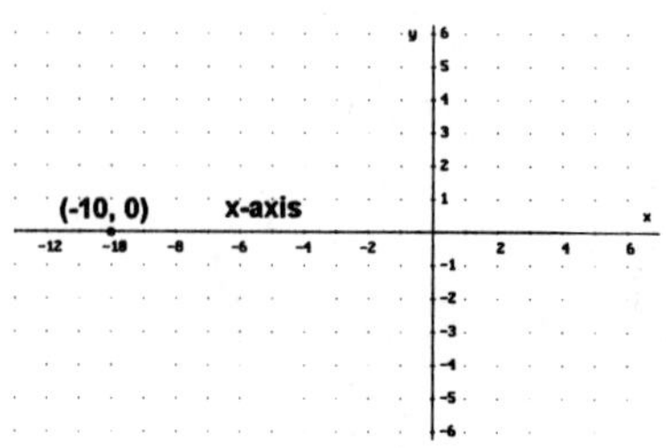

29. \$8 billion

30. \$3 billion

31. \$5.2 billion

32. From 1993 to 1994.

Chapter 2 - Cumulative Review

1a. $9 \leq 11$

b. $8 > 1$

c. $3 \neq 4$

3a. $-1 < 0$

b. $7 = \frac{14}{2}$

c. $-5 > -6$

5a. $\frac{42}{49} = \frac{7 \bullet 6}{7 \bullet 7} = \frac{6}{7}$

b. $\frac{11}{27}$

c. $\frac{88}{20} = \frac{4 \bullet 22}{4 \bullet 5} = \frac{22}{5}$

7a. $\sqrt{9} = 3$

b. $\sqrt{25} = 5$

c. $\sqrt{\frac{1}{4}} = \frac{1}{2}$

9a. $2x - y$

$2(3) - (2)$

$6 - 2$

4

b. $\frac{3x}{2y}$

$\frac{3(3)}{2(2)}$

$\frac{9}{4}$

c. $\frac{x}{y} + \frac{y}{2}$

$\frac{3}{2} + \frac{2}{2}$

$\frac{5}{2}$

d. $x^2 - y^2$

$3^2 - 2^2$

$9 - 4$

5

11a. $7x - 3x$

$4x$

b. $10y^2 + y^2$

$11y^2$

c. $8x^2 + 2x - 3x$

$8x^2 - x$

13. $2x + 3x - 5 + 7 = 10x + 3 - 6x - 4$

$5x + 2 = 4x - 1$

$5x + 2 - 2 = 4x - 1 - 2$

$5x = 4x - 3$

$5x - 4x = 4x - 4x - 3$

$x = -3$

$\{-3\}$

15. $2(x-3) = 5x - 9$

$2x - 6 = 5x - 9$

$2x - 6 + 6 = 5x - 9 + 6$

$2x = 5x - 3$

$2x - 5x = 5x - 5x - 3$

$-3x = -3$

$x = \frac{-3}{-3}$

$x = 1$

$\{1\}$

17a. One number $= 3$
Other number $= 8 - 3 = 5$

b. One number $= x$
Other number $= 8 - x$

19. $P = 21 + 2w$

$P - 21 = 21 - 21 + 2w$

$P - 21 = 2w$

$\frac{P - 21}{2} = \frac{2w}{2}$

$\frac{P-2l}{2}=w$

21a. 80 beats per minutes.

b. 5 minutes before lighting a cigarette.

c. Between 0 and 5 minutes after lighting a cigarette.

Exercise Set 3.1

1. $\frac{2}{15}$

3. $\frac{\$120}{8}=\frac{\$15}{1}$

5. $\frac{50}{1}$

7. $\frac{2}{3}=\frac{x}{6}$

$2\bullet 6=3\bullet x$

$12=3x$

$4=\frac{12}{3}=x$

$\{4\}$

9. $\frac{x}{10}=\frac{5}{9}$

$x\bullet 9=10\bullet 5$

$9x=50$

$x=\frac{50}{9}$

$\left\{\frac{50}{9}\right\}$

11. $\frac{9}{5}=\frac{12}{3x+2}$

$9\bullet(3x+2)=5\bullet 12$

$27x+18=60$

$27x=60-18$

$27x=42$

$x=\frac{42}{27}=\frac{14}{9}$

$\left\{\frac{14}{9}\right\}$

13. $\frac{3}{x+1}=\frac{5}{2x}$

$3\bullet 2x=5\bullet(x+1)$

$6x=5x+5$

$6x-5x=5$

$x=5$

$\{5\}$

15. $\frac{2x-1}{7}=\frac{x}{2}$

$2(2x-1)=7x$

$4x-2=7x$

$4x-4x-2=7x-4x$

$\frac{-2}{3}=\frac{3x}{3}$

$-\frac{3}{2}=x$

$\left\{-\frac{2}{3}\right\}$

17. $\frac{x}{24}=\frac{40}{32}$

$24\bullet\frac{x}{24}=24\bullet\frac{40}{32}$

$x=30$ feet

19. $\frac{y}{5}=\frac{3}{2}$

$5\bullet\frac{y}{5}=5\bullet\frac{3}{2}$

$y=\frac{15}{2}$ cm

21. $\frac{3}{100}=\frac{x}{4100}$

$4100\bullet\frac{3}{100}=4100\bullet\frac{x}{4100}$

123 pounds $=x$

23. $\frac{65}{170}=\frac{x}{9,000}$

$9,000\bullet\frac{65}{170}=9,000\bullet\frac{x}{9,000}$

3441 pounds $\approx x$

25. $\frac{4x}{6}=\frac{7}{2}$

$4x\bullet 2=6\bullet 7$

$8x=42$

$x=\frac{42}{8}=\frac{21}{4}$

$\left\{\frac{21}{4}\right\}$

27. $\frac{a}{25}=\frac{12}{10}$

$a \bullet 10=25 \bullet 12$

$10a=300$

$a=\frac{300}{10}=30$

$\{30\}$

29. $\frac{x-3}{x}=\frac{4}{7}$

$7 \bullet (x-3)=4 \bullet x$

$7x-21=4x$

$-21=4x-7x$

$-21=-3x$

$7=\frac{-21}{-3}=x$

$\{7\}$

31. $\frac{5x+1}{x}=\frac{6}{3}$

$3 \bullet (5x+1)=6 \bullet x$

$15x+3=6x$

$3=6x-15x$

$3=-9x$

$-\frac{1}{3}=-\frac{3}{9}=x$

$\left\{-\frac{1}{3}\right\}$

33. $\frac{x+1}{2x+3}=\frac{2}{3}$

$3 \bullet (x+1)=2 \bullet (2x+3)$

$3x+3=4x+6$

$3-6=4x-3x$

$-3=x$

$\{-3\}$

35. $\frac{110}{28.4}=\frac{x}{42.6}$

$110 \bullet 42.6=28.4 \bullet x$

$4686=28.4x$

$\frac{4686}{28.4}=x$

$165 \text{ cal}=x$

37. $\frac{4}{1}=\frac{x}{5}$

$4 \bullet 5=1 \bullet x$

$20 \text{ tablespoons}=x$

39. $\frac{418.5 \text{ miles}}{13.5 \text{ gal}}=31 \text{ mpg}$

41. $\frac{1}{6}=\frac{x}{23,000}$

$23,000 \bullet \frac{1}{6}=23,000 \bullet \frac{x}{23,000}$

$3,833 \approx x$

43. $A=20(12)$

$A=240 \text{ sq. ft.}$

$\frac{1}{9}=\frac{x}{240}$

$240 \bullet \frac{1}{9}=240 \bullet \frac{x}{240}$

$26 \text{ students} \approx x$

45. $\frac{343}{7}=\frac{x}{5}$

$7x=1715$

$x=245 \text{ miles}$

47. $\frac{8}{2}=\frac{36}{x}$

$8 \bullet x=2 \bullet 36$

$8x=72$

$x=9 \text{ gallons}$

49. $\frac{\$153}{8 \text{ hours}}=\$19.125/\text{hour} \approx \$19.13/\text{hour}.$

51. $\frac{\$35,063}{26 \text{ weeks}}=\$1348.58 \text{ per week.}$

$\left(6 \text{ months}=\frac{1}{2} \text{ year}=\frac{1}{2}\times 52 \text{ weeks}=26 \text{ weeks}\right)$

53. $\frac{11}{12}=\frac{y}{9}$

$9 \bullet \frac{11}{12}=9 \bullet \frac{y}{9}$

$8\frac{1}{4} \text{ kilometers}=y$

55. $\frac{5}{8}=\frac{x}{80}$

$80\bullet\frac{5}{8}=80\bullet\frac{x}{80}$

50 feet = x

57. $\frac{30 \text{ minutes}}{4 \text{ pages}}=\frac{x \text{ minutes}}{30 \text{ pages}}$

$30\bullet\frac{30}{4}=30\bullet\frac{x}{30}$

225 minutes = x

$\frac{225 \text{ minutes}}{60 \text{ minutes/hour}}=3.75$ hours

59. $1,568-97$

1471 megawatts

61. $2,976+1,471$

4447 megawatts

63. answers vary

$\frac{x}{(\text{population of your town})}=\frac{1000}{560,000}$

65. $\frac{y-b}{x-a}$

$\frac{5-(5)}{-3-(4)}$

$\frac{0}{-7}$

0

67. Let x = number

$2(4+x)+10=12$

$8+2x+10=12$

$2x+18=12$

$2x+18-18=12-18$

$2x=-6$

$x=-\frac{6}{2}$

$x=-3$

69. Let x = number

$2(x+3)=42$

$2x+6=42$

$2x+6-6=42-6$

$2x=36$

$x=\frac{36}{2}$

$x=18$

71. -2^5

-32

73. $(-2)^4$

16

75. $\frac{x}{y}=\frac{\text{length of chin to top of head}}{\text{length of chin to top of ear}}$

Exercise Set 3.2

1. 120% = 1.20

3. 22.5% = 0.225

5. 0.12% = 0.0012

7. 0.75 = 75%

9. 2 = 200%

11. $\frac{1}{8}=0.125=12.5\%$

13. 38%

15. 38% + 16%

54%

17. 0.38(360)

136.8°

19. answers vary

0.38(number of homeowners)

21. $x=0.16\times 70$

$x=11.2$

23. $28.6=x\bullet 52$

$\frac{28.6}{52}=x$

$0.55=x$

$55\%=x$

25. $45=0.25\bullet x$

$\frac{45}{0.25}=x$

$180 = x$

27. $0.25(156)$
$39 decrease
$156 − $39
$117 sale price

29. $110,000 − $95,500
$14,500 amount of increase
$\frac{14,500}{95,500} = 0.152$
$0.152 = 15.2\%$ increase

31. $0.23(20)$
4.6

33. $40 = 0.80 \bullet x$
$\frac{40}{0.80} = x$
$50 = x$

35. $144 = x \bullet 480$
$\frac{144}{480} = x$
$0.3 = x$
$30\% = x$

37. $447.2(0.448)$
200.3 feet increase
$447.2 + 200.3$
647.5 feet

39. 55.40%

41. $0.2370(230)$
approximately 54 people

43. No, many people surveyed used several different kinds of medications.

45. 70¢ − 40¢
30¢ increase
$\frac{30}{40} = 0.75$
$0.75 = 75\%$ increase

47. $x = \frac{230}{2400}$
$x \approx 0.096$
$x = 9.6\%$

49. $\frac{35}{130} = 0.269$
26.9%; Yes

51. $\frac{4 \text{ cal.}}{1 \text{ gram}} = \frac{x \text{ cal.}}{12 \text{ gram}}$
$x = 48$ calories
$\frac{48}{280} = 0.171$
17.1% cal. from protein

53. $0.14(2000) = 280$
$280 of clothing budget spent on women and girls.

55. $15.65 - 12.62 = 3.03$
$x = \frac{3.03}{12.62}$
$x = 0.24$
24% increase; Yes

57. $5000 - 3 = 4997$
$x = \frac{4997}{3}$
$x = 1665.667$
166,567% increase

59. 88%

61. $0.90(20) = 18$
18 supermarkets

63. More supermarkets offered selected services in 1992 than in 1990.

65. $-3a + 2c - b$
$-3(-2) + 2(-7) - 6$
$6 + (-14) - 6$

$-8-6$

-14

67. $ab+6bc$

$(0)(-1)+6(-1)(9)$

$0+(-6)(9)$

$0+(-54)$

-54

69. $2n^2+3m^2$

$2(-2)^2+3(7)^2$

$2(4)+3(49)$

$8+147$

155

71. $I=PRT$

$125=P(0.05)\left(\frac{5}{2}\right)$

$125=P(0.125)$

$\frac{125}{0.125}=P$

$\$1{,}000=P$

73. $d=rt$

$590=55t$

$\frac{590}{55}=t$

$10.7 \text{ hours}=t$

Exercise Set 3.3

1. Let $r=$ his speed for the first 3 hours and $r-20=$ his speed for the last hour. We must have (using $d=rt$):

$r \bullet 3+(r-20) \bullet 1=200$

$3r+r-20=200$

$4r-20=200$

$4r=220$

$r=55$

so, $r-20=35$

Hence, his speed was 55 mph for the first 3 hours and then 35 mph the last hour.

3. Let x be the time it took to travel to Los Angeles. Then the distance to Los Angeles is 200x. But this is equal to the distance it took to travel back from Los Angeles which is $300(2-x)$.

$200x=300(2-x)$

$200x=600-300x$

$500x=600$

$x=\frac{6}{5}$ hrs.

The distance is thus

$(200)\left(\frac{6}{5}\right)=240$ miles.

5. Let $n=$ the number of ounces of 20% codeine solution and $6-n$ $=$ the number of ounces of 50% codeine solution. Then:

$0.20n+0.50(6-n)=0.30(6)$

$2n+5(6-n)=3(6)$

$2n+30-5n=18$

$30-3n=18$

$12=3n$

$4=n$

$n=4$

so, $6-n=2$

Therefore, he should use 4 ounces of the 20% codeine solution and 2 ounces of the 50% codeine solution.

7. Let x be the amount of pure acid.

$0.10(4)+x=0.25(4+x)$

$0.40+x=1+0.25x$

$0.75x=0.60$

$x=\frac{0.60}{0.75}=\frac{60}{75}=\frac{4}{5}=0.8$ liter

9. Let $x=$ amount invested in the mutual fund and $24{,}000-x=$ amount invested in a CD. Then:

$0.08x+0.09(24{,}000-x)=2020$

$8x+9(24{,}000-x)=202{,}000$

$8x + 216,000 - 9x = 202,000$

$216,000 - x = 202,000$

$x = 14,000$

so, $24,000 - x = 10,000$

She invested $14,000 in the mutual fund and $10,000 in the CD.

11. Let x be the amount invested in the savings account. Then $3200 + x$ is the amount invested in the bond. The yearly income is

$0.06x + 0.08(3200 + x) = 1656$

$0.06x + 256 + 0.08x = 1656$

$0.14x = 1400$

$x = 10,000$

The amount invested in the bond is $3,200 + 10,000 = \$13,200$.

13. Let $x =$ amount invested at 9%.
$2x =$ amount invested at 10%.
$3x =$ amount invested at 11%.

$0.09x + 0.10(2x) + 0.11(3x) = 8370$

$9x + 10(2x) + 11(3x) = 837,000$

$9x + 20x + 33x = 837,000$

$62x = 837,000$

$x = 13,500$
$2x = 27,000$
$3x = 40,500$

She invested $13,500 at 9%, $27,000 at 10%, and $40,500 at 11%.

15. Let x be the amount deposited in the account that pays 7% annual interest.

$0.10(7000) + 0.07x = 0.09(7000 + x)$

$700 + 0.07x = 630 + 0.09x$

$70 = 0.02x$

$\$3500 = x$

17. First note that $3.75 - 0.25 = 3.5$ is the number of hours spent traveling. Now let $t =$ the time traveled before the gas stop and $3.5 - t =$ time traveled after gas stop. (using $d = rt$)

$70t + 60(3.5 - t) = 225$

$70t + 210 - 60t = 225$

$10t + 210 = 225$

$10t = 15$

$t = 1.5$

so, $70t = 105$

Thus, he drove 105 miles before the gas stop.

19. Let x be the amount of $6/lb. coffee. Then $100 - x$ is the amount of $5.90/lb. coffee.

$6x + 5.80(100 - x) = 5.85(100)$

$6x + 580 - 5.8x = 585$

$0.2x = 5$

$x = \frac{5}{0.2} = 25$

He should use 25 lbs. of the $6/lb. coffee and $100 - 25 = 75$ lbs. of the $5.80/lb. coffee.

21. 1st investment at $11\% = x$
2nd investment at 4% loss $= 10,000 - x$

$0.11(x) - 0.04(10,000 - x) = 650$

$11(x) - 4(10,000 - x) = 65,000$

$11x - 40,000 + 4x = 65,000$

$15x - 40,000 = 65,000$

$\frac{15x}{15} = \frac{105,000}{15}$

$x = 7000$

$10,000 - x = 3000$

$7,000 at 11% profit
$3,000 at 4% loss

23. amount invested at $10\% = x$
amount invested at $12\% = 2x$

$2890 = 0.10(x) + 0.12(2x)$

$289,000 = 10x + 24x$

$\frac{289,000}{34} = \frac{34x}{34}$

$8500 = x$

$17{,}000 = 2x$

\$8,500 invested at 10%
\$17,000 invested at 12%

25.

	distance = rate • time		
Bus	$60x$	60 mph	x
Car	$40(x+1.5)$	40 mph	$(x+1.5)$

$60x = 40(x+1.5)$

$60x = 40x+60$

$20x = 60$

$x = 3$ hours

27.

	distance = rate • time		
Bus on Level Road	$3(x+20)$	$x+20$	3
Bus on Winding Rd.	$4x$	x	4

$305 = 3(x+20)+4$

$305 = 3x+60+4x$

$\frac{245}{7} = \frac{7x}{7}$

$x = 35$ mph

$x+20 = 55$ mph

55 mph on level road.

29. Quantity of 60% solution = 10 cc.
Quantity of 25% solution = x cc.
Quantity of 30% solution = $(x+10)$ cc.

$0.25(x)+0.60(10) = 0.30(x+10)$

$25x+60(10) = 30(x+10)$

$25x+600 = 30x+300$

$300 = 5x$

$60 = x$

60 cc.

31. Quantity of \$4 per lb. coffee = 14 lbs.
Quantity of \$7 per lb. coffee = x
Quantity of \$5 per lb. coffee = $x+14$

$4(14)+7(x) = 5(x+14)$

$56+7x = 5x+70$

$\frac{2x}{2} = \frac{14}{2}$

$x = 7$

7 lbs.

33. 1st investment = x
2nd investment = $20{,}000-x$

$0.12(x)-0.04(20{,}000-x) = 0$

$12x-80{,}000+4x = 0$

$\frac{16x}{16} = \frac{80{,}000}{16}$

$x = 5000$

$20{,}000-x = 15{,}000$

5,000 at 12%
15,000 at 4%

35. amount invested at 9% = x
amount invested at 10% = $2x$
amount invested at 11% = $3x$

$\$2790 = 0.09(x)+0.10(2x)+0.11(3x)$

$279{,}000 = 9x+20x+33x$

$\frac{279{,}000}{62} = \frac{62x}{62}$

$x = 4{,}500$

$2x = 9{,}000$

$3x = 13{,}000$

\$4,500 at 9%
\$9,000 at 10%
\$13,500 at 11%

37.

	distance = rate • time		
Alan	$55(x+1)$	55	$x+1$
Dave	$65(x)$	65	x

$55(x+1)+65(x) = 250$

$55x+55+65x = 250$

$120x+55 = 250$

$\frac{120x}{120} = \frac{195}{120}$

$x = 1.625$

0.625×60 minutes $= 37\frac{1}{2}$ minutes

$x+1 = 2$ hrs. $37\frac{1}{2}$ minutes.

39. Quantity of 70% solution =
Quantity of 30% solution
of water = 30.
Quantity of 100% solution = x

$100\%(x) + 30\%(30) = 40\%(x + 30)$

$100x + 30(30) = 40(x + 30)$

$100x + 900 = 40x + 1200$

$60x = 300$

$\frac{60x}{60} = \frac{300}{60}$

$x = 5$ gallons

41.

	distance = rate • time		
Charlie	2x	x	2
Cindy	2(x + 1.1)	x + 1.1	2

$2x + 2(x + 1.1) = 11$

$2x + 2x + 2.2 = 11$

$4x + 2.2 = 11$

$4x + 2.2 - 2.2 = 11 - 2.2$

$4x = 8.8$

$x = 2.2$ miles per hours

Charlie hiked at 2.2 mph and
Cindy hiked at 3.3 mph.

43.

	distance = rate • time		
Upstream	5x	5	x
Downstream	11(4 − x)	11	4 − x

$5x = 11(4 - x)$

$5x = 44 - 11x$

$\frac{16x}{16} = \frac{44}{16}$

$x = 2.75$

Distance =

$5x = 5(2.75) = 13.75$

$11(4 - x) = 11(4 - 2.75) =$

$11(1.75) = 13.75 \times 2 =$

27.5 miles

45. Let t be the number of hours
he rows upstream.

	distance = rate • time		
Upstream	1.5t	3 − 1.5	t
Downstream	4.5(4 − t)	3 + 1.5	4 − t

$(3 - 1.5)t = (3 + 1.5)(4 - t)$

$1.5t = 18 - 4.5t$

$6t = 18$

$t = 3$ hrs.

47. Let x = the number of lbs. of
ground sirloin used and
500 − x = the number of lbs.
of hamburger used.

$2.25x + 1.00(500 - x) = 1.50(500)$

$225x + 100(500 - x) = 150(500)$

$225x + 50{,}000 - 100x = 75{,}000$

$125x = 25{,}000$

$x = 200$

$500 - x = 300$

Thus, he uses 200 lbs. of ground
sirloin and 300 lbs. of hamburger.

49. Let x = the number of bikes washed.
350 − x = the number of cars washed.

$0.75x + 2.00(350 - x) = 450$

$0.75x + 700 - 2x = 450$

$-1.25x = -250$

$x = 200$

200 bikes were washed.

51. Let x = the amount of 40%
antifreeze solution that must
be drained.

$0.40(6 - x) + 1.00x = 0.60(6)$

$4(6 - x) + 10x = 6(6)$

$24 - 4x + 10x = 36$

$24 + 6x = 36$

$6x = 12$

$x = 2$

Thus, 2 gallons of 40% antifreeze solution must be drained and replaced by pure antifreeze.

53. Solve the equation $C = R$ or

$100 + 20x = 24x$

$100 = 4x$

$25 = x$

$x = 25$

Therefore, the manufacturer must produce and sell 25 skateboards in order to break even.

55. Solve $C = R$

$4.50x + 2400 = 7.50x$

$2400 = 3x$

$800 = x$

$x = 800$

800 books must be produced and sold in order to break even.

57. $3 + (-7)$

-4

59. $4 - 16$

-12

61. $-5 - (-1)$

$-5 + (+1)$

-4

63. $5x + 20 = 8 - x$

$5x + 20 - 20 = 8 - 20 - x$

$5x = -12 - x$

$5x + x = -12 - x + x$

$6x = -12$

$x = -\frac{12}{6}$

$x = -2$

$\{-2\}$

65. $6(x-3) + 10 = -8$

$6x - 18 + 10 = -8$

$6x - 8 = -8$

$6x - 8 + 8 = -8 + 8$

$6x = 0$

$x = \frac{0}{6}$

$x = 0$

$\{0\}$

67. $\frac{6(3-z)}{5} = -z$

$5 \bullet \left[\frac{6(3-z)}{5}\right] = 5(-z)$

$6(3-z) = -5z$

$18 - 6z = -5z$

$18 - 6z + 6z = -5z + 6z$

$18 = z$

$\{18\}$

69. A(2, 2) B(0, 0)

C(−3, 2) D(−6, −1)

E(4, −4) F(0, −3)

Exercise Set 3.4

1. $|x| = 7$

$x = 7$ or $x = -7$

$\{7, -7\}$

3. $|3x| = 12$

$3x = 12$ or $3x = -12$

$x = 4$ or $x = -4$

$\{4, -4\}$

5. $|2x-5| = 9$

$2x - 5 = 9$ or $2x - 5 = -9$

$2x = 14$ or $2x = -4$

$x = 7$ or $x = -2$

$\{7, -2\}$

7. $\left|\frac{x}{2}-3\right|=1$

$\frac{x}{2}-3=1$ or $\frac{x}{2}-3=-1$

$\frac{x}{2}=4$ or $\frac{x}{2}=2$

$x=8$ or $x=4$

$\{8, 4\}$

9. $|z|+4=9$

$|z|=5$

$z=5$ or $z=-5$

$\{5, -5\}$

11. $|3x|+5=14$

$|3x|=9$

$3x=9$ or $3x=-9$

$x=3$ or $x=-3$

$\{3, -3\}$

13. $|2x|=0$

$2x=0$

$x=0$

$\{0\}$

15. $|4n+1|+10=4$

$|4n+1|=-6$

which is impossible.

$\{\ \}$

17. $|5x-1|=0$

$5x-1=0$

$5x=1$

$x=\frac{1}{5}$

$\left\{\frac{1}{5}\right\}$

19. $|5x-7|=|3x+11|$

$5x-7=3x+11$ or $5x-7=-(3x+11)$

$2x=18$ or $5x-7=-3x-11$

$x=9$ or $8x=-4$

$x=-\frac{1}{2}$

$\left\{9, -\frac{1}{2}\right\}$

21. $|z+8|=|z-3|$

$z+8=z-3$ or $z+8=-(z-3)$

$8=-3$ or $z+8=-z+3$

which is impossible or $2z=-5$

$z=-\frac{5}{2}$

$\left\{-\frac{5}{2}\right\}$

23. $|x|=4$

$x=4$ or $x=-4$

$\{4, -4\}$

25. $|y|=0$

$y=0$

$\{0\}$

27. $|z|=-2$

which is impossible.

$\{\ \}$

29. $|7-3x|=7$

$7-3x=7$ or $7-3x=-7$

$-3x=0$ or $-3x=-14$

$x=0$ or $x=\frac{14}{3}$

$\left\{0, \frac{14}{3}\right\}$

31. $|6x|-1=11$

$|6x|=12$

$6x=12$ or $6x=-12$

$x=2$ or $x=-2$

$\{2, -2\}$

33. $|4p|=-8$

which is impossible.

$\{\ \}$

35. $|x-3|+3=7$

$|x-3|=4$

$x-3=4$ or $x-3=-4$

$x=7$ or $x=-1$

$\{7, -1\}$

37. $\left|\frac{z}{4}+5\right| = -7$

which is impossible.

$\{\ \}$

39. $|9v-3| = -8$

which is impossible.

$\{\ \}$

41. $|8n+1| = 0$

$8n+1=0$

$8n = -1$

$n = -\frac{1}{8}$

$\left\{-\frac{1}{8}\right\}$

43. $|1+6c| - 7 = -3$

$|1+6c| = 4$

$1+6c = 4$ or $1+6c = -4$

$6c = 3$ or $6c = -5$

$c = \frac{1}{2}$ or $c = -\frac{5}{6}$

$\left\{\frac{1}{2}, -\frac{5}{6}\right\}$

45. $|5x+1| = 11$

$5x+1 = 11$ or $5x+1 = -11$

$5x = 10$ or $5x = -12$

$x = 2$ or $x = -\frac{12}{5}$

$\left\{2, -\frac{12}{5}\right\}$

47. $|4x-2| = |-10|$

$|4x-2| = 10$

$4x-2 = 10$ or $4x-2 = -10$

$4x = 12$ or $4x = -8$

$x = 3$ or $x = -2$

$\{3, -2\}$

49. $|5x+1| = |4x-7|$

$5x+1 = 4x-7$ or $5x+1 = -(4x-7)$

$x = -8$ or $5x+1 = -4x+7$

$9x = 6$

$x = \frac{2}{3}$

$\left\{-8, \frac{2}{3}\right\}$

51. $|6+2x| = -|-7|$

$|6+2x| = -7$

which is impossible

$\{\ \}$

53. $|2x-6| = |10-2x|$

$2x-6 = 10-2x$ or $2x-6 = -(10-2x)$

$4x = 16$ or $2x-6 = -10+2x$

$x = 4$ or $-6 = -10$

which is impossible

$\{4\}$

55. $\left|\frac{2x-5}{3}\right| = 7$

$\frac{2x-5}{3} = 7$ or $\frac{2x-5}{3} = -7$

$2x-5 = 21$ or $2x-5 = -21$

$2x = 26$ or $2x = -16$

$x = 13$ or $x = -8$

$\{13, -8\}$

57. $2+|5n| = 17$

$|5n| = 15$

$5n = 15$ or $5n = -15$

$n = 3$ or $n = -3$

$\{3, -3\}$

59. $\left|\frac{2x-1}{3}\right| = |-5|$

$\left|\frac{2x-1}{3}\right| = 5$

$\frac{2x-1}{3} = 5$ or $\frac{2x-1}{3} = -5$

$2x-1 = 15$ or $2x-1 = -15$

$2x = 16$ or $2x = -14$

$x = 8$ or $x = -7$

$\{8, -7\}$

61. $|2y-3| = |9-4y|$

$2y-3 = 9-4y$ or $2y-3 = -(9-4y)$

$6y = 12$ or $2y-3 = -9+4y$

$y = 2$ or $6 = 2y$

$3 = y$

$\{2, 3\}$

63. $\left|\frac{3n+2}{8}\right| = |-1|$

$\left|\frac{3n+2}{8}\right| = 1$

$\frac{3n+2}{8} = 1$ or $\frac{3n+2}{8} = -1$

$3n+2 = 8$ or $3n+2 = -8$

$3n = 6$ or $3n = -10$

$n = 2$ or $n = -\frac{10}{3}$

$\left\{2, -\frac{10}{3}\right\}$

65. $|x+4| = |7-x|$

$x+4 = 7-x$ or $x+4 = -(7-x)$

$2x = 3$ or $x+4 = -7+x$

$x = \frac{3}{2}$ or $4 = -7$

which is impossible

$\left\{\frac{3}{2}\right\}$

67. $\left|\frac{8c-7}{3}\right| = -|-5|$

$\left|\frac{8c-7}{3}\right| = -5$

which is impossible.

{ }

69. $-(5) = -5$

71. $-(-8) = 8$

73. $\frac{1}{-3} = -\frac{1}{3}$

75. $\frac{1}{\frac{5}{9}} = \frac{9}{5}$

77. $\frac{x}{3} = \frac{x-4}{5}$

$5x = 3(x-4)$

$5x = 3x - 12$

$5x - 3x = 3x - 3x - 12$

$2x = -12$

$x = -\frac{12}{2}$

$x = -6$

$\{-6\}$

79. $\frac{2x-1}{6} = \frac{3x}{10}$

$10(2x-1) = 6(3x)$

$20x - 10 = 18x$

$20x - 20x - 10 = 18x - 20x$

$-10 = -2x$

$\frac{-10}{-2} = x$

$5 = x$

$\{5\}$

Exercise Set 3.5

1. $(-\infty, -3)$

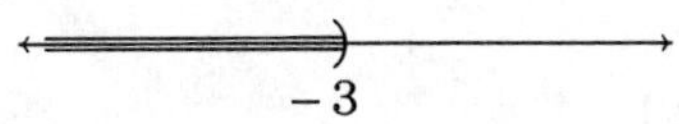

3. $[0.3, \infty)$

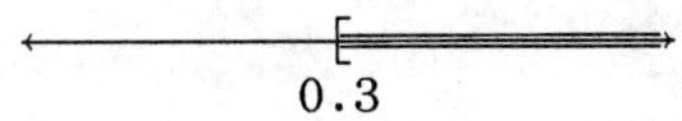

5. $(5, \infty)$

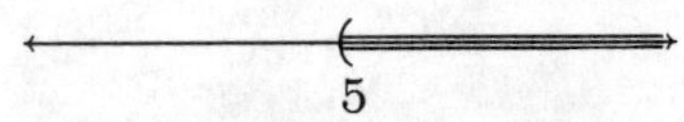

7. $(-2, 5)$

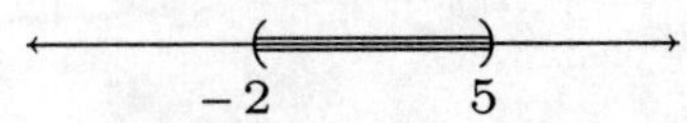

9. $(-1, 5)$

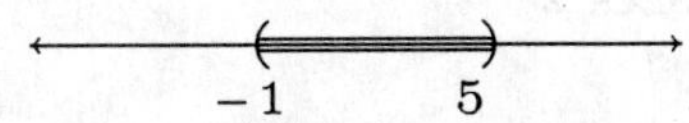

11. $2x < -6$

$\frac{2x}{2} < \frac{-6}{2}$

$x < -3$

$(-\infty, -3)$

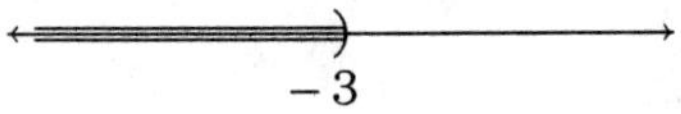

13. $x-2 \geq -7$

$x-2+2 \geq -7+2$

$x \geq -5$

$[-5, \infty)$

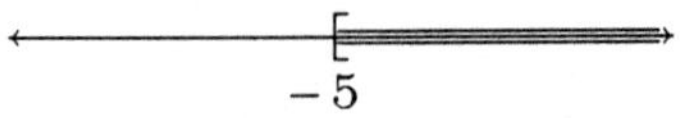

15. $-8x \leq 16$

$\frac{-8x}{-8} \geq \frac{16}{-8}$

$x \geq -2$

$[-2, \infty)$

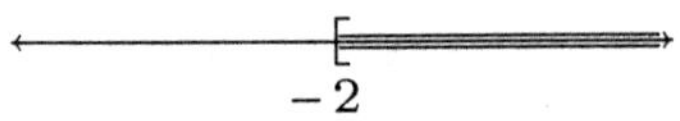

17. $15+2x \geq 4x-7$

$22 \geq 2x$

$11 \geq x$

$x \leq 11$

$(-\infty, 11]$

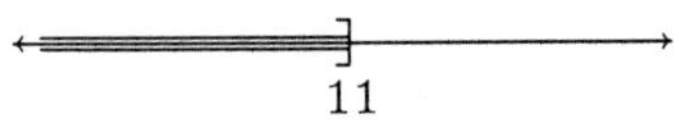

19. $\frac{3x}{4} \geq 2$

$x \geq \frac{8}{3}$

$\left[\frac{8}{3}, \infty\right)$

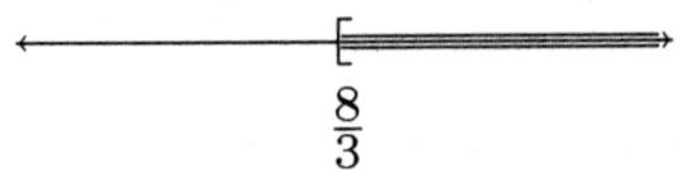

21. $3(x-5) < 2(2x-1)$

$3x-15 < 4x-2$

$-13 < x$

$x > -13$

$(-13, \infty)$

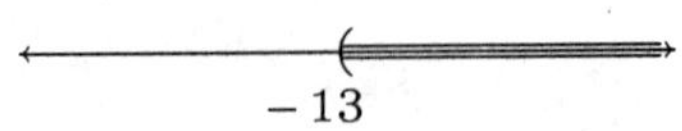

23. $\frac{1}{2}+\frac{2}{3} \geq \frac{x}{6}$

$\frac{7}{6} \geq \frac{x}{6}$

$7 \geq x$

$x \leq 7$

$(-\infty, 7]$

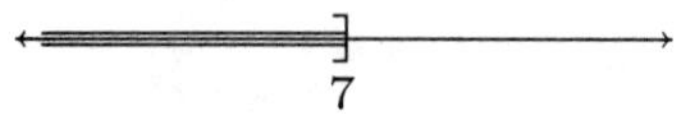

25. $4(x-1) \geq 4x-8$

$4x-4 \geq 4x-8$

$-4 \geq -8$

All real numbers.

$(-\infty, \infty)$

27. $7x < 7(x-2)$

$7x < 7x-14$

$0 < -14$

No solution exists.

$\{ \}$

29. Let $x =$ the weight of the luggaga and cargo.

$6(160)+x \leq 2000$

$960+x \leq 2000$

$x \leq 1040$

The plane can carry a maximum of 1040 lbs. of luggage and cargo.

31. Let $x =$ the weight of the envelope.

$0.32(1)+0.23(x-1) \leq 4.23$

$0.32+0.23x-0.23 \leq 4.23$

$0.09+0.23x \leq 4.23$

$\frac{0.23x}{0.23} \leq \frac{4.14}{0.23}$

$x \leq 18$

At most 18 ounces can be mailed for \$4.23.

33. $5x+3>2+4x$

$x>-1$

$(-1,\ \infty)$

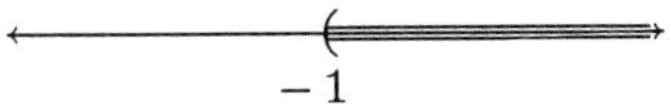

35. $8x-7\le 7x-5$

$x\le 2$

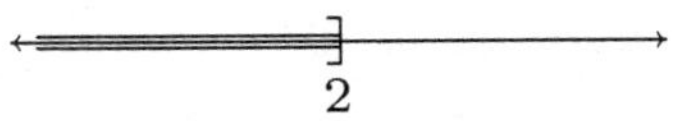

37. $5x>10$

$x>2$

$(2,\ \infty)$

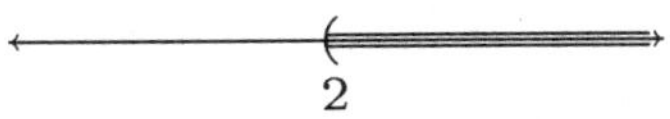

39. $-4x\le 32$

$x\ge -8$

$[-8,\ \infty)$

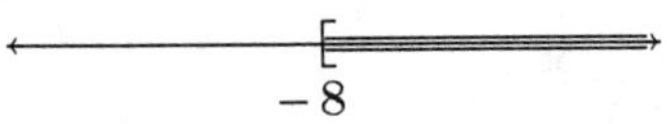

41. $-2x+7\ge 9$

$-2x\ge 2$

$x\le -1$

$(-\infty,-1]$

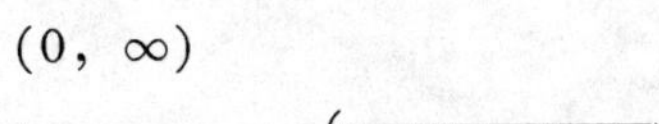

43. $4(2x+1)>4$

$2x+1>1$

$2x>0$

$x>0$

$(0,\ \infty)$

45. $\frac{x+7}{5}>1$

$x+7>5$

$x>-2$

$(-2,\ \infty)$

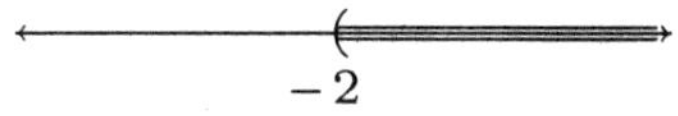

47. $-6x+2\ge 2(5-x)$

$-6x+2\ge 10-2x$

$-6x+2x+2\ge 10-2x+2x$

$-4x+2\ge 10$

$-4x+2-2\ge 10-2$

$-4x\ge 8$

$\frac{-4x}{-4}\le\frac{8}{-4}$

$x\le -2$

$(-\infty,-2]$

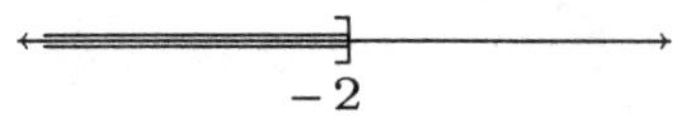

49. $4(3x-1)\le 5(2x-4)$

$12x-4\le 10x-20$

$12x\quad 10x-4\le 10x-10x-20$

$2x-4\le -20$

$2x-4+4\le -20+4$

$2x\le -16$

$\frac{2x}{2}\le\frac{-16}{2}$

$x\le -8$

$(-\infty,-8]$

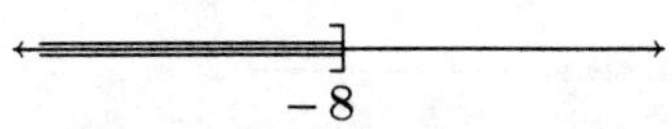

51. $\frac{-5x+11}{2}\le 7$

$-5x+11\le 14$

$-5x\le 3$

$x\ge -\frac{3}{5}$

$\left[-\frac{3}{5},\ \infty\right)$

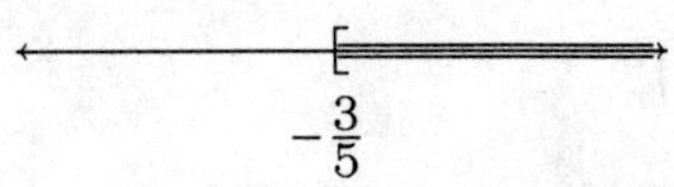

53. $8x-16\le 10x+2$

$-18\le 2x$

$-9\le x$

$x\ge -9$

$[-9, \infty)$

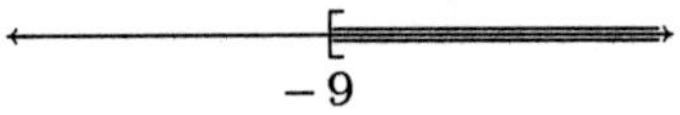

55. $2(x-3) > 70$

$x-3 > 35$

$x > 38$

$(38, \infty)$

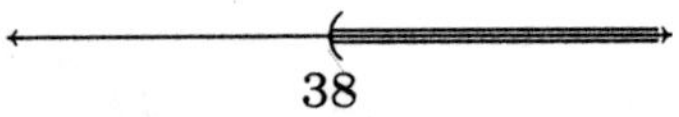

57. $-5x+4 \leq -4(x-1)$

$-5x+4 \leq -4x+4$

$0 \leq x$

$x \geq 0$

$[0, \infty)$

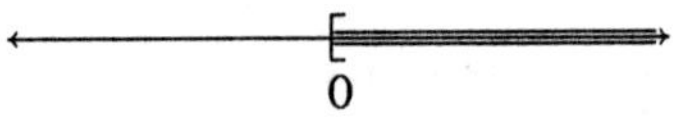

59. $\frac{1}{4}(x-7) \geq x+2$

$x-7 \geq 4x+8$

$-15 \geq 3x$

$-5 \geq x$

$x \leq -5$

$(-\infty, -5]$

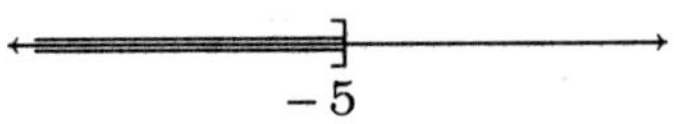

61. $\frac{2}{3}(x+2) < \frac{1}{5}(2x+7)$

$10(x+2) < 3(2x+7)$

$10x+20 < 6x+21$

$4x < 1$

$x < \frac{1}{4}$

$\left(-\infty, \frac{1}{4}\right)$

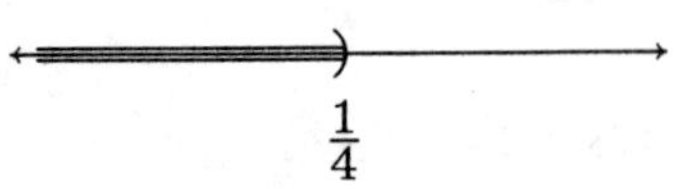

63. $4(x-6)+2x-4 \geq 3(x-7)+10x$

$4x-24+2x-4 \geq 3x-21+10x$

$6x-28 \geq 13x-21$

$-7 \geq 7x$

$-1 \geq x$

$x \leq -1$

$(-\infty, -1]$

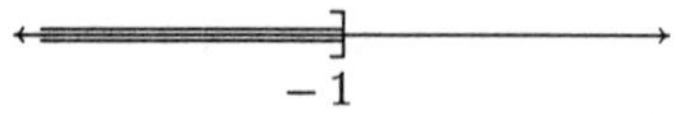

65. $\frac{5x+1}{7} - \frac{2x-6}{4} \geq -4$

$4(5x+1) - 7(2x-6) \geq -112$

$20x+4-14x+42 \geq -112$

$6x+46 \geq -112$

$6x \geq -158$

$x \geq -\frac{79}{3}$

$\left[-\frac{79}{3}, \infty\right)$

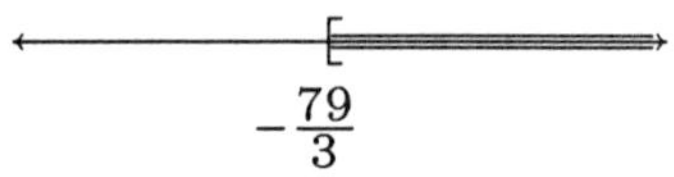

67. $\frac{-x+2}{2} - \frac{1-5x}{8} < -1$

$4(-x+2) - (1-5x) < -8$

$-4x+8-1+5x < -8$

$x+7 < -8$

$x < -15$

$(-\infty, -15)$

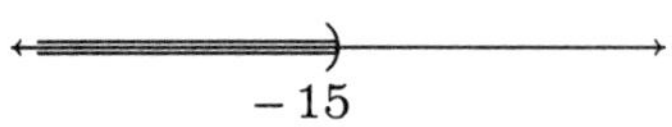

69. Let $x =$ her score on the final.

$\frac{72+67+82+79+2x}{6} \geq 60$

$300+2x \geq 360$

$2x \geq 60$

$x \geq 30$

Therefore, she must score at least 30% on the final exam.

71. $\frac{(3.52)+(4.04)+(3.87)+x}{4} < 4$

$\frac{11.43+x}{4} < 4$

$11.43 + x < 16$

$x < 4.57$ minutes

73. Let $x =$ score in the 3rd game.

$\frac{146 + 201 + x}{3} \geq 180$

$\frac{347 + x}{3} \geq 180$

$347 + x \geq 3(180)$

$347 + x \geq 540$

$x \geq 193$

He must score at least 193.

75. $P \leq 100$

$21 + 2w \leq 100$

$21 + 2(15) \leq 100$

$21 + 30 \leq 100$

$21 \leq 70$

$l \leq 35$ cm.

77. $\sqrt{25} = 5$

79. $\sqrt[3]{8} = 2$

81. $\sqrt[4]{16} = 2$

83. $-\sqrt{4} = -2$

85. $\{x | 0 \leq x \leq 5\}$

[0, 5]

87. $\{x | 3 \leq x < 10\}$

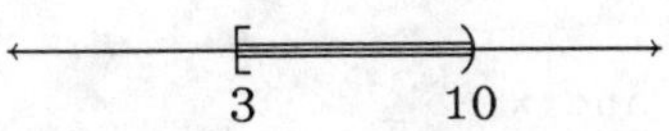

[3, 10)

89. 32 million

91. The greatest income is from 1991 to 1992.

Exercise Set 3.6

1. $x < 5$ and $x > -2$

$-2 < x < 5$

$(-2, 5)$

3. $x + 1 \geq 7$ and $3x - 1 \geq 5$

$x \geq 6$ and $3x \geq 6$

$x \geq 2$

$x \geq 6$

$[6, \infty)$

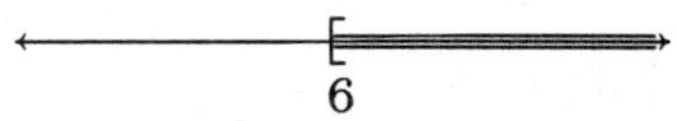

5. $4x + 2 \leq -10$

$4x \leq -12$

$x \leq -3$

$(-\infty, -3]$

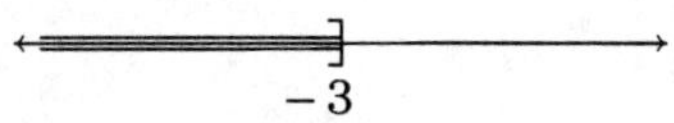

7. $5 < x - 6 < 11$

$11 < x < 17$

$(11, 17)$

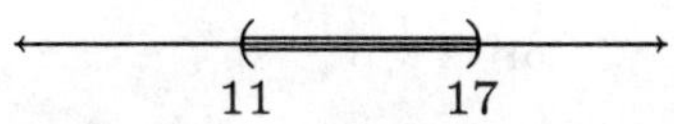

9. $-2 \leq 3x - 5 \leq 7$

$3 \leq 3x \leq 12$

$1 \leq x \leq 4$

$[1, 4]$

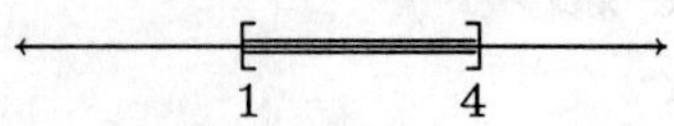

11. $1 \leq \frac{2}{3}x + 3 \leq 4$

$-2 \leq \frac{2}{3}x \leq 1$

$-3 \leq x \leq \frac{3}{2}$

$\left[-3, \frac{3}{2}\right]$

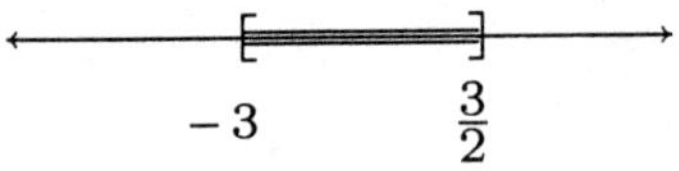

13. $-5 \le \frac{x+1}{4} \le -2$

$-20 \le x+1 \le -8$

$-21 \le x \le -9$

$[-21, -9]$

15. $x < -1$ or $x > 0$

$(-\infty, -1) \cup (0, \infty)$

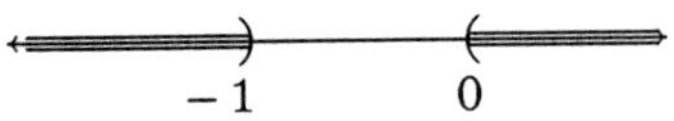

17. $-2x \le -4$ or $5x - 20 \ge 5$

$x \ge 2$ or $5x \ge 25$

$x \ge 5$

$x \ge 2$

$[2, \infty)$

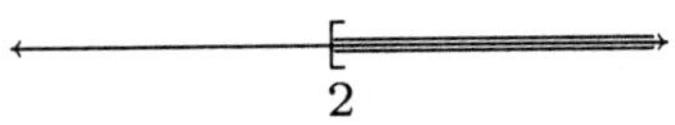

19. $3(x-1) < 12$ or $x+7 > 10$

$x - 1 < 4$ or $x > 3$

$x < 5$

All real numbers

$(-\infty, \infty)$

21. $x < 2$ and $x > -1$

$-1 < x < 2$

$(-1, 2)$

23. $x < 2$ or $x > -1$

All real numbers

$(-\infty, \infty)$

25. $x \ge -5$ and $x \ge -1$

$x \ge -1$

$[-1, \infty)$

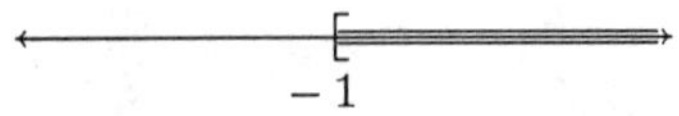

27. $x \ge -5$ or $x \ge -1$

$x \ge -5$

$[-5, \infty)$

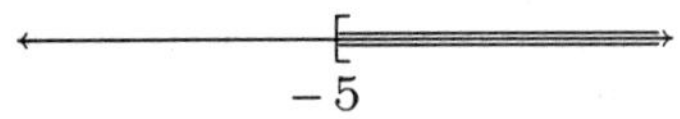

29. $0 < 2x - 3 \le 9$

$3 \le 2x \le 12$

$\frac{3}{2} \le x \le 6$

$\left[\frac{3}{2}, 6\right]$

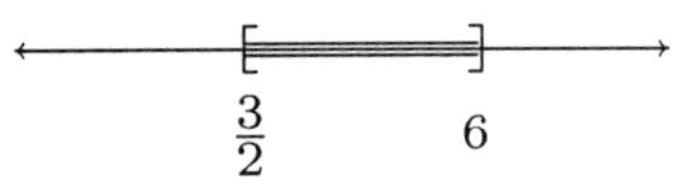

31. $\frac{1}{2} < x - \frac{3}{4} < 2$

$\frac{5}{4} < x < \frac{11}{4}$

$\left(\frac{5}{4}, \frac{11}{4}\right)$

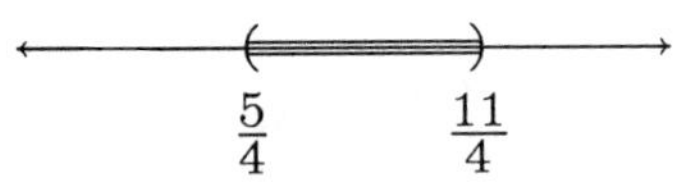

33. $x + 3 \ge 3$ and $x + 3 \le 2$

$x \ge 0$ and $x \le -1$

No solution.

$\{\ \}$

35. $3x \ge 5$ or $-x - 6 < 1$

$x \ge \frac{5}{3}$ or $-x < 7$

$$x > -7$$

$x > -7$

$(-7,\ \infty)$

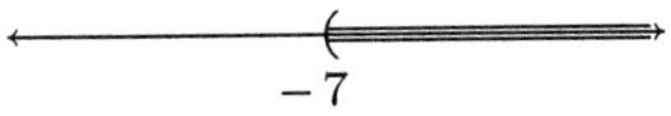

37. $0 < \frac{5-2x}{3} < 5$

$0 < 5-2x < 15$

$-5 < -2x < 10$

$-5 < x < \frac{5}{2}$

$\left(-5,\ \frac{5}{2}\right)$

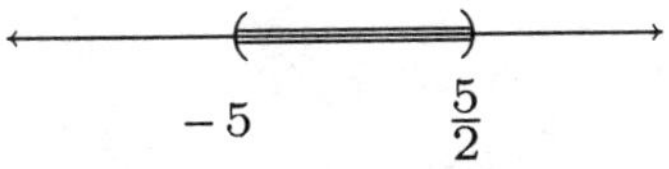

39. $-6 < 3(x-2) \le 8$

$-2 < x-2 \le \frac{8}{3}$

$0 < x \le \frac{14}{3}$

$\left(0,\ \frac{14}{3}\right]$

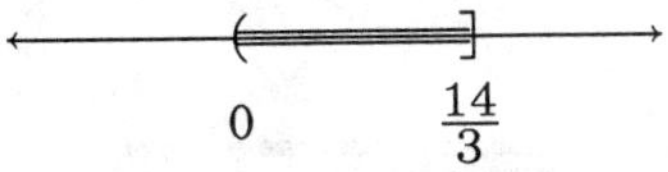

41. $-x+5 > 6$ and $1+2x \le -5$

$-x > 1$ and $2x \le -6$

$x < -1$ and $x \le -3$

$x \le -3$

$(-\infty, -3]$

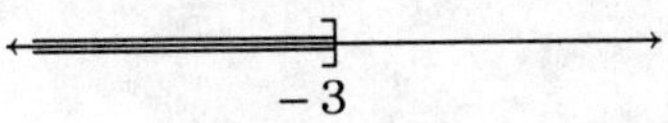

43. $3x+2 \le 5$ or $7x > 29$

$3x \le 3$ or $x > \frac{29}{7}$

$x \le 1$

$(-\infty,\ 1] \cup \left(\frac{29}{7},\ \infty\right)$

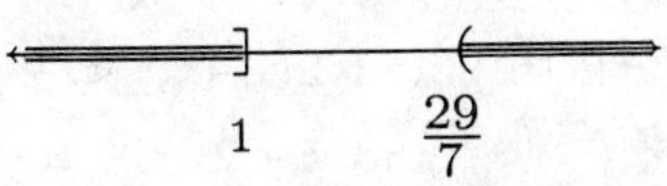

45. $5-x > 7$ and $2x+3 \ge 13$

$-x > 7-5$ and $2x \ge 13-3$

$-x > 2$ and $2x \ge 10$

$x < -2$ and $x \ge 5$

No solution.

$\{\ \}$

47. $-\frac{1}{2} \le \frac{4x-1}{6} < \frac{5}{6}$

$-3 \le 4x-1 < 5$

$-2 \le 4x < 6$

$-\frac{1}{2} \le x < \frac{3}{2}$

$\left[-\frac{1}{2},\ \frac{3}{2}\right)$

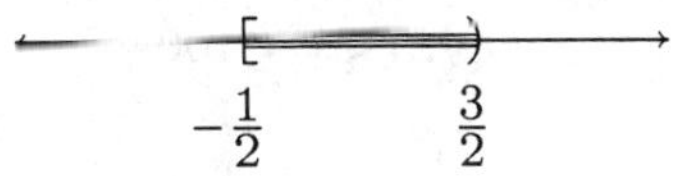

49. $\frac{1}{15} < \frac{8-3x}{15} < \frac{4}{5}$

$1 < 8-3x < 12$

$-7 < -3x < 4$

$-\frac{4}{3} < x < \frac{7}{3}$

$\left(-\frac{4}{3},\ \frac{7}{3}\right)$

51. $0.3 < 0.2x - 0.9 < 1.5$

$1.2 < 0.2x < 2.4$

$6 < x < 12$

$(6,\ 12)$

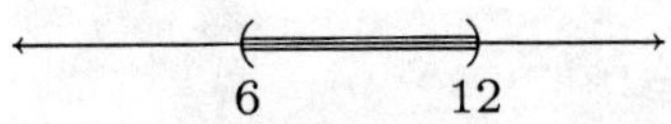

53. $-39^\circ \le C \le 45^\circ$

$-39 \le \frac{5}{9}(F-32) \le 45$

$\frac{9}{5}(-39) \le \frac{9}{5} \bullet \frac{5}{9}(F-32) \le \frac{9}{5}(45)$

$-70.2 \le F - 32 \le 81$

$-70.2 + 32 \le F - 32 + 32 \le 81 + 32$

$-38.2^\circ \le F \le 113^\circ$

55. Let $x =$ grade of final exam.

$90 < \dfrac{(85 + 95 + 92 + 3x)}{6} < 100$

$6(90) \le 6 \bullet \dfrac{(85 + 95 + 92 + 3x)}{6} \le 6(100)$

$540 \le 85 + 95 + 92 + 3x \le 600$

$540 \le 272 + 3x \le 600$

$540 - 272 \le 272 - 272 + 3x \le 600 - 272$

$268 \le 3x \le 328$

$\dfrac{268}{3} \le \dfrac{3x}{3} \le \dfrac{328}{3}$

$89.3 \le x \le 109.3$

Since grades can not exceed 100 the range is $89.3 \le x \le 100$.

57. $2.9 \le C \le 3.1$

$2.9 \le 3.14d \le 3.1$

$\dfrac{2.9}{3.14} \le \dfrac{3.14d}{3.14} \le \dfrac{3.1}{3.14}$

$0.924 \le d \le 0.987$

59. $|-3| = 3$

61. $|7| = 7$

63. $|7 - 15|$

$|-8| = 8$

65. $\left|\dfrac{10(5)}{-15-10}\right|$

$\left|\dfrac{50}{-25}\right|$

$|-2| = 2$

67. $|x - 2| = 19$

$x - 2 = 19$ or $x - 2 = -19$

$x = 19 + 2$ or $x = -19 + 2$

$x = 21$ or $x = -17$

$\{-17, 21\}$

69. $|2x + 1| + 7 = -4$

$|2x + 1| + 7 - 7 = -4 - 7$

$|2x + 1| = -11$

No solution.

{ }

71. $|x - 3| = |x + 11|$

$x - 3 = x + 11$ or $x - 3 = -(x + 11)$

$x - x - 3 = x - x + 11$ or $x - 3 = -x - 11$

$-3 = 11$ or $x + x - 3 = x - x - 11$

No solution or $2x - 3 = -11$

$2x = -11 + 3$

$2x = -8$

$x = -4$

$\{-4\}$

73. $2x - 3 < 3x + 1 < 4x - 5$

$2x - 3 < 3x + 1$ and $3x + 1 < 4x - 5$

$-3 < x + 1$ and $1 < x - 5$

$-4 < x$ and $6 < x$

$x > 6$

$(6, \infty)$

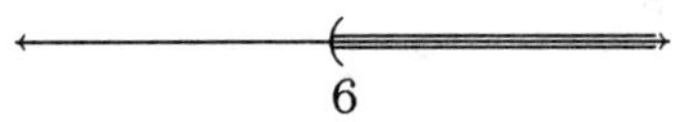

75. $-3(x - 2) \le 3 - 2x \le 10 - 3x$

$-3(x - 2) \le 3 - 2x$ and $3 - 2x \le 10 - 3x$

$-3x + 6 \le 3 - 2x$ and $3 + x \le 10$

$6 \le 3 + x$ and $x \le 7$

$3 \le x$

$x \ge 3$

$3 \le x \le 7$

$[3, 7]$

77. $5x - 8 < 2(2 + x) < -2(1 + 2x)$

$5x - 8 < 2(2 + x)$ and $2(2 + x) < -2(1 + 2x)$

$5x - 8 < 4 + 2x$ and $4 + 2x < -2 - 4x$

$3x - 8 < 4$ and $4 + 6x < -2$

$3x < 12$ and $6x < -6$

$x < 4$ and $x < -1$

$x < -1$

$(-\infty, -1)$

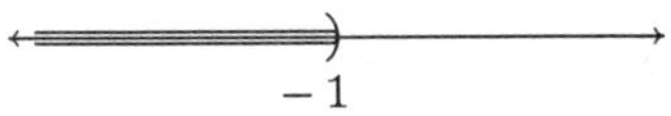

Exercise Set 3.7

1. $|x| \le 4$

$-4 \le x \le 4$

$[-4, 4]$

3. $|x - 3| < 2$

$-2 < x - 3 < 2$

$1 < x < 5$

$(1, 5)$

5. $|x + 3| < 2$

$-2 < x + 3 < 2$

$-5 < x < -1$

$(-5, -1)$

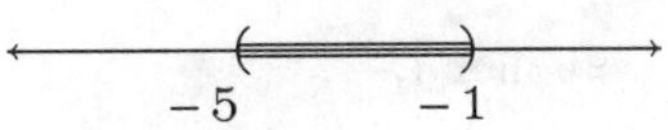

7. $|2x + 7| \le 13$

$-13 \le 2x + 7 \le 13$

$-20 \le 2x \le 6$

$-10 \le x \le 3$

$[-10, 3]$

9. $|x| + 7 \le 12$

$|x| \le 5$

$-5 \le x \le 5$

$[-5, 5]$

11. $|3x - 1| < -5$

No real solutions.

$\{ \}$

13. $|x - 6| - 7 \le -1$

$|x - 6| \le 6$

$-6 \le x - 6 \le 6$

$0 \le x \le 12$

$[0, 12]$

15. $|x| > 3$

$x < -3$ or $x > 3$

$(-\infty, -3) \cup (3, \infty)$

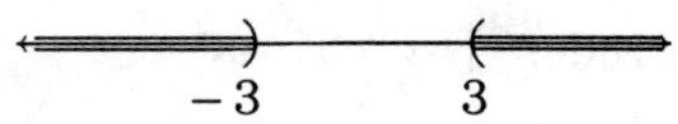

17. $|x + 10| \ge 14$

$x + 10 \le -14$ or $x + 10 \ge 14$

$x \le -24$ or $x \ge 4$

$(-\infty, -24] \cup [4, \infty)$

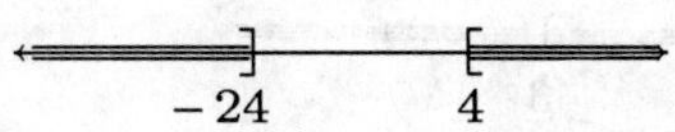

19. $|x| + 2 > 6$

$|x| > 4$

$x < -4$ or $x > 4$

$(-\infty, -4) \cup (4, \infty)$

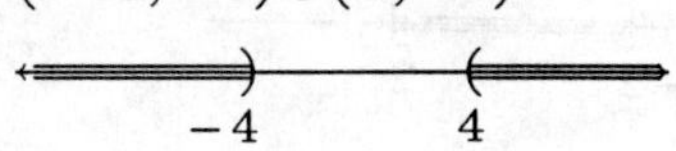

21. $|5x| > -4$

All real numbers.

$(-\infty, \infty)$

23. $|6x-8|+3>7$

$|6x-8|>4$

$6x-8<-4$ or $6x-8>4$

$6x<4$ or $6x>12$

$x<\frac{2}{3}$ or $x>2$

$\left(-\infty, \frac{2}{3}\right)\cup(2, \infty)$

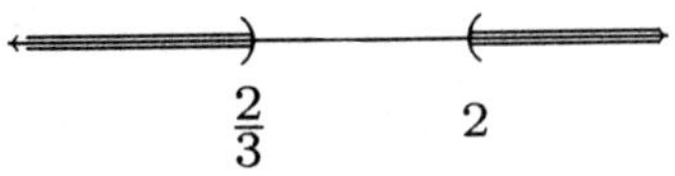

25. $|x|\le 0$

$|x|=0$

$x=0$

$\{0\}$

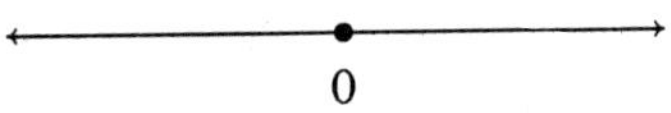

27. $|8x+3|>0$

only excludes $|8x+3|=0$

$8x+3=0$

$8x=-3$

$x=-\frac{3}{8}$

$\left(-\infty, -\frac{3}{8}\right)\cup\left(-\frac{3}{8}, \infty\right)$

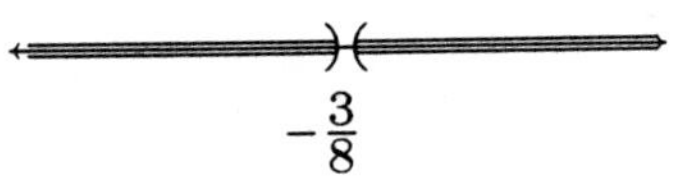

29. $|x|\le 2$

$-2\le x\le 2$

$[-2, 2]$

31. $|y|>1$

$y<-1$ or $y>1$

$(-\infty, -1)\cup(1, \infty)$

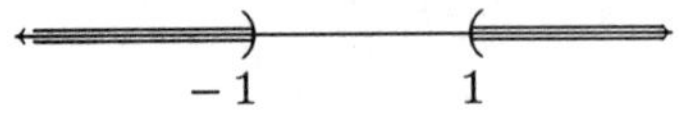

33. $|x-3|<8$

$-8<x-3<8$

$-5<x<11$

$(-5, 11)$

35. $|6x-8|>4$

$6x-8<-4$ or $6x-8>4$

$6x<4$ or $6x>12$

$x<\frac{2}{3}$ or $x>2$

$\left(-\infty, \frac{2}{3}\right)\cup(2, \infty)$

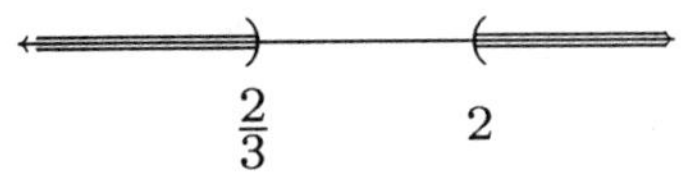

37. $5+|x|\le 2$

$|x|\le -3$

No real solution.

$\{\ \}$

39. $|x|>-4$

All real numbers.

$(-\infty, \infty)$

41. $|2x-7|\le 11$

$-11\le 2x-7\le 11$

$-2\le x\le 9$

$[-2, 9]$

43. $|x+5|+2 \geq 8$

$|x+5| \geq 6$

$x+5 \leq -6$ or $x+5 \geq 6$

$x \leq -11$ or $x \geq 1$

$(-\infty, -11] \cup [1, \infty)$

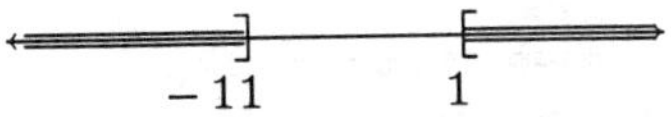

45. $|x| > 0$

excludes only $|x| = 0$

$x = 0$

All reals except $x = 0$

$(-\infty, 0) \cup (0, \infty)$

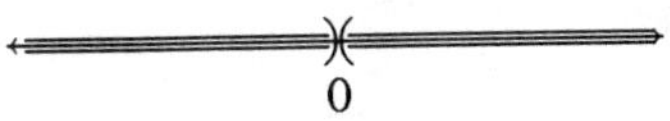

47. $9 + |x| > 7$

$|x| > -2$

All real numbers.

$(-\infty, \infty)$

49. $6 + |4x-1| \leq 9$

$|4x-1| \leq 3$

$-3 \leq 4x-1 \leq 3$

$-2 \leq 4x \leq 4$

$-\frac{1}{2} \leq x \leq 1$

$\left[-\frac{1}{2}, 1\right]$

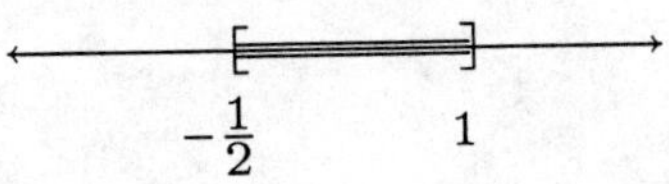

51. $\left|\frac{2}{3}x+1\right| > 1$

$\frac{2}{3}x+1 < -1$ or $\frac{2}{3}x+1 > 1$

$\frac{2}{3}x < -2$ or $\frac{2}{3}x > 0$

$x < -3$ or $x > 0$

$(-\infty, -3) \cup (0, \infty)$

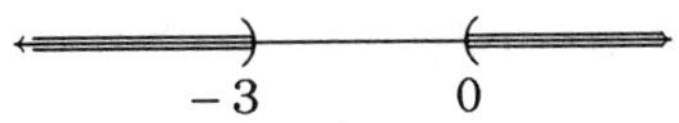

53. $|5x+3| < -6$

No real numbers.

{ }

55. $|8x+3| \geq 0$

All real numbers.

$(-\infty, \infty)$

57. $|1+3x|+4 < 5$

$|1+3x| < 1$

$-1 < 1+3x < 1$

$-2 < 3x < 0$

$-\frac{2}{3} < x < 0$

$\left(-\frac{2}{3}, 0\right)$

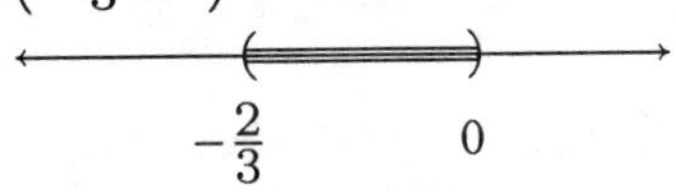

59. $|x| - 3 \geq -3$

$|x| \geq 0$

All real numbers.

61. $|8x| - 10 > -2$

$|8x| > 8$

$8x < -8$ or $8x > 8$

$x < -1$ or $x > 1$

$(-\infty, -1) \cup (1, \infty)$

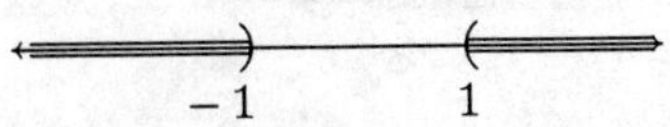

63. $\left|\frac{x+6}{3}\right| > 2$

$\frac{x+6}{3} < -2$ or $\frac{x+6}{3} > 2$

$x+6<-6$ or $x+6>6$

$x<-12$ or $x>0$

$(-\infty, -12)\cup(0, \infty)$

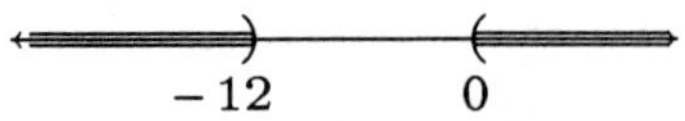

65. $|2(3+x)|>6$

$2|3+x|>6$

$|3+x|>3$

$3+x<-3$ or $3+x>3$

$x<-6$ or $x>0$

$(-\infty, -6)\cup(0, \infty)$

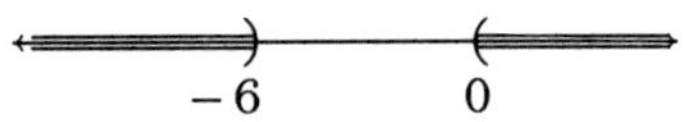

67. $\left|\frac{5(x+2)}{3}\right|<7$

$\frac{5}{3}|x+2|<7$

$|x+2|<\frac{21}{5}$

$\frac{-21}{5}<x+2<\frac{21}{5}$

$\frac{-31}{5}<x<\frac{11}{5}$

$\left(-\frac{31}{5}, \frac{11}{5}\right)$

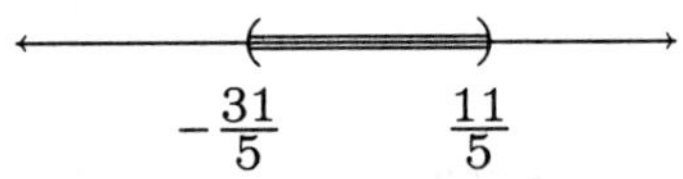

69. $-15+|2x-7|\le -6$

$|2x-7|\le 9$

$-9\le 2x-7\le 9$

$-2\le 2x\le 16$

$-1\le x\le 8$

$[-1, 8]$

71. $\left|2x+\frac{3}{4}\right|-7\le -2$

$\left|2x+\frac{3}{4}\right|\le 5$

$-5\le 2x+\frac{3}{4}\le 5$

$\frac{-23}{4}\le 2x\le \frac{17}{4}$

$\frac{-23}{8}\le x\le \frac{17}{8}$

$\left[-\frac{23}{8}, \frac{17}{8}\right]$

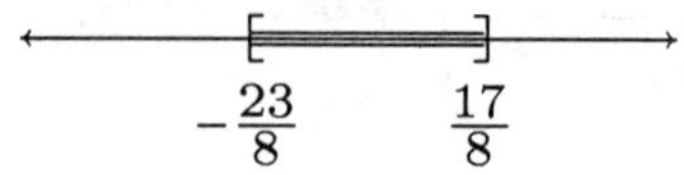

73. $|2x-3|<7$

$-7<2x-3<7$

$-4<2x<10$

$-2<x<5$

$(-2, 5)$

75. $|2x-3|=7$

$2x-3=7$ or $2x-3=-7$

$2x=10$ or $2x=-4$

$x=5$ or $x=-2$

$\{5, -2\}$

77. $|x-5|\ge 12$

$x-5\le -12$ or $x-5\ge 12$

$x\le -7$ or $x\ge 17$

$(-\infty, -7]\cup[17, \infty)$

79. $|9+4x|=0$

$9+4x=0$

$4x=-9$

$x=-\frac{9}{4}$

$\left\{-\frac{9}{4}\right\}$

81. $|2x+1|+4<7$

$|2x+1|<3$

$-3<2x+1<3$

$-4<2x<2$

$-2<x<1$

$(-2, 1)$

83. $|3x-5|+4=5$

$|3x-5|=1$

$3x-5=-1$ or $3x-5=1$

$3x=4$ or $3x=6$

$x=\frac{4}{3}$ or $x=2$

$\left\{\frac{4}{3},\ 2\right\}$

85. $|x+11|=-1$

No real solution.

{ }

87. $\left|\frac{2x-1}{3}\right|=6$

$\frac{2x-1}{3}=-6$ or $\frac{2x-1}{3}=6$

$2x-1=-18$ or $2x-1=18$

$2x=-17$ or $2x=19$

$x=\frac{-17}{2}$ or $x=\frac{19}{2}$

$\left\{-\frac{17}{2},\ \frac{19}{2}\right\}$

89. $\left|\frac{3x-5}{6}\right|>5$

$\frac{3x-5}{6}<-5$ or $\frac{3x-5}{6}>5$

$3x-5<-30$ or $3x-5>30$

$3x<-25$ or $3x>35$

$x<\frac{-25}{3}$ or $x>\frac{35}{3}$

$\left(-\infty,-\frac{25}{3}\right)\cup\left(\frac{35}{3},\infty\right)$

91. {1, 3, 5, 7, 9}

93. { }

95. $(-3)^2+(-5)^2$

$9+25$

34

97. $\frac{2-(-7)}{3^2}$

$\frac{2+7}{9}$

$\frac{9}{9}$

1

99. $100\%-(20\%+45\%)$

$100\%-65\%$

35%

101. ($9.75 billion)(0.45)

S4.39 billion

103.

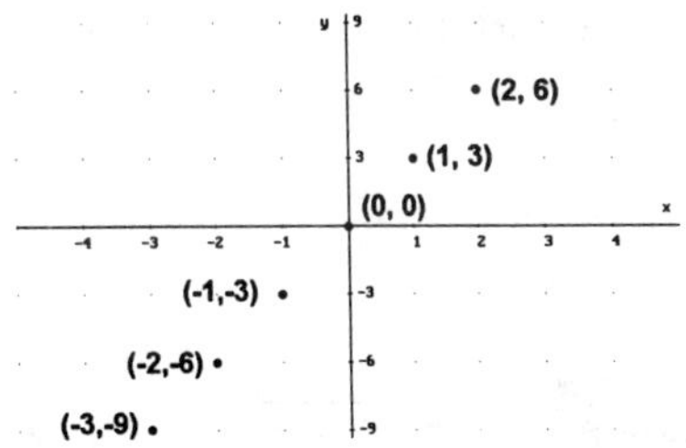

Chapter 3 - Review

1. $\frac{\text{20 frames}}{\text{1 dollar}}$

3. $\frac{x}{2}=\frac{12}{4}$

$4x=2(12)$

$4x=24$

$x=6$

$\{6\}$

5. $\frac{32}{100}=\frac{100}{x}$

$32x=100(100)$

$32x=10{,}000$

$x=\frac{10{,}000}{32}$

$x=312.5$

$\{312.5\}$

7. $\frac{2}{x-1}=\frac{3}{x+3}$

$2(x+3)=3(x-1)$

$2x+6=3x-3$

$2x-2x+6=3x-2x-3$

$6 = x - 3$

$6 + 3 = x - 3 + 3$

$9 = x$

$\{9\}$

9. $\frac{y+2}{y} = \frac{5}{3}$

$3(y+2) = 5y$

$3y + 6 = 5y$

$3y - 3y + 6 = 5y - 3y$

$6 = 2y$

$3 = y$

$\{3\}$

11. $\frac{300 \text{ parts}}{20 \text{ minutes}} = \frac{x \text{ parts}}{45 \text{ minutes}}$

$20x = 300(45)$

$20x = 13500$

$x = \frac{13500}{20}$

$x = 675$ parts

13. $\frac{100 \text{ letters}}{35 \text{ minutes}} = \frac{x \text{ letters}}{55 \text{ minutes}}$

$35x = 100(55)$

$35x = 5500$

$x = \frac{5500}{35}$

$x = 157.14$

157 letters

15. $\frac{7}{x} = \frac{9}{27}$

$9x = 7(27)$

$9x = 189$

$x = \frac{189}{9}$

$x = 21$ cm.

17. 110% of 85

1.10(85)

93.5

19. $59.5 = x(85)$

$\frac{59.5}{85} = x$

$0.7 = x$

$70\% = x$

21. $768 = 0.60(x)$

$\frac{768}{0.60} = x$

$1280 = x$

23. 6%

25. 0.40(300)

120 travelers

27. $210 - 180 = 30$

$\frac{\text{amount of decrease}}{\text{original amount}}$

$\frac{30}{210} = 0.143$

$0.143 = 14.3\%$ decrease

29. Let x be the time the car traveled at 70 mph.

$70x + 60(5 - x) = 320$

$70x + 300 - 60x = 320$

$10x = 20$

$x = 2$ hrs.

31. Let x be the amount invested at an 11% profit.

$0.11x - 0.04(10{,}000 - x) = 650$

$0.11x - 400 + 0.04x = 650$

$0.15x = 1050$

$x = 7000$

He invested \$7,000 at an 11% profit and $\$10{,}000 - \$7{,}000 = \$3{,}000$ at a 4% loss.

33. Let $x =$ the number of gallons of water which must evaporate. Note that $0.04(200) = 8$ gallons of saline.

$\frac{8}{200 - x} = 0.06$

$\frac{8}{0.06} = 200 - x$

$133\frac{1}{3} = 200 - x$

$x = 200 - 133\frac{1}{3}$

$x = 66\frac{2}{3}$

Therefore, $66\frac{2}{3}$ gallons of water must evaporate.

35. Let x be the distance he rowed upstream.

$\frac{x}{5} + \frac{x}{11} = 4$

$55\left(\frac{x}{5} + \frac{x}{11}\right) = 4(55)$

$11x + 5x = 220$

$16x = 220$

$x = 13.75$ miles

37. Let x = the number of centiliters of the 15% solution used and 150 − x = the number of centiliters of the 45% solution used.

$0.15x + 0.45(150 - x) = 0.35(150)$

$0.15x + 67.5 - 0.45x = 52.5$

$-0.30x = -15$

$x = 50$

$150 - x = 100$

Therefore, he should use 50 cl of the 15% solution and 100 cl of the 45% solution.

39. $|8 - x| = 3$

$8 - x = 3$ or $8 - x = -3$

$5 = x$ or $11 = x$

$\{5, 11\}$

41. $|-3x + 4| = 7$

$-3x + 4 = 7$ or $-3x + 4 = -7$

$-3x = 3$ or $-3x = -11$

$x = -1$ or $x = \frac{11}{3}$

$\left\{-1, \frac{11}{3}\right\}$

43. $5 + |6x + 1| = 5$

$|6x + 1| = 0$

$6x + 1 = 0$

$x = -\frac{1}{6}$

$\left\{-\frac{1}{6}\right\}$

45. $|5 - 6x| + 8 = 3$

$|5 - 6x| = -5$

No solution

{ }

47. $-8 = |x - 3| - 10$

$2 = |x - 3|$

$x - 3 = 2$ or $x - 3 = -2$

$x = 5$ or $x = 1$

$\{1, 5\}$

49. $\left|\frac{9 - 2x}{5}\right| = -3$

No solution

{ }

51. $|x - 3| = |7 + 2x|$

$x - 3 = 7 + 2x$ or $x - 3 = -(7 + 2x)$

$-10 = x$ or $x - 3 = -7 - 2x$

$3x = -4$

$x = \frac{-4}{3}$

$\left\{-10, -\frac{4}{3}\right\}$

53. $-2(x + 7) \geq 3(x + 2)$

$-2x - 14 \geq 3x + 6$

$-5x \geq 20$

$x \leq -4$

$(-\infty, -4]$

55. $3(x - 8) < 7x + 2(5 - x)$

$3x - 24 < 7x + 10 - 2x$

$-2x < 34$

$x > -17$

$(-17,\ \infty)$

57. $48 + x \geq 5(2x+4) - 2x$

$48 + x \geq 10x + 20 - 2x$

$-7x \geq -28$

$x \leq 4$

$(-\infty,\ 4]$

59. $x + \frac{3}{4} < \frac{-x}{2} + \frac{9}{4}$

$4x + 3 < -2x + 9$

$6x < 6$

$x < 1$

$(-\infty,\ 1)$

61. $\frac{3(x-2)}{5} > \frac{-5(x-2)}{3}$

$9(x-2) > -25(x-2)$

$9x - 18 > -25x + 50$

$34x > 68$

$x > 2$

$(2,\ \infty)$

63. $500 \leq \frac{9}{5}C + 32 \leq 1000$

$2500 \leq 9C + 160 \leq 5000$

$2340 \leq 9C \leq 4840$

$260 \leq C \leq 538$

65. $4000 \leq 2x + 500 \leq 8000$

$3500 \leq 2x \leq 7500$

$1750 \leq x \leq 3750$

67. $0 \leq -5x \leq 20$

$\frac{0}{-5} \geq \frac{-5x}{-5} \geq \frac{20}{-5}$

$0 \geq x \geq -4$

$[-4,\ 0]$

69. $-2 \leq 8 + 5x < -1$

$-10 \leq 5x < -9$

$-2 \leq x < -\frac{9}{5}$

$\left[-2,\ -\frac{9}{5}\right)$

71. $-6 < x - (3 - 4x) < -3$

$-6 < 5x - 3 < -3$

$-3 < 5x < 0$

$-\frac{3}{5} < x < 0$

$\left(-\frac{3}{5},\ 0\right)$

73. $0 \leq \frac{2(3x+4)}{5} \leq 3$

$0 \leq 2(3x+4) \leq 15$

$0 \leq 6x + 8 \leq 15$

$-8 \leq 6x \leq 7$

$-\frac{4}{3} \leq x \leq \frac{7}{6}$

$\left[-\frac{4}{3},\ \frac{7}{6}\right]$

75. $x \leq 2$ or $x > -5$

$(-\infty,\ \infty)$

77. $-2x \leq 6$ and $-2x + 3 < -7$

$x \geq -3$ and $-2x < -10$

$x > 5$

$x > 5$

$(5,\ \infty)$

79. $|6 + 4x| \geq 10$

$6 + 4x \geq 10$ or $6 + 4x \leq -10$

$4x \geq 4$ or $4x \leq -16$

$x \geq 1$ or $x \leq -4$

$(-\infty, -4] \cup [1,\ \infty)$

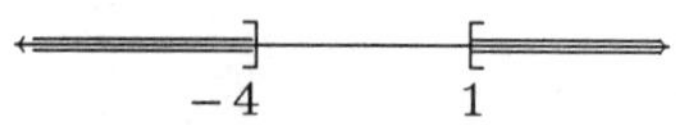

81. $9 + |5x| < 24$

$|5x| < 15$

$-15 < 5x < 15$

$-3 < x < 3$

$(-3,\ 3)$

83. $|6x-5| \geq -1$

$(-\infty,\ \infty)$

85. $\left|\frac{4x-3}{5}\right| < 1$

$-1 < \frac{4x-3}{5} < 1$

$-5 < 4x-3 < 5$

$-2 < 4x < 8$

$-\frac{1}{2} < x < 2$

$\left(-\frac{1}{2},\ 2\right)$

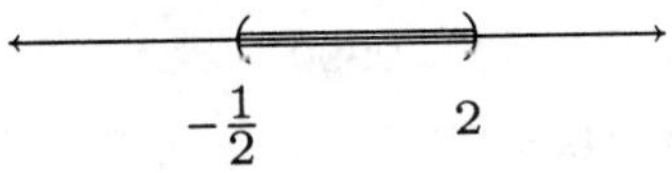

87. $\left|\frac{4(x-1)}{7}\right| + 10 < 2$

$\left|\frac{4(x-1)}{7}\right| < -8$

No solution

$\{\ \}$

Chapter 3 - Test

1. $\frac{5}{y+1} = \frac{4}{y+2}$

$4(y+1) = 5(y+2)$

$4y+4 = 5y+10$

$4y-4y+4 = 5y-4y+10$

$4 = y+10$

$4-10 = y+10-10$

$-6 = y$

$\{-6\}$

2. $|6x-5| = 1$

$6x-5 = -1$ or $6x-5 = 1$

$6x = 4$ or $6x = 6$

$x = \frac{2}{3}$ or $x = 1$

$\left\{\frac{2}{3},\ 1\right\}$

3. $|8-2t| = -6$

No solution

$\{\ \}$

4. $\left|\frac{x+3}{2}\right| = 7$

$\frac{x+3}{2} = 7$ or $\frac{x+3}{2} = -7$

$x+3 = 2(7)$ or $x+3 = -7(2)$

$x+3 = 14$ or $x+3 = -14$

$x = 11$ or $x = -17$

$\{-17,\ 11\}$

5. $3(2x-7)-4x > -(x+6)$

$6x-21-4x > -x-6$

$2x-21 > -x-6$

$3x > 15$

$x > 5$

$(5,\ \infty)$

6. $8-\frac{x}{2} \leq 7$

$1 \leq \frac{x}{2}$

$2 \leq x$

$[2,\ \infty)$

7. $-3 < 2(x-3) \leq 4$

$-3 < 2x-6 \leq 4$

$3 < 2x \leq 10$

$\frac{3}{2} < x \leq 15$

$\left(\frac{3}{2},\ 5\right]$

8. $|3x+1| > 5$

$3x+1 < -5$ or $3x+1 > 5$

$3x < -6$ or $3x > 4$

$x < -2$ or $x > \frac{4}{3}$

$(-\infty, -2) \cup \left(\frac{4}{3}, \infty\right)$

9. $x \geq 5$ and $x \geq 4$

$x \geq 5$

$[5, \infty)$

10. $x \geq 5$ or $x \geq 4$

$x \geq 4$

$[4, \infty)$

11. $-x > 1$ and $3x + 3 \geq x - 3$

$x < -1$ and $2x \geq -6$

$x \geq -3$

$-3 \leq x < -1$

$[-3, -1)$

12. $6x + 1 > 5x + 4$ or $1 - x > -4$

$x > 3$ or $5 > x$

$x < 5$

$(-\infty, \infty)$

13. 85% of 200

$0.85(200)$

170

14. $35 = x(140)$

$\frac{35}{140} = x$

$0.25 = x$

$25\% = x$

15. $31.5 = 0.35(x)$

$\frac{31.5}{0.35} = x$

$90 = x$

16. $\$3.95 - \$3.50 = \$0.45$

$\frac{\text{amount of increase}}{\text{original amount}} = \frac{0.45}{3.50} = 0.129$

12.9% increase

17. 81.3%

18. $126.2(0.047)$

$5.93 billion

19. 6.7% of 360°

$0.067(360^\circ)$

24.12°

20. Solve $R > C$

$7.4x > 3910 + 2.8x$

$4.6x > 3910$

$x > 850$

Therefore, 850 sunglasses must be produced and sold in oreder for them to yield a profit.

21. Let $x =$ amount invested at 10% and $2x =$ amount invested at 12%.

$0.10x + 0.12(2x) = 2890$

$0.10x + 0.24x = 2890$

$0.34x = 2890$

$x = 8500$

Therefore, he invested $8500 at 10% and $17,000 (twice $8500) at 12% annual interest.

22. First note that the cars are separating at $55 + 65 = 120$ mph. Using $d = rt$ we have:

$250 = 120t$

$t = \frac{250}{120} = 2\frac{1}{12}$ hrs

$t = 2$ hrs 5 min

Therefore, they can talk on their car phones for 2 hours and 5 minutes.

23. 2 hours = 12 minutes

$\frac{5 \text{ cars}}{30 \text{ minutes}} = \frac{x \text{ cars}}{120 \text{ minutes}}$

$30x = 5(120)$

$30x = 600$

$x = \frac{600}{30}$

$x = 20$ cars

24. Let $x =$ the number of liters of the 12% solution, so $x + 10 =$ the number of liters of the 20% solution.

$0.12x + 0.25(10) = 0.20(x + 10)$

$0.12x + 2.5 = 0.2x + 2$

$0.5 = 0.08x$

$\frac{50}{8} = x$

$x = 6\frac{1}{4}$

Therefore, $6\frac{1}{4}$ liters of a 12% solution must be added to the 10 liters of 25% solution.

Chapter 3 - Cumulative Review

1a. $\{11, 112\}$

b. $\{0, 11, 112\}$

c. $\{-3, -2, 0, 11, 112\}$

d. $\{-3, -2, 0, \frac{1}{4}, 11, 112\}$

e. $\{\sqrt{2}\}$

f. $\{-3, -2, 0, \frac{1}{4}, \sqrt{2}, 11, 112\}$

$\frac{4}{5} \div \frac{5}{16}$

$\frac{4}{5} \bullet \frac{16}{5}$

$\frac{64}{25}$

b. $\frac{7}{10} \div 14$

$\frac{7}{10} \bullet \frac{1}{14}$

$\frac{\cancel{7}}{10} \bullet \frac{1}{\cancel{7} \times 2}$

$\frac{1}{20}$

c. $\frac{3}{8} \div \frac{3}{10}$

$\frac{3}{8} \bullet \frac{10}{3}$

$\frac{\cancel{3}}{4 \times \cancel{2}} \bullet \frac{5 \times \cancel{2}}{\cancel{3}}$

$\frac{5}{4}$

5. $3x - 10 = 2x$

$3(10) - 10 \stackrel{?}{=} 2(10)$

$30 - 10 \stackrel{?}{=} 20$

$20 = 20$

Yes, 10 is a solution.

7a. $(7)(0)(-6)$

$(0)(-6)$

0

b. $(-2)(-3)(-4)$

$(+6)(-4)$

-24

c. $(-1)(5)(-9)$

$(-5)(-9)$

45

d. $(-2)^3$

$(-2)(-2)(-2)$

$4(-2)$

-8

e. $(-4)(-11) - (5)(-2)$

$44 - (-10)$

$44 + (+10)$

54

9a. $2(x + y)$

$2x + 2y$

b. $-5(-3 + z)$

$15 - 5z$

c. $5(x + y - z)$

$5x + 5y - 5z$

d. $-1(2 - y)$

$-2 + y$

e. $-(3 + x - w)$

$-3 - x + w$

11a. $2x+6$

b. $\frac{x-4}{7}$

c. $5+3(x+1)$

$5+3x+3$

$8+3x$

13. Let $x=$ number

$2x+7=x-3$

$x+7=-3$

$x=-10$

15. $C=\frac{5}{9}(F-32)$

$C=\frac{5}{9}(59-32)$

$C=\frac{5}{9}(27)$

$C=15^\circ$

17. $\$37.47(5)=3x$

$\$187.35=3x$

$\$62.45=x$

19. $|5w+3|=7$

$5w+3=7$ or $5w+3=-7$

$5w=4$ or $5w=-10$

$w=\frac{4}{5}$ or $w=-2$

$\left\{-2,\ \frac{4}{5}\right\}$

21. Let $x=$ number of people invited.

$100+14x\le 1000$

$14x\le 900$

$x\le 64.29$

Therefore, at most 64 people could be invited.

23. $|m-6|<2$

$-2<m-6<2$

$4<m<8$

$(4,\ 8)$

Graphing Calculator Exercise 4.1

1. $y=-3x+7$

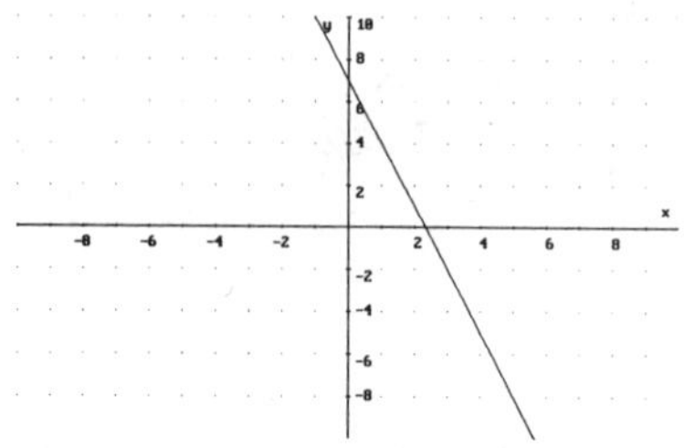

3. $y=\frac{1}{4}x-2$

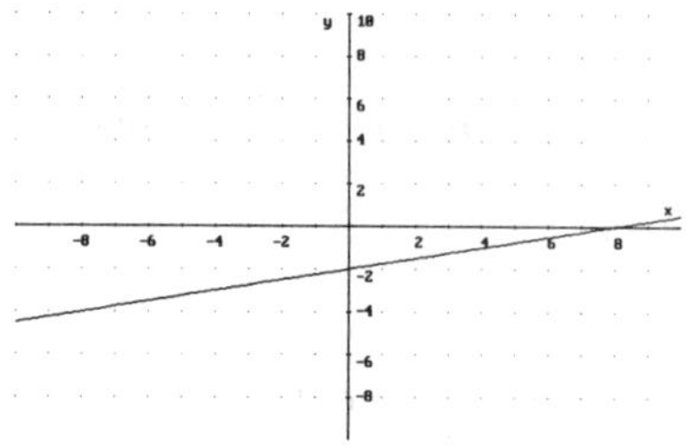

5. $y=|x-3|+2$

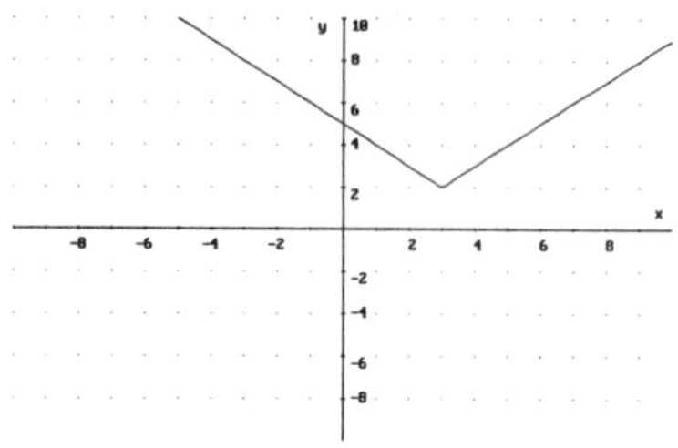

7. $y=x^2+3$

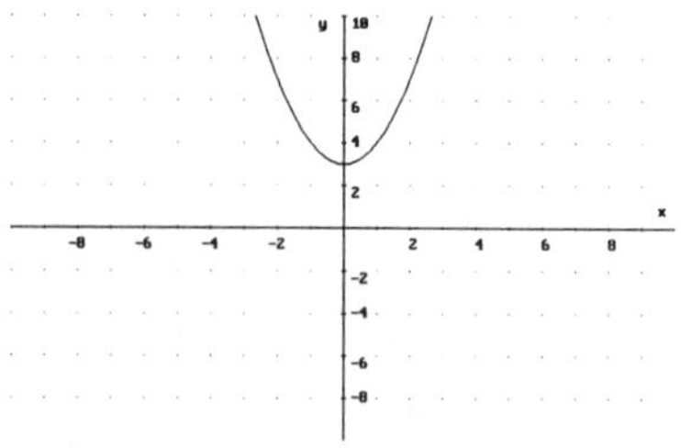

Exercise Set 4.1

1\.

(3,1) yes

$$\begin{array}{r|l} 2x+y= & 7 \\ \hline 2(3)+1 & 7 \\ 6+1 & 7 \\ 7=7 & \end{array}$$

(7,0) no

$$\begin{array}{r|l} 2x+y= & 7 \\ \hline 2(7)+0 & 7 \\ 14+0 & 7 \\ 14\neq 7 & \end{array}$$

(0,7) yes

$$\begin{array}{r|l} 2x+y= & 7 \\ \hline 2(0)+7 & 7 \\ 0+7 & 7 \\ 7=7 & \end{array}$$

3\.

(−1,−5) no

$$\begin{array}{r|l} y= & -5x \\ \hline -5 & -5(-1) \\ -5\neq +5 & \end{array}$$

(0,0) yes

$$\begin{array}{r|l} y= & -5x \\ \hline 0 & -5(0) \\ 0=0 & \end{array}$$

(2,−10) yes

$$\begin{array}{r|l} y= & -5x \\ \hline -10 & -5(2) \\ -10=-10 & \end{array}$$

5\. $x=5$

(4,5) $4\neq 5$ no

(5,4) $5=5$ yes

(5,0) $5=5$ yes

7\. $x+3y=6;$ (0,)

$0+3y=6$

$3y=6$

$y=2$ (0,2)

$x+3y=6;$ (,0)

$x+3(0)=6$

$x+0=6$

$x=6$ (6,0)

$x+3y=6;$ (,1)

$x+3(1)=6$

$x+3=6$

$x=3$ (3,1)

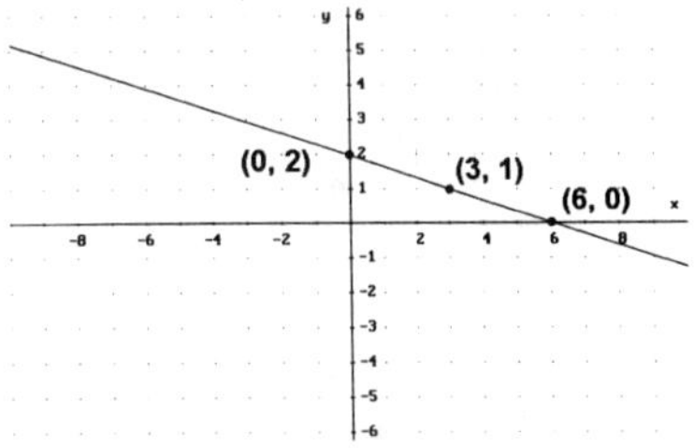

9\. $2x-y=12;$ (0,)

$2(0)-y=12$

$-y=12$

$y=-12$ (0,−12)

$2x-y=12;$ (,−2)

$2x-(-2)=12$

$2x+2=12$

$2x=10$

$x=5$ (5,−2)

$2x-y=12;$ (−3,)

$2(-3)-y=12$

$-6-y=12$

$-y=18$

$y=-18$ (−3,−18)

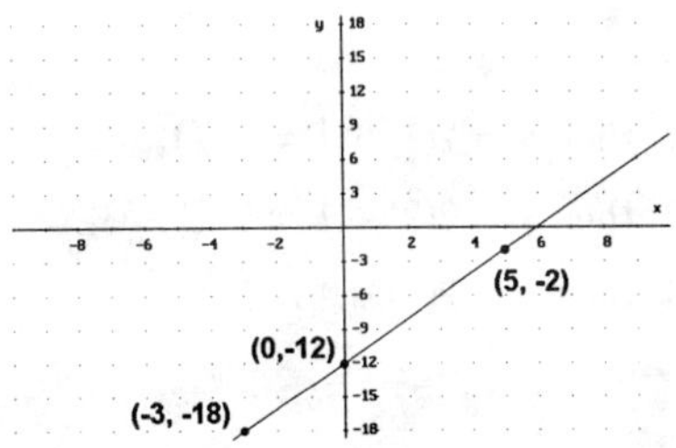

11\. $2x+7y=5;$ (0,)

$2(0)+7y=5$

$7y=5$

$y=\frac{5}{7}$ $\left(0,\frac{5}{7}\right)$

$2x+7y=5;$ (,0)

$2x+7(0)=5$

$2x=5$

$x=\frac{5}{2}$ $\left(\frac{5}{2},0\right)$

$2x+7y=5;$ (,1)

$2x+7(1)=5$

$2x+7=5$

$2x=-2$

$x=-1$ (−1,1)

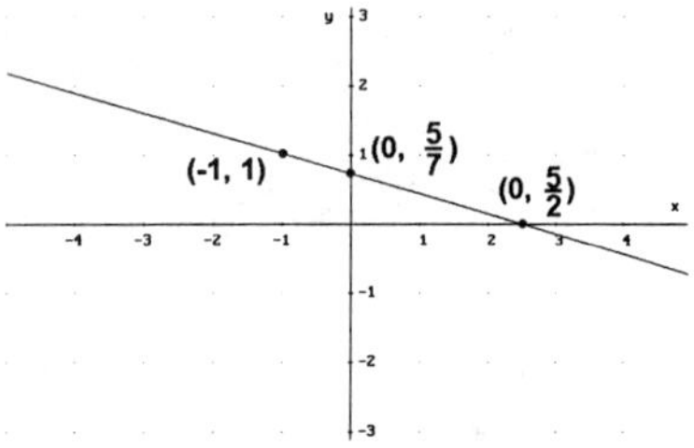

13. $y = 2x$

If $x = 1$, then $y = 2(1) = 2$ $(1, 2)$

If $x = 3$, then $y = 2(3) = 6$ $(3, 6)$

If $x = -2$, then $y = 2(-2) = -4$ $(-2, -4)$

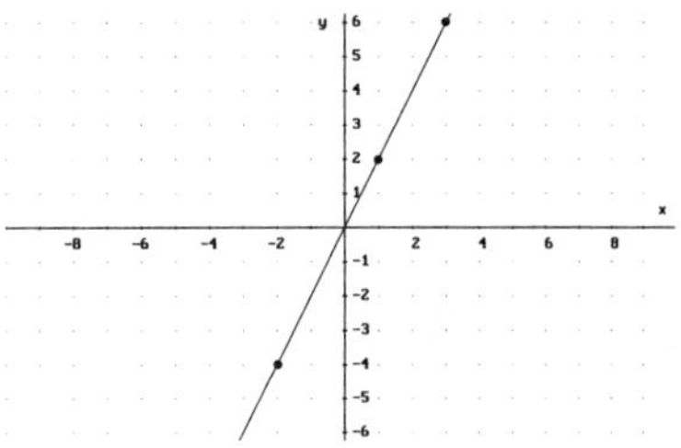

15. $y = 2x + 1$

If $x = 1$, then $y = 2(1) + 1 = 3$ $(1, 3)$

If $x = 2$, then $y = 2(2) + 1 = 5$ $(2, 5)$

If $x = 0$, then $y = 2(0) + 1 = 1$ $(0, 1)$

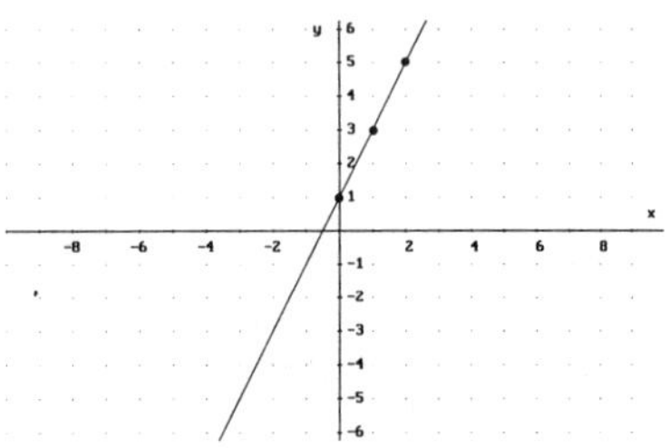

17. $y = \frac{1}{4}x$

If $x = 4$, then $y = \frac{1}{4}(4) = 1$ $(4, 1)$

If $x = 0$, then $y = \frac{1}{4}(0) = 0$ $(0, 0)$

If $x = -4$, then $y = \frac{1}{4}(-4)$ $(-4, -1)$

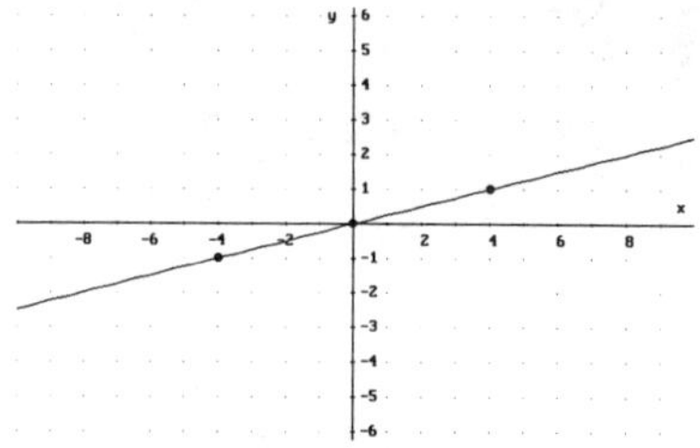

19. $y = 3x - 2$

If $x = 1$, then $y = 3(1) - 2 = 1$ $(1, 1)$

If $x = 0$, then $y = 3(0) - 2 = -2$ $(0, -2)$

If $x = -1$, then $y = 3(-1) - 2 = -5$ $(-1, -5)$

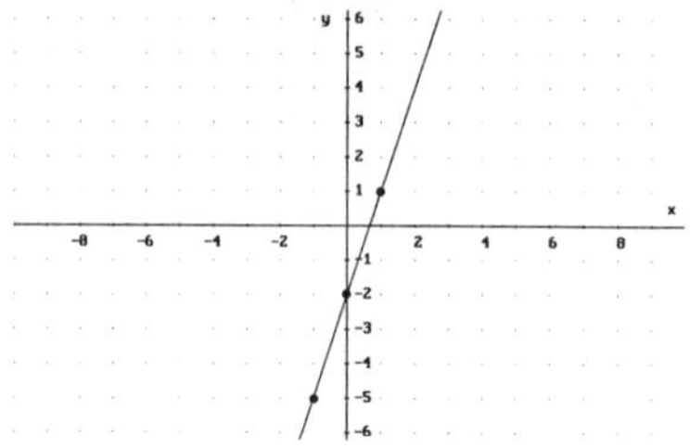

21. $y = x^2 + 2$

If $x = -3$, then $y = (-3)^2 + 2 = 11$ $(-3, 11)$

If $x = -2$, then $y = (-2)^2 + 2 = 6$ $(-2, 6)$

If $x = -1$, then $y = (-1)^2 + 2 = 3$ $(-1, 3)$

If $x = 0$, then $y = 0^2 + 2 = 2$ $(0, 2)$

If $x = 1$, then $y = 1^2 + 2 = 3$ $(1, 3)$

If $x = 2$, then $y = 2^2 + 2 = 6$ $(2, 6)$

If $x = 3$, then $y = 3^2 + 2 = 11$ $(3, 11)$

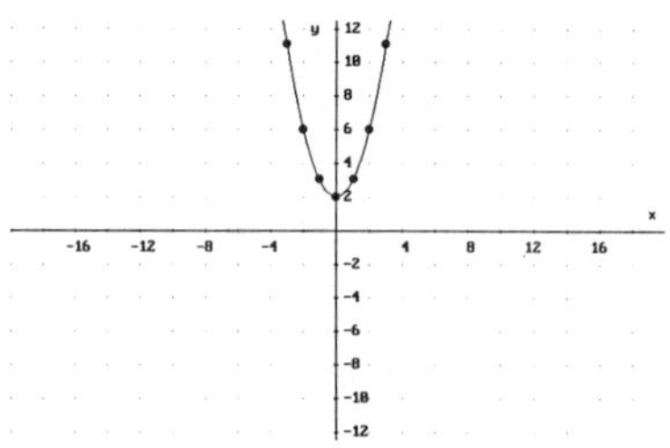

23. $y = |x| - 1$

If $x = -2$, then $y = |-2| - 1 = 1$ $(-2, 1)$

If $x = -1$, then $y = |-1| - 1 = 0$ $(-1, 0)$

If $x = 0$, then $y = |0| - 1 = -1$ $(0, -1)$

If $x = 1$, then $y = |1| - 1 = 0$ $(1, 0)$

If $x = 2$, then $y = |2| - 1 = 1$ $(2, 1)$

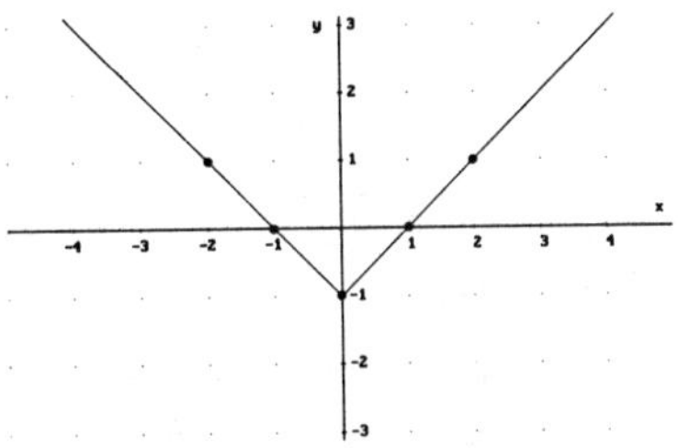

25. $y = -x^2$

If $x = -3$, then $y = -(-3)^2 = -9$ $(-3, -9)$

If $x = -2$, then $y = -(-2)^2 = -4$ $(-2, -4)$

If $x = -1$, then $y = -(-1)^2 = -1$ $(-1, -1)$

If $x = 0$, then $y = -(0)^2 = 0$ $(0, 0)$

If $x = 1$, then $y = -(1)^2 = -1$ $(1, -1)$

If $x = 2$, then $y = -(2)^2 = -4$ $(2, -4)$

If $x = 3$, then $y = -(3)^2 = -9$ $(3, -9)$

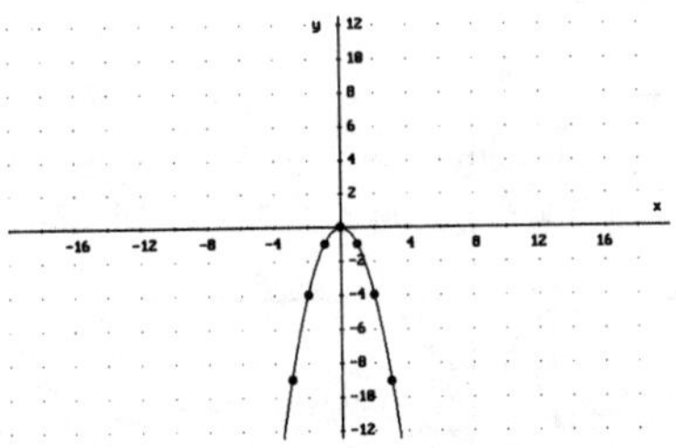

27. $y = |x| + 5$

If $x = -2$, then $y = |-2| + 5 = 7$ $(-2, 7)$

If $x = -1$, then $y = |-1| + 5 = 6$ $(-1, 6)$

If $x = 0$, then $y = |0| + 5 = 5$ $(0, 5)$

If $x = 1$, then $y = |1| + 5 = 6$ $(1, 6)$

If $x = 2$, then $y = |2| + 5 = 7$ $(2, 7)$

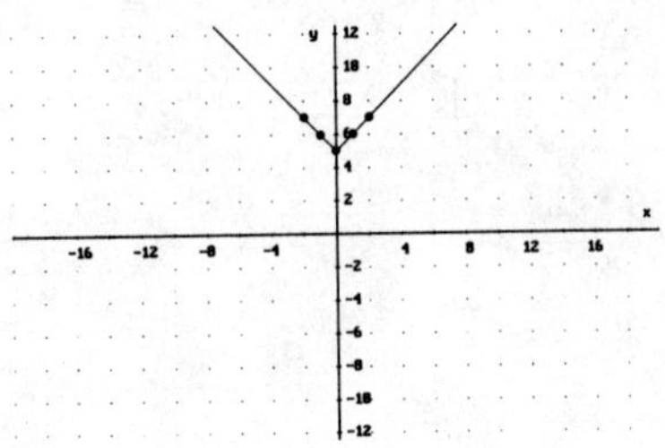

29. $x + 2y = 9$; $(5,2)$

$$\begin{array}{r|l} 5+2(2) & 9 \\ 5+4 & 9 \end{array}$$
$9 = 9$ yes

$x + 2y = 9$; $(0,9)$

$$\begin{array}{r|l} 0+2(9) & 9 \end{array}$$
$18 \neq 9$ no

31. $2x - y = 11$; $(3, -4)$

$$\begin{array}{r|l} 2(3)-(-4) & 11 \\ 6+4 & 11 \end{array}$$
$10 \neq 11$ no

$2x - y = 11$; $(9,8)$

$$\begin{array}{r|l} 2(9)-8 & 11 \\ 18-8 & 11 \end{array}$$
$10 \neq 11$ no

33. $x = \frac{1}{3}y$; $(0,0)$

$$\begin{array}{r|l} 0 & \frac{1}{3}(0) \end{array}$$
$0 = 0$ yes

$x = \frac{1}{3}y$; $(3,9)$

$$\begin{array}{r|l} 3 & \frac{1}{3}(9) \end{array}$$
$3 = 3$ yes

35. $y = 2x^2$; $(1, 2)$

$$\begin{array}{r|l} 2 & 2(1)^2 \\ 2 & 2(1) \end{array}$$
$2 = 2$ yes

$y = 2x^2$; $(3, 18)$

$$\begin{array}{r|l} 18 & 2(3)^2 \\ 18 & 2(9) \end{array}$$
$18 = 18$ yes

37. $y = x^3$; $(2, 8)$

$$\begin{array}{r|l} 8 & (2)^3 \\ 8 & 8 \end{array}$$
$8 = 8$ yes

$y = x^3$;		(3, 9)
9	$(3)^3$	
9	27	
$9 \neq 27$		no

39. linear

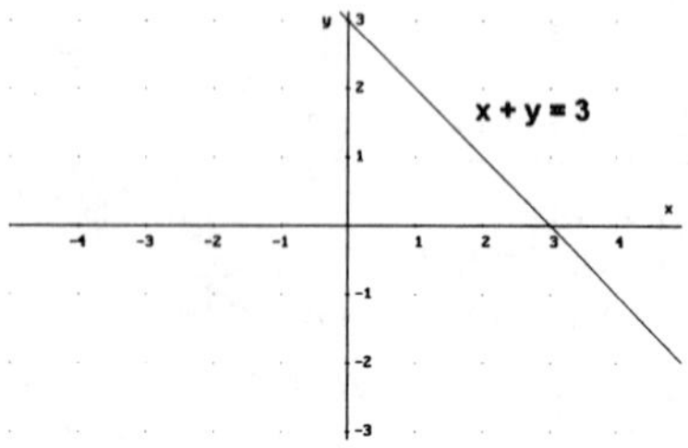

41. linear

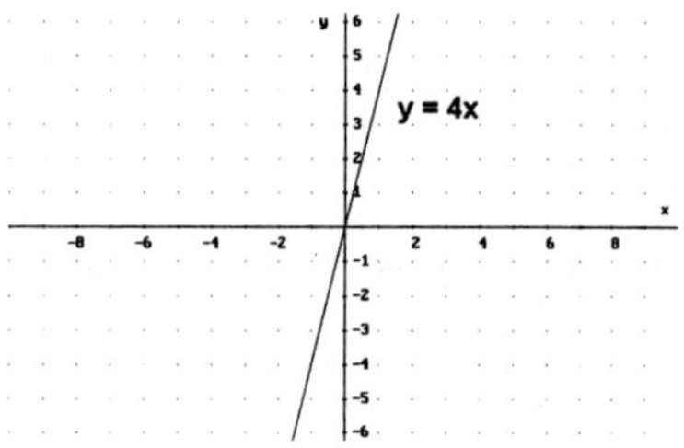

43. linear

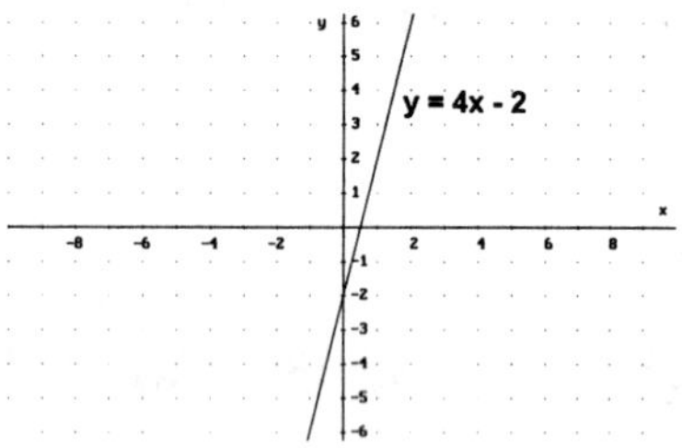

45. not linear

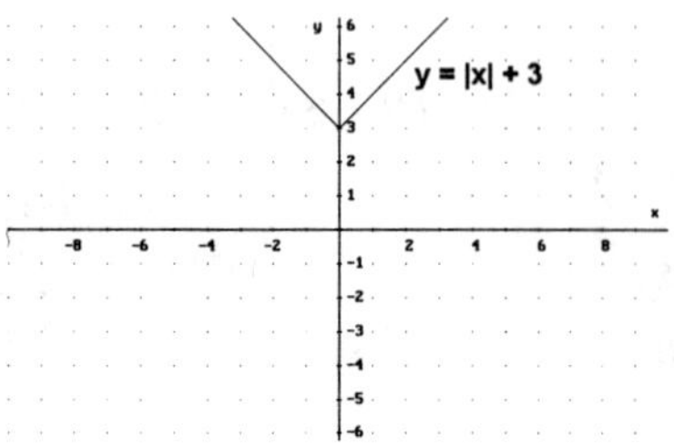

47. linear

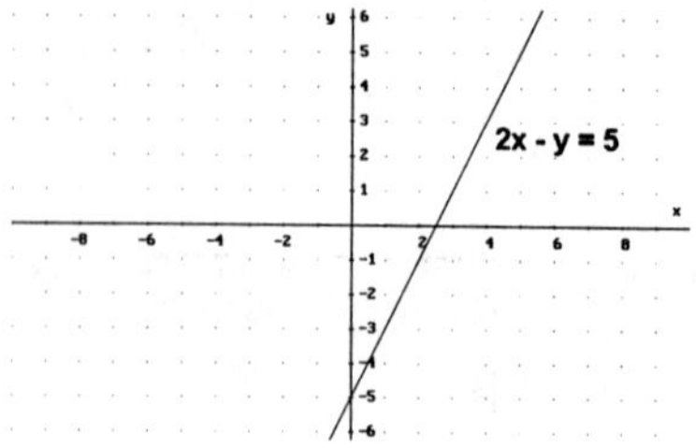

49. not linear

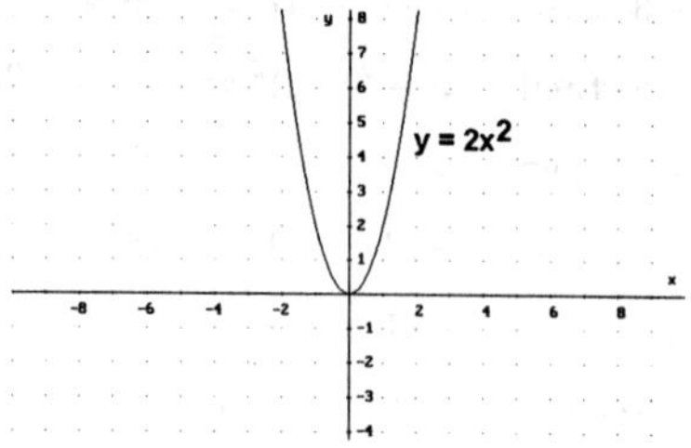

51. not linear

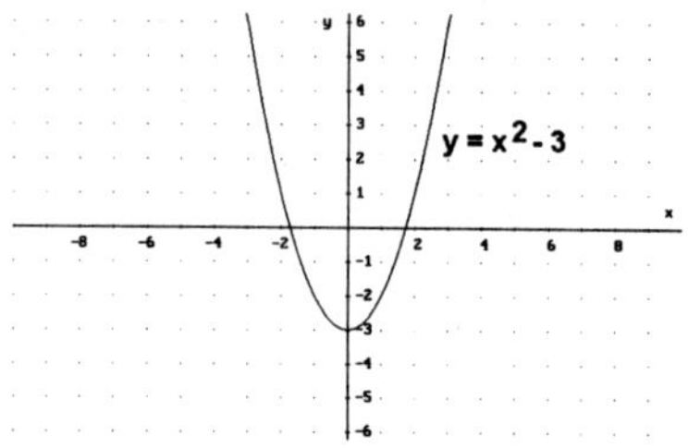

53. linear

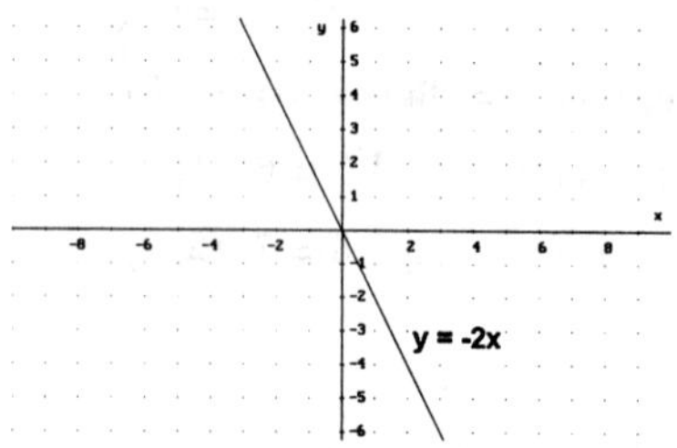

55. linear

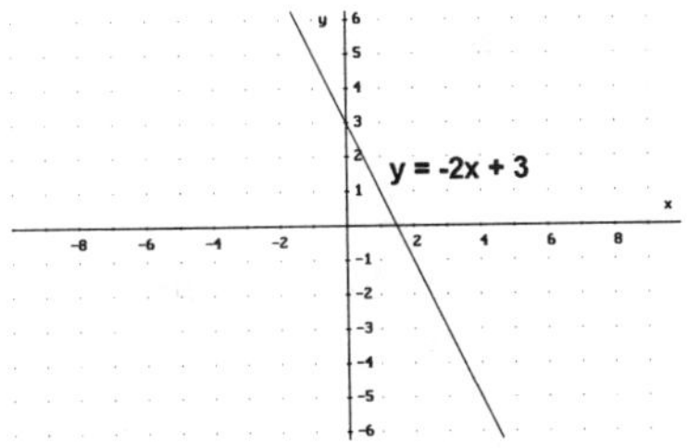

57. $7,000

59. $7,000 − $6,500

$500

61. The amount of depreciation is the same from year to year.

63.

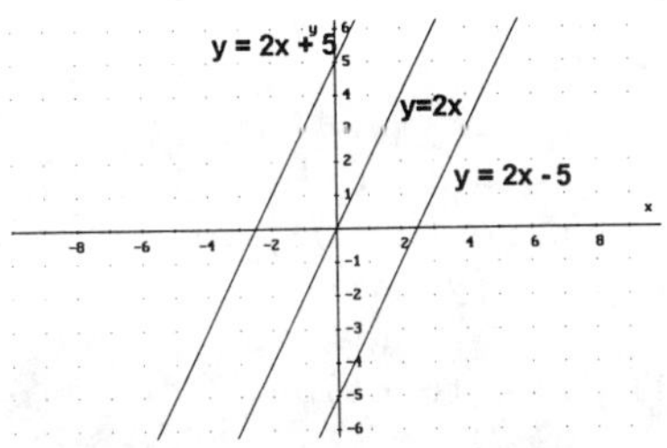

65. $y = x + 5$

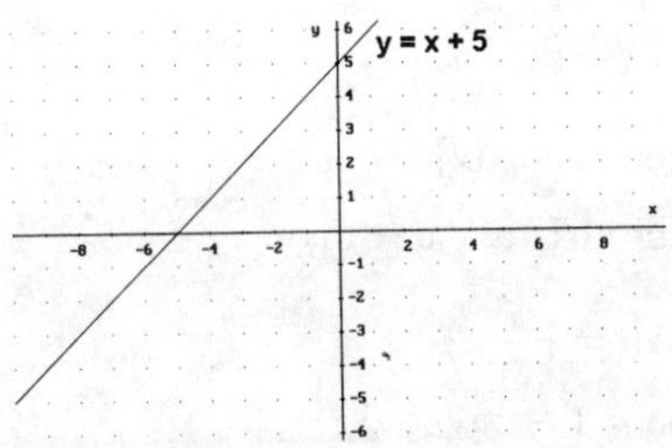

67.

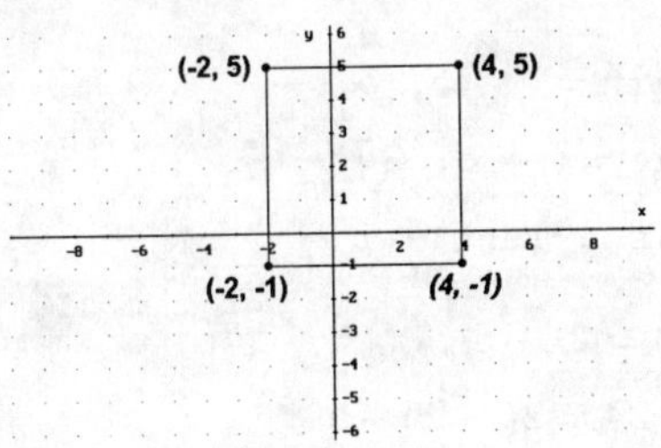

69. $3(x-2)+5x=6x-16$

$3x-6+5x=6x-16$

$8x-6=6x-16$

$2x-6=-16$

$2x=-10$

$x=-5$

$\{-5\}$

71. $3x+\frac{2}{5}=\frac{1}{10}$

$3x+\frac{2}{5}-\frac{2}{5}=\frac{1}{10}-\frac{2}{5}$

$3x=\frac{1}{10}-\frac{4}{10}$

$3x=-\frac{3}{10}$

$\frac{1}{3}(3x)=\frac{1}{3}\left(-\frac{3}{10}\right)$

$x=-\frac{1}{10}$

$\left\{-\frac{1}{10}\right\}$

73. $3x \le -15$

$x \le -5$

75. $2x-5>4x+3$

$2x>4x+8$

$-2x>8$

$\frac{-2x}{-2}<\frac{8}{-2}$

$x<-4$

Graphing Calculator Exercise 4.2

1. $f(x)=|x|$

$g(x)=|x|+1$

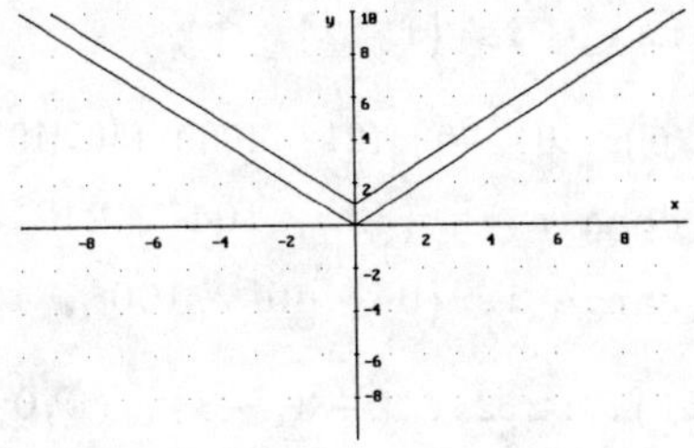

3. $f(x)=x$

$H(x) = x - 6$

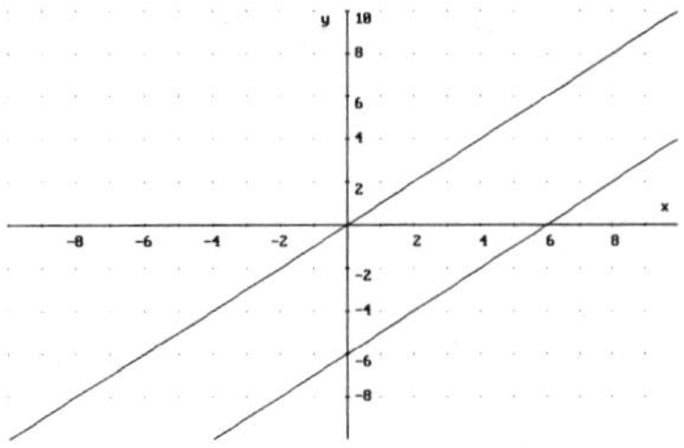

5. $f(x) = -x^2$

$F(x) = x^2 + 7$

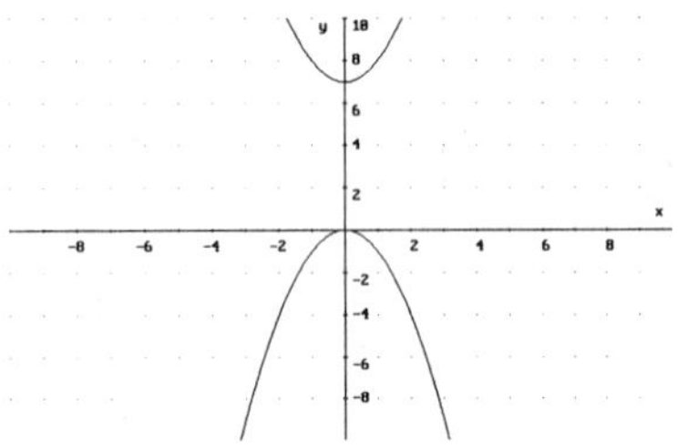

Exercise Set 4.2

1. $\{(2,4), (0,0), (-7,10), (10,-7)\}$

   The domain is $\{-7, 0, 2, 10\}$.

   The range is $\{-7, 0, 4, 10\}$.

3. $\{(0,-2), (1,-2), (5,-2)\}$

   The domain is $\{0, 1, 5\}$.

   The range is $\{-2\}$.

5. $\{(-1, 2), (1, 1), (2, 1), (3, 1)\}$

   The domain is $\{-1, 1, 2, 3\}$.

   The range is $\{1, 2\}$.

7. $\{(32^\circ, 0^\circ), (104^\circ, 40^\circ), (212^\circ, 100^\circ), (50^\circ, 10^\circ)\}$

   The domain is $\{32^\circ, 104^\circ, 212^\circ, 50^\circ\}$.

   The range is $\{0^\circ, 40^\circ, 100^\circ, 10^\circ\}$.

9. $\{(1,1), (2,2), (-3,-3), (0,0)\}$

   Yes, it is a function.

11. $\{(-1,0), (-1,6), (-1,8)\}$

    No, the x value -1 has
    more than one y value.

13. $y = x + 1$

    Yes, it is a function.
    Each x value will produce
    exactly one y value.

15. $x = 2y^2$

    No, it is not a function.
    The ordered pairs $(2,1)$ and $(2,-1)$ make
    the equation true. Therefore an x
    value has more than on y value, so it
    is not a function.

17. $y - x = 7$

    Yes, it is a function.
    Each x value will produce
    exactly one y value.

19. $y = \frac{1}{x}$

    Yes, it is a function.
    Each x value $(x \neq 0)$, will produce
    exactly one y value.

21. Yes it is a function.

23. No it is not a function.

25. Yes it is a function.

27. Domain $= [2, 7]$

    Range $= [1, 6]$

    It is not a function.

29. Domain $= \{-2\}$

    Range $= (-\infty, \infty)$

    It is not a function.

31. Domain $= (-\infty, \infty)$

    Range $= (-\infty, 3]$

    It is a function.

33. $f(x) = 2x - 5$

    a. $f(-2) = 2(-2) - 5$
    $f(-2) = -4 - 5$
    $f(-2) = -9$

b. $f(0)=2(0)-5$
$f(0)=0-5$
$f(0)=-5$

c. $f(3)=2(3)-5$
$f(3)=6-5$
$f(3)=1$

35. $h(x)=x^2+2$

a. $h(-3)=(-3)^2+2$
$h(-3)=9+2$
$h(-3)=11$

b. $h\left(\frac{1}{4}\right)=\left(\frac{1}{4}\right)^2+2$
$h\left(\frac{1}{4}\right)=\frac{1}{16}+2$
$h\left(\frac{1}{4}\right)=2\frac{1}{16}$

c. $h(3)=(3)^2+2$
$h(3)=9+2$
$h(3)=11$

37. $h(x)=x^3$

a. $h(-2)=(-2)^3$
$h(-2)=-8$

b. $h(-6)=(-6)^3$
$h(-6)=-216$

c. $h(0)=(0)^3$
$h(0)=0$

39. $f(x)=|x|$

a. $f(7)=|7|$
$f(7)=7$

b. $f(-7)=|-7|$
$f(-7)=7$

c. $f(0)=|0|$
$f(0)=0$

41. 6.3 billion dollars

43. Domain $=\{-1, 0, -2, 5\}$
Range $=\{7, 6, 2\}$
It is a function.

45. Domain $=\{-2, 6, -7\}$
Range $=\{4, -3, -8\}$
It is not a function.

47. Domain $=\{1\}$
Range $=\{1, 2, 3, 4\}$
It is not a function.

49. Domain $=\left\{\frac{3}{2}, 0\right\}$
Range $=\left\{\frac{1}{2}, -7, \frac{4}{5}\right\}$
It is not a function.

51. Domain $=\{-3, 0, 3\}$
Range $=\{-3, 0, 3\}$
It is a function.

53. $\{(2, 0), (-1, 0), (5, 0), (100, 0)\}$
Domain $=\{2, -1, 5, 100\}$
Range $=\{0\}$
It is a function.

55.

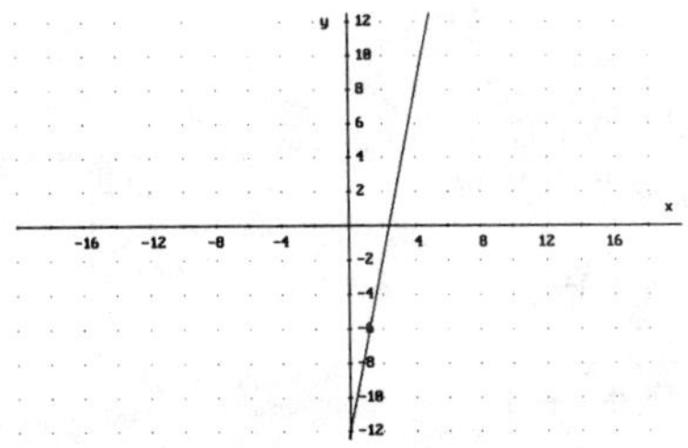

It is a function.

57.

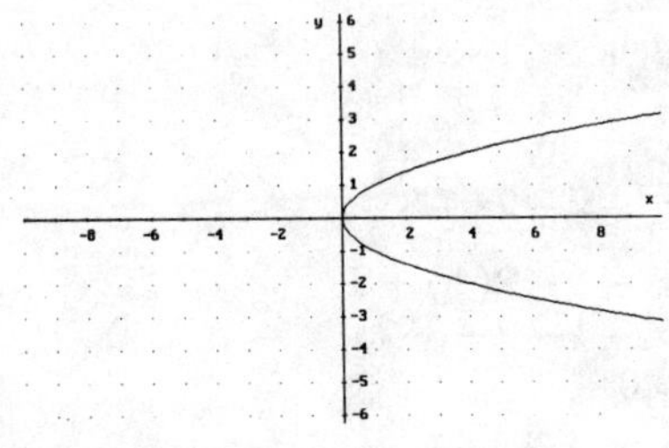

It is not a function.

59. Domain $=[0, \infty)$
Range $=(-\infty, \infty)$
It is not a function.

61. Domain $= [-1, 1]$

Range $= (-\infty, \infty)$

It is not a function.

63. Domain $= (-\infty, \infty)$

Range $= (-\infty, -3] \cup [3, \infty)$

It is not a function.

65. $f(x) = 5x$

a. $f(0) = 5(0)$
$f(0) = 0$

b. $f(2) = 5(2)$
$f(2) = 10$

c. $f(-2) = 5(-2)$
$f(-2) = -10$

67. $g(x) = 2x^2 + 3$

a. $g(-11) = 2(-11)^2 + 3$
$g(-11) = 2(121) + 3$
$g(-11) = 242 + 3$
$g(-11) = 245$

b. $g(-1) = 2(-1)^2 + 3$
$g(-1) = 2(1) + 3$
$g(-1) = 2 + 3$
$g(-1) = 5$

c. $g\left(\frac{1}{2}\right) = 2\left(\frac{1}{2}\right)^2 + 3$

$g\left(\frac{1}{2}\right) = 2\left(\frac{1}{4}\right) + 3$

$g\left(\frac{1}{2}\right) = \frac{2}{4} + 3$

$g\left(\frac{1}{2}\right) = \frac{1}{2} + 3$

$g\left(\frac{1}{2}\right) = 3\frac{1}{2}$

69. $f(x) = -x - 2x + 3$

a. $f(1) = -1 - 2(1) + 3$
$f(1) = -1 - 2 + 3$
$f(1) = 0$

b. $f(-1) = -(-1) - 2(-1) + 3$
$f(-1) = 1 + 2 + 3$
$f(-1) = 6$

71. $f(x) = 6$

a. $f(2) = 6$

b. $f(0) = 6$

c. $f(606) = 6$

73. $A(r) = \pi r^2$

$A(5) = \pi(5)^2$

$A(5) = \pi(25)$

$A(5) = 25\pi$ sq. cm.

75. $V(x) = x^3$

$V(14) = 14^3$

$V(14) = 2744$ cu. in.

77. $H(f) = 2.59f + 47.24$

$H(46) = 2.59(46) + 47.24$

$H(46) = 166.38$ cm.

79. $D(x) = \frac{136}{25}x$

$D(30) = \frac{136}{25}(30)$

$D(30) = 163.2$ mg.

81. $x < 4$ and $x > -1$

$-1 < x < 4$

$(-1, 4)$

83. $-2x > -10$ and $x + 7 < 15$

$\frac{-2x}{-2} > \frac{-10}{-2}$ and $x < 8$

$x < 5$ and $x < 8$

$x < 5$

$(-\infty, 5)$

85. $x =$ one angle
$180 - x =$ other angle

$x = 3(180 - x)$

$x = 540 - 3x$

$\frac{4x}{4} = \frac{540}{4}$

$x = 135^\circ$

$180 - x = 45^\circ$

87. $f(x) = 2x + 7$

a. $f(2) = 2(2) + 7$

$f(2) = 4 + 7$

$f(2) = 11$

b. $f(a) = 2a + 7$

89. $h(x) = x^2 + 7$

a. $h(3) = (3)^2 + 7$

$h(3) = 9 + 7$

$h(3) = 16$

b. $h(a) = a^2 + 7$

Graphing Calculator Exercise 4.3

1. $x = 3y$

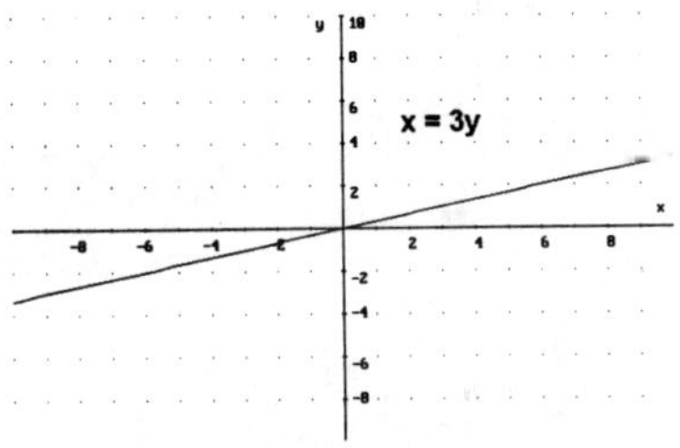

3. $3x + 7y = 21$

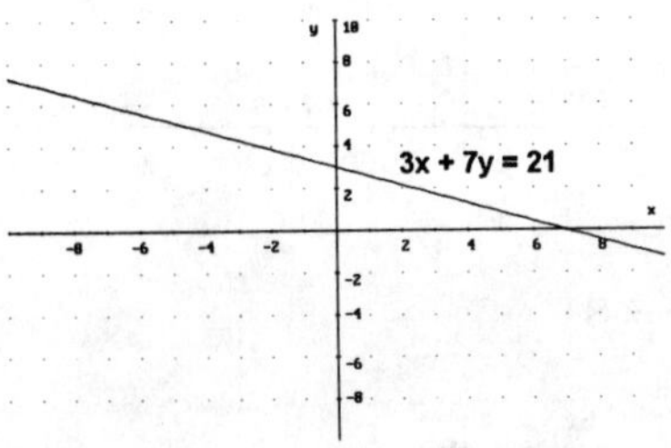

5. $-2.2x + 6.8y = 15.5$

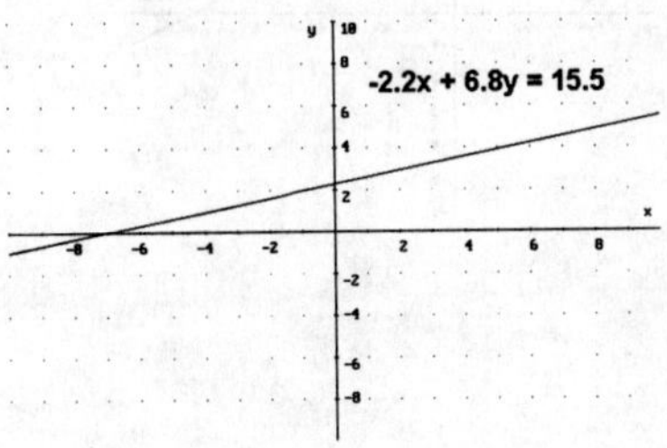

Exercise Set 4.3

1. $f(x) = -2x$

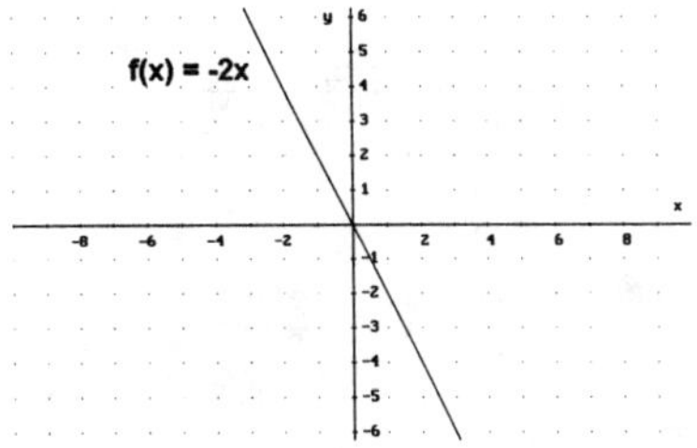

3. $f(x) = -2x + 3$

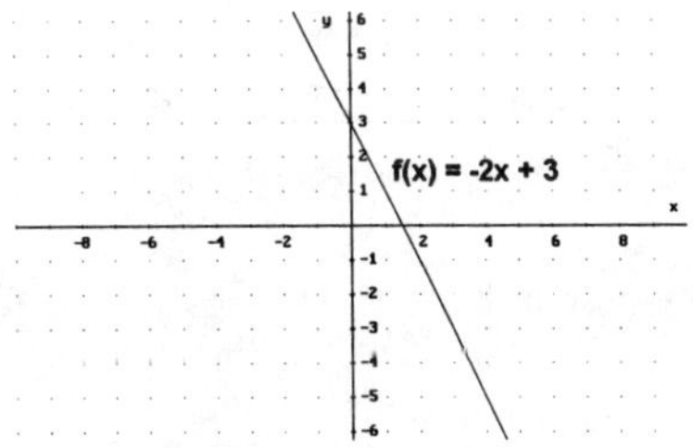

5. $f(x) = \frac{1}{2}x$

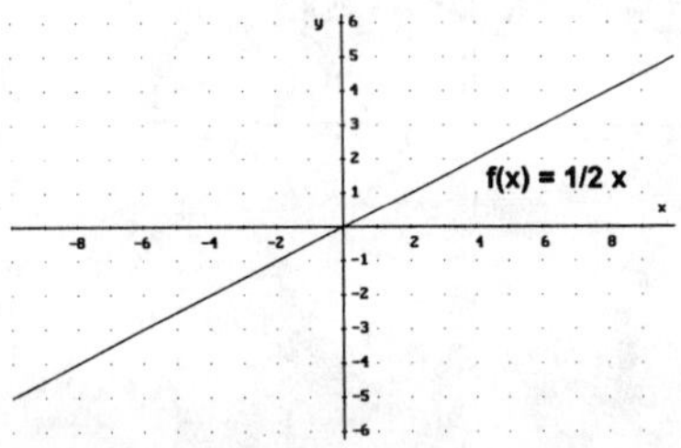

7. $f(x) = \frac{1}{2}x - 4$

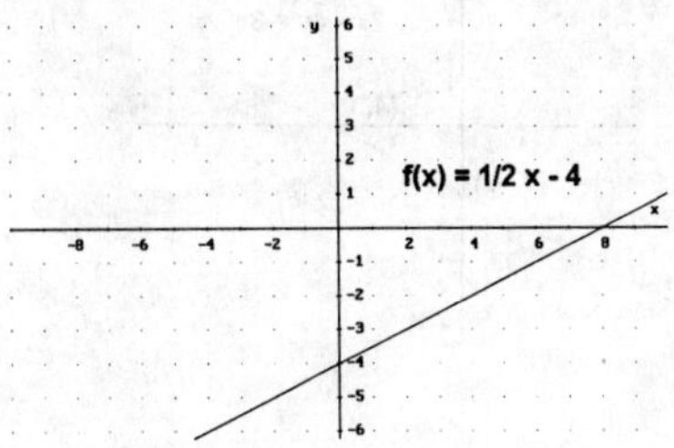

9. $x - y = 3$

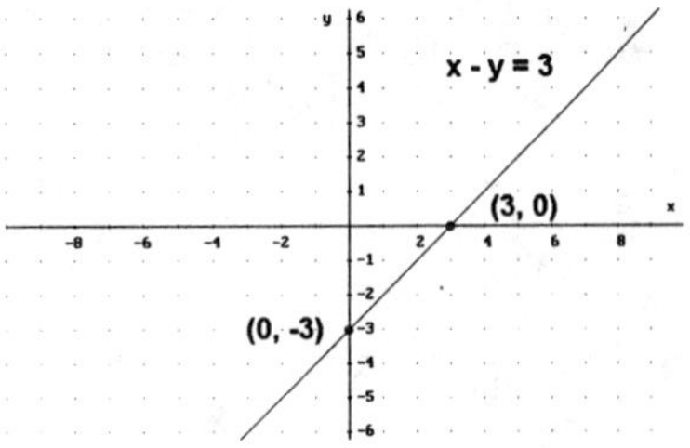

11. $x = 5y$

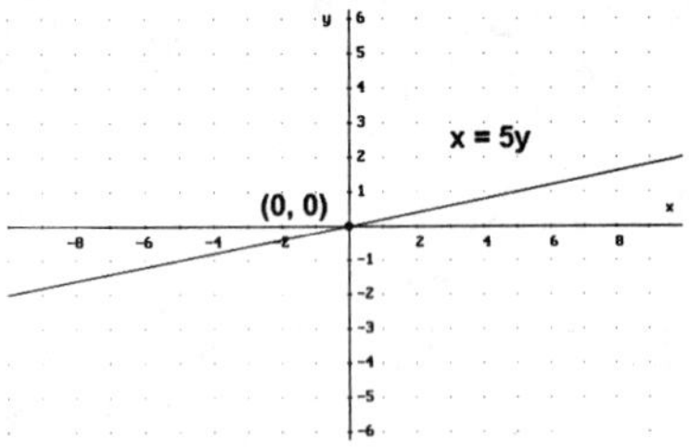

13. $-x + 2y = 6$

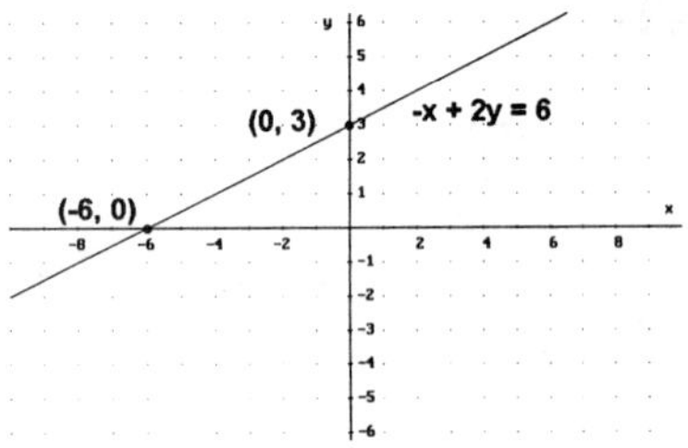

15. $2x - 4y = 8$

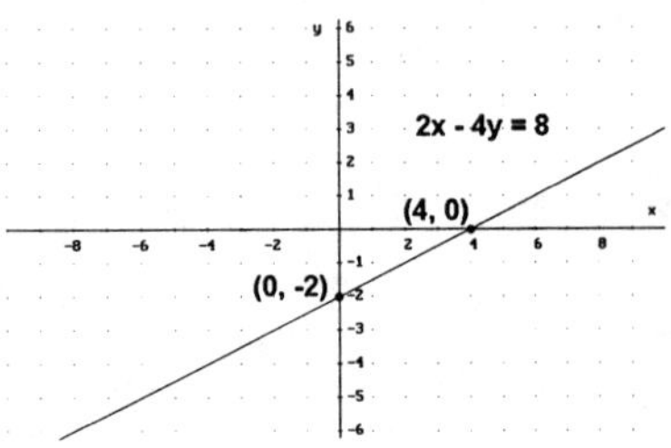

17. $x = -1$

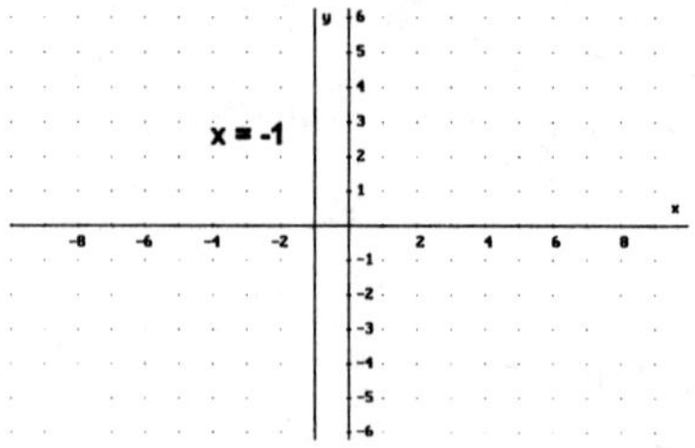

19. $y = 0$

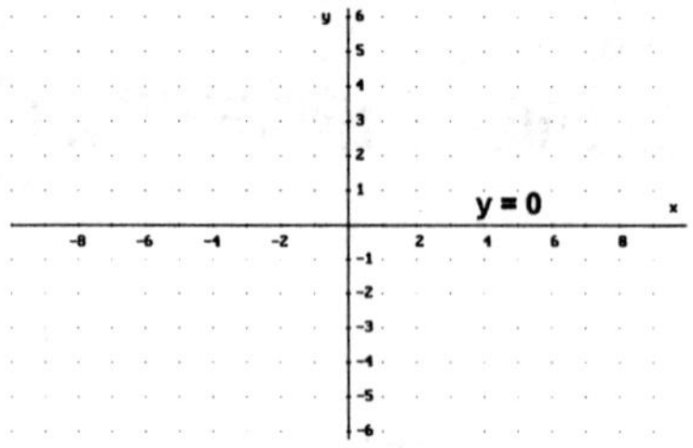

21. $y + 7 = 0$

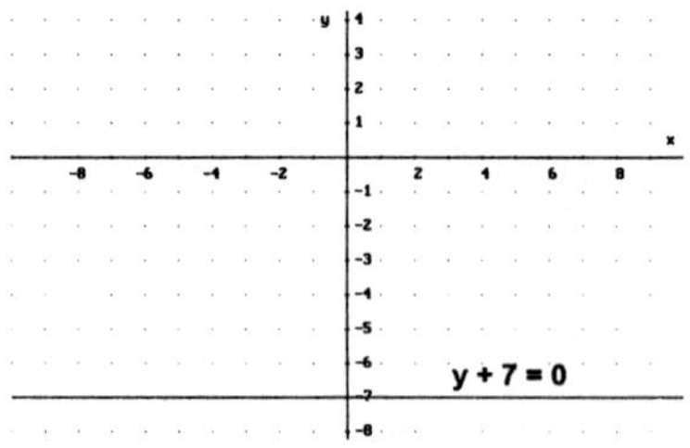

23. $x + 2y = 8$

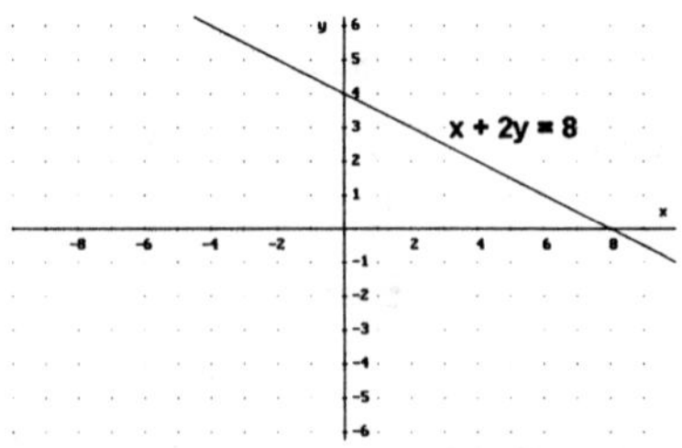

25. $f(x) = \frac{3}{4}x + 2$

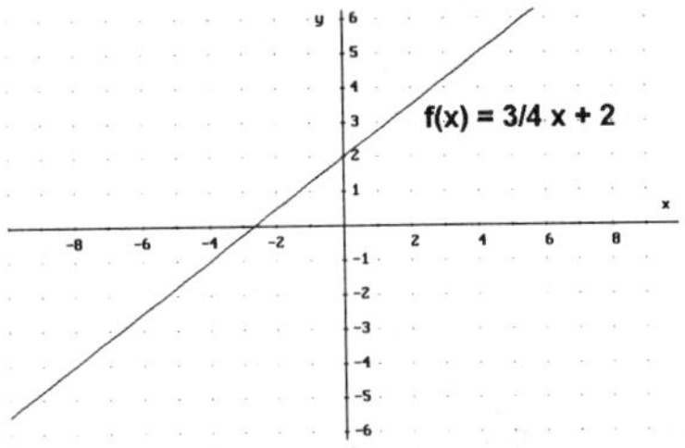

33. $x + 8y = 8$

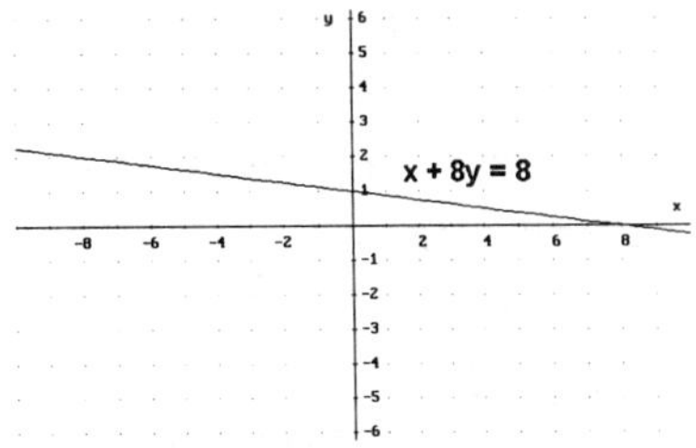

27. $x = -3$

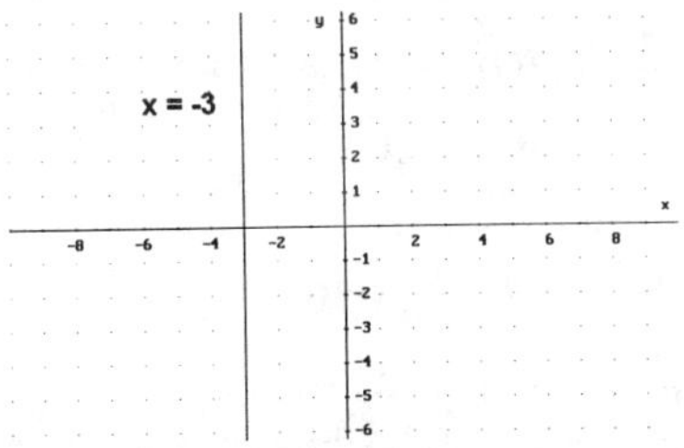

35. $5 = 6x - y$

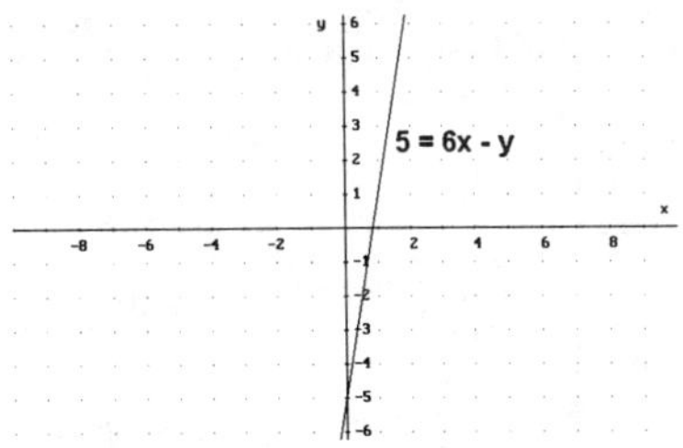

29. $3x + 5y = 7$

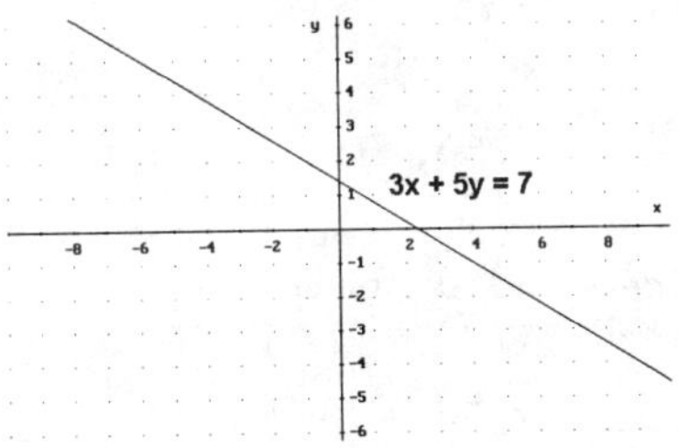

37. $-x + 10y = 11$

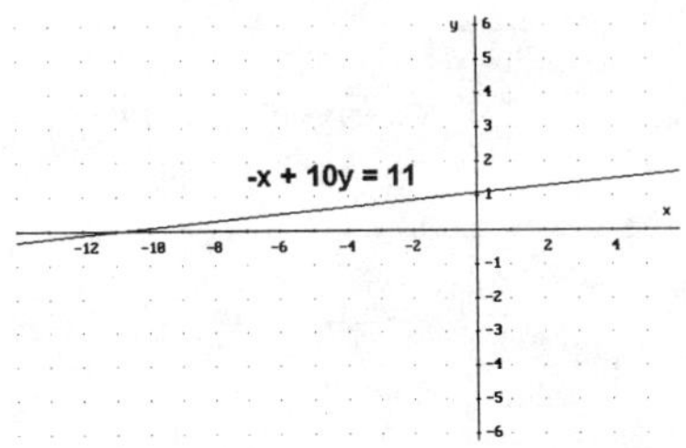

31. $f(x) = x$

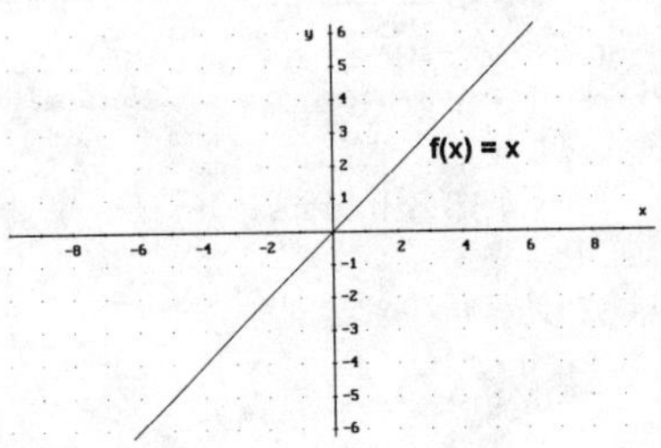

39. $y = 1$

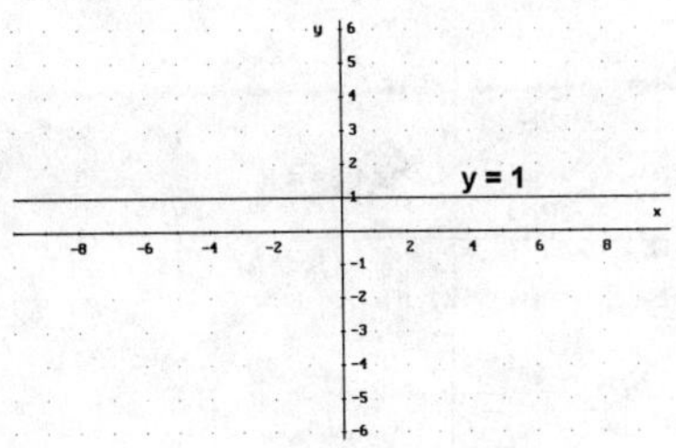

41. $f(x) = \frac{1}{2}x$

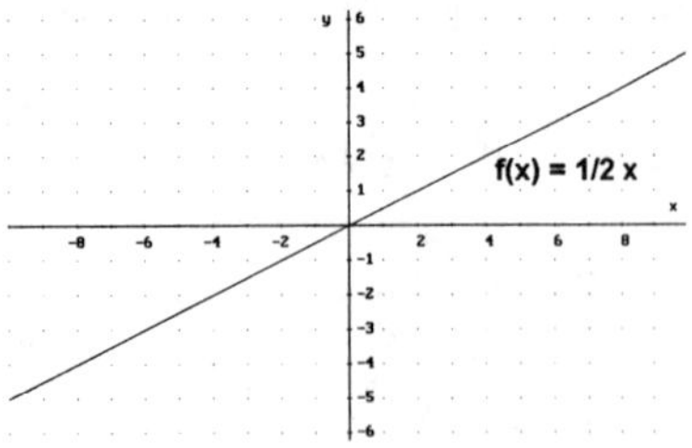

43. $x + 3 = 0$

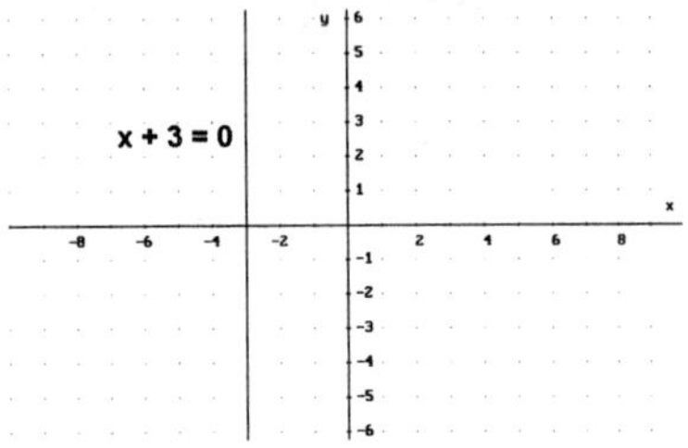

45. $f(x) = 4x - \frac{1}{3}$

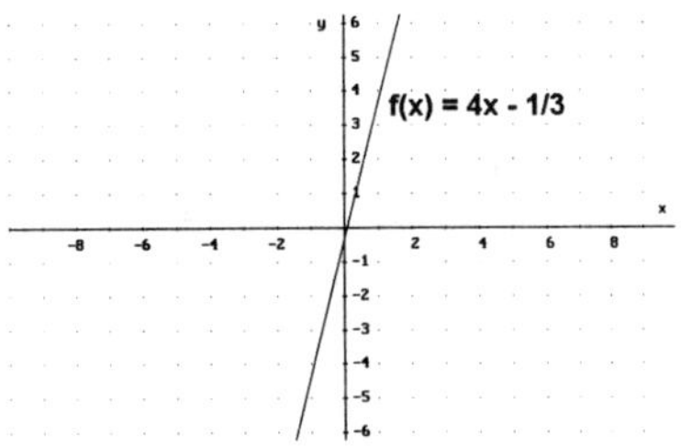

47. $2x + 3y = 6$

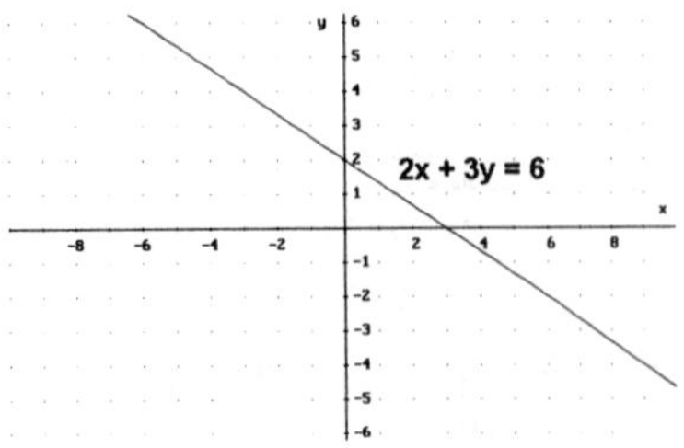

49a. $P(x) = 2x + 6$

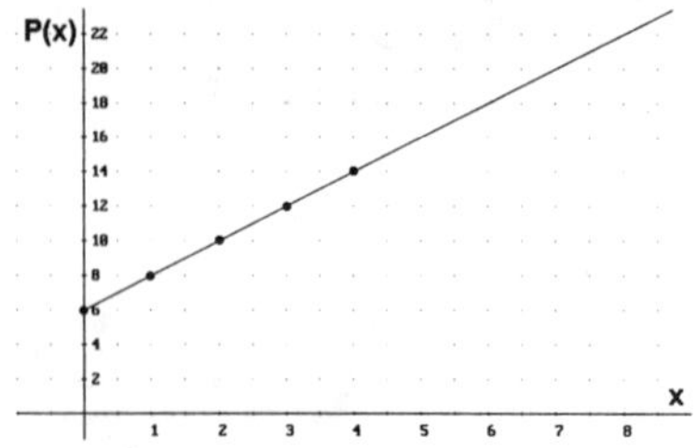

b. If $x = 4$, $P(4) = 14$

51. $2x + 3y = 1500$

a. $x = 0$: $2(0) + 3y = 1500$

$3y = 1500$

$y = 500$

$(0,\ 500)$

This represents 0 tables produced and 500 chairs produced.

b. $y = 0$: $2x + 3(0) = 1500$

$2x = 1500$

$x = 750$

$(750,\ 0)$

This represents 750 tables produced and 0 chairs produced.

c. $x = 50$: $2(50) + 3y = 1500$

$100 + 3y = 1500$

$3y = 1400$

$y = \frac{1400}{3}$

$y = 466\frac{2}{3}$

466 chairs

53. $|x - 3| = 6$

$x - 3 = -6$ or $x - 3 = 6$

$x = -3$ or $x = 9$

$\{-3,\ 9\}$

55. $|2x + 5| > 3$

$2x + 5 < -3$ or $2x + 5 > 3$

$2x < -8 \quad \text{or} \quad 2x > -2$

$x < -4 \quad \text{or} \quad x > -1$

$(-\infty, -4) \cup (-1, \infty)$

57. $|3x - 4| \leq 2$

$-2 \leq 3x - 4 \leq 2$

$2 \leq 3x \leq 6$

$\frac{2}{3} \leq x \leq 2$

$\left[\frac{2}{3}, 2\right]$

59. $\frac{-6-3}{2-8} = \frac{-9}{-6} = \frac{3}{2}$

61. $\frac{-8-(-2)}{-3-(-2)} = \frac{-8+2}{-3+2} = \frac{-6}{-1} = 6$

63. $\frac{0-6}{5-0} = -\frac{6}{5}$

Graphing Calculator Exercise 4.4

1. $y = x$; $y = 6x$; $y = -6x$

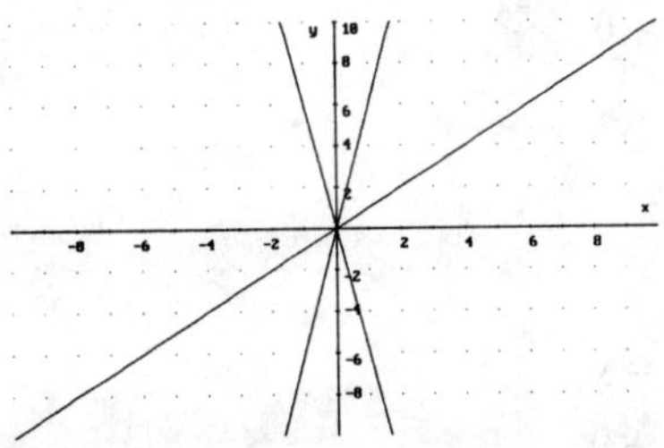

3. $y = \frac{1}{2}x + 2$; $y = \frac{3}{4}x + 2$; $y = x + 2$

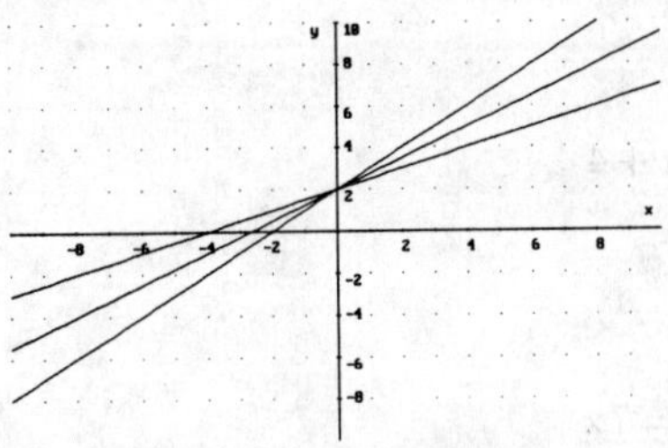

5. $y = -7x + 5$; $y = 7x + 5$

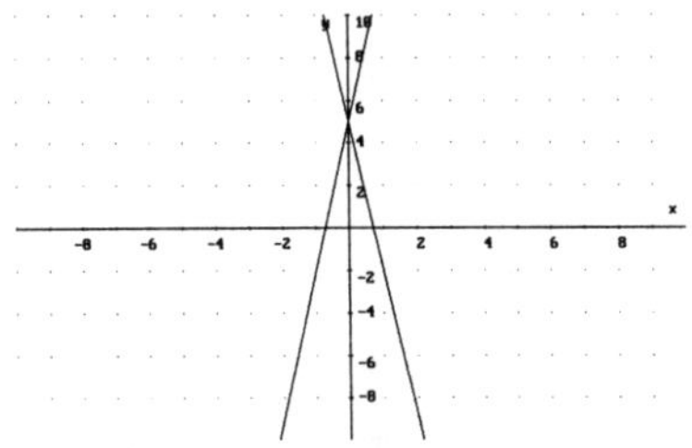

Exercise Set 4.4

1. (0,0) and (7,8)

$m = \frac{8-0}{7-0} = \frac{8}{7}$

3. (−1,5) and (6,−2)

$m = \frac{-2-5}{6-(-1)} = \frac{-7}{6+1} = \frac{-7}{7} = -1$

5. (1,4) and (5,3)

$m = \frac{3-4}{5-1} = \frac{-1}{4} = -\frac{1}{4}$

7. (−4,3) and (−4,5)

$m = \frac{5-3}{-4-(-4)} = \frac{2}{0}$

Undefined, division by zero is not defined.

9. $y = 5x - 2$

$m = 5$

$b = -2$

11. $2x + y = 7$

$y = -2x + 7$

$m = -2$

$b = 7$

13. $2x - 3y = 10$

$-3y = -2x + 10$

$y = \frac{-2}{-3}x + \frac{10}{-3}$

$y = \frac{2}{3}x - \frac{10}{3}$

$m = \frac{2}{3}$

$b = -\frac{10}{3}$

15. $f(x) = \frac{1}{2}x$

$m = \frac{1}{2}$

$b = 0$

17. $y = -3x + 6$ $\quad$ $y = 3x + 5$

$m = -3$ $\quad$ $m = 3$

neither

19. $-4x + 2y = 5$ $\quad$ $2x - y = 7$

$2y = 4x + 5$ $\quad$ $-y = -2x + 7$

$y = 2x + \frac{5}{2}$ $\quad$ $y = 2x - 7$

$m = 2$ $\quad$ $m = 2$

parallel, slopes are equal

21. $-2x + 3y = 1$ $\quad$ $3x + 2y = 12$

$3y = 2x + 1$ $\quad$ $2y = -3x + 12$

$y = \frac{2}{3}x + \frac{1}{3}$ $\quad$ $y = -\frac{3}{2}x + 6$

$m = \frac{2}{3}$ $\quad$ $m = -\frac{3}{2}$

perpendicular, slopes are negative reciprocals

23. $x = 1$

vertical line

slope is undefined

25. $y = -3$

horizontal line

$m = 0$

27. $x + 2 = 0$

$x = -2$

vertical line

slope is undefined

29. $(-2,8)$ and $(1,6)$

$m = \frac{6-8}{1-(-2)} = \frac{-2}{1+2} = -\frac{2}{3}$

31. $(1,0)$ and $(1,1)$

$m = \frac{1-0}{1-1} = \frac{1}{0}$

undefined

33. $(5,-11)$ and $(1,-11)$

$m = \frac{-11-(-11)}{1-5} = \frac{-11+11}{-4} = \frac{0}{-4} = 0$

35. $(0,6)$ and $(-3,0)$

$m = \frac{0-6}{-3-0} = \frac{-6}{-3} = 2$

37. $(-1,2)$ and $(-3,4)$

$m = \frac{4-2}{-3-(-1)} = \frac{2}{-3+1} = \frac{2}{-2} = -1$

39. $f(x) = -x + 5$

$m = -1$, $b = 5$

41. $-6x + 5y = 30$

$5y = 6x + 30$

$y = \frac{6}{5}x + 6$

$m = \frac{6}{5}$

$b = 6$

43. $3x + 9 = y$

$y = 3x + 9$

$m = 3$

$b = 9$

45. $y = 4$

$y = 0x + 4$

$m = 0$

$b = 4$

47. $f(x) = 7x$

$m = 7$, $b = 0$

49. $6 + y = 0$

$y = -6$

$y = 0x - 6$

$m = 0$

$b = -6$

51. $2 - x = 3$

$-x = 1$

$x = -1$

slope is undefined;
no y-intercept

53. $m = \frac{\text{change in rise}}{\text{change in run}} = \frac{8}{12} = \frac{2}{3}$

55. 2.5 miles × 5280 feet/mile = 13,200 feet

$\frac{1600}{13200} = \frac{4}{33}$

$m = \frac{4}{33}$

57. $y = -\frac{7}{2}x - 6$

$m = -\frac{7}{2}$

Slope of the parallel
line is the same,

$m = -\frac{7}{2}$.

59. $y = -\frac{7}{2}x - 6$

$m = -\frac{7}{2}$

Slope of the perpendicular
line is the negative reciprocal,

$m = \frac{2}{7}$.

61. $(-7, -5)$, $(-2, -6)$

$m = \frac{-6-(-5)}{-2-(-7)} = \frac{-6+5}{-2+7} = -\frac{1}{5}$

The slope of the parallel
line is the same,

$m = -\frac{1}{5}$.

63. (0, 0), (1, −3)

$m = \frac{-3-0}{1-0} = \frac{-3}{1} = -3$

The slope of the perpendicular
line is the negative reciprocal,

$m = \frac{1}{3}$.

65. $|-6| = 6$

67. $-|-1| = -1$

69. \$70

71. \$90

73. The greatest increase
is from 1990 to 1991.

75. $y - 2 = 5(x + 6)$

$y - 2 = 5x + 30$

$y = 5x + 32$

77. $y - 0 = -3[x - (-10)]$

$y = -3(x + 10)$

$y = -3x - 30$

Exercise Set 4.5

1. Slope −1; y-intercept 1

$y = mx + b$

$y = -1x + 1$

3. Slope 2; y-intercept $\frac{3}{4}$

$y = mx + b$

$y = 2x + \frac{3}{4}$

5. Slope $\frac{2}{7}$; y-intercept 0

$y = mx + b$

$y = \frac{2}{7}x + 0$

$y = \frac{2}{7}x$

7.

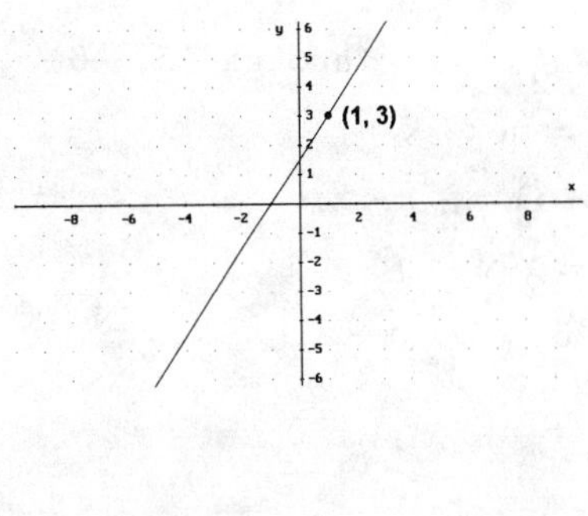

9.

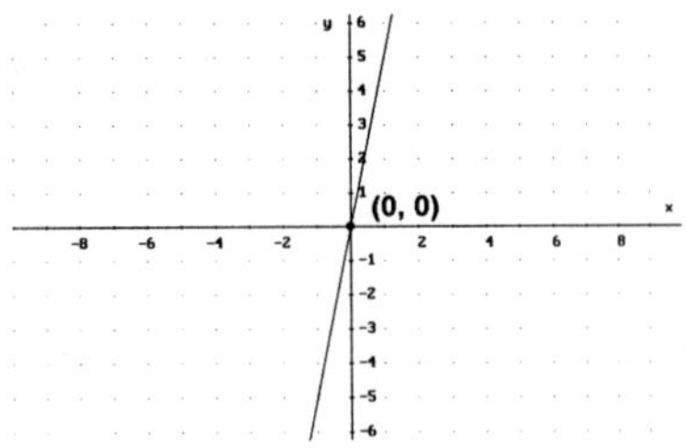

11.

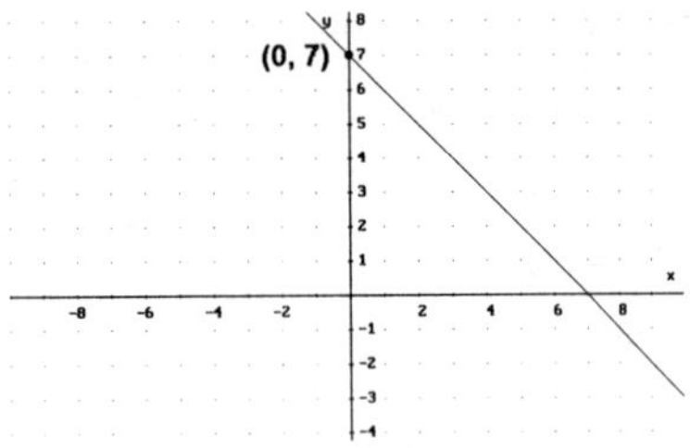

13. Slope 6; through (2,2)

$y - y_1 = m(x - x_1)$

$y - 2 = 6(x - 2)$

$y - 2 = 6x - 12$

$-2 = 6x - y - 12$

$-2 + 12 = 6x - y$

$10 = 6x - y$

$6x - y = 10$

15. Slope -8; through $(-1, -5)$

$y - y_1 = m(x - x_1)$

$y - (-5) = -8[x - (-1)]$

$y + 5 = -8(x + 1)$

$y + 5 = -8x - 8$

$8x + y + 5 = -8$

$8x + y = -8 - 5$

$8x + y = -13$

17. Slope $\frac{1}{2}$; through $(5, -6)$

$y - y_1 = m(x - x_1)$

$y - (-6) = \frac{1}{2}(x - 5)$

$y + 6 = \frac{1}{2}(x - 5)$

$2(y + 6) = 2\left[\frac{1}{2}(x - 5)\right]$

$2y + 12 = x - 5$

$+12 = x - 2y - 5$

$12 + 5 = x - 2y$

$17 = x - 2y$

$x - 2y = 17$

19. Through (3,2) and (5,6)

$m = \frac{6 - 2}{5 - 3} = \frac{4}{2} = 2$

$y - y_1 = m(x - x_1)$

$y - 2 = 2(x - 3)$

$y - 2 = 2x - 6$

$y = 2x - 4$

$f(x) = 2x - 4$

21. Through $(-1,3)$ and $(-2, -5)$

$m = \frac{-5 - 3}{-2 - (-1)} = \frac{-8}{-2 + 1} = \frac{-8}{-1} = 8$

$y - y_1 = m(x - x_1)$

$y - 3 = 8[x - (-1)]$

$y - 3 = 8(x + 1)$

$y - 3 = 8x + 8$

$y = 8x + 11$

$f(x) = 8x + 11$

23. Through (2,3) and $(-1, -1)$

$m = \frac{-1 - 3}{-1 - 2} = \frac{-4}{-3} = \frac{4}{3}$

$y - y_1 = m(x - x_1)$

$y - 3 = \frac{4}{3}(x - 2)$

$3(y - 3) = 3\left[\frac{4}{3}(x - 2)\right]$

$3(y - 3) = 4(x - 2)$

$3y - 9 = 4x - 8$

$3y = 4x + 1$

$y = \frac{4x}{3} + \frac{1}{3}$

$f(x) = \frac{4}{3}x + \frac{1}{3}$

25. Vertical line through (0,2)
On a vertical line, the
x-coordinate stays the same.

$x = 0$

27. Horizontal line through $(-1,3)$
On a horizontal line, the y-coordinate stays the same.

$y=3$

29. Vertical line through $(-7,-2)$
On a vertical line, the x-coordinate stays the same.

$x=-7$

31. $y=4x-2$ so $m=4$

$y-8=4(x-3)$

$y-8=4x-12$

$f(x)=4x-4$

33. $3y=x-6$ or $y=\frac{1}{3}x-2$

so $m_{\perp}=\frac{1}{3}$ and $m=-3$

$y-(-5)=-3(x-2)$

$y+5=-3x+6$

$f(x)=-3x+1$

35. $3x+2y=5$

$2y=-3x+5$

$y=-\frac{3}{2}x+\frac{5}{2}$ so $m=-\frac{3}{2}$

$y-(-3)=-\frac{3}{2}[x-(-2)]$

$2(y+3)=-3(x+2)$

$2y+6=-3x-6$

$2y=-3x-12$

$f(x)=-\frac{3}{2}x-6$

37. Slope $-\frac{1}{2}$; through $\left(0,\frac{5}{3}\right)$

$y-y_1=m(x-x_1)$

$y-\frac{5}{3}=-\frac{1}{2}(x-0)$

$y-\frac{5}{3}=-\frac{1}{2}x$

$6\left(y-\frac{5}{3}\right)=6\left(-\frac{1}{2}x\right)$

$6y-10=-3x$

$3x+6y-10=0$

$3x+6y=10$

39. Slope 1; through $(-7,9)$

$y-y_1=m(x-x_1)$

$y-9=1[x-(-7)]$

$y-9=1(x+7)$

$y-9=x+7$

$-9=x-y+7$

$-9-7=x-y$

$-16=x-y$

$x-y=-16$

41. Through $(10,7)$ and $(7,10)$

$m=\frac{10-7}{7-10}=\frac{3}{-3}=-1$

$y-y_1=m(x-x_1)$

$y-7=-1(x-10)$

$y-7=-x+10$

$x+y-7=10$

$x+y=10+7$

$x+y=17$

43. Through $(6,7)$ parallel to x-axis.

The x-axis is a horizontal line, so the parallel line is horizontal.

On a horizontal line, the y-coordinate stays the same.

$y=7$

45. Slope $-\frac{4}{7}$, through $(-1,-2)$

$y-y_1=m(x-x_1)$

$y-(-2)=-\frac{4}{7}[x-(-1)]$

$y+2=-\frac{4}{7}(x+1)$

$7(y+2)=7\left[-\frac{4}{7}(x+1)\right]$

$7(y+2)=-4(x+1)$

$7y+14=-4x-4$

$4x+7y+14=-4$

$4x+7y=-4-14$

$4x+7y=-18$

47. $y-3=2[x-(-2)]$

$y-3=2(x+2)$

$y-3=2x+4$

$2x-y=-7$

49. $m=\frac{2-6}{5-1}=\frac{-4}{4}=-1$

$y-6=-1(x-1)$

$y-6=-x+1$

$x+y=7$

51. $y=-\frac{1}{2}x+11$

$2y=-x+22$

$x+2y=22$

53. $m=\frac{-6-(-4)}{0-(-7)}=\frac{-2}{7}$

$y=-\frac{2}{7}x-6$

$7y=-2x-42$

$2x+7y=-42$

55. $y-0=\frac{-4}{3}[x-(-5)]$

$3y=-4(x+5)$

$3y=-4x-20$

$4x+3y=-20$

57. $x=-2$

59. $2x+4y=9$

$4y=-2x+9$

$y=-\frac{1}{2}x+\frac{9}{4}$ so $m=-\frac{1}{2}$

$y-(-2)=-\frac{1}{2}(x-6)$

$2(y+2)=-x+6$

$2y+4=-x+6$

$x+2y=2$

61. $y=12$

63a. (1, 32), (3, 96)

$m=\frac{96-32}{3-1}=\frac{64}{2}=32$

$y-32=32(x-1)$

$y-32=32x-32$

$y=32x$

$R(x)=32x$

b. $R(4)=32(4)$

$R(4)=128$ ft. per sec.

65a. (1, 30000), (4, 66000)

$m=\frac{66000-30000}{4-1}=\frac{36000}{3}=12{,}000$

$y-30000=12000(x-1)$

$y-30000=12000x-12000$

$y=12000x+18000$

$P(x)=12000x+18000$

b. $P(7)=12000(7)+18000$

$P(7)=84000+18000$

$P(7)=102{,}000$

c. $126000=12000x+18000$

$108000=12000x$

$9=x$

After 9 years the profit will be $126,000.

67. Let $y=$ temperature in K°
$x=$ temperature in C°

(0, 273), (100, 373)

$m=\frac{373-273}{100-0}=\frac{100}{100}=1$

$y-273=1(x-0)$

$y-273=x$

$y=x+273$

$K=C+273$

69. $\frac{2x}{zx-y^2}$

$x=1,\ y=-4,\ z=0$

$\frac{2(1)}{0(1)-(-4)^2}=\frac{2}{0-(16)}=\frac{2}{-16}=-\frac{1}{8}$

71. $\frac{|x|+3z}{2y}$

$x=1,\ y=-4,\ z=0$

$\frac{|1|+3(0)}{2(-4)}=\frac{1+0}{-8}=-\frac{1}{8}$

73. $-3x+1>0$

$-3x>-1$

$\frac{-3x}{-3}<\frac{-1}{-3}$

$x<\frac{1}{3}$

$\left(-\infty,\ \frac{1}{3}\right)$

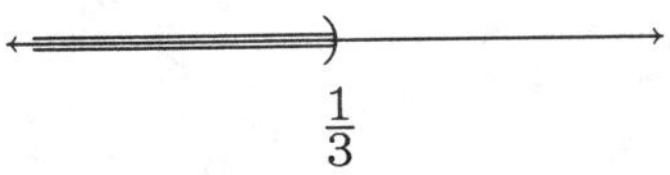

75. $-2(x+1)\le -x+10$

$-2x-2\le -x+10$

$-2\le x+10$

$-12\le x$

$[-12,\ \infty)$

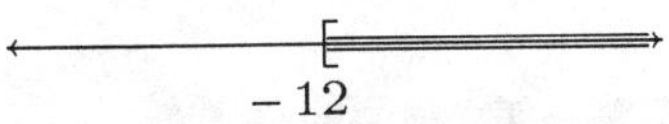

77. $\frac{x}{5}-\frac{3}{10}\ge\frac{x}{2}-1$

$10\left(\frac{x}{5}\right)-10\left(\frac{3}{10}\right)\ge 10\left(\frac{x}{2}\right)-10(1)$

$2x-3\ge 5x-10$

$-3\ge 3x-10$

$7\ge 3x$

$\frac{7}{3}\ge x$

$x\le\frac{7}{3}$

$\left(-\infty,\ \frac{7}{3}\right]$

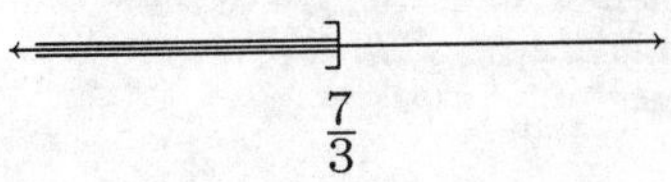

Exercise Set 4.6

1. $x<2$

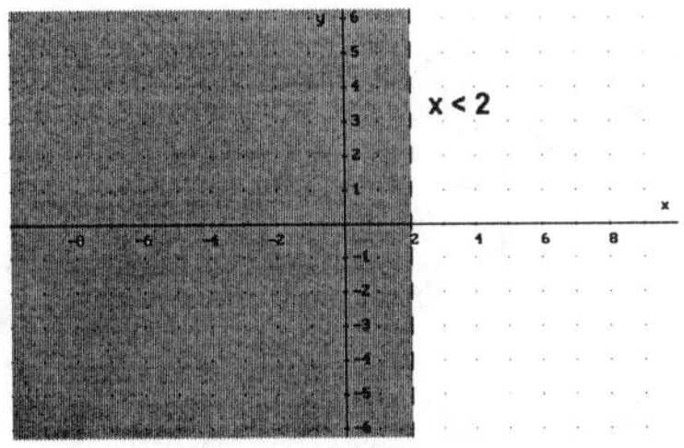

3. $x-y\ge 7$

$y\le x-7$

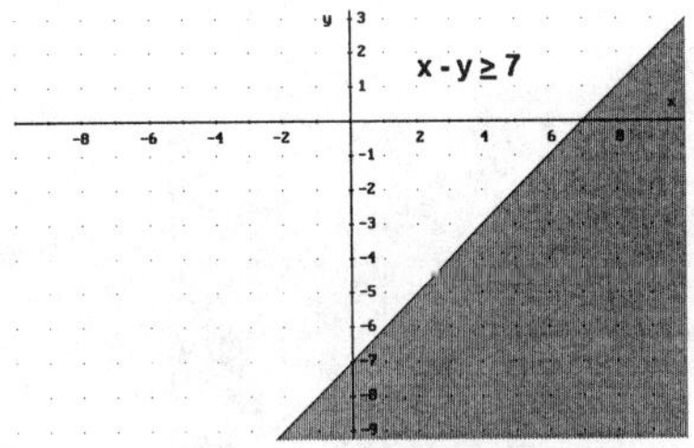

5. $3x+y>6$

$y>-3x+6$

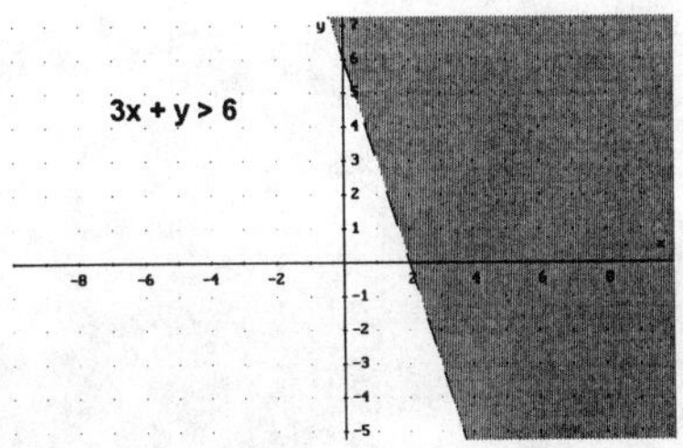

7. $y\le -2x$

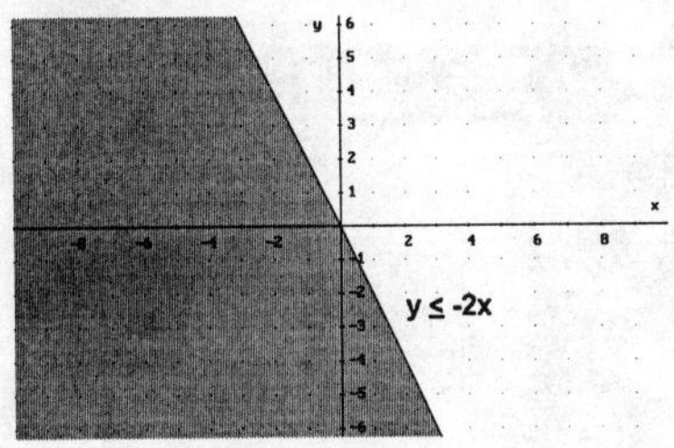

9. $2x + 4y \geq 8$

$4y \geq -2x + 8$

$y \geq -\frac{1}{2}x + 2$

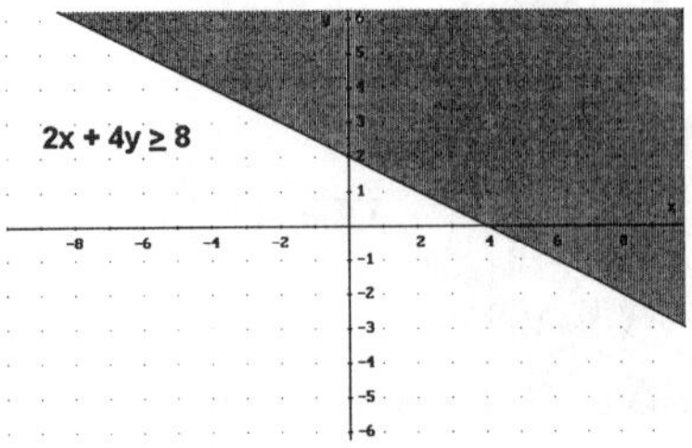

11. $5x + 3y > -15$

$3y > -5x - 15$

$y > -\frac{5}{3}x - 5$

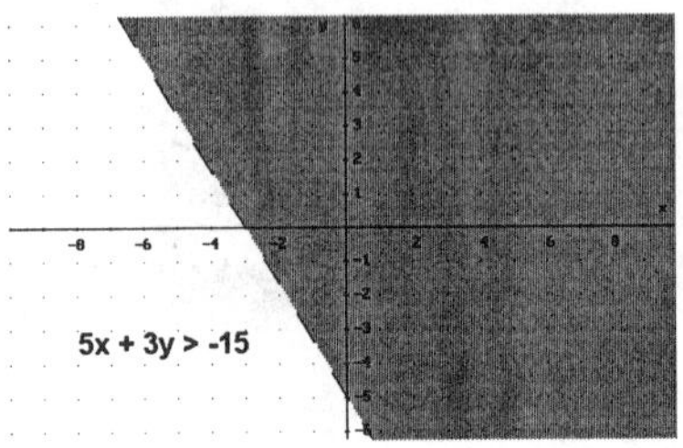

13. $x \geq 3$ and $y \leq -2$

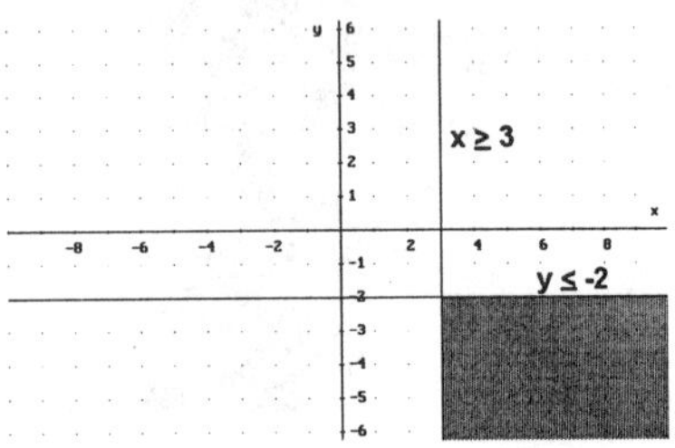

15. $x \leq -2$ or $y \geq 4$

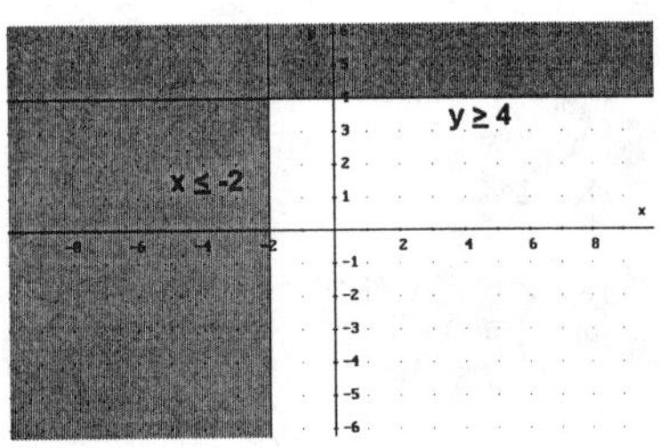

17. $x - y < 3$ and $x > 4$

$y > x - 3$ and $x > 4$

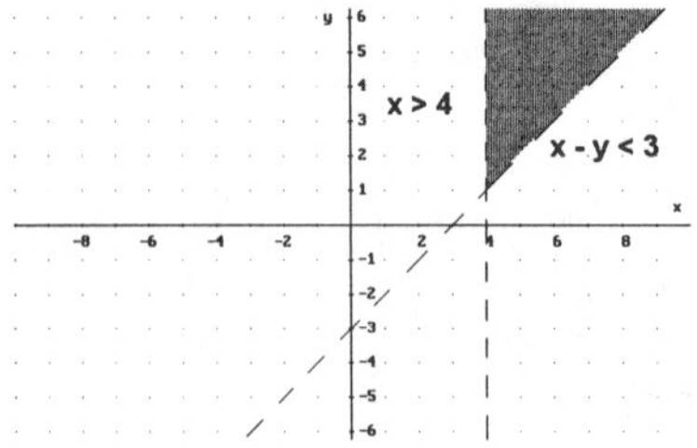

19. $x + y \leq 3$ or $x - y \geq 5$

$y \leq -x + 3$ or $y \leq x - 5$

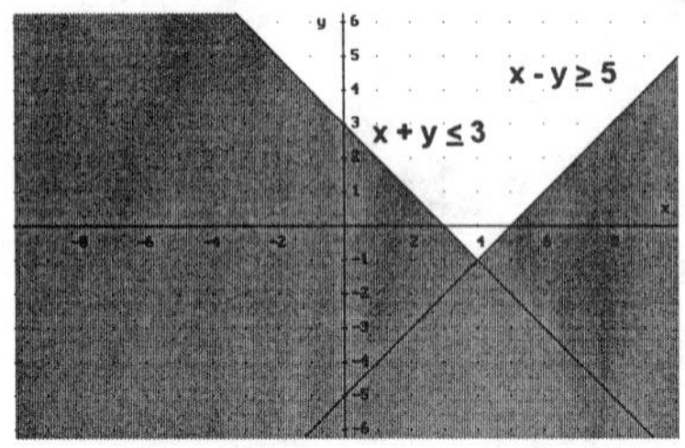

21. $y \geq -2$

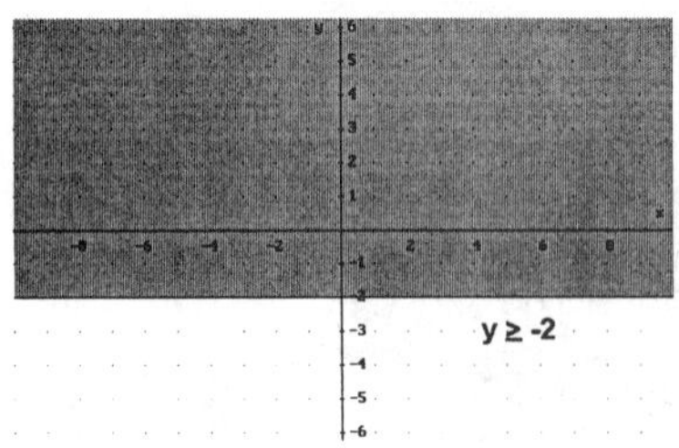

23. $x - 6y < 12$

$x - 12 \leq 6y$

$y > \frac{1}{6}x - 2$

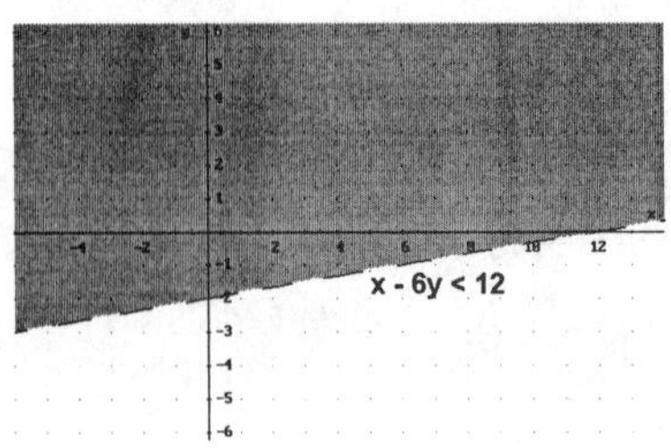

25. $x > 5$

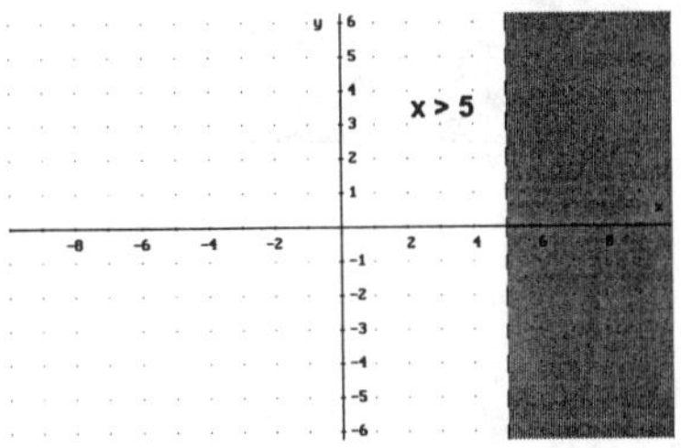

27. $-2x + y \leq 4$

$y \leq 2x + 4$

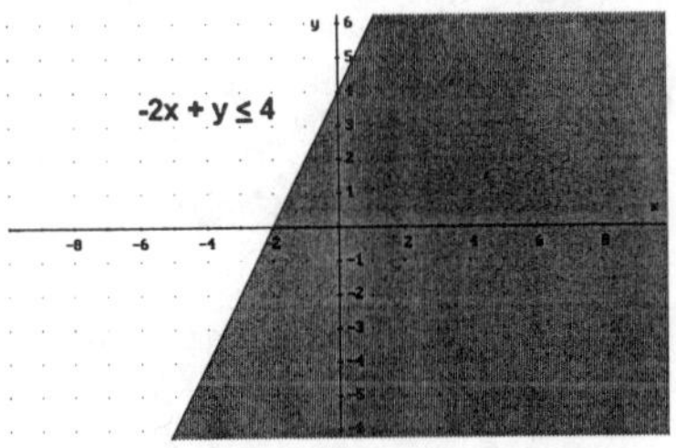

29. $x - 3y < 0$

$x < 3y$

$y > \frac{x}{3}$

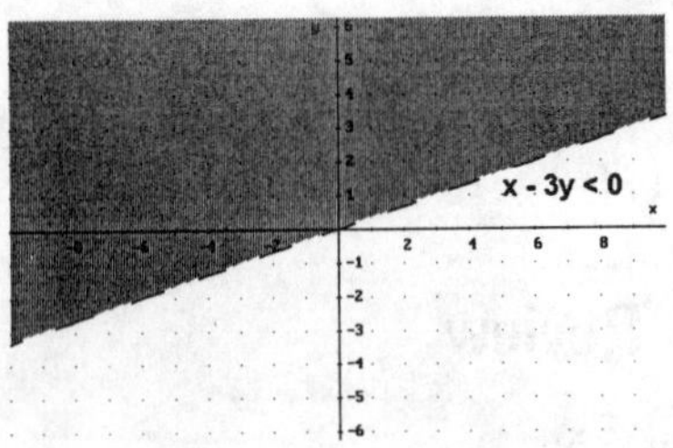

31. $3x - 2y \leq 12$

$3x - 12 \leq 2y$

$y \geq \frac{3}{2}x - 6$

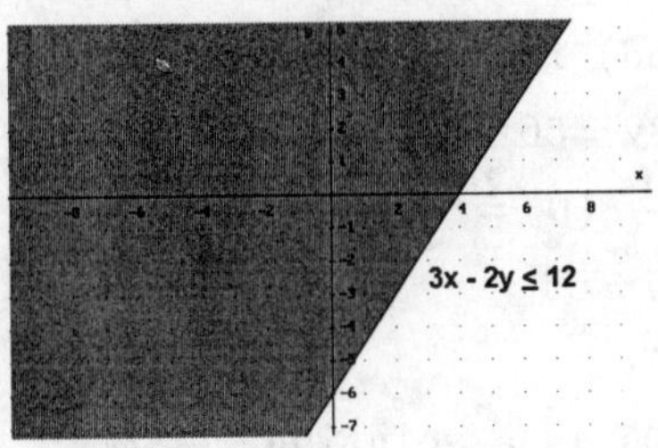

33. $x - y \geq 2$ or $y < 5$

$y \leq x - 2$ or $y < 5$

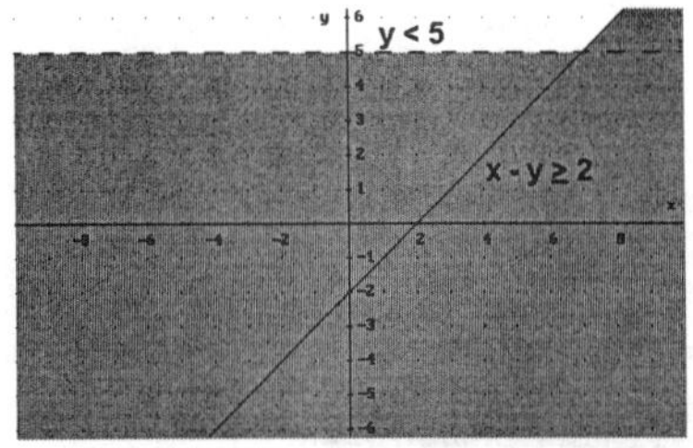

35. $x + y \leq 1$ and $y \leq -1$

$y \leq -x + 1$ and $y \leq -1$

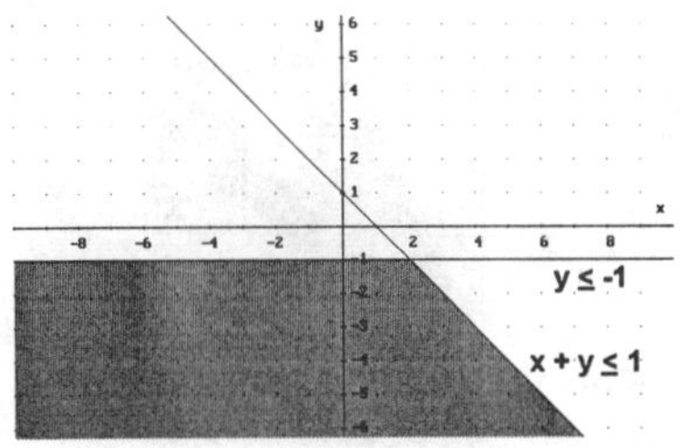

37. $2x + y > 4$ or $x \geq 1$

$y > -2x + 4$ or $x \geq 1$

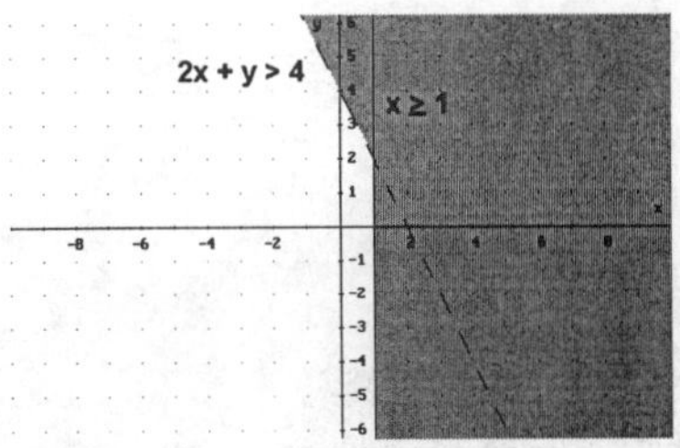

39. $-2 \leq x \leq 1$

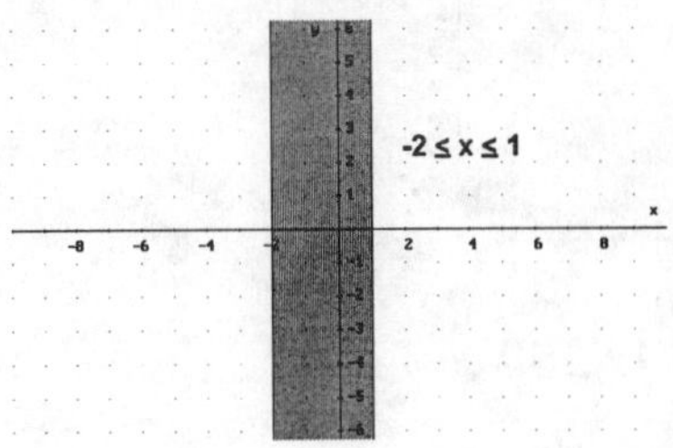

41. $x+y \le 0$ and $3x-6y \ge 12$

$y \le -x$ and $3x-12 \ge 6y$

$y \le -x$ and $y \le \frac{1}{2}x-2$

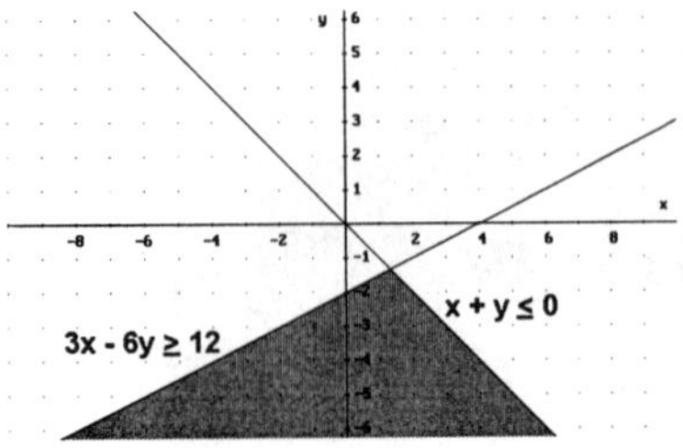

43. $2x-y>3$ and $x \ge 0$

$y<2x-3$ and $x \ge 0$

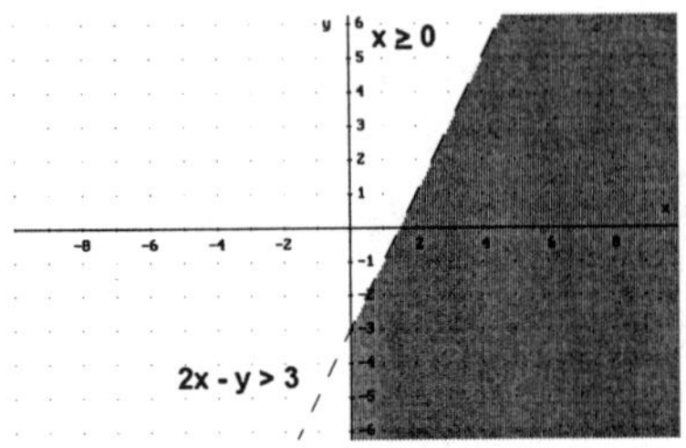

45. $x \ge 2$

47. $y \le -3$

49. $y>4$

51. $x<1$

53. $x \le 20$ and $y \ge 10$

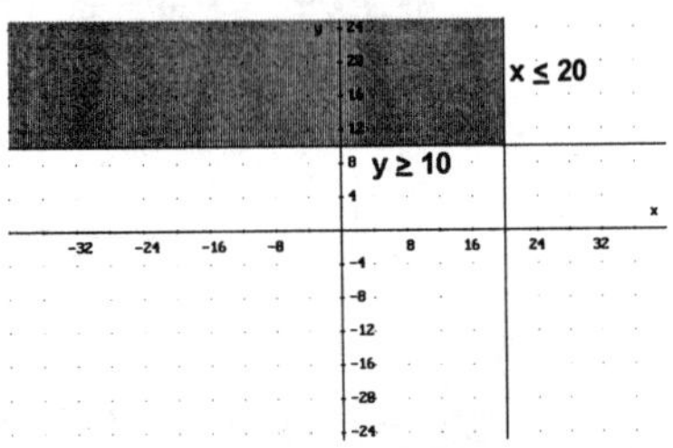

55. $\begin{cases} x \ge 0 \\ y \ge 0 \\ 2x+4y \le 40 \end{cases}$

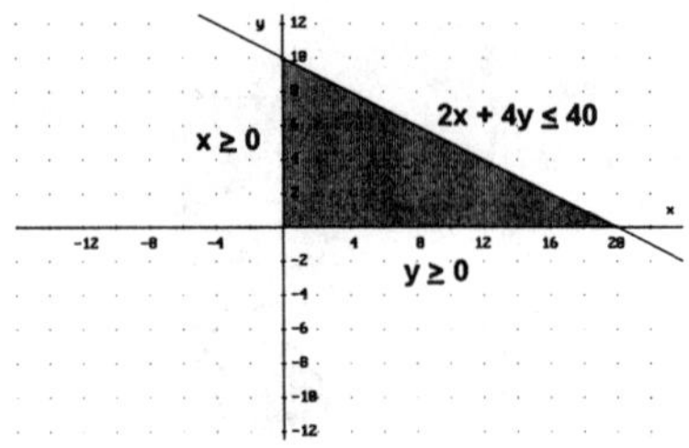

57. $3^2 = 3 \bullet 3 = 9$

59. $(-5)^2 = (-5)(-5) = 25$

61. -2^4

$-1 \bullet 2^4$

$-1 \bullet 16$

-16

63. $\left(\frac{2}{7}\right)^2 = \frac{2}{7} \bullet \frac{2}{7} = \frac{4}{49}$

65. $\frac{x}{3} = \frac{7}{5}$

$x = \frac{7}{5} \bullet 3$

$x = \frac{21}{5}$

$x = 4\frac{1}{5}$ inches

67. Domain: $\{x \mid x < -2 \text{ or } x > 2\}$

Range: $\{y \mid y \text{ is a real number}\}$

Chapter 4 Review

1. $7x-8y=56$

$(0,\ 56)$

$7(0)-8(56) \stackrel{?}{=} 56$

$-8(56) \stackrel{?}{=} 56$

$-448 \ne 56$

(0, 56) is not a solution.

$7x-8y=56$

$7(8)-8(0) \stackrel{?}{=} 56$

$56-0 \stackrel{?}{=} 56$

$56=56$

(8, 0) is a solution.

3. $x = 13$ (13, 5)

$13 = 13$

(13, 5) is a solution.

$x = 13$ (13, 13)

$13 = 13$

(13, 13) is a solution.

5. $-2 + y = 6x$ (7,)

$-2 + y = 6(7)$

$-2 + y = 42$

$y = 44$

(7, 44)

7. $9 = -3x + 4y$

a. (, 0) $9 = -3x + 4(0)$

$9 = -3x$

$-3 = x$

$(-3, 0)$

b. (, 3) $9 = -3x + 4(3)$

$9 = -3x + 12$

$-3 = -3x$

$1 = x$

(1, 3)

c. (9,) $9 = -3(9) + 4y$

$9 = -27 + 4y$

$36 = 4y$

$9 = y$

(9, 9)

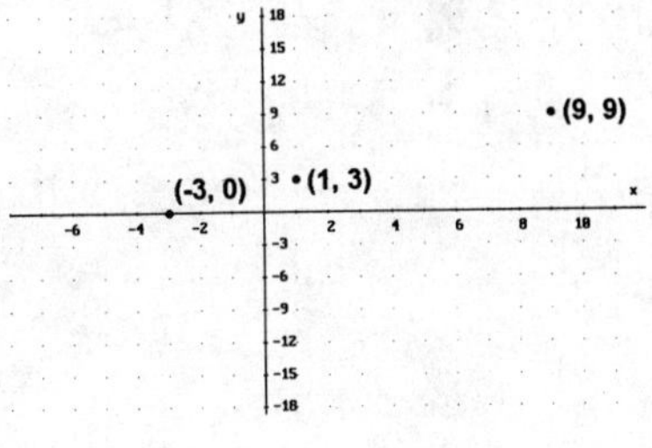

9. $x = 2y$

a. (, 0) $x = 2(0)$

$x = 0$

(0, 0)

b. (, 5) $x = 2(5)$

$x = 10$

(10, 5)

c. (, −5) $x = 2(-5)$

$x = -10$

$(-10, -5)$

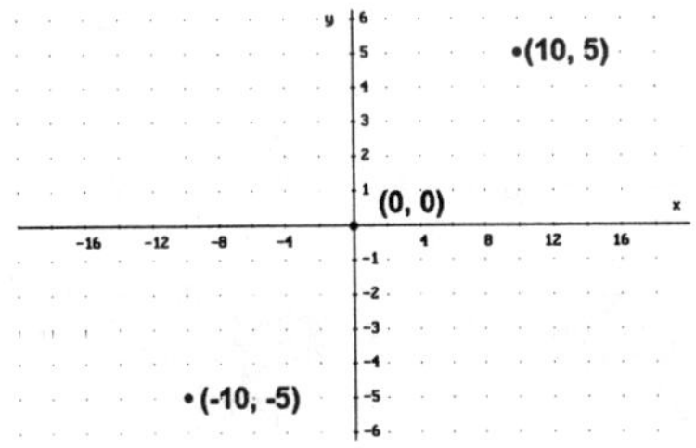

11. $x - 3y = 2$

linear

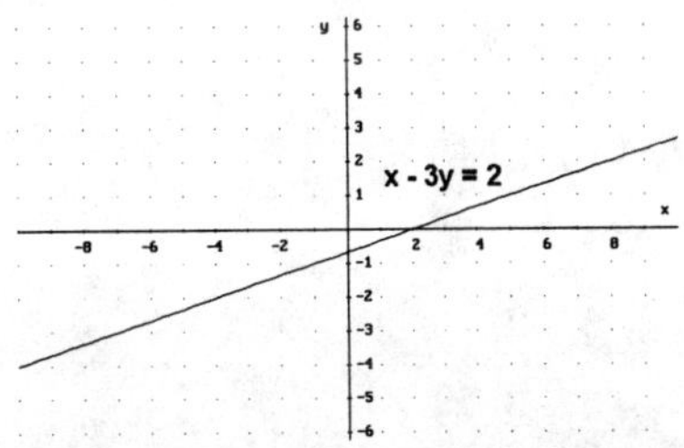

13. $y = x^2 + 4$

not linear

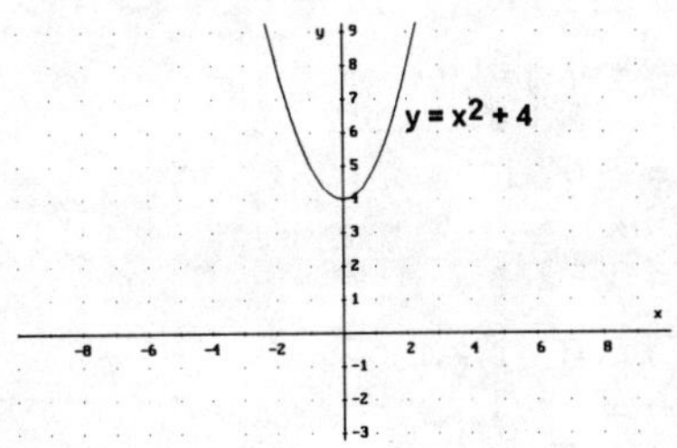

15. $y = -x + 5$

linear

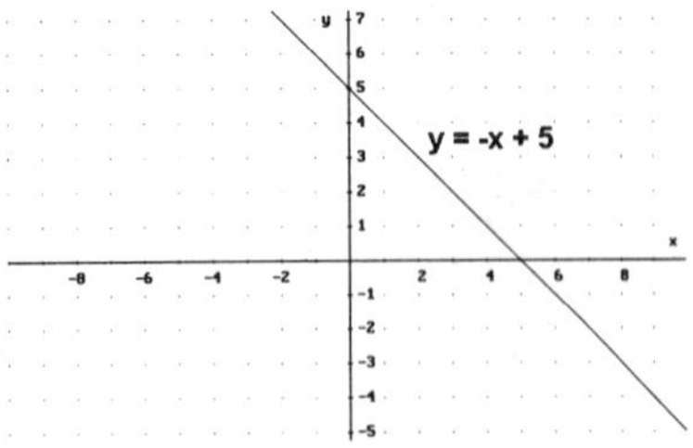

17. Domain: $\{\frac{3}{4}, 0.75, -12, 25\}$

Range: $\{-\frac{1}{2}, 6, 0, 25\}$

It is not a function.

19. Domain: {triangle, square, rectangle, parallelogram}

Range: $\{3, 4\}$

It is a function.

21. Domain: $\{-3\}$

Range: $\{y \mid y$ is a real number$\}$

It is not a function.

23. Domain: $\{x \mid -1 \leq x \leq 1\}$

Range: $\{y \mid -1 \leq y \leq 1\}$

It is not a function.

25. $h(x) = -5 - 3x$

a. $h(2) = -5 - 3(2)$
$h(2) = -5 - 6$
$h(2) = -11$

b. $h(-3) = -5 - 3(-3)$
$h(-3) = -5 + 9$
$h(-3) = 4$

c. $h(0) = -5 - 3(0)$
$h(0) = -5 + 0$
$h(0) = -5$

27. $h(x) = 6 - x^2$

a. $h(-1) = 6 - (-1)^2$
$h(-1) = 6 - 1$
$h(-1) = 5$

b. $h(1) = 6 - (1)^2$
$h(1) = 6 - 1$
$h(1) = 5$

c. $h(-4) = 6 - (-4)^2$
$h(-4) = 6 - (16)$
$h(-4) = 6 - 16$
$h(-4) = -10$

29. $J(x) = 2.54x$

$J(2000) = 2.54(2000)$

$J(2000) = 5080$

31. $x + y = 6$

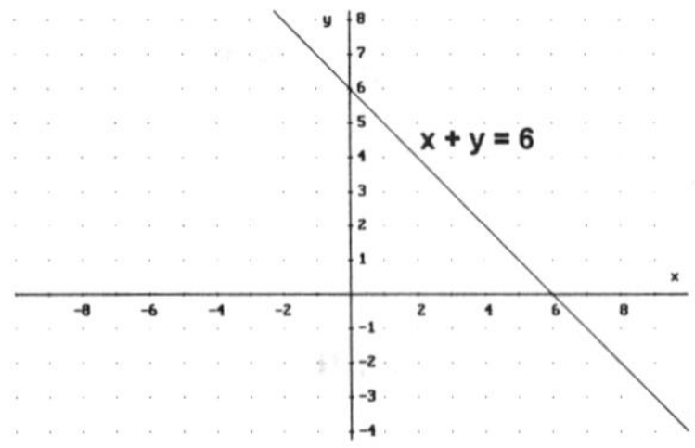

33. $f(x) = 5x + 8$

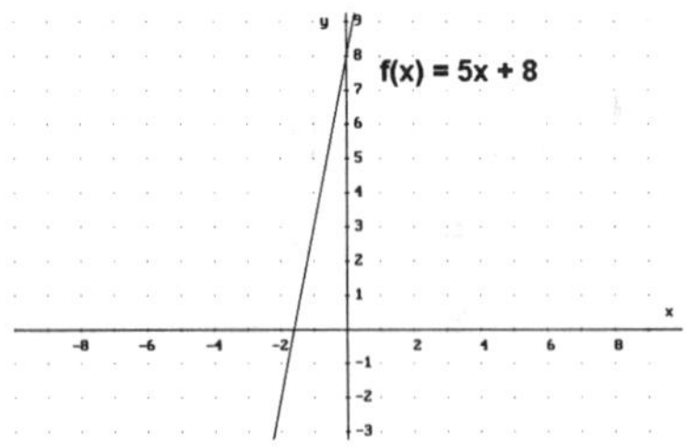

35. $y = -2x$

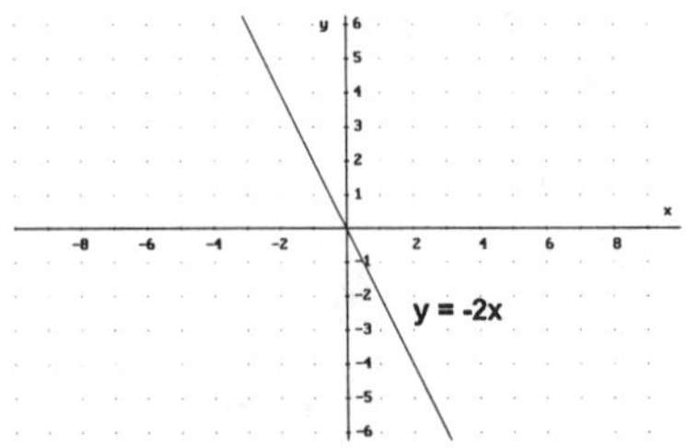

37. $y = -2$

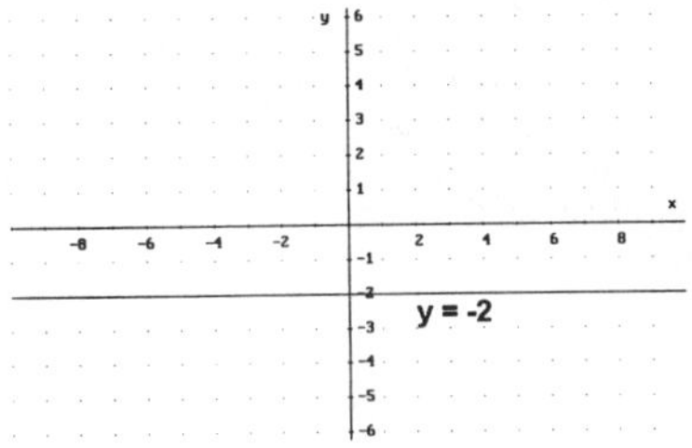

39. $4x - 3y = 12$

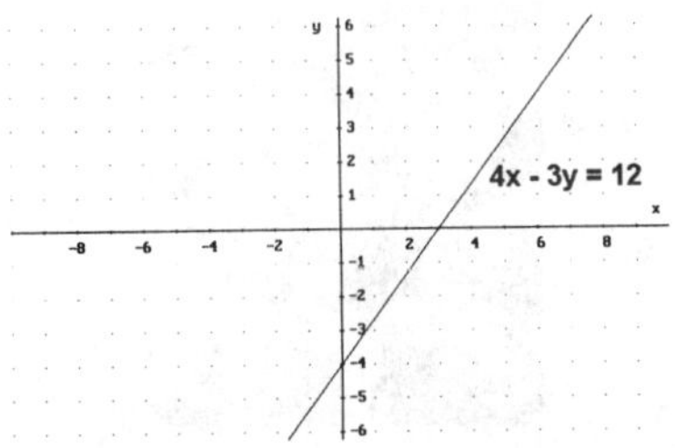

41. $(4,7)$ and $(1,2)$

$m = \frac{2-7}{1-4} = \frac{-5}{-3} = \frac{5}{3}$

43. $(-4,1)$ and $(3,-6)$

$m = \frac{-6-1}{3-(-4)} = \frac{-7}{3+4} = \frac{-7}{7} = -1$

45. $x - 2y = 4$

$-2y = -x + 4$

$\frac{-2y}{-2} = \frac{-x}{-2} + \frac{4}{-2}$

$y = \frac{x}{2} - 2$

$y = \frac{1}{2}x - 2$

$m = \frac{1}{2}, \ b = -2$

47. $4x - 5y = 9$

$-5y = -4x + 9$

$\frac{-5y}{-5} = \frac{-4x}{-5} + \frac{9}{-5}$

$y = \frac{4x}{5} - \frac{9}{5}$

$y = \frac{4}{5}x - \frac{9}{5}$

$m = \frac{4}{5}, \ b = -\frac{9}{5}$

49. $x = -3$

The slope is undefined.
No y-intercept.

51. $3x + y = 7$

$y = -3x + 7, \ m = -3$

$-3x - y = 10$

$-3x - 10 = y, \ m = -3$

parallel

53. Vertical; through $(-2,-4)$

$x = -2$

55. Slope 0; through (2, 5)

$y = 5$

57. $y - y_1 = m(x - x_1)$

$y - (-2) = 2(x - 5)$

$y + 2 = 2x - 10$

$y = 2x - 12$

$f(x) = 2x - 12$

59. $y = mx + b$

$y = -x - 2$

$f(x) = -x - 2$

61. The slope of $3x + 2y = 8$ or $y = -\frac{3}{2}x + 4$ is $-\frac{3}{2}$. Any line parallel to it must have a slope of $-\frac{3}{2}$. If the line also goes through the point $(-4,-2)$ its equation is

$y - (-2) = -\frac{3}{2}[x - (-4)]$

$2y + 4 = -3x - 12$

$2y = -3x - 16$

$y = \frac{-3x - 16}{2}$

$f(x) = -\frac{3}{2}x - 8$

63. The slope of $2x-3y=6$ or $y=\frac{2}{3}x-2$ is $\frac{2}{3}$. Any line perpendicular to it must have a slope of $-\frac{3}{2}$. If the line also goes through point $(-4, 5)$, its equation is

$y-5=-\frac{3}{2}[x-(-4)]$

$2y-10=-3x-12$

$2y=-3x-2$

$y=\frac{-3x-2}{2}$

$f(x)=-\frac{3}{2}x-1$

65. $m=\frac{y_2-y_1}{x_2-x_1}=\frac{-8-3}{-4-(-5)}=\frac{-11}{1}=-11$

$y-y_1=m(x-x_1)$

$y-3=-11[x-(-5)]$

$y-3=-11x-55$

$y=-11x-52$

$f(x)=-11x-52$

67. Any line parallel to $y=8$ must be of the form $y=c$. Since the line goes through the point $(-2,-5)$, its equation is $y=-5$.

$f(x)=-5$

69. $\frac{1}{2}x-y<2$

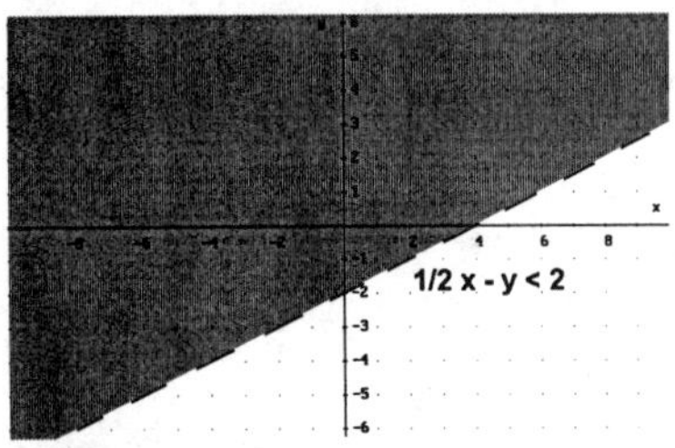

71. $3y \geq x$

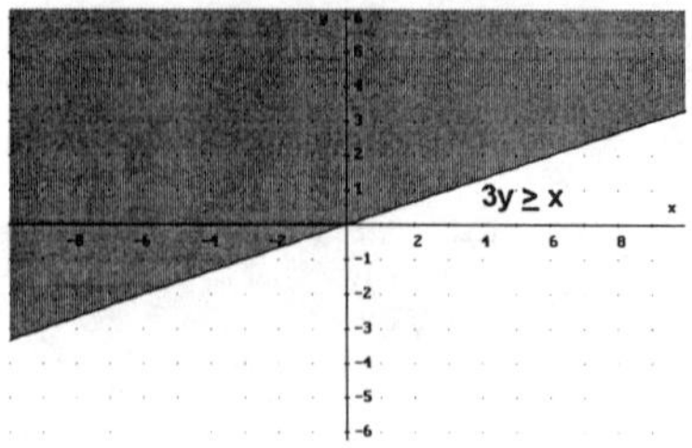

73. $x>-2$

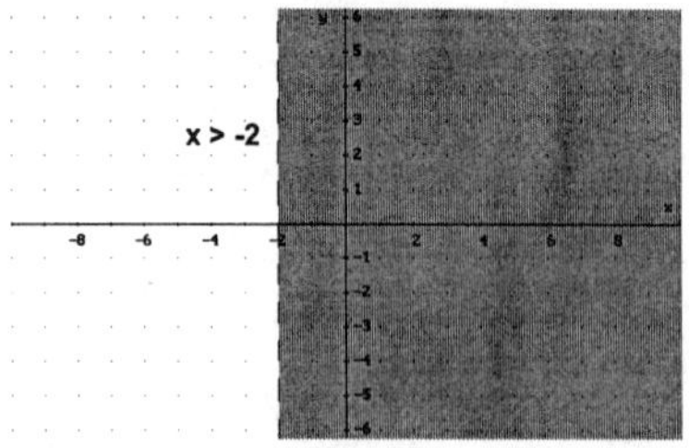

75. $2x<3y+8$ and $y \geq -2$

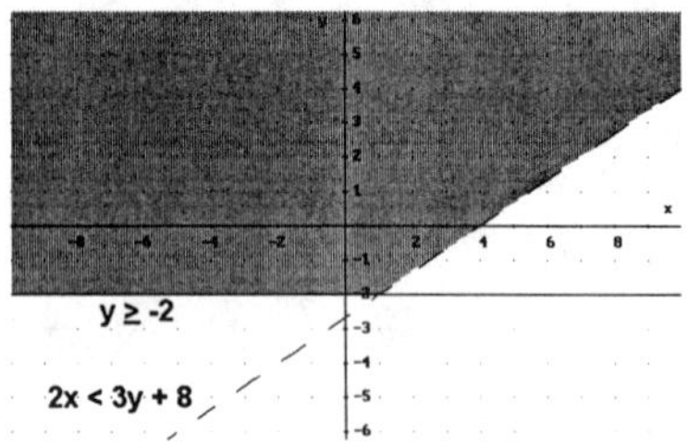

Chapter 4 Test

1. $12y-7x=5;$ $(1,\ )$

$12y-7(1)=5$

$12y-7=5$

$12y=5+7$

$12y=12$

$y=1$ $(1,1)$

2. $y=17;$ $(-4,\ )$

$y=17$ $(-4,17)$

3. $x - 2y = 3$; (1,1)

$x - 2y$	3
$1 - 2(1)$	3
$1 - 2$	3
-1	3

$-1 \neq 3$ no

4. $2x + 3y = 6$; (0, −2)

$2x + 3y$	6
$2(0) + 3(-2)$	6
$0 - 6$	6
-6	6

$-6 \neq 6$ no

5. $-3x + 5 = y$

$y = -3x + 5$

$m = -3$

6. Through (6, −5) and (−1,2)

$$m = \frac{2-(-5)}{-1-6} = \frac{2+5}{-7} = \frac{7}{-7} = -1$$

7. $f(x) = -2x + 8$

$y = -2x + 8$

Find the intercepts.

Let $x = 0$, $y = -2(0) + 8$, $y = 8$, (0,8)

Let $y = 0$, $0 = -2x + 8$, $2x = 8$, $x = 4$, (4,0)

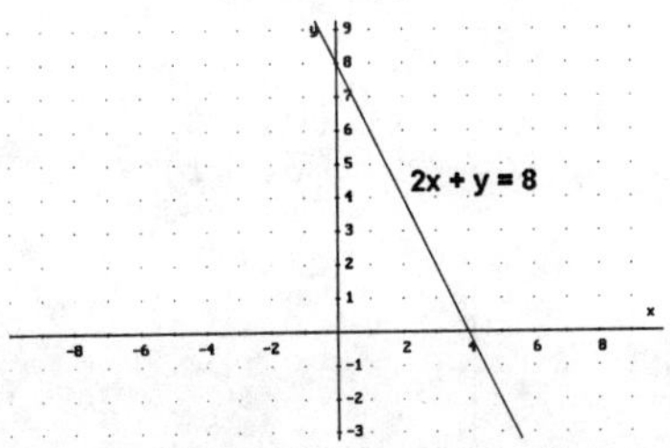

8. $f(x) = \frac{1}{4}x + \frac{5}{4}$

$y = \frac{1}{4}x + \frac{5}{4}$

Find the intercepts.

Let $x = 0$, $y = \frac{1}{4}(0) + \frac{5}{4}$, $y = \frac{5}{4}$, $\left(0, \frac{5}{4}\right)$

Let $y = 0$, $0 = \frac{1}{4}x + \frac{5}{4}$, $-\frac{1}{4}x = \frac{5}{4}$, $x = -5$, (−5,0)

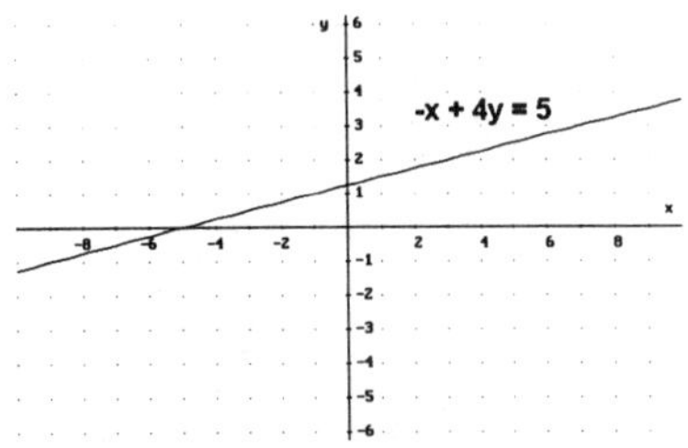

9. $x - y \geq -2$

Find the intercepts.

Let $x = 0$, $0 - y = -2$, $-y = -2$,

$y = \frac{-2}{-1} = 2$, (0,2)

Let $y = 0$, $x - 0 = -2$, $x = -2$, (−2,0)

The boundary line is solid.

Choose (0,0) as a test point.

$x - y \geq$	-2
$0 - 0$	-2
0	-2

Since $0 \geq -2$ the side containing (0,0) is shaded.

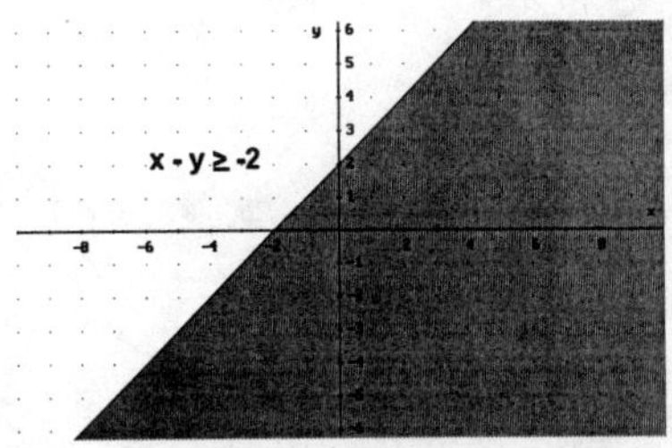

10. $y \geq -4x$

Find two points.

Let $x = 0$, $y = -4(0)$, $y = 0$, (0,0)

Let $x = 1$, $y = -4(1)$, $y = -4$, (1, −4)

The boundary line is solid.

Choose (5,0) as a test point.

$y \geq$	$-4x$
0	$-4(5)$
0	-20

Since $0 \geq -20$, the side containing (5,0) is shaded.

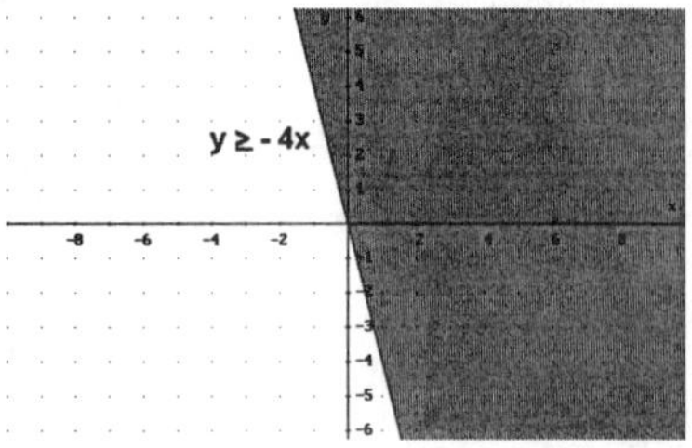

11. $5x - 7y = 10$

Find the intercepts.
Let $x = 0$, $5(0) - 7y = 10$, $-7y = 10$,
$y = -\frac{10}{7}$, $\left(0, -\frac{10}{7}\right)$
Let $y = 0$, $5x - 7(0) = 10$, $5x = 10$, $x = 2$,
$(2,0)$

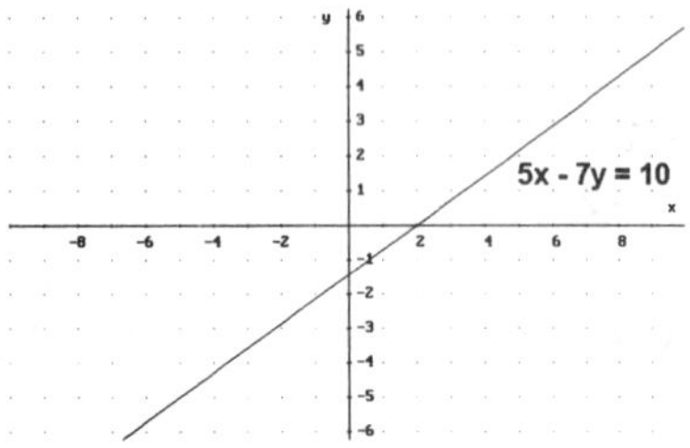

12. $2x - 3y > -6$

Find the intercepts.
Let $x = 0$, $2(0) - 3y = -6$, $-3y = -6$,
$y = \frac{-6}{-3} = 2$, $(0,2)$
Let $y = 0$, $2x - 3(0) = -6$, $2x = -6$,
$x = -3$, $(-3,0)$

The boundary line is dashed.

Choose $(0,0)$ for a test point.

$2x - 3y >$	-6
$2(0) - 3(0)$	-6
$0 + 0$	-6
0	-6

Since $0 > -6$, the side containing $(0,0)$ is shaded.

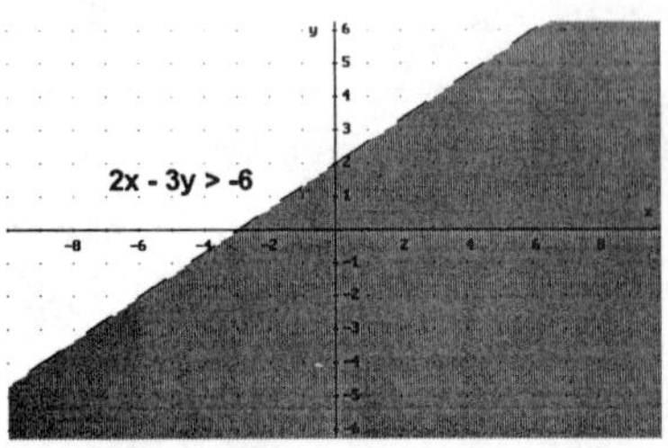

13. $6x + y > -1$

Find the intercepts.
Let $x = 0$, $6(0) + y = -1$, $y = -1$, $(0, -1)$
Let $y = 0$, $6x + 0 = -1$, $6x = -1$, $x = -\frac{1}{6}$,
$\left(-\frac{1}{6}, 0\right)$

The boundary line is dashed.

Choose $(0,0)$ as a test point.

$6x + y >$	-1
$6(0) + 0$	-1
$0 + 0$	-1
0	-1

Since $0 > -1$ the side containing $(0,0)$ is shaded.

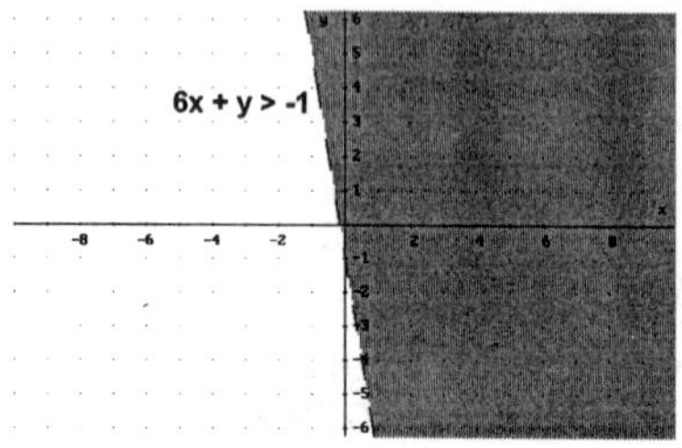

14. $y = -1$

Find two points.
Let $x = 0$, $y = -1$, $(0, -1)$
Let $x = 3$, $y = -1$, $(3, -1)$

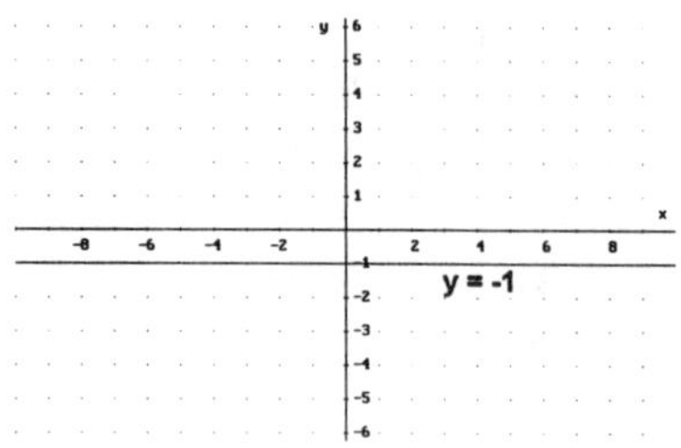

15. $x - 3 = 0$

$x = 3$

Find two points.
Let $y = 0$, $x = 3$, $(3,0)$
Let $y = 2$, $x = 3$, $(3,2)$

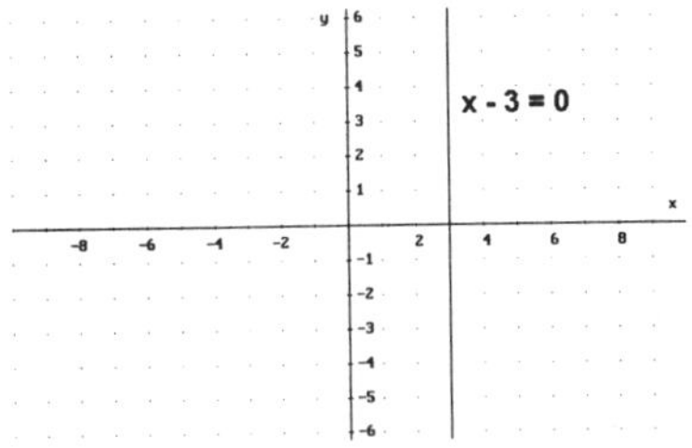

16. $5x - 3y = 15$

Find the intercepts.
Let $x = 0$, $5(0) - 3y = 15$, $-3y = 15$,
$y = -5$, $(0, -5)$
Let $y = 0$, $5x - 3(0) = 15$, $5x = 15$, $x = 3$
$(3,0)$

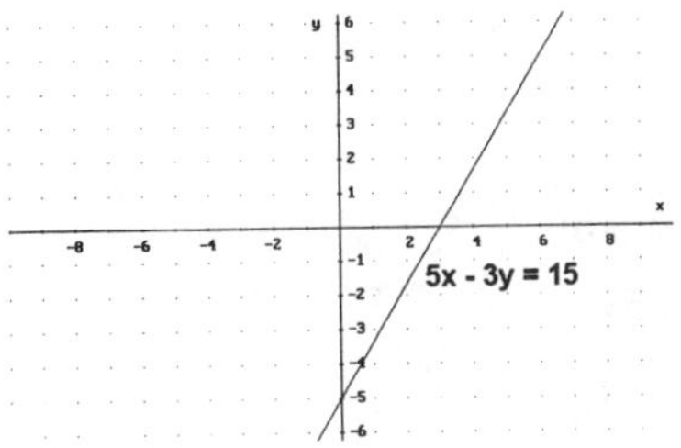

17. $y = -x^2$

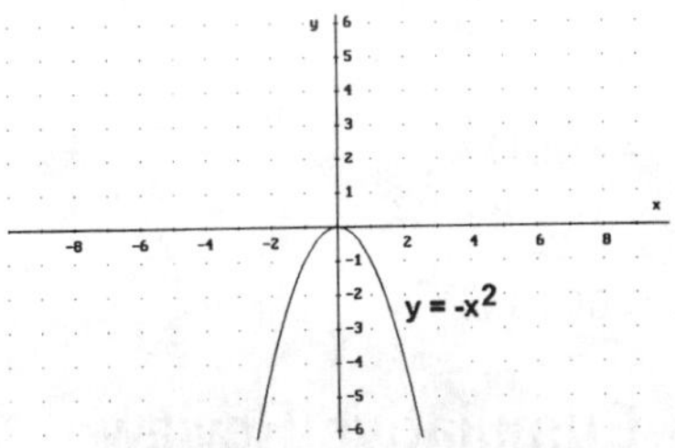

18. $y = 3|x| + 2$

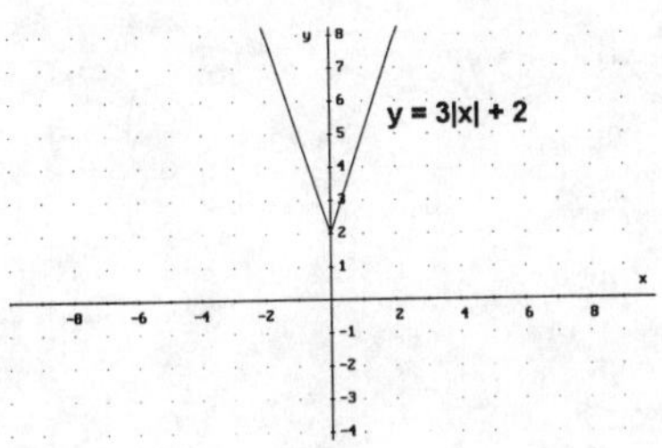

19. Domain: $\{x|x \text{ is a real number}\}$.

Range: $\{y|y \text{ is a real number}\}$.

Yes, it is a function.

20. Domain: $\{x|x \geq 0\}$.

Range: $\{y|y \text{ is a real number}\}$.

No, a vertical line could pass through the graph at two points.

21. Domain: $\{-2\}$

Range: $\{y|y \text{ is a real number}\}$.

No, a vertical line could pass through the graph at more than one point.

22. $f(x) = 2x - 4$

a. $f(-2) = 2(-2) - 4$
$f(-2) = -4 - 4$
$f(-2) = -8$

b. $f(0.2) = 2(0.2) - 4$
$f(0.2) = 0.4 - 4$
$f(0.2) = -3.6$

c. $f(0) = 2(0) - 4$
$f(0) = -4$

23. $h(x) = x^3 - x$

a. $h(-1) = (-1)^3 - (-1)$
$h(-1) = -1 + 1$
$h(-1) = 0$

b. $h(0) = 0^3 - 0$
$h(0) = 0 + 0$
$h(0) = 0$

c. $h(4) = 4^3 - 4$
$h(4) = 64 - 4$
$h(4) = 60$

24. $g(x) = 6$

a. $g(0) = 6$

b. $g(a) = 6$

c. $g(242) = 6$

25. Through the origin and $(6, -7)$.
$(0,0)$ and $(6, -7)$

$$m = \frac{-7 - 0}{6 - 0} = -\frac{7}{6}$$

$$y - y_1 = m(x - x_1)$$

$$y - 0 = -\frac{7}{6}(x - 0)$$

$$y = -\frac{7}{6}x$$

$f(x) = -\frac{7}{6}x$

26. Through $(2, -5)$ and $(1,3)$.

$m = \frac{3-(-5)}{1-2} = \frac{3+5}{-1} = \frac{8}{-1} = -8$

$y - y_1 = m(x - x_1)$

$y-(-5) = -8(x-2)$

$y+5 = -8x+16$

$8x+y+5 = 16$

$8x+y = 16-5$

$y = -8x+11$

$f(x) = -8x+11$

27. Through $(-5,-1)$, parallel to $y=7$.

$y=7$ is a horizontal line, so the parallel line would be the same, a horizontal line.

On a horizontal line, the y-coordinate stays the same.

$y = -1$

$f(x) = -1$

28. Slope $\frac{1}{8}$, through $(0,12)$.

$y - y_1 = m(x - x_1)$

$y-12 = \frac{1}{8}(x-0)$

$y-12 = \frac{1}{8}x$

$y = \frac{1}{8}x+12$

$f(x) = \frac{1}{8}x+12$

29. $3x-y=4$

$y = 3x-4$

so $m_{\perp} = 3$ and $m = \frac{-1}{3}$

$y-2 = \frac{-1}{3}[x-(-1)]$

$3(y-1) = -(x+1)$

$3y-6 = -x-1$

$3y = -x+5$

$y = \frac{-x+5}{3}$

$f(x) = -\frac{1}{3}x+\frac{5}{3}$

30. $2y+x=3$

$2y = -x+3$

$y = -\frac{1}{2}x+\frac{3}{2}$

so $m = -\frac{1}{2}$

$y-(-2) = -\frac{1}{2}(x-3)$

$2(y+2) = -(x-3)$

$2y+4 = -x+3$

$2y = -x-1$

$y = \frac{-x-1}{2}$

$f(x) = -\frac{1}{2}x-\frac{1}{2}$

31. $C(d) = \pi d$

$C(5) = \pi(5)$

$C(5) = 5\pi$

$C(5) \approx 15.7$ m

32. $r = 8m$

$d = 2r = 2(8) = 16m$

$C(d) = \pi d$

$C(16) = \pi(16)$

$C(16) = 16\pi$

$C(16) \approx 50.3$ m

Chapter 4 Cumulative Review

1. $\frac{2}{15} \bullet \frac{5}{13}$

$\frac{2}{\cancel{5} \bullet 3} \bullet \frac{\cancel{5}}{13}$

$\frac{2}{39}$

3a. $x+3$

b. $3x$

c. $2x$

d. $10-x$

e. $5x+7$

5a. $\frac{(-12)(-3)+4}{-7-(-2)}$

$\frac{36+4}{-7+2}=\frac{40}{-5}=-8$

b. $\frac{2(-3)^2-20}{-5+4}$

$\frac{18-20}{-1}=\frac{-2}{-1}=2$

7. $\frac{5}{2}x=15$

$\frac{2}{5}\left(\frac{5}{2}x\right)=\frac{2}{5}(15)$

$x=6$

$\{6\}$

9. width $= x$
length $= 3x-2$

$P=2l+2w$

$28=2(3x-2)+2x$

$28=6x-4+2x$

$28=8x-4$

$32=8x$

$4=x$

The width is 4 feet and the length is 10 feet.

$\frac{r}{16}=\frac{9}{6}$

$r=\frac{9}{6}\bullet 16$

$r=24$ cm.

13. Let x = time traveling.

Distance for level roads = rate × time
$d_l=18x$

Distance for hilly roads = rate × time
$d_h=10x$

Total distance $= d_l+d_h$

$98=18x+10x$

$98=28x$

$\frac{98}{28}=x$

3.5 hours $= x$

Entire trip took $2(3.5)=7$ hours.

15. $-(x-3)+2<3(2x-5)+x$

$-x+3+2<6x-15+x$

$-x+5<7x-15$

$-8x+5<-15$

$-8x<-20$

$\frac{-8x}{-8}>\frac{-20}{-8}$

$x>\frac{5}{2}$

$\left(\frac{5}{2},\ \infty\right)$

17a. $\{(-1,-1),\ (2,\ 3),\ (7,\ 3),\ (8,\ 6)\}$

It is a function.

b. $\{(0,-2),\ (1,\ 5),\ (0,\ 3),\ (7,\ 7)\}$

Not a function.

19. $m=\frac{4-(-2)}{2-(-1)}=\frac{4+2}{2+1}=\frac{6}{3}=2$

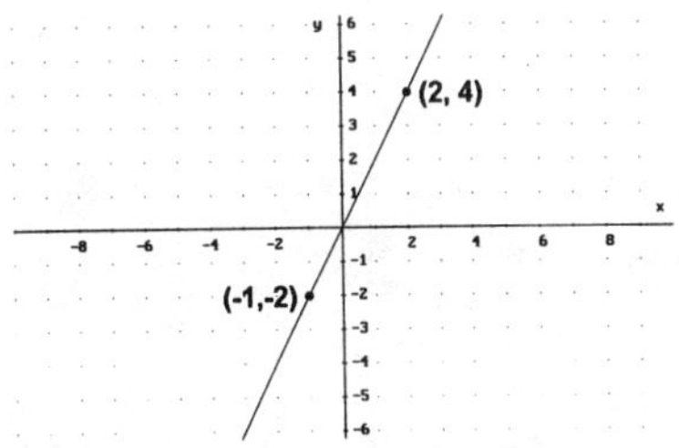

21. $2x-y<6$

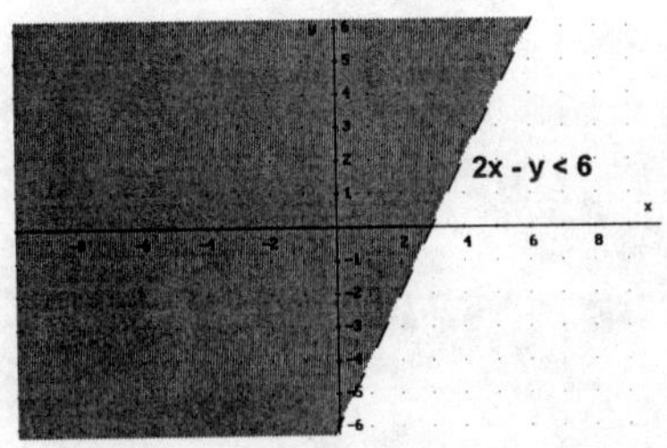

Exercise Set 5.1

1. 7^2

$7\bullet 7$

49

3. $(-5)^1$

-5

5. -2^4

$-(2 \bullet 2 \bullet 2 \bullet 2)$

$-(16)$

-16

7. $(-2)^4$

$(-2)(-2)(-2)(-2)$

16

9. x^2x^5

x^{2+5}

x^7

11. $(5y^4)(3y)$

$(5)(3)y^{4+1}$

$15y^5$

13. $(4z^{10})(-6z^7)(z^3)$

$(4)(-6)(z^{10+7+3})$

$-24z^{20}$

15. $(pq)^7$

$p^{1\cdot 7}q^{1\cdot 7}$

p^7q^7

17. $(\frac{m}{n})^9$

$\frac{m^{1\cdot 9}}{n^{1\cdot 9}}$

$\frac{m^9}{n^9}$

19. $(x^2y^3)^5$

$x^{2\cdot 5}y^{3\cdot 5}$

$x^{10}y^{15}$

21. $\left(\frac{-2xz}{y^5}\right)^2$

$\frac{(-2)^2x^{1\cdot 2}z^{1\cdot 2}}{y^{5\cdot 2}}$

$\frac{4x^2z^2}{y^{10}}$

23. $\frac{x^3}{x}$

x^{3-1}

x^2

25. $\frac{(-2)^5}{(-2)^3}$

$(-2)^{5-3}$

$(-2)^2$

4

27. $\frac{p^7q^{20}}{pq^{15}}$

$p^{7-1}q^{20-15}$

p^6q^5

29. $\frac{7x^2y^6}{14x^2y^3}$

$\frac{7}{14}x^{2-2}y^{6-3}$

$\frac{1}{2}x^0y^3$

$\frac{1}{2}(1)y^3$

$\frac{y^3}{2}$

31. $(2x)^0$

1

33. $-2x^0$

$-2(1)$

-2

35. 5^0+y^0

$1+1$

2

37. $\frac{5p^3q^2}{pq}$

$5p^{3-1}q^{2-1}$

$5p^2q$

39. $\dfrac{(3x)^4yz^3}{zx^2}$

$\dfrac{3^4x^4yz^3}{zx^2}$

$3^4x^{4-2}yz^{3-1}$

$81x^2yz^2$

41. $\dfrac{(6mn)^5}{mn^2}$

$\dfrac{6^{1\cdot 5}m^{1\cdot 5}n^{1\cdot 5}}{mn^2}$

$\dfrac{6^5m^5n^5}{mn^2}$

$6^5m^{5-1}n^{5-2}$

$6^5m^4n^3$

43. $\dfrac{a^5b^7}{a^4b^3}$

$a^{5-4}b^{7-3}$

ab^4

45. -5^1

-5

47. $(-4)^3$

$(-4)(-4)(-4)$

-64

49. $(6b)^0$

1

51. 2^3+2^5

$2\bullet 2\bullet 2+2\bullet 2\bullet 2\bullet 2\bullet 2$

$8+32$

40

53. b^4b^2

b^{4+2}

b^6

55. $a^2a^3a^4$

a^{2+3+4}

a^9

57. $(2x^3)(-8x^4)$

$(2)(-8)x^{3+4}$

$-16x^7$

59. $2x^3-8x^4$

Cannot be combined

61. $(4a)^3$

$4^{1\cdot 3}a^{1\cdot 3}$

4^3a^3

$64a^3$

63. $(-6xyz^3)^2$

$(-6)^2x^{1\cdot 2}y^{1\cdot 2}z^{3\cdot 2}$

$36x^2y^2z^6$

65. $\left(\dfrac{3y^5}{6x^4}\right)^3$

$\left(\dfrac{y^5}{2x^4}\right)^3$ Reduce Fraction

$\dfrac{y^{5\cdot 3}}{2^{1\cdot 3}x^{4\cdot 3}}$

$\dfrac{y^{15}}{2^3x^{12}}$

$\dfrac{y^{15}}{8x^{12}}$

67. $\dfrac{x^5}{x^4}$

x^{5-4}

x

69. $\dfrac{2x^3y^2z}{xyz}$

$2x^{3-1}y^{2-1}z^{1-1}$

$2x^2y^1z^0$

$2x^2y(1)$

$2x^2y$

71. $\dfrac{10a^9y^{12}}{35a^4y^7}$

$\dfrac{10a^{9-4}y^{12-7}}{35}$

$\dfrac{2a^5y^5}{7}$

73. $\dfrac{3x^4y^6}{-2xy^2}$

$\dfrac{3x^{4-1}y^{6-2}}{-2}$

$-\dfrac{3x^3y^4}{2}$

75. $\left(\dfrac{a^3}{q^2}\right)^5$

$\dfrac{a^{3\cdot5}}{q^{2\cdot5}}$

$\dfrac{a^{15}}{q^{10}}$

77. $\left(\dfrac{y^3y^5}{xy^2}\right)^3$

$\left(\dfrac{y^{3+5}}{xy^2}\right)^3$

$\left(\dfrac{y^8}{xy^2}\right)^3$

$\left(\dfrac{y^{8-2}}{x}\right)^3$

$\left(\dfrac{y^6}{x}\right)^3$

$\dfrac{y^{6\cdot3}}{x^{1\cdot3}}$

$\dfrac{y^{18}}{x^3}$

79. $\left(\dfrac{5xy}{5^2x^2}\right)^2$

$\left(\dfrac{\overset{1}{\cancel{5}}\overset{1}{\cancel{x}}y}{\underset{1}{\cancel{5}}\bullet 5\underset{1}{\cancel{x}}\bullet x}\right)^2$

$\left(\dfrac{y}{5x}\right)^2$

$\dfrac{y^{1\cdot2}}{5^{1\cdot2}x^{1\cdot2}}$

$\dfrac{y^2}{5^2x^2}$

$\dfrac{y^2}{25x^2}$

81. $\dfrac{(3x^2)^5}{x^3}$

$\dfrac{3^{1\cdot5}x^{2\cdot5}}{x^3}$

$\dfrac{3^5x^{10}}{x^3}$

3^5x^{10-3}

$243x^7$

83. $\dfrac{7(xy)^3}{(7xy)^2}$

$\dfrac{7x^{1\cdot3}y^{1\cdot3}}{7^{1\cdot2}x^{1\cdot2}y^{1\cdot2}}$

$\dfrac{7x^3y^3}{7^2x^2y^2}$

$\dfrac{7x^{3-2}y^{3-2}}{49}$

$\dfrac{xy}{7}$

85. $\dfrac{(-5)^2}{-q}$

$\dfrac{(-5)(-5)}{-q}$

$\dfrac{25}{-q}$

$-\dfrac{25}{q}$

87. $A = l \bullet w$

$A = (4x^2)(5x^3)$

$A = 20x^5$ sq. ft.

89. $V = s^3$

$V = (3y^4)^3$

$V = 3^3y^{12}$

$V = 27y^{12}$ cu. ft.

91. $y = -2x + 7$

$m = -2$

93. $3x - 5y = 14$

$-5y = -3x + 14$

$y = \frac{-3}{-5}x + \frac{14}{-5}$

$y = \frac{3}{5}x - \frac{14}{5}$

$m = \frac{3}{5}$

95. It is a function.

97. 0.33(59,000)

19,470 households

99. $x^{5a}x^{4a}$

x^{5a+4a}

x^{9a}

101. $(a^b)^5$

a^{5b}

103. $\frac{x^{9a}}{x^{4a}}$

x^{9a-4a}

x^{5a}

105. $(x^a y^b z^c)^{5a}$

$x^{a(5a)}y^{b(5a)}z^{c(5a)}$

$x^{5a^2}y^{5ab}z^{5ac}$

Exercise Set 5.2

1. 4^{-3}

$\frac{1}{4^3}$

$\frac{1}{64}$

3. $7x^{-3}$

$7\left(\frac{1}{x^3}\right)$

$\frac{7}{x^3}$

5. $\left(\frac{1}{4}\right)^{-3}$

$\frac{1^{-3}}{4^{-3}}$

$\frac{4^3}{1^3}$

$\frac{64}{1}$

64

7. $3^{-1} + 2^{-1}$

$\frac{1}{3} + \frac{1}{2}$

$\frac{1}{3} \bullet \frac{2}{2} + \frac{1}{2} \bullet \frac{3}{3}$

$\frac{2}{6} + \frac{3}{6}$

$\frac{5}{6}$

9. $\frac{1}{p^{-3}}$

p^3

11. $\frac{p^{-5}}{q^{-4}}$

$\frac{q^4}{p^5}$

13. $\frac{x^{-2}}{x}$

x^{-2-1}

x^{-3}

$\frac{1}{x^3}$

15. $\frac{z^{-4}}{z^{-7}}$

$z^{-4-(-7)}$

z^{-4+7}

z^3

17. $(a^{-5})^{-6}$

$a^{-5 \cdot -6}$

a^{30}

19. $\left(\frac{x^{-2}y^4}{x^3y^7}\right)^2$

$(x^{-2-3}y^{4-7})^2$

$(x^{-5}y^{-3})^2$

$x^{-10}y^{-6}$

$\frac{1}{x^{10}y^6}$

21. $\frac{4^2z^{-3}}{4^3z^{-5}}$

$4^{2-3}z^{-3-(-5)}$

$4^{-1}z^{-3+(+5)}$

$4^{-1}z^2$

$\frac{z^2}{4}$

23. 78,000

7.8×10^4

25. 0.00000167

1.67×10^{-6}

27. 93,000,000

9.3×10^7

29. 7.86×10^8

786,000,000

31. 8.673×10^{-10}

0.0000000008673

33. 6.25×10^{18}

6,250,000,000,000,000,000

35. $(4\times 10^4)(2\times 10^6)$

$4\times 2\times 10^{4+6}$

8×10^{10}

80,000,000,000

37. $\frac{3\times 10^7}{2\times 10^3}$

$\frac{3}{2}\times 10^{7-3}$

1.5×10^4

15,000

39. $(-3)^{-2}$

$\frac{1}{(-3)^2}$

$\frac{1}{9}$

41. $\frac{-1}{p^{-4}}$

$-1p^4$

$-p^4$

43. -2^0-3^0

$-(1)-(1)$

$-1-1$

-2

45. $\frac{r}{r^{-3}r^{-2}}$

$r\ r^3r^2$

r^6

47. $(x^5y^3)^{-3}$

$x^{5\cdot -3}y^{3\cdot -3}$

$x^{-15}y^{-9}$

$\frac{1}{x^{15}y^9}$

49. 2^0+3^{-1}

$1+\frac{1}{3}$

$\frac{3}{3}+\frac{1}{3}$

$\frac{4}{3}$

51. $\frac{2^{-3}x^{-4}}{2^2x}$

$\frac{1}{2^22^3xx^4}$

$\frac{1}{2^5x^5}$

$\frac{1}{32x^5}$

53. $\frac{7ab^{-4}}{7^{-1}a^{-3}b^2}$

$\frac{7 \bullet 7aa^3}{b^4b^2}$

$\frac{7^2a^4}{b^6}$

$\frac{49a^4}{b^6}$

55. $\left(\frac{a^{-5}b}{ab^3}\right)^{-4}$

$(a^{-5-1}b^{1-3})^{-4}$

$(a^{-6}b^{-2})^{-4}$

$a^{-6\cdot-4}b^{-2\cdot-4}$

$a^{24}b^8$

57. $\frac{(xy^3)^5}{(xy)^{-4}}$

$\frac{x^{1\cdot5}y^{3\cdot5}}{x^{1\cdot-4}y^{1\cdot-4}}$

$\frac{x^5y^{15}}{x^{-4}y^{-4}}$

$x^{5-(-4)}y^{15-(-4)}$

$x^{5+4}y^{15+4}$

x^9y^{19}

59. $\frac{(-2xy^{-3})^{-3}}{(xy^{-1})^{-1}}$

$\frac{(-2)^{1\cdot-3}x^{1\cdot-3}y^{-3\cdot-3}}{x^{1\cdot-1}y^{-1\cdot-1}}$

$\frac{(-2)^{-3}x^{-3}y^9}{x^{-1}y^1}$

$(-2)^{-3}x^{-3-(-1)}y^{9-1}$

$(-2)^{-3}x^{-3+1}y^8$

$(-2)^{-3}x^{-2}y^8$

$\frac{y^8}{(-2)^3x^2}$

$\frac{y^8}{-8x^2}$

$-\frac{y^8}{8x^2}$

61. 0.00635

6.35×10^{-3}

63. 1,160,000

1.16×10^6

65. 20,000,000

2×10^7

67. 3.3×10^{-2}

0.033

69. 2.032×10^4

20,320

71. 9.460×10^{12}

9,460,000,000,000

73. $(1.2\times10^{-3})(3\times10^{-2})$

$1.2\times3\times10^{-3+(-2)}$

3.6×10^{-5}

0.000036

75. $(4\times10^{-10})(7\times10^{-9})$

$4\times7\times10^{-10+(-9)}$

28×10^{-19}

0.0000000000000000028

77. $\frac{8\times10^{-1}}{16\times10^5}$

$\frac{8}{16}\times10^{-1-5}$

0.5×10^{-6}

0.0000005

79. $\frac{1.4\times10^{-2}}{7\times10^{-8}}$

$0.2\times10^{-2-(-8)}$

$0.2\times10^{-2+8}$

0.2×10^6

200,000

81. $\frac{6{,}000\times0.006}{0.009\times400}$

$\frac{(6\times10^{3})(6\times10^{-3})}{(9\times10^{-3})(4\times10^{2})}$

$\frac{36\times10^{3-3}}{36\times10^{-3+2}}$

$\frac{10^{0}}{10^{-1}}$

$10^{0-(-1)}$

$10^{1}=10$

83. $\frac{0.00064\times2{,}000}{16{,}000}$

$\frac{(6.4\times10^{-4})(2\times10^{3})}{1.6\times10^{4}}$

$\frac{12.8\times10^{-4+3}}{1.6\times10^{4}}$

$8\times10^{-1-4}$

8×10^{-5}

0.00008

85. $\frac{66{,}000\times0.001}{0.002\times0.003}$

$\frac{(6.6\times10^{4})(1\times10^{-3})}{(2\times10^{-3})(3\times10^{-3})}$

$\frac{6.6\times10^{4-3}}{6\times10^{-3-3}}$

$\frac{1.1\times10^{1}}{10^{-6}}$

$1.1\times10^{1-(-6)}$

1.1×10^{7}

$11{,}000{,}000$

87. $200{,}000\times10^{-8}$

$2\times10^{5}\times10^{-8}$

2×10^{-3} sec.

89. $(4.2\times10^{6})(3600)$

$(4.2\times10^{6})(3.6\times10^{3})$

$4.2\times3.6\times10^{6+3}$

15.12×10^{9}

$15{,}120{,}000{,}000$ cu. ft.

1.512×10^{10} cu. ft.

91. $V=s^{3}$

$V=\left(\frac{2x^{-2}}{y}\right)^{3}$

$V=\frac{2^{3}x^{-6}}{y^{3}}$

$V=\frac{8}{x^{6}y^{3}}$ cu. m.

93. $7x+5-9x-10$

$-2x-5$

95. $-3(y-6)+2(y+4)$

$-3y+18+2y+8$

$-y+26$

97. $P=4s$

$P=4(3x)$

$P=12x$

99. $5x+2=3x+8$

$2x+2=8$

$2x=6$

$x=3$

$\{3\}$

101. $\frac{x}{2}+\frac{1}{4}=6$

$4\left(\frac{x}{2}\right)+4\left(\frac{1}{4}\right)=4(6)$

$2x+1=24$

$2x=23$

$x=\frac{23}{2}$

$\left\{\frac{23}{2}\right\}$

103. $a^{-4m}\bullet a^{5m}$

a^{m}

105. $(3y^{2z})^{3}$

$3^{3}y^{6z}$

$27y^{6z}$

107. $\frac{y^{4a}}{y^{-a}}$

$y^{4a-(-a)}$

y^{4a+a}

y^{5a}

109. $(z^{3a+2})^{-2}$

$z^{-2(3a+2)}$

z^{-6a-4}

Exercise Set 5.3

1. 4 has degree 0.

3. $5x^2$ has degree 2.

5. $-3x^2y$ has degree $1+2=3$.

7. $6x+3$ has degree 1 and is a binomial.

9. $3x^2-2x+5$ has degree 2 and is a trinomial.

11. $-xyz$ has degree $1+1+1=3$ and is a monomial.

13. x^2y-4xy^2+5x+y has degree $2+1=3$ and is none of these.

15. $P(x)=x^2+x+1$

$P(7)=7^2+7+1$

$P(7)=49+7+1$

$P(7)=57$

17. $Q(x)=5x^2-1$

$Q(-10)=5(-10)^2-1$

$Q(-10)=5(100)-1$

$Q(-10)=500-1$

$Q(-10)=499$

19. $P(x)=x^2+x+1$

$P(0)=0^2+0+1$

$P(0)=1$

21. $P(t)=-16t^2+1821$

$P(2)=-16(2)^2+1821$

$P(2)=-16(4)+1821$

$P(2)=-64+1821$

$P(2)=1757$ feet

23. $P(t)=-16t^2+1821$

$P(6)=-16(6)^2+1821$

$P(6)=-16(36)+1821$

$P(6)=-576+1821$

$P(6)=1245$ feet

25. $5y+y=6y$

27. $4x+7x-3=11x-3$

29. $4xy+2x-3xy-1$

$xy+2x-1$

31. $(9y^2-8)+(9y^2-9)$

$18y^2-17$

33.
$$\begin{array}{r} x^2+\ xy-\ y^2 \\ +\ \underline{2x^2-4xy+7y^2} \\ 3x^2-3xy+6y^2 \end{array}$$

35.
$$\begin{array}{r} x^2-6x+3 \\ +\ \underline{\qquad 2x+5} \\ x^2-4x+8 \end{array}$$

37.
$$\begin{array}{r} 9y^2-7y+5 \\ -\ \underline{8y^2-7y+2} \\ y^2\qquad +3 \end{array}$$

39.
$$\begin{array}{r} 4x^2+2x \\ -\ \underline{6x^2-3x} \\ -2x^2+5x \end{array}$$

41.
$$\begin{array}{r} 3x^2-4x+8 \\ -\ \underline{5x^2\qquad -7} \\ -2x^2-4x+15 \end{array}$$

43.
$$\begin{array}{r} 5x-11 \\ +\ \underline{-x-\ 2} \\ 4x-13 \end{array}$$

45.
$$\begin{array}{r} 7x^2+x+1 \\ -\ \underline{6x^2+x-1} \\ x^2\qquad +2 \end{array}$$

47. $(7x^3-4x+8)+(5x^3+4x+8x)$

$7x^3-4x+8+5x^3+12x$

$12x^3+8x+8$

49.
$$\begin{array}{rl} & 9x^3-2x^2+4x-7 \\ - & \underline{2x^3-6x^2-4x+3} \\ & 7x^3+4x^2+8x-10 \end{array}$$

51.
$$\begin{array}{rl} & y^2+\ 4y+7 \\ + & \underline{-19y^2+\ 7y+7} \\ & -18y^2+11y+14 \end{array}$$

53.
$$\begin{array}{rl} & 3x^3-b+2a-6 \\ + & \underline{-4x^3+b+6a-6} \\ & -x^3 \qquad +8a-12 \end{array}$$

55.
$$\begin{array}{rl} & 4x^2-6x+2 \\ - & \underline{-x^2+3x+5} \\ & 5x^2-9x-3 \end{array}$$

57.
$$\begin{array}{rl} & -3x+8 \\ + & \underline{-3x^2+3x-5} \\ & -3x^2 \qquad +3 \end{array}$$

59.
$$\begin{array}{rl} & 4x^2+7xy-3 \\ + & \underline{2x^3-\ x^2+\ xy} \\ & 2x^3+3x^2+8xy-3 \end{array}$$

61.
$$\begin{array}{rl} & 6y^2-6y+4 \\ - & \underline{-y^2-6y+7} \\ & 7y^2 \qquad -3 \end{array}$$

63.
$$\begin{array}{rl} & 3x^2+15x+8 \\ + & \underline{(2x^2+\ 7x+8)} \\ & 5x^2+22x+16 \end{array}$$

65.
$$\begin{array}{rl} & 5q^4-2q^2-3q \\ + & \underline{-6q^4+3q^2 \qquad +5} \\ & -q^4+\ q^2-3q+5 \end{array}$$

67.
$$\begin{array}{rl} & 7x^2+\ 4x+9 \\ + & \underline{8x^2+\ 7x-8} \\ & 15x^2+11x+1 \\ - & \underline{3x+7} \\ & 15x^2+\ 8x-6 \end{array}$$

69.
$$\begin{array}{rl} & 4x^4-7x^2+3 \\ + & \underline{-3x^4 \qquad +2} \\ & x^4-7x^2+5 \end{array}$$

71. $P(4)=3(4)+3$

$12+3=15$

73. $R(-3)=5(-3)^2-7$

$5(9)-7$

$45-7$

38

75. $Q(2)=4(2)^2-6(2)+3$

$4(4)-12+3$

$16-12+3$

$4+3$

7

77. $Q(0)=4(0)^2-6(0)+3$

3

79. $P=a+b+c$

$P=(-x^2+3x)+(2x^2+5)+(4x-1)$

$P=-x^2+3x+2x^2+5+4x-1$

$P=(x^2+7x+4)$ ft.

81. $(4y^2+4y+1)-(y^2-10)$

$4y^2+4y+1-y^2+10$

$(3y^2+4y+11)$ meters

83.
$$\begin{array}{rl} & 7x^2 \qquad -4 \\ - & \underline{3x^2+2x-5} \\ & (4x^2-2x+1) \text{ cm.} \end{array}$$

85. $P(t)=-16t^2+300t$

a. $P(1)=-16(1)^2+300(1)$

$P(1)=-16(1)+300$

$P(1)=-16+300$

$P(1)=284$ feet

b. $P(2)=-16(2)^2+300(2)$

$P(2)=-16(4)+600$

$P(2)=-64+600$

$P(2) = 536$ feet

c. $P(3) = -16(3)^2 + 300(3)$

$P(3) = -16(9) + 900$

$P(3) = -144 + 900$

$P(3) = 756$ feet

d. $P(4) = -16(4)^2 + 300(4)$

$P(4) = -16(16) + 1200$

$P(4) = -256 + 1200$

$P(4) = 944$ feet

87. $P(t) = -16t^2 + 300t$

$0 = -16t^2 + 300t$

Using a calculator and a trial and error process, the projectile will hit the ground around 18 or 19 seconds.

$P(18) = -16(18)^2 + 300(18)$

$P(18) = 216$

$P(19) = -16(19)^2 + 300(19)$

$P(19) = -76$

89. $C(x) = 0.8x + 10{,}000$

$C(20{,}000) = 0.8(20{,}000) + 10{,}000$

$C(20{,}000) = \$26{,}000$

91. $3x(2x)$

$6x^2$

93. $5y^2(-2y)$

$-10y^3$

95. $(-12x^3)(-x^5)$

$-12x^8$

97. $\frac{1}{5} = \frac{x}{9}$

$5x = 1(9)$

$5x = 9$

$x = \frac{9}{5}$

$\left\{\frac{9}{5}\right\}$

99. $\frac{x+6}{16} = \frac{3x-2}{8}$

$8(x+6) = 16(3x-2)$

$8x + 48 = 48x - 32$

$-40x + 48 = -32$

$-40x = -80$

$x = \frac{-80}{-40}$

$x = 2$

$\{2\}$

101. $(0.15)(1600) = 240$

240 women

103. $P(x) = 2x - 3$

a. $P(a) = 2a - 3$

b. $P(-x) = 2(-x) - 3$

$P(-x) = -2x - 3$

c. $P(x+h) = 2(x+h) - 3$

$P(x+h) = 2x + 2h - 3$

105. $P(x) = 4x$

a. $P(a) = 4a$

b. $P(-x) = 4(-x)$

$P(-x) = -4x$

c. $P(x+h) = 4(x+h)$

$P(x+h) = 4x + 4h$

107. $P(x) = 4x - 1$

a. $P(a) = 4a - 1$

b. $P(-x) = 4(-x) - 1$

$P(-x) = -4x - 1$

c. $P(x+h) = 4(x+h) - 1$

$P(x+h) = 4x + 4h - 1$

Exercise Set 5.4

1. $(-4x^3)(3x^2) = -12x^5$

3. $(-xyz)(-9xy^2z^2) = 9x^2y^3z^3$

5.
$$\begin{array}{l} 4x + 7 \\ \underline{3x \qquad\quad} \\ 12x^2 + 21x \end{array}$$

7. $-6xy(4x+y)$

$-6xy(4x) - 6xy(y)$

$-24x^2y - 6xy^2$

9. $-4ab(xa^2 + ya^2 - 3)$

$-4ab(xa^2) - 4ab(ya^2) - 4ab(-3)$

$-4xa^3b - 4ya^3b + 12ab$

11.
$$\begin{array}{r} 2x + 4 \\ x - 3 \\ \hline -6x - 12 \\ 2x^2 + 4x \qquad \\ \hline 2x^2 - 2x - 12 \end{array}$$

13.
$$\begin{array}{rrrr} x^3 & & -x & +2 \\ & & 2x & +3 \\ \hline 3x^3 & & -3x & +6 \\ 2x^4 \qquad & -2x^2 & +4x & \\ \hline 2x^4 + 3x^3 & -2x^2 & +x & +6 \end{array}$$

15.
$$\begin{array}{r} x^2 + 2x - 1 \\ x^2 + 2x - 1 \\ \hline -x^2 - 2x + 1 \\ 2x^3 + 4x^2 - 2x \qquad \\ x^4 + 2x^3 - x^2 \qquad\qquad \\ \hline x^4 + 4x^3 + 2x^2 - 4x + 1 \end{array}$$

17.
$$\begin{array}{r} 3x + 2 \\ x + 4 \\ \hline 12x + 8 \\ 3x^2 + 2x \qquad \\ \hline 3x^2 + 14x + 8 \end{array}$$

19.
$$\begin{array}{r} 2x^2 - 4x + 2 \\ x - 5 \\ \hline -10x^2 + 20x - 10 \\ 2x^3 - 4x^2 + 2x \qquad\quad \\ \hline 2x^3 - 14x^2 + 22x - 10 \end{array}$$

21.
$$\begin{array}{r} a^2 - 4a - 3 \\ a^2 - 2a - 5 \\ \hline -5a^2 + 20a + 15 \\ -2a^3 + 8a^2 + 6a \qquad \\ a^4 - 4a^3 - 3a^2 \qquad\qquad \\ \hline a^4 - 6a^3 \qquad + 26a + 15 \end{array}$$

23.
$$\begin{array}{r} 2a^2 + ab + b^2 \\ 3a^2 - ab + b^2 \\ \hline 2a^2b^2 + ab^3 + b^4 \\ -2a^3b - a^2b^2 - ab^3 \qquad \\ 6a^4 + 3a^3b + 3a^2b^2 \qquad\qquad \\ \hline 6a^4 + a^3b + 4a^2b^2 \qquad + b^4 \end{array}$$

25.
$$\begin{array}{r} x - 3 \\ x + 4 \\ \hline 4x - 12 \\ x^2 - 3x \qquad \\ \hline x^2 + x - 12 \end{array}$$

27.
$$\begin{array}{r} 2x - 8 \\ 2x - 4 \\ \hline -8x + 32 \\ 4x^2 - 16x \qquad \\ \hline 4x^2 - 24x + 32 \end{array}$$

29.
$$\begin{array}{r} 3x - 1 \\ x + 3 \\ \hline 9x - 3 \\ 3x^2 - x \qquad \\ \hline 3x^2 + 8x - 3 \end{array}$$

31.
$$\begin{array}{r} 3x + \frac{1}{2} \\ 3x - \frac{1}{2} \\ \hline -\frac{3}{2}x - \frac{1}{4} \\ 9x^2 + \frac{3}{2}x \qquad \\ \hline 9x^2 \qquad - \frac{1}{4} \end{array}$$

33. $(x+4)^2$

$x^2+2(x)4+4^2$

$x^2+8x+16$

35. $(6y-1)(6y+1)$

$(6y)^2-1^2$

$36y^2-1$

37. $(3x-y)^2$

$(3x)^2-2(3x)y+y^2$

$9x^2-6xy+y^2$

39. $(3b-6y)(3b+6y)$

$(3b)^2-(6y)^2$

$9b^2-36y^2$

41. $[3+(4b+1)]^2$

$3^2+2(3)(4b+1)+(4b+1)^2$

$9+6(4b+1)+(4b)^2+2(4b)1+1^2$

$9+24b+6+16b^2+8b+1$

$16b^2+32b+16$

43. $[(2s-3)-1][(2s-3)+1]$

$(2s-3)^2-1^2$

$(2s)^2-2(2s)3+3^2-1$

$4s^2-12s+9-1$

$4s^2-12s+8$

45. $[(xy+4)-6]^2$

$(xy+4)^2-2(6)(xy+4)+6^2$

$(xy)^2+2(xy)(4)+4^2-12(xy+4)+36$

$x^2y^2+8xy+16-12xy-48+36$

$x^2y^2-4xy+4$

47. $f(x)=x^2-3x$

$f(a)=a^2-3a$

49. $f(a+5)=(a+5)^2-3(a+5)$

$f(a+5)=a^2+5a+5a+25-3a-15$

$f(a+5)=a^2+7a+10$

51. $(3ab)(-4b)=-12ab^2$

53. $4y(x^2+y+z)$

$4y(x^2)+4y(y)+4y(z)$

$4x^2y+4y^2+4yz$

55.
$$\begin{array}{r} 3x+1 \\ \underline{3x+5} \\ 15x+5 \\ \underline{9x^2+\ \ 3x\qquad} \\ 9x^2+18x+5 \end{array}$$

57.
$$\begin{array}{rrrrrr} & & 2x^3 & & & +5 \\ & & & \underline{5x^2+} & \underline{4x} & \underline{+1} \\ & & 2x^3 & & & +5 \\ & 8x^4 & & & +20x & \\ \underline{10x^5} & & & \underline{+25x^2} & & \\ 10x^5 & +8x^4 & +2x^3 & +25x^2 & +20x & +5 \end{array}$$

59. $(7x+3)(7x-3)$

$(7x)^2-3^2$

$49x^2-9$

61.
$$\begin{array}{r} 3x^2+\ \ 4x-\ \ 4 \\ \underline{3x+\ \ 6} \\ 18x^2+24x-24 \\ \underline{9x^3+12x^2-12x\qquad} \\ 9x^3+30x^2+12x-24 \end{array}$$

63.
$$\begin{array}{r} 4x+\frac{1}{3} \\ \underline{4x-\frac{1}{2}} \\ -2x-\frac{1}{6} \\ \underline{16x^2+\frac{4}{3}x\qquad} \\ 16x^2-\frac{2}{3}x-\frac{1}{6} \end{array}$$

65. $(6x+1)^2$

$(6x)^2+2(6x)1+1^2$

$36x^2+12x+1$

67. $(x^2+2y)(x^2-2y)$

$(x^2)^2-(2y)^2$

x^4-4y^2

69.
$$\begin{array}{r} 5a^2b^2-6a-6b \\ -6a^2b^2 \\ \hline -30a^4b^4+36a^3b^2+36a^2b^3 \end{array}$$

71.
$$\begin{array}{r} a-\ 4 \\ \underline{2a-\ 4} \\ -\ 4a+16 \\ \underline{2a^2-\ 8a\quad\quad} \\ 2a^2-12a+16 \end{array}$$

73. $(7ab+3c)(7ab-3c)$

$(7ab)^2-(3c)^2$

$49a^2b^2-9c^2$

75. $[4-(3x+1)][4+(3x+1)]$

$4^2-(3x+1)^2$

$16-[(3x)^2+2(3x)1+1^2]$

$16-9x^2-6x-1$

$-9x^2-6x+15$

77. $(m-4)^2$

$m^2-2(m)4+4^2$

$m^2-8m+16$

79. $[3+(2y-c)]^2$

$3^2+2(3)(2y-c)+(2y-c)^2$

$9+6(2y-c)+(2y)^2-2(2y)c+c^2$

$9+12y-6c+4y^2-4yc+c^2$

81. $[(5x-2y)-4][(5x-2y)+4]$

$(5x-2y)^2-4^2$

$(5x)^2-2(5x)(2y)+(2y)^2-16$

$25x^2-20xy+4y^2-16$

83. $(3x+1)^2$

$(3x)^2+2(3x)1+1^2$

$9x^2+6x+1$

85.
$$\begin{array}{r} y-\ 4 \\ \underline{y-\ 3} \\ -3y+12 \\ \underline{y^2-4y\quad\quad} \\ y^2-7y+12 \end{array}$$

87. $[4-(2x+y)][4+(2x+y)]$

$4^2-(2x+y)^2$

$16-[(2x)^2+2(2x)y+y^2]$

$16-4x^2-4xy-y^2$

$-4x^2-4xy-y^2+16$

89.
$$\begin{array}{r} x+y \\ \underline{2x-1} \\ -x-y \\ \underline{2x^2+2xy\quad\quad\quad} \\ 2x^2+2xy-x-y \\ \underline{x+1} \\ 2x^2+2xy-x-y \\ \underline{2x^3+2x^2y-x^2-\ xy\quad\quad\quad} \\ 2x^3+2x^2y+x^2+xy-x-y \end{array}$$

91.
$$\begin{array}{r} 3x^2+2x-1 \\ \underline{3x^2+2x-1} \\ -3x^2-2x+1 \\ 6x^3+4x^2-2x\quad \\ \underline{9x^4+\ 6x^3-3x^2\quad\quad\quad} \\ 9x^4+12x^3-2x^2-4x+1 \end{array}$$

93.
$$\begin{array}{r} 4x^2-\ 2x+5 \\ \underline{3x+1} \\ 4x^2-\ 2x+5 \\ \underline{12x^3-6x^2+15x\quad\quad} \\ 12x^3-2x^2+13x+5 \end{array}$$

95. $R(x)=x+5$

a. $R(x)+R(x)$

$x+5+x+5$

$2x+10$

b. $R(x)\bullet R(x)$

$(x+5)(x+5)$

$x^2+5x+5x+25$

$x^2+10x+25$

97. $P(x)=3x^2+1$

a. $P(a)=3(a)^2+1$

$P(a)=3a^2+1$

b. $P(a-1)=3(a-1)^2+1$

$P(a-1)=3(a^2-a-a+1)+1$

$P(a-1)=3(a^2-2a+1)+1$

$P(a-1)=3a^2-6a+3+1$

$P(a-1)=3a^2-6a+4$

99. $A=lw$

$A=(2x+5)(2x-5)$

$A=2x(2x)+2x(-5)+5(2x)+5(-5)$

$A=4x^2-10x+10x-25$

$A=(4x^2-25)$ sq. yds.

101. $A=\frac{1}{2}bh$

$A=\frac{1}{2}(4x)(3x-2)$

$A=(2x)(3x-2)$

$A=(6x^2-4x)$ sq. inches.

103. $V=lwh$

$V=(2x)(3)(x^2+6x-1)$

$V=6x(x^2+6x-1)$

$(6x^3+36x^2-6x)$ cu. ft.

105. $\frac{3x^3y^2}{12x}=\frac{x^{3-1}y^2}{4}=\frac{x^2y^2}{4}$

107. $\frac{144x^5y^5}{-16x^2y}=-9x^{5-2}y^{5-1}=-9x^3y^4$

109. $|x-5|=9$

$x-5=-9$ or $x-5=9$

$x=-4$ or $x=14$

$\{-4,\ 14\}$

111. $\left|\frac{x}{2}+7\right|+1=8$

$\left|\frac{x}{2}+7\right|=7$

$\frac{x}{2}+7=7$ or $\frac{x}{2}+7=-7$

$\frac{x}{2}=0$ or $\frac{x}{2}=-14$

$x=2(0)$ or $x=2(-14)$

$x=0$ or $x=-28$

$\{0,\ -28\}$

113. $|x+3|<10$

$-10<x+3<10$

$-10-3<x+3-3<10-3$

$-13<x<7$

$(-13,\ 7)$

115. $|3x-6|\geq 3$

$3x-6\leq -3$ or $3x-6\geq 3$

$3x\leq 3$ or $3x\geq 9$

$x\leq 1$ or $x\geq 3$

$(-\infty,\ 1]\cup[3,\ \infty)$

117. $5x^{-1}(x^{-2}+3x^{-1}+2)$

$5x^{-3}+15x^{-2}+10x^{-1}$

119. $(x^{-2}+2y)(x^{-2}-2y)$

$x^{-4}+2x^{-2}y-2x^{-2}y-4y^2$

$x^{-4}-4y^2$

121. $(3a+y^{-4})(a+y^{-2})$

$3a^2+3ay^{-2}+ay^{-4}+y^{-6}$

123. $6a^4(3a^{n+1}-6)$

$18a^{n+1+4}-36a^4$

$18a^{n+5}-36a^4$

125. $(3x^y+7)^2$

$(3x^y)^2+2(3x^y)(7)+(7)^2$

$9x^{2y}+42x^y+49$

Exercise Set 5.5

1. $\frac{50b^{10}}{25b^5}=2b^{10-5}=2b^5$

3. $\frac{26x^2y^3z^7}{13x^6bz^5}=\frac{2y^3z^{7-5}}{x^{6-2}b}=\frac{2y^3z^2}{x^4b}$

5. $\frac{-2x^4y^2}{6x^4y^4}=\frac{-1}{3y^{4-2}}=-\frac{1}{3y^2}$

7. $\frac{4a^2+8a}{2a}=\frac{4a^2}{2a}+\frac{8a}{2a}=2a+4$

9. $\dfrac{12a^5b^2+16a^4b}{4a^4b}$

$\dfrac{12a^5b^2}{4a^4b}+\dfrac{16a^4b}{4a^4b}$

$3ab+4$

11. $\dfrac{4x^2y^2+6xy^2-4y^2}{2y^2}$

$\dfrac{4x^2y^2}{2y^2}+\dfrac{6xy^2}{2y^2}-\dfrac{4y^2}{2y^2}$

$2x^2+3x-2$

13. $\dfrac{4x^2+8x+4}{4}=\dfrac{4x^2}{4}+\dfrac{8x}{4}+\dfrac{4}{4}$

x^2+2x+1

15.
$$\begin{array}{r} x+1 \\ x+2\;\overline{)\;x^2+3x+3} \\ \underline{x^2+2x} \\ x+3 \\ \underline{x+2} \\ 1 \end{array}$$

$x+1+\dfrac{1}{x+2}$

17.
$$\begin{array}{r} 2x-8 \\ x+1\;\overline{)\;2x^2-6x-8} \\ \underline{2x^2+2x} \\ -8x-8 \\ \underline{-8x-8} \\ 0 \end{array}$$

$2x-8$

19.
$$\begin{array}{r} x-\frac{1}{2} \\ 2x+4\;\overline{)\;2x^2+3x-2} \\ \underline{2x^2+4x} \\ -x-2 \\ \underline{-x-2} \\ 0 \end{array}$$

$x-\frac{1}{2}$

21.
$$\begin{array}{r} 2x^2-\frac{1}{2}x+5 \\ 2x+4\;\overline{)\;4x^3+7x^2+8x+20} \\ \underline{4x^3+8x^2} \\ -x^2+8x \\ \underline{-x^2-2x} \\ 10x+20 \\ \underline{10x+20} \\ 0 \end{array}$$

$2x^2-\frac{1}{2}x+5$

23. $\dfrac{25a^2b^{12}}{10a^5b^7}=\dfrac{5b^{12-7}}{2a^{5-2}}=\dfrac{5b^5}{2a^3}$

25. $\dfrac{x^6y^6-x^3y^3}{x^3y^3}=\dfrac{x^6y^6}{x^3y^3}-\dfrac{x^3y^3}{x^3y^3}=x^3y^3-1$

27.
$$\begin{array}{r} a+3 \\ a+1\;\overline{)\;a^2+4a+3} \\ \underline{a^2+a} \\ 3a+3 \\ \underline{3a+3} \\ 0 \end{array}$$

$a+3$

29.
$$\begin{array}{r} 2x+5 \\ x-2\;\overline{)\;2x^2+x-10} \\ \underline{2x^2-4x} \\ 5x-10 \\ \underline{5x-10} \\ 0 \end{array}$$

$2x+5$

31. $\dfrac{-16y^3+24y^4}{-4y^2}$

$\dfrac{16y^3}{-4y^2}+\dfrac{24y^4}{-4y^2}$

$4y-6y^2$

33.
$$\begin{array}{r} 2x+23 \\ x-5\;\overline{)\;2x^2+13x+15} \\ \underline{2x^2-10x} \\ 23x+15 \\ \underline{23x-115} \\ 130 \end{array}$$

$2x+23+\dfrac{130}{x-5}$

35. $\dfrac{20x^2y^3 + 6xy^4 - 12x^3y^5}{2xy^3}$

$\dfrac{20x^2y^3}{2xy^3} + \dfrac{6xy^4}{2xy^3} - \dfrac{12x^3y^5}{2xy^3}$

$10x + 3y - 6x^2y^2$

37.

$$\begin{array}{r|l} & 2x + 4 \\ \hline 3x+2 & 6x^2 + 16x + 8 \\ & \underline{6x^2 + 4x} \\ & 12x + 8 \\ & \underline{12x + 8} \\ & 0 \end{array}$$

$2x + 4$

39.

$$\begin{array}{r|l} & y + 5 \\ \hline 2y-3 & 2y^2 + 7y - 15 \\ & \underline{2y^2 - 3y} \\ & 10y - 15 \\ & \underline{10y - 15} \\ & 0 \end{array}$$

$y + 5$

41.

$$\begin{array}{r|l} & 2x + 3 \\ \hline 2x-3 & 4x^2 \quad - 9 \\ & \underline{4x^2 - 6x} \\ & 6x - 9 \\ & \underline{6x - 9} \\ & 0 \end{array}$$

$2x + 3$

43.

$$\begin{array}{r|l} & 2x^2 - 8x + 38 \\ \hline x+4 & 2x^3 \quad + 6x - 4 \\ & \underline{2x^3 + 8x^2} \\ & -8x^2 + 6x \\ & \underline{-8x^2 - 32x} \\ & 38x - 4 \\ & \underline{38x + 152} \\ & -156 \end{array}$$

$2x^2 - 8x + 38 - \dfrac{156}{x+4}$

45.

$$\begin{array}{r|l} & 3x + 3 \\ \hline x-1 & 3x^2 \quad - 4 \\ & \underline{3x^2 - 3x} \\ & 3x - 4 \\ & \underline{3x - 3} \\ & -1 \end{array}$$

$3x + 3 - \dfrac{1}{x-1}$

47.

$$\begin{array}{r|l} & -2x^3 + 3x^2 - x + 4 \\ \hline -x+5 & 2x^4 - 13x^3 + 16x^2 - 9x + 20 \\ & \underline{2x^4 - 10x^3} \\ & -3x^3 + 16x^2 \\ & \underline{-3x^3 + 15x^2} \\ & x^2 - 9x \\ & \underline{x^2 - 5x} \\ & -4x + 20 \\ & \underline{-4x + 20} \\ & 0 \end{array}$$

$-2x^3 + 3x^2 - x + 4$

49.

$$\begin{array}{r|l} & 3x^3 \quad + 5x + 4 \\ \hline x^2-2 & 3x^5 - x^3 + 4x^2 - 12x - 8 \\ & \underline{3x^5 - 6x^3} \\ & 5x^3 + 4x^2 - 12x - 8 \\ & \underline{5x^3 \quad - 10x} \\ & 4x^2 - 2x - 8 \\ & \underline{4x^2 \quad - 8} \\ & -2x \end{array}$$

$3x^3 + 5x + 4 - \dfrac{2x}{x^2 - 2}$

51. $\dfrac{3x^3 - 5}{3x^2} = \dfrac{3x^3}{3x^2} - \dfrac{5}{3x^2} = x - \dfrac{5}{3x^2}$

53. Perimeter = 4 times a side
$12x^3 + 4x - 16 = 4 \bullet s$

$4s = 12x^3 + 4x - 16$

$s = \dfrac{12x^3 + 4x - 16}{4}$

$s = \dfrac{12x^3}{4} + \dfrac{4x}{4} - \dfrac{16}{4}$

$s = (3x^3 + x - 4)$ ft.

55. $A = lw$

$49x^2 + 70x - 200 = (7x + 20) \bullet w$

$\dfrac{49x^2 + 70x - 200}{7x + 20} = w$

$$\begin{array}{r|l} & 7x - 10 \\ \hline 7x+20 & 49x^2 + 70x - 200 \\ & \underline{49x^2 + 140x} \\ & -70x - 200 \\ & \underline{-70x - 200} \\ & 0 \end{array}$$

$w = (7x - 10)$ inches

57. $\dfrac{36x^5 - 12x^3 + 6x^2}{(2x)(3x)}$

$\dfrac{36x^5 - 12x^3 + 6x^2}{6x^2}$

$\dfrac{36x^5}{6x^2} - \dfrac{12x^3}{6x^2} + \dfrac{6x^2}{6x^2}$

$(6x^3 - 2x + 1)$ feet

59. $A = bh$

$2x^2 - 17x + 35 = (2x - 7) \bullet h$

$\dfrac{2x^2 - 17x + 35}{2x - 7} = h$

$$\begin{array}{r|l} & \quad\quad\quad x - 5 \\ 2x - 7 & 2x^2 - 17x + 35 \\ & \underline{2x^2 - 7x} \\ & \quad - 10x + 35 \\ & \quad \underline{- 10x + 35} \\ & \quad\quad\quad\quad 0 \end{array}$$

$h = (x - 5)$ cm.

61. $P(x) = x^3 - 4x^2 - 3x + 5$

$P(-2) = (-2)^3 - 4(-2)^2 - 3(-2) + 5$

$P(-2) = -8 - 4(+4) - 3(-2) + 5$

$P(-2) = -8 - 16 + 6 + 5$

$P(-2) = -13$

$$\begin{array}{r|l} & \quad x^2 - 6x + 9 \\ x + 2 & x^3 - 4x^2 - 3x + 5 \\ & \underline{x^3 + 2x^2} \\ & \quad - 6x^2 - 3x \\ & \quad \underline{- 6x^2 - 12x} \\ & \quad\quad\quad\quad 9x + 5 \\ & \quad\quad\quad\quad \underline{9x + 18} \\ & \quad\quad\quad\quad\quad - 13 \end{array}$$

The remainder is -13.
$P(-2)$ is equal to the remainder.

63. $18 - 24$ years old.

65. Answers vary.

67. Let $x =$ lowest elevation in Louisiana
$x + 103 =$ lowest elevation in Vermont.

$x + x + 103 = 87$

$2x + 103 = 87$

$2x = 87 - 103$

$2x = -16$

$x = -8$

$x + 103 = -8 + 103 = 95$

-8 feet is the lowest elevation in Louisiana and 95 feet is the lowest elevation in Vermont.

69.

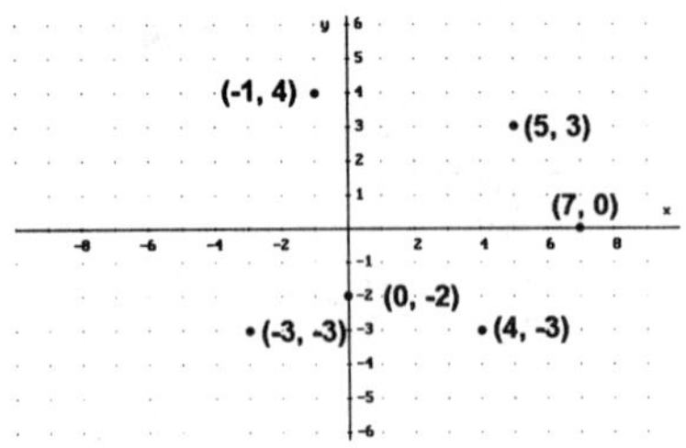

71. $-3(x - 2) < -4$

$-3x + 6 < -4$

$-3x < -10$

$\dfrac{-3x}{-3} > \dfrac{-10}{-3}$

$x > \dfrac{10}{3}$

$\left(\dfrac{10}{3}, \infty\right)$

73. $\dfrac{5x}{20} - 2 \geq \dfrac{x - 2}{10}$

$20\left(\dfrac{5x}{20}\right) - 20(2) \geq 20\left(\dfrac{x - 2}{10}\right)$

$5x - 40 \geq 2(x - 2)$

$5x - 40 \geq 2x - 4$

$5x \geq 2x + 36$

$3x \geq 36$

$x \geq 12$

$[12, \infty)$

75.
$$\begin{array}{r} 2x^2+\frac{1}{2}x-5 \\ x+2\,\overline{)\,2x^3+\frac{9}{2}x^2-4x-10} \\ \underline{2x^3+4x^2} \\ \frac{1}{2}x^2-4x \\ \underline{\frac{1}{2}x^2+x} \\ -5x-10 \\ \underline{-5x-10} \\ 0 \end{array}$$

$2x^2+\frac{1}{2}x-5$

77.
$$\begin{array}{r} 2x^3+\frac{9}{2}x^2+10x+21 \\ x-2\,\overline{)\,2x^4+\frac{1}{2}x^3+x^2+x+0} \\ \underline{2x^4-4x^3} \\ \frac{9}{2}x^3+x^2 \\ \underline{\frac{9}{2}x^3-9x^2} \\ 10x^2+x \\ \underline{10x^2-20x} \\ 21x+0 \\ \underline{21x-42} \\ 42 \end{array}$$

$2x^3+\frac{9}{2}x^2+10x+21+\frac{42}{x-2}$

79.
$$\begin{array}{r} 3x^4-2x \\ 3x+2\,\overline{)\,9x^5+6x^4\qquad-6x^2-4x} \\ \underline{9x^5+6x^4} \\ 0\qquad-6x^2-4x \\ \underline{-6x^2-4x} \\ 0 \end{array}$$

$3x^4-2x$

Exercise Set 5.6

1.
$$\begin{array}{r|rrr} 5 & 1 & 3 & -40 \\ & & 5 & 40 \\ \hline & 1 & 8 & 0 \end{array}$$

$x+8$

3.
$$\begin{array}{r|rrr} -6 & 1 & 5 & -6 \\ & & -6 & 6 \\ \hline & 1 & -1 & 0 \end{array}$$

$x-1$

5.
$$\begin{array}{r|rrrr} 2 & 1 & -7 & -13 & 5 \\ & & 2 & -10 & -46 \\ \hline & 1 & -5 & -23 & -41 \end{array}$$

$x^2-5x-23-\frac{41}{x-2}$

7.
$$\begin{array}{r|rrr} 2 & 4 & 0 & -9 \\ & & 8 & 16 \\ \hline & 4 & 8 & 7 \end{array}$$

$4x+8+\frac{7}{x-2}$

9a. $P(2)=3(2)^2-4(2)-1$

$P(2)=12-8-1=3$

b.
$$\begin{array}{r|rrr} 2 & 3 & -4 & -1 \\ & & 6 & 4 \\ \hline & 3 & 2 & 3 \end{array}$$

So, $P(2)=3$

11a. $P(-2)=4(-2)^4+7(-2)^2+9(-2)-1$

$P(2)=64+28-18-1$

$P(2)=73$

b.
$$\begin{array}{r|rrrrr} -2 & 4 & 0 & 7 & 9 & -1 \\ & & -8 & 16 & -46 & 74 \\ \hline & 4 & -8 & 23 & -37 & 73 \end{array}$$

So, $P(-2)=73$

13a. $P(-1)=(-1)^5+3(-1)^4+3(-1)-7$

$P(-1)=-1+3-3-7$

$P(-1)=-8$

b.
$$\begin{array}{r|rrrrrr} -1 & 1 & 3 & 0 & 0 & 3 & -7 \\ & & -1 & -2 & 2 & -2 & -1 \\ \hline & 1 & 2 & -2 & 2 & 1 & -8 \end{array}$$

So, $P(-1)=-8$

15.
$$\begin{array}{r|rrrr} 3 & 1 & -3 & 0 & 2 \\ & & 3 & 0 & 0 \\ \hline & 1 & 0 & 0 & 2 \end{array}$$

$x^2+\frac{2}{x-3}$

17.
$$\begin{array}{r|rrr} -1 & 6 & 13 & 8 \\ & & -6 & -7 \\ \hline & 6 & 7 & 1 \end{array}$$

$6x+7+\frac{1}{x+1}$

19.
$$\begin{array}{r|rrrrr} 5 & 2 & -13 & 16 & -9 & 20 \\ & & 10 & -15 & 5 & -20 \\ \hline & 2 & -3 & 1 & -4 & 0 \end{array}$$

$2x^3 - 3x^2 + x - 4$

21.
$$\begin{array}{r|rrr} -3 & 3 & 0 & -15 \\ & & -9 & 27 \\ \hline & 3 & -9 & 12 \end{array}$$

$3x - 9 + \frac{12}{x+3}$

23.
$$\begin{array}{r|rrrr} \frac{1}{2} & 3 & -6 & 4 & 5 \\ & & \frac{3}{2} & \frac{-9}{4} & \frac{7}{8} \\ \hline & 3 & \frac{-9}{2} & \frac{7}{4} & \frac{47}{8} \end{array}$$

$3x^2 - \frac{9}{2}x + \frac{7}{4} + \frac{\frac{47}{8}}{x - \frac{1}{2}}$

25.
$$\begin{array}{r|rrrr} \frac{1}{3} & 3 & 2 & -4 & 1 \\ & & 1 & 1 & -1 \\ \hline & 3 & 3 & -3 & 0 \end{array}$$

$3x^2 + 3x - 3$

27.
$$\begin{array}{r|rrrr} -1 & 3 & 7 & -4 & 12 \\ & & -3 & -4 & 8 \\ \hline & 3 & 4 & -8 & 20 \end{array}$$

$3x^2 + 4x - 8 + \frac{20}{x+1}$

29.
$$\begin{array}{r|rrrr} 1 & 1 & 0 & 0 & -1 \\ & & 1 & 1 & 1 \\ \hline & 1 & 1 & 1 & 0 \end{array}$$

$x^2 + x + 1$

31.
$$\begin{array}{r|rrr} -6 & 1 & 0 & -36 \\ & & -6 & 36 \\ \hline & 1 & -6 & 0 \end{array}$$

$x - 6$

33.
$$\begin{array}{r|rrrr} 1 & 1 & 3 & -7 & 4 \\ & & 1 & 4 & -3 \\ \hline & 1 & 4 & -3 & 1 \end{array}$$

Thus, $P(1) = 1$

35.
$$\begin{array}{r|rrrr} -3 & 3 & -7 & -2 & 5 \\ & & -9 & 48 & -138 \\ \hline & 3 & -16 & 46 & -133 \end{array}$$

Thus, $P(-3) = -133$

37.
$$\begin{array}{r|rrrrr} -1 & 4 & 0 & 1 & 0 & -2 \\ & & -4 & 4 & -5 & 5 \\ \hline & 4 & -4 & 5 & -5 & 3 \end{array}$$

Thus, $P(-1) = 3$

39.
$$\begin{array}{r|rrrrr} \frac{1}{3} & 2 & 0 & -3 & 0 & -2 \\ & & \frac{2}{3} & \frac{2}{9} & \frac{-25}{27} & -\frac{25}{81} \\ \hline & 2 & \frac{2}{3} & \frac{-25}{9} & \frac{-25}{27} & \frac{-187}{81} \end{array}$$

Thus, $P\left(\frac{1}{3}\right) = \frac{-187}{81}$

41.
$$\begin{array}{r|rrrrrr} \frac{1}{2} & 1 & 1 & -1 & 0 & 0 & 3 \\ & & \frac{1}{2} & \frac{3}{4} & \frac{-1}{8} & \frac{-1}{16} & \frac{-1}{32} \\ \hline & 1 & \frac{3}{2} & \frac{-1}{4} & \frac{-1}{8} & \frac{-1}{16} & \frac{95}{32} \end{array}$$

Thus, $P\left(\frac{1}{2}\right) = \frac{95}{32}$

43.
$$\begin{array}{r|rrrr} -3 & 1 & 3 & 4 & 12 \\ & & -3 & 0 & -12 \\ \hline & 1 & 0 & 4 & 0 \end{array}$$

$(x+3)(x^2+4) = x^3 + 3x^2 + 4x + 12$

45. $P(x)$ is equal to the remainder when $P(x)$ is divided by $x - c$. Therefore, $P(c) = 0$.

47. Multiply $(x^2 - x + 10)$ by $(x + 3)$ and add the remainder, -2.

$(x^2 - x + 10)(x + 3)$

$x^3 - x^2 + 10x + 3x^2 - 3x + 30$

$x^3 + 2x^2 + 7x + 30$

$\underline{\qquad\qquad\qquad\quad -2}$

$x^3 + 2x^2 + 7x + 28$

49. $V = lwh$

$w = \frac{V}{lh}$

$w = \frac{x^4 + 6x^3 - 7x^2}{x^2(x+7)}$

$w = \frac{x^4 + 6x^3 - 7x^2}{x^3 + 7x^2}$

$$\begin{array}{r} x - 1 \\ x^3 + 7x^2 \overline{\big)\, x^4 + 6x^3 - 7x^2} \\ \underline{x^4 + 7x^3 \qquad} \\ -1x^3 - 7x^2 \\ \underline{-1x^3 - 7x^2} \\ 0 \end{array}$$

The width is $(x-1)$ meters.

51. $f(x) - h(x)$

$3x^2 + 5 - (x^2 + 3)$

$3x^2 + 5 - x^2 - 3$

$2x^2 + 2$

53. $3 \bullet h(x) + f(x)$

$3(x^2 + 3) + 3x^2 + 5$

$3x^2 + 9 + 3x^2 + 5$

$6x^2 + 14$

55. $h(x) \bullet h(x)$

$(x^2 + 3)(x^2 + 3)$

$x^4 + 3x^2 + 3x^2 + 9$

$x^4 + 6x^2 + 9$

57. $g(x) \div f(x)$

$\frac{g(x)}{f(x)}$

$\frac{x - 5}{3x^2 + 5}$

59. $(-5)^2$ __ 5^2

$25 = 25$

61. 3^4 __ $(-3)^4$

$81 = 81$

Graphing Calculator Exercise 5.7

1. $f(x) = x^2$

$g(x) = x$

$(f + g)(x) = x^2 + x$

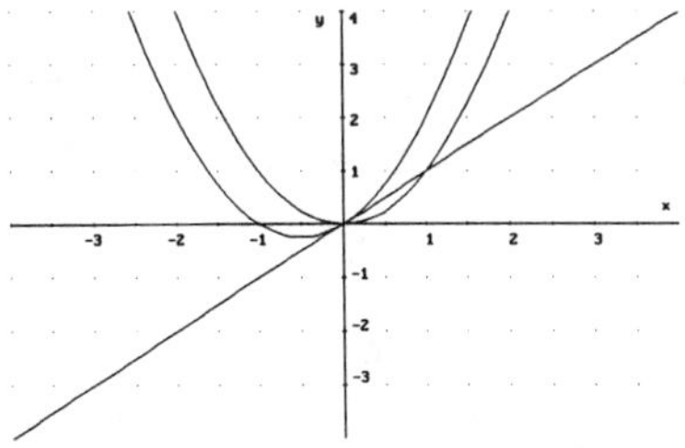

Exercise Set 5.7

1. $f(5) = 3(5) = 15$

3. $g(-2) = 2(-2)^2 - 5 = 2 \bullet 4 - 5 = 3$

5. $h(16) = \sqrt{16} = 4$

7. $h\left(\frac{1}{9}\right) = \sqrt{\frac{1}{9}} = \frac{1}{3}$

9. $f(x) = 2x$

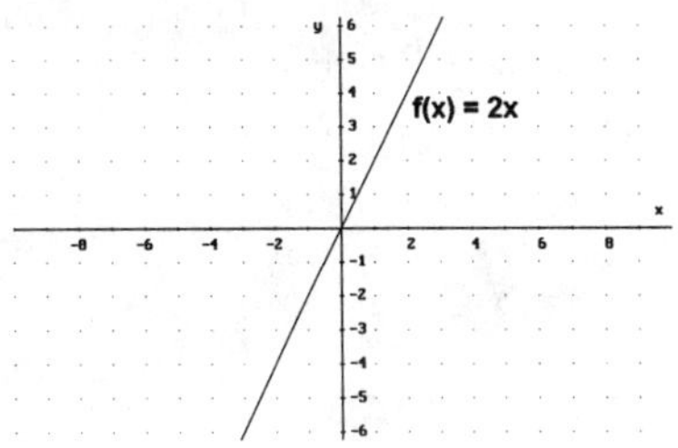

11. $h(x) = x - 3$

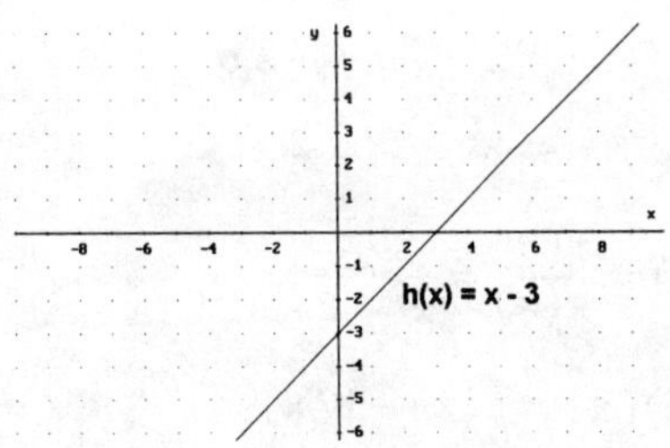

13. $g(x) = -1$

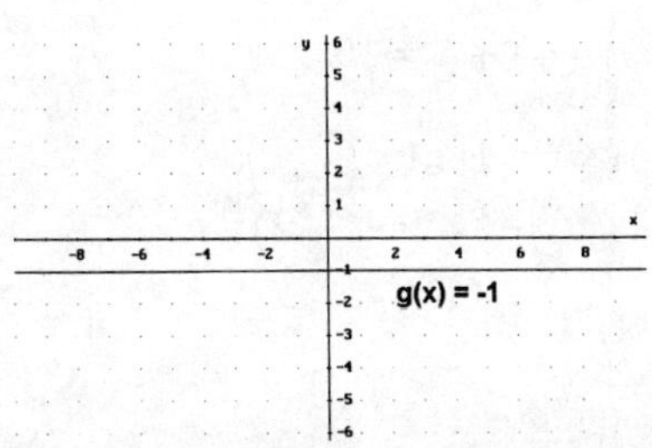

15. $(f+g)(x) = f(x)+g(x)$
$= (x^2+1)+5x$
$= x^2+5x+1$

17. $(f-g)(x) = f(x)-g(x)$
$= (x^2+1)-5x$
$= x^2-5x+1$

19. $\left(\frac{g}{f}\right)(x) = \frac{g(x)}{f(x)} = \frac{5x}{x^2+1}$

21. $(f \circ g)(x) = f[g(x)]$
$= (5x)^2+1$
$= 25x^2+1$

23. $(f \circ f)(x) = f[f(x)]$
$= (x^2+1)^2+1$
$= (x^4+2x^2+1)+1$
$= x^4+2x^2+2$
$(f \circ f)(1) = 1^4+2(1)^2+2$
$= 1+2+2$
$= 5$

25. $g(7) = 7^2+2 = 51$

27. $f(0) = -2(0) = 0$

29. $(f+g)(x) = f(x)+g(x)$
$= -2x+(x^2+2)$
$= x^2-2x+2$

31. $\left(\frac{f}{g}\right)(x) = \frac{f(x)}{g(x)} = \frac{-2x}{x^2+2}$

33. $(g-h)(x) = g(x)-h(x)$
$= (x^2+2)-(4x+3)$
$= x^2-4x-1$

35. $h(4) = 4(4)+3 = 19$

37. $(f \circ g)(x) = f[g(x)]$
$= -2(x^2+2)$
$= -2x^2-4$

39. $(h \circ f)(x) = h[f(x)]$
$= 4(-2x)+3$
$= -8x+3$
$(h \circ f)(-3) = -8(-3)+3$
$= 24+3$
$= 27$

41. $(h+f)(x) = h(x)+f(x)$
$= (4x+3)+(-2x)$
$= 2x+3$

43. $(f \circ f)(x) = f[f(x)]$
$= f(-2x)$
$= -2(-2x)$
$= 4x$

45. $f(a+b) = -2(a+b)$
$= -2a-2b$

47. $\left(\frac{f}{h}\right)(x) = \frac{f(x)}{h(x)} = \frac{-2x}{4x+3}$

49. $(g \circ h)(x) = g[h(x)]$
$= (4x+3)^2+2$
$= (16x^2+24x+9)+2$
$= 16x^2+24x+11$

51. $g(x) = -x$

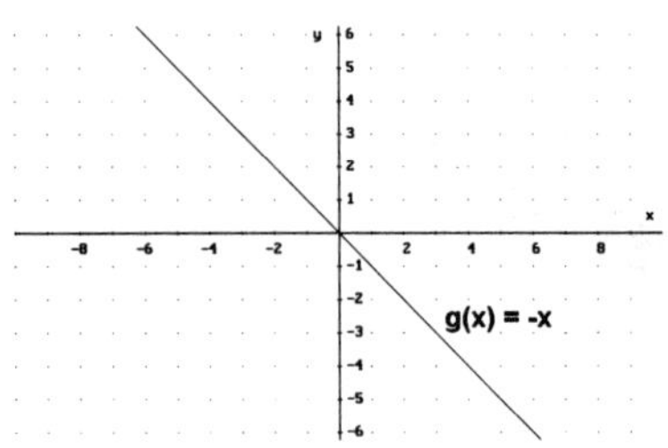

53. $g(x) = 3x+2$

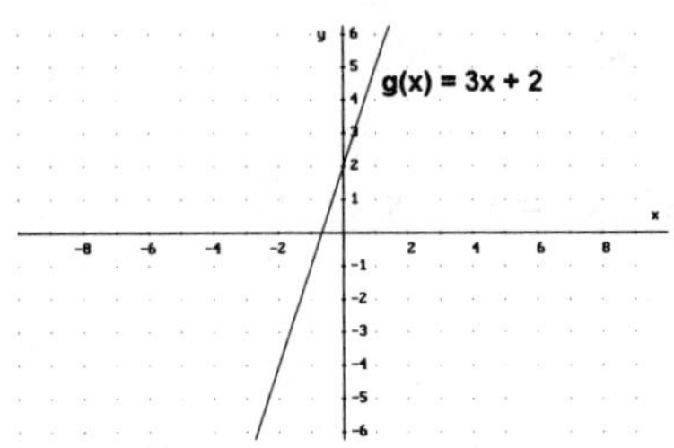

55. $h(x) = -x - 3$

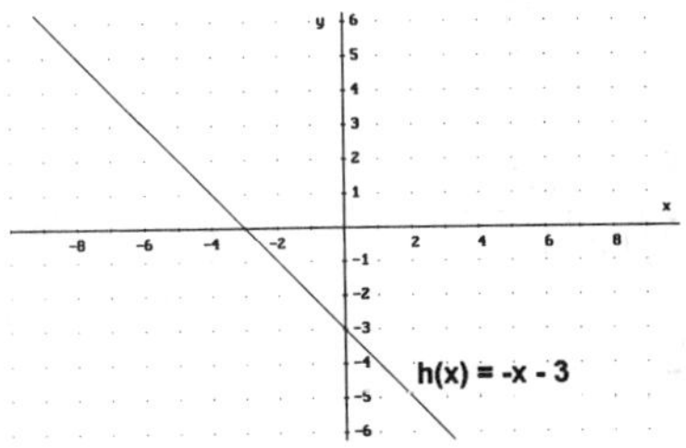

57.

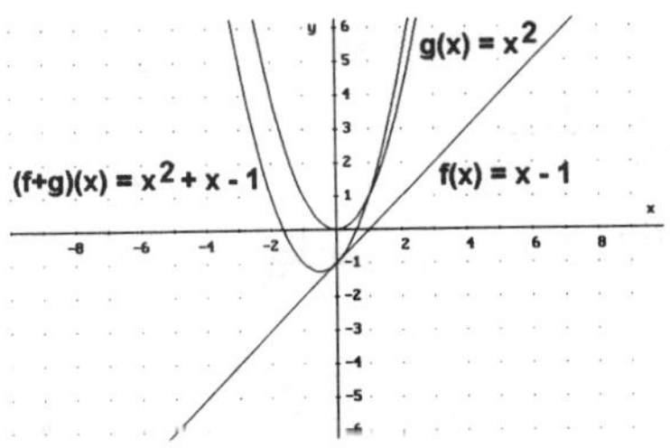

59.

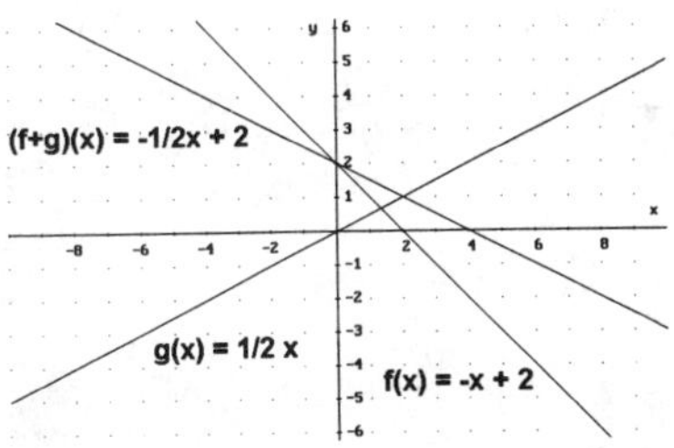

61. $80 - 29$
51 pounds

63. Beef consumption is decreasing and chicken consumption is increasing.

65. $(f \circ g)(x) = f[g(x)]$
$= 2\left(\frac{1}{2}x - 2\right) + 4$
$= x - 4 + 4$
$= x$
$(g \circ f)(x) = g[f(x)]$
$= \frac{1}{2}(2x + 4) - 2$
$= x + 2 - 2$
$= x$

67. $P(x) = R(x) - C(x)$

69. $A(10) = \pi 10^2 = 100\pi$ cm^2

71a. $W(x) = 2x$

b. First, $h = 5'5''$
$= [5(12) + 5]''$
$= 65''$
Then, $W(65) = 2(65) = 130$ lbs.

73. $7x(9x - 1)$
$63x^2 - 7x$

75. $-9xy(-9x + 4)$
$81x^2y - 36xy$

77. $-2(x + 7) + 14 = -3x$
$-2x - 14 + 14 = -3x$
$-2x = -3x$
$x = 0$
$\{0\}$

79. $\frac{2x}{5} - \frac{1}{3} = \frac{4}{5}$
$3(2x) - 5(1) = 3(4)$
$6x - 5 = 12$
$6x = 17$
$x = \frac{17}{6}$
$\left\{\frac{17}{6}\right\}$

81. $7 - (4^2 - 3)$
$7 - (16 - 3)$
$7 - (13)$
$7 - 13$
-6

83. $(-2, 4)$ and $(0, 6)$
$m = \frac{6 - 4}{0 - (-2)} = \frac{2}{2} = 1$
$y - 6 = 1(x - 0)$
$y - 6 = x$
$y = x + 6$

Chapter 5 Review

1. 3^2; base = 3, exponent = 2

3. -5^4; base = 5, exponent = 4

5. $(-6)^2$

$(-6)(-6)$

36

7. $-4^3 - 4^0$

$-(64) - (1)$

$-64 - 1$

-65

9. $\frac{8b}{8b}$

1

11. $2^3 \bullet x^0$

$8 \bullet 1$

8

13. $(2x^3)(-5x^2)$

$(2)(-5)(x^3)(x^2)$

$-10x^5$

15. $\left(\frac{3ab^2}{6ab}\right)^4$

$\left(\frac{b}{2}\right)^4$

$\frac{b^4}{2^4}$

$\frac{b^4}{16}$

17. $\frac{2x^7y^8}{8xy^2}$

$\frac{x^6y^6}{4}$

19. $5a^7(2a^4)^3$

$5a^7(2^3a^{12})$

$5a^7(8a^{12})$

$40a^{19}$

21. $\frac{(-4)^2(3^3)}{(4^5)(3^2)}$

$\frac{(-1 \bullet 4)^2(3^3)}{(4^5)(3^2)}$

$\frac{(-1)^2(4^2)(3^3)}{(4^5)(3^2)}$

$\frac{(1)(3)}{(4^3)}$

$\frac{3}{64}$

23. $\frac{(2x)^0(-4)^2}{16x}$

$\frac{1 \bullet (16)}{16x}$

$\frac{1}{x}$

25. $m^0 + p^0 + 3q^0$

$1 + 1 + 3(1)$

$1 + 1 + 3$

5

27. $(3xy^2 + 8x + 9)^0$

1

29. $6(a^2b^3)^3$

$6(a^6b^9)$

$6a^6b^9$

31. 7^{-2}

$\frac{1}{7^2}$

$\frac{1}{49}$

33. $2x^{-4}$

$2\left(\frac{1}{x^4}\right)$

$\frac{2}{x^4}$

35. $\left(\frac{1}{5}\right)^{-3}$

$\frac{1^{-3}}{5^{-3}}$

$\frac{5^3}{1^3}$

$\frac{125}{1}$

125

37. 2^0+2^{-4}

$1+\frac{1}{2^4}$

$1+\frac{1}{16}$

$\frac{16}{16}+\frac{1}{16}$

$\frac{17}{16}$

39. $\frac{1}{(2q)^{-3}}$

$1(2q)^3$

$1(2^3q^3)$

$1(8q^3)$

$8q^3$

41. $\frac{r^{-3}}{s^{-4}}$

$\frac{s^4}{r^3}$

43. $\frac{-6}{8x^{-3}r^4}$

$\frac{-6x^3}{8r^4}$

$-\frac{3x^3}{4r^4}$

45. $(2x^{-5})^{-3}$

$2^{-3}x^{15}$

$\frac{x^{15}}{2^3}$

$\frac{x^{15}}{8}$

47. $(3a^{-1}b^{-1}c^{-2})^{-2}$

$3^{-2}a^2b^2c^4$

$\frac{a^2b^2c^4}{3^2}$

$\frac{a^2b^2c^4}{9}$

49. $\frac{5^{-2}x^8}{5^{-3}x^{11}}$

$5^{-2-(-3)}x^{8-11}$

$5^{-2+3}x^{8-11}$

5^1x^{-3}

$\frac{5}{x^3}$

51. $\left(\frac{bc^{-2}}{bc^{-3}}\right)^4$

$(b^{1-1}c^{-2-(-3)})^4$

$(b^0c^{-2+3})^4$

$(1 \bullet c^1)^4$

1^4c^4

c^4

53. $\frac{x^{-4}y^{-6}}{x^2y^7}$

$x^{-4-2}y^{-6-7}$

$x^{-6}y^{-13}$

$\frac{1}{x^6y^{13}}$

55. -2^0+2^{-4}

$-(1)+\frac{1}{2^4}$

$-1+\frac{1}{16}$

$-\frac{16}{16}+\frac{1}{16}$

$-\frac{15}{16}$

57. $a^{6m}a^{5m}$

a^{11m}

59. $(3xy^{2z})^3$

$3^3x^3y^{2z(3)}$

$27x^3y^{6z}$

61. 0.00027

2.7×10^{-4}

63. 80,800,000

8.08×10^7

65. 258,000,000

2.58×10^8

67. 8.67×10^5

867,000

69. 8.6×10^{-4}

0.00086

71. 1×10^{20}

100,000,000,000,000,000,000

73. $(8 \times 10^4)(2 \times 10^{-7})$

$8 \times 2 \times 10^{4+(-7)}$

16×10^{-3}

0.016

75. $-3xy^2z$ has degree $1+2+1=4$.

77. $3x$ has degree 1.

79. $3x+2$ has degree 1.

81. $-8xy^3+4xy^3-3x^3y$

$(-8+4)xy^3-3x^3y$

$-4xy^3-3x^3y$

83.
$$\begin{array}{rrr} & 4x^2-6xy+9y^2 \\ - & \underline{8x^2-6xy-\ \ y^2} \\ & -4x^2 \qquad\quad +10y^2 \end{array}$$

85.
$$\begin{array}{rr} & 4x^2+\ 9xy \qquad\ +18 \\ + & \underline{-4x^3 \qquad\ +\ 7xy-9x \qquad} \\ & -4x^3+4x^2+16xy-9x+18 \end{array}$$

87.
$$\begin{array}{rr} & x^2-5x+7 \\ - & \underline{x+4} \\ & x^2-6x+3 \end{array}$$

89. $P(6)=9(6)^2-7(6)+8=290$

91. $P(-3)=9(-3)^2-7(-3)+8=110$

93. $P(t)=-16t^2+1001$

$P(5)=-16(5)^2+1001$

$P(5)=-16(25)+1001$

$P(5)=-400+1001$

$P(5)=601$ (units unknown)

95.
$$\begin{array}{r} 4xy-6x+1 \\ \underline{-6xy^3} \\ -24x^2y^4+36x^2y^3-6xy^3 \end{array}$$

97. $(x-4)(2x+9)$

$2x^2+9x-8x-36$

$2x^2+x-36$

99. $(-3xa+4b)^2$

$(-3xa)^2+2(-3xa)(4b)+(4b)^2$

$9x^2a^2-24xab+16b^2$

101. $(5x-9)(3x+9)$

$15x^2+45x-27x-81$

$15x^2+18x-81$

103. $(3x-y)^2$

$(3x)^2-2(3x)y+y^2$

$9x^2-6xy+y^2$

105. $(x+3y)(x-3y)$

$x^2-(3y)^2$

x^2-9y^2

107. $[4+(3a-b)][4-(3a-b)]$

$4^2-(3a-b)^2$

$16-[(3a)^2-2(3a)b+b^2]$

$16-(9a^2-6ab+b^2)$

$-9a^2+6ab-b^2+16$

109. $[(9y-3)-y^2]^2$

$(9y-3)^2-2(9y-3)y^2+(y^2)^2$

$(9y^2)-2(9y)3+3^2-2y^2(9y-3)+y^4$

$81y^2-54y+9-18y^3+6y^2+y^4$

$y^4-18y^3+87y^2-54y+9$

111. $(4y^3+3x^2)^2$

$(4y^3)^2+2(4y^3)(3x^2)+(3x^2)^2$

$4^2(y^3)^2+24x^2y^3+3^2(x^2)^2$

$16y^6+24x^2y^3+9x^4$

113. $(4xy^z-b)^2$

$(4xy^z)^2-2(4xy^z)b+b^2$

$4^2x^2(y^z)^2-8xy^zb+b^2$

$16x^2y^{2z}-8xy^zb+b^2$

115. $f(x)=5x^2+2x$

a. $f(a)=5a^2+2a$

b. $f(a+h)=5(a+h)^2+2(a+h)$

$=5(a^2+2ah+h^2)+2(a+h)$

$=5a^2+10ah+5h^2+2a+2h$

c. $f(x)\bullet f(x)$

$(5x^2+2x)(5x^2+2x)$

$25x^4+10x^3+10x^3+4x^2$

$25x^4+20x^3+4x^2$

117. $\dfrac{-9xb^4z^3}{-4axb^2}=\dfrac{9}{4a}x^{1-1}b^{4-2}z^3=\dfrac{9b^2z^3}{4a}$

119. $\dfrac{12xb^2+16xb^4}{4xb^3}$

$\dfrac{12xb^2}{4xb^3}+\dfrac{16xb^4}{4xb^3}$

$\dfrac{3}{b}+4b$

121.

$$
\begin{array}{r|l}
 & 2x^3+6x^2+17x+56 \\
x-3 & 2x^4 \qquad -x^2+5x-12 \\
 & \underline{2x^4-6x^3} \\
 & 6x^3-x^2 \\
 & \underline{6x^3-18x^2} \\
 & 17x^2+5x \\
 & \underline{17x^2-51x} \\
 & 56x-12 \\
 & \underline{56x-168} \\
 & 156
\end{array}
$$

$2x^3+6x^2+17x+56+\dfrac{156}{x-3}$

123.

$$
\begin{array}{r|l}
 & x^2+\frac{7}{2}x-\frac{1}{4} \\
x-\frac{1}{2} & x^3+3x^2-2x+2 \\
 & \underline{x^3-\frac{1}{2}x^2} \\
 & \frac{7}{2}x^2-2x \\
 & \underline{\frac{7}{2}x^2-\frac{7}{4}x} \\
 & -\frac{1}{4}x+2 \\
 & \underline{-\frac{1}{4}x+\frac{1}{8}} \\
 & \frac{15}{8}
\end{array}
$$

$x^2+\frac{7}{2}x-\frac{1}{4}+\dfrac{\frac{15}{8}}{x-\frac{1}{2}}$

125.

$$
\begin{array}{r|l}
 & 3x^2 \qquad +6 \\
3x^2-2x-5 & 9x^4-6x^3+3x^2-12x-30 \\
 & \underline{9x^4-6x^3-15x^2} \\
 & 18x^2-12x-30 \\
 & \underline{18x^2-12x-30} \\
 & 0
\end{array}
$$

$3x^2+6$

127.

$$
\begin{array}{r|l}
 & 3x^2-\frac{5}{2}x-\frac{1}{4} \\
x+\frac{3}{2} & 3x^3+2x^2-4x-1 \\
 & \underline{3x^3+\frac{9}{2}x^2} \\
 & -\frac{5}{2}x^2-4x \\
 & \underline{-\frac{5}{2}x^2-\frac{15}{4}x} \\
 & -\frac{1}{4}x-1 \\
 & \underline{-\frac{1}{4}x-\frac{3}{8}} \\
 & -\frac{5}{8}
\end{array}
$$

$3x^2-\frac{5}{2}x-\frac{1}{4}-\dfrac{\frac{5}{8}}{x+\frac{3}{2}}$

129.

$$\begin{array}{r} x^2+3x+9 \\ x-3\,\overline{)\,x^3 \qquad\qquad -81} \\ \underline{x^3-3x^2} \qquad\qquad \\ 3x^2 \qquad\qquad \\ \underline{3x^2-9x} \qquad \\ 9x-81 \\ \underline{9x-27} \\ -54 \end{array}$$

$$x^2+3x+9-\frac{54}{x-3}$$

131.

$$\begin{array}{r} 3x^3-6x^2+10x-20 \\ x+2\,\overline{)\,3x^4 \qquad -2x^2 \qquad +10} \\ \underline{3x^4+6x^3} \qquad\qquad\qquad \\ -6x^3-2x^2 \qquad\qquad \\ \underline{-6x^3-12x^2} \qquad\qquad \\ 10x^2 \qquad\qquad \\ \underline{10x^2+20x} \qquad \\ -20x+10 \\ \underline{-20x-40} \\ 50 \end{array}$$

$$3x^3-6x^2+10x-20+\frac{50}{x+2}$$

133. $P(x)=3x^5-9x+7$

$$P(-5)=3(-5)^5-9(-5)+7$$
$$=3(-3125)+45+7$$
$$=-9323$$

135. $P(x)=3x^5-9x+7$

$$P\left(-\frac{1}{2}\right)=3\left(-\frac{1}{2}\right)^5-9\left(-\frac{1}{2}\right)+7$$
$$=\frac{-3}{32}+\frac{9}{2}+7$$
$$=\frac{-3+144+244}{32}=\frac{365}{32}$$

137. $(f+g)(x)=f(x)+g(x)$

$$=(x^2-2)+(x+1)$$
$$=x^2+x-1$$

139. $\frac{h}{g}(x)=\frac{h(x)}{g(x)}=\frac{x^3-x^2}{x+1}$

$$\begin{array}{r} x^2-2x+2 \\ x+1\,\overline{)\,x^3-x^2 \qquad\qquad} \\ \underline{x^3+x^2} \qquad\qquad \\ -2x^2 \qquad\quad \\ \underline{-2x^2-2x} \quad \\ 2x \\ \underline{2x+2} \\ -2 \end{array}$$

$$\frac{h}{g}(x)=x^2-2x+2-\frac{2}{x+1}$$

141. $(f\circ g)(x)=f[g(x)]$

$$=(x+1)^2-2$$
$$=x^2+2x+1-2$$
$$=x^2+2x-1$$

143. $(h\circ g)(2)=h[g(2)]$

$$=h(2+1)$$
$$=h(3)$$
$$=3^3-3^2$$
$$=27-9$$
$$=18$$

145. $(f\circ g)(-1)=f[g(-1)]$

$$=f(-1+1)$$
$$=f(0)$$
$$=0^2-2$$
$$=-2$$

147.

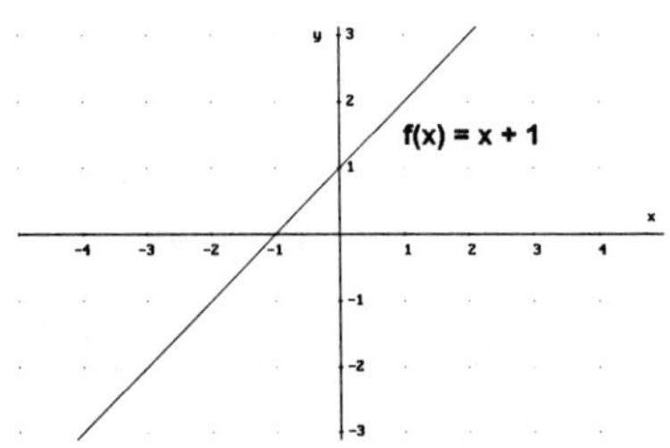

149. $f(x)=x-5$
$g(x)=x^2$
$(f+g)(x)=x^2+x-5$

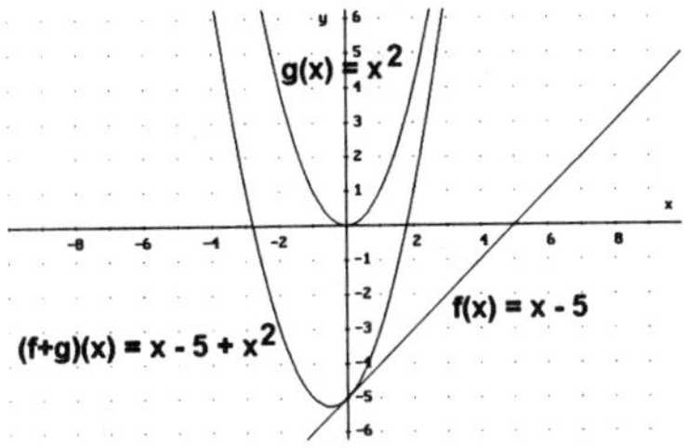

Chapter 5 Test

1. $(-2)^3 = (-2)(-2)(-2) = -8$

2. $6^{-2} = \frac{1}{6^2} = \frac{1}{36}$

3. $-3xy^{-2}(4xy^2)z = -12x^{1+1}y^{-2+2}z$
$-12x^2y^0z = -12x^2(1)z = -12x^2z$

4. $(-9x)^{-2} = \frac{1}{(-9x)^2} = \frac{1}{(-9)^2x^2} = \frac{1}{81x^2}$

5. $\left(\frac{-xy^{-5}z}{xy^3}\right)^{-5} = \left(\frac{-z}{y^{3-(-5)}}\right)^{-5}$
$\left(\frac{-z}{y^8}\right)^{-5} = \frac{-(y^8)^5}{z^5} = \frac{-y^{40}}{z^5}$

6. $\frac{144(xy^{-3}z)^3}{12(xy)^{-2}} = \frac{12x^3(y^{-9})z^3}{x^{-2}y^{-2}}$
$\frac{12x^{3-(-2)}y^{-9}z^3}{y^{-2}} = \frac{12x^5z^3}{y^{-2-(-9)}} = \frac{12x^5z^3}{y^7}$

7. $630,000,000 = 6.3 \times 10^8$

8. $0.01200 = 1.2 \times 10^{-2}$

9. $5.0 \times 10^{-6} = 0.000005$

10. $\frac{(0.0024)(0.00012)}{(0.00032)}$
$\frac{(2.4 \times 10^{-3})(1.2 \times 10^{-4})}{(3.2 \times 10^{-4})}$
$0.9 \times 10^{-3} = 0.0009$

11. $\begin{array}{r} 4x^3 \quad -3x-4 \\ -\ \underline{9x^2 \quad +8x+5} \\ -5x^3-11x-9 \end{array}$

12. $\begin{array}{r} 12x^6-6xy^2 \qquad +15 \\ +\ \underline{2x^6+3xy^2+6y^2 \qquad} \\ 14x^6-3xy^2+6y^2+15 \end{array}$

13. $P(-3) = -3(-3)^3 - 4(-3) + 2$
$-3(-27) + 12 + 2 = 81 + 14 = 95$

14. $-3xy(4x+y)$
$-3xy(4x) - 3xy(y)$
$-12x^2y - 3xy^2$

15. $(3x+4)(4x-7)$
$12x^2 - 21x + 16x - 28$
$12x^2 - 5x - 28$

16. $(9x^2+4y+2)^2$
$(9x^2)^2 + (4y)^2 + 2^2 + 2(9x^2)(4y) + 2(9x^2)2 + 2(4y)2$
$81x^4 + 16y^2 + 4 + 72x^2y + 36x^2 + 16y$
$81x^4 + 72x^2y + 36x^2 + 16y^2 + 16y + 4$

17. $[3-(4x-y)]^2$
$3^2 - 2(3)(4x-y) + (4x-y)^2$
$9 - 6(4x-y) + (4x)^2 - 2(4x)y + y^2$
$9 - 24x + 6y + 16x^2 - 8xy + y^2$
$16x^2 - 8xy + y^2 - 24x + 6y + 9$

18. $\frac{4x^2y + 9x + z}{3xz}$
$\frac{4x^2y}{3xz} + \frac{9x}{3xz} + \frac{z}{3xz}$
$\frac{4xy}{3z} + \frac{3}{z} + \frac{1}{3x}$

19.

$$\begin{array}{r} x^5 + 5x^4 + 8x^3 + 16x^2 + 33x + 63 \\ x-2 \overline{\big) x^6 + 3x^5 - 2x^4 \qquad + x^2 - 3x + 2} \end{array}$$

$$\underline{x^6 - 2x^5}$$

$$5x^5 - 2x^4$$

$$\underline{5x^5 - 10x^4}$$

$$8x^4$$

$$\underline{8x^4 - 16x^3}$$

$$16x^3 + x^2$$

$$\underline{16x^3 - 32x^2}$$

$$33x^2 - 3x$$

$$\underline{33x^2 - 66x}$$

$$63x + 2$$

$$\underline{63x - 126}$$

$$128$$

$$x^5 + 5x^4 + 8x^3 + 16x^2 + 33x + 63 + \frac{128}{x-2}$$

20.

$\frac{2}{3}$	4	-3	2	-1	-1
		$\frac{8}{3}$	$-\frac{2}{9}$	$\frac{32}{27}$	$\frac{10}{81}$
	4	$-\frac{1}{3}$	$\frac{16}{9}$	$\frac{5}{27}$	$-\frac{71}{81}$

$$4x^3 - \frac{1}{3}x^2 + \frac{16}{9}x + \frac{5}{27} - \frac{\frac{71}{81}}{x - \frac{2}{3}}$$

21.

-2	4	0	7	-2	-5
		-8	16	-46	96
	4	-8	23	-48	91

Thus, $P(-2) = 91$

22. $(h-g)(x) = h(x) - g(x)$
$= (x^2 - 6x + 5) - (x - 7)$
$= x^2 - 6x + 5 - x + 7$
$= x^2 - 7x + 12$

23. $(h \bullet f)(x) = h(x) \bullet f(x)$
$= (x^2 - 6x + 5)(x)$
$= x^3 - 6x^2 + 5x$

24. $(g \circ f)(x) = g[f(x)]$
$= g(x)$
$= x - 7$

25. $(g \circ h)(x) = g[h(x)]$
$= g(x^2 - 6x + 5)$
$= (x^2 - 6x + 5) - 7$
$= x^2 - 6x - 2$

26. $f(x) = 2x - 4$

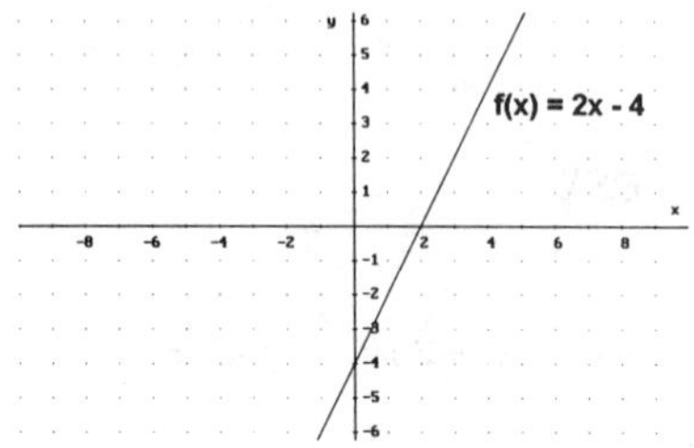

27. $f(x) = 2x^2 - 4$

a. $f(a) = 2a^2 - 4$

b. $f(a+2) = 2(a+2)^2 - 4$
$f(a+2) = 2(a^2 + 4a + 4) - 4$
$f(a+2) = 2a^2 + 8a + 8 - 4$
$f(a+2) = 2a^2 + 8a + 4$

c. $f(x) \bullet f(x) = (2x^2 - 4)(2x^2 - 4)$
$f(x) \bullet f(x) = 4x^4 - 8x^2 - 8x^2 + 16$
$f(x) \bullet f(x) = 4x^2 - 16x^2 + 16$

28. Side of shaded square $= x - 4$
$A = s^2$
$A = (x - 4)^2$
$A = x^2 - 8x + 16$

29. $P(x) = R(x) - C(x)$
$P(x) = 2x - (0.8x + 10{,}000)$
$P(x) = 2x - 0.8x - 10{,}000$
$P(x) = 1.2x - 10{,}000$
$P(20{,}000) = 1.2(20{,}000) - 10{,}000$
$P(20{,}000) = 24{,}000 - 10{,}000$
$P(20{,}000) = 14{,}000$

Chapter 5 Cumulative Review

1a. $\frac{2}{5}+\frac{1}{4}=\frac{8}{20}+\frac{5}{20}=\frac{13}{20}$

b. $\frac{1}{2}+\frac{17}{22}-\frac{2}{11}=\frac{11}{22}+\frac{17}{22}-\frac{4}{22}$

$\frac{28}{22}-\frac{4}{22}=\frac{24}{22}=\frac{12}{11}$

c. $3\frac{1}{6}-1\frac{11}{12}=\frac{19}{6}-\frac{23}{12}$

$\frac{38}{12}-\frac{23}{12}=\frac{15}{12}=\frac{5}{4}$

3. $-4-8=-12$

5. $I=Prt$

$I=800(0.05)(3)$

$I=\$120$

$\$120$ per person $\times 3$ people $=\$360$

They will not have enough money.

7. $|p|=2$

$p=2$ or $p=-2$

$\{-2, 2\}$

9. $2<4-x<7$

$2-4<4-4-x<7-4$

$-2<-x<3$

$\frac{-2}{-1}>\frac{-x}{-1}>\frac{3}{-1}$

$2>x>-3$

$-3<x<2$

$(-3, 2)$

11. $y=3x$

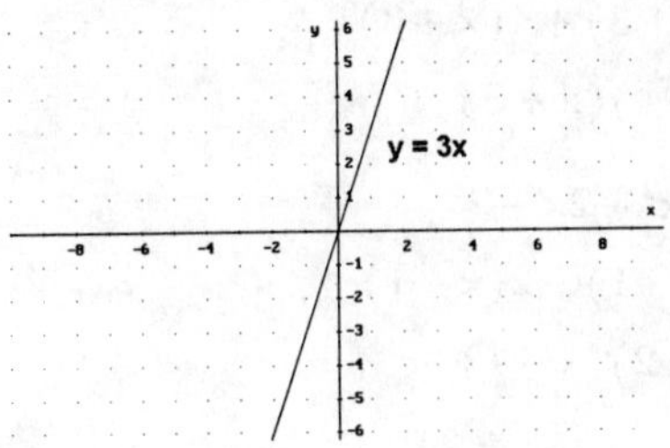

13. $m=-2,\ (-1, 5)$

$y-5=-2[x-(-1)]$

$y-5=-2(x+1)$

$y-5=-2x-2$

$2x+y-5=-2$

$2x+y=3$

15a. $\frac{x^5}{x^2}=x^{5-2}=x^3$

b. $\frac{4^7}{4^3}=4^{7-3}=4^4$

c. $\frac{(-3)^5}{(-3)^2}=(-3)^{5-2}=(-3)^3=-27$

d. $\frac{2x^5y^2}{xy}=2x^{5-1}y^{2-1}=2x^4y$

17. $(11x^3-12x^2+x-3)+(x^3-10x+5)$

$12x^3-12x^2-9x+2$

19. $\frac{7a^2b-2ab^2}{2ab^2}=\frac{7a^2b}{2ab^2}-\frac{2ab^2}{2ab^2}=\frac{7a}{2b}-1$

21.
$$\begin{array}{r|rrrrr} -2 & 1 & -2 & -11 & 5 & 34 \\ & & -2 & 8 & 6 & -22 \\ \hline & 1 & -4 & -3 & 11 & 12 \end{array}$$

$x^3-4x^2-3x+11+\frac{12}{x+2}$

Exercise Set 6.1

1. The GCF of 24 and 30 is 6.

3. The GCF of 84 and 140 is 28.

5. The GCF of 20, 36, and 60 is 4.

7. The GCF of 30, 48, and 72 is 6.

9. a^8, a^5, and a^3 have GCF a^3.

11. $x^2y^3z^3$, y^2z^3, xy^2z^2 have GCF y^2z^2.

13. $6x^3y$, $9x^2y^2$, $12x^2y$ have GCF $3x^2y$.

15. $10x^3yz^3$, $20x^2z^5$, $45xz^3$ have GCF $5xz^3$.

17. $18x-12=6(3x-2)$

19. $4y^2 - 16xy^3 = 4y^2(1-4xy)$

21. $6x^5 - 8x^4 + 2x^3 = 2x^3(3x^2 - 4x + 1)$

23. $8a^3b^3 - 4a^2b^2 + 4ab + 16ab^2$

$4ab(2a^2b^2 - ab + 1 + 4b)$

25. $6(x+3) + 5a(x+3)$

$(6+5a)(x+3)$

27. $2x(z+7) + (z+7)$

$(2x+1)(z+7)$

29. $3x(x^2+5) - 2(x^2+5)$

$(3x-2)(x^2+5)$

31. $ab + 3a + 2b + 6$

$a(b+3) + 2(b+3)$

$(a+2)(b+3)$

33. $ac + 4a - 2c - 8$

$a(c+4) - 2(c+4)$

$(a-2)(c+4)$

35. $2xy - 3x - 4y + 6$

$x(2y-3) - 2(2y-3)$

$(x-2)(2y-3)$

37. $12xy - 8x - 3y + 2$

$4x(3y-2) - (3y-2)$

$(4x-1)(3y-2)$

39. $6x^3 + 9 = 3(2x^3+3)$

41. $x^3 + 3x^2 = x^2(x+3)$

43. $8a^3 - 4a = 4a(2a^2-1)$

45. $-20x^2y + 16xy^3$

$-4xy(5x - 4y^2)$

47. $10a^2b^3 + 5ab^2 - 15ab^3$

$5ab^2(2ab + 1 - 3b)$

49. $9abc^2 + 6a^2bc - 6ab + 3bc$

$3b(3ac^2 + 2a^2c - 2a + c)$

51. $4x(y-2) - 3(y-2)$

$(4x-3)(y-2)$

53. $2m(n-8) - (n-8)$

$(2m-1)(n-8)$

55. $15x^3y^2 - 18x^2y^2$

$3x^2y^2(5x-6)$

57. $6xy + 10x + 9y + 15$

$2x(3y+5) + 3(3y+5)$

$(2x+3)(3y+5)$

59. $xy + 3y - 5x - 15$

$y(x+3) - 5(x+3)$

$(y-5)(x+3)$

61. $6ab - 2a - 9b + 3$

$2a(3b-1) - 3(3b-1)$

$(2a-3)(3b-1)$

63. $12xy + 18x + 2y + 3$

$6x(2y+3) + 1(2y+3)$

$(6x+1)(2y+3)$

65. $2x^2 + 3xy + 4x + 6y$

$x(2x+3y) + 2(2x+3y)$

$(x+2)(2x+3y)$

67. $5x^2 + 5xy - 3x - 3y$

$5x(x+y) - 3(x+y)$

$(5x-3)(x+y)$

69. $x^3 + 3x^2 + 4x + 12$

$x^2(x+3) + 4(x+3)$

$(x^2+4)(x+3)$

71. $x^3 - x^2 - 2x + 2$

$x^2(x-1) - 2(x-1)$

$(x^2-2)(x-1)$

73. $2\pi r^2 + 2\pi rh$

$2\pi r(r+h)$

75. $A = P + PRT$

$A = P(1 + RT)$

77. $h(t) = -16t^2 + 64t$

$h(t) = -16t(t-4)$

79. $(5x^2)(11x^5)$

$5 \bullet 11 \bullet x^2 \bullet x^5$

$55x^7$

81. $(5x^2)^3$

$5x^2 \bullet 5x^2 \bullet 5x^2$

$5 \bullet 5 \bullet 5 \bullet x^2 \bullet x^2 \bullet x^2$

$125x^6$

83. $(x+2)(x-5)$

$x^2 - 5x + 2x - 10$

$x^2 - 3x - 10$

85. $(x+3)(x+2)$

$x^2 + 2x + 3x + 6$

$x^2 + 5x + 6$

87. $(y-3)(y-1)$

$y^2 - y - 3y + 3$

$y^2 - 4y + 3$

89. $9x^2 - 6 - (x^2 - 2x + 1)$

$9x^2 - 6 - x^2 + 2x - 1$

$8x^2 + 2x - 7$

91. $x^{3n} - 2x^{2n} + 5x^n$

$x^n(x^{2n} - 2x^n + 5)$

93. $6x^{8a} - 2x^{5a} - 4x^{3a}$

$2x^{3a}(3x^{5a} - x^{2a} - 2)$

95. $3x^{-2} + 8x^{-1} = x^{-2}(3 + 8x)$

97. $3x^2y^{-3} + 2xy^{-1} = xy^{-3}(3x + 2y^2)$

99. $6x^{-2}y^{-1} - 2x^{-2}y^{-4} + 8xy^{-2}$

$2x^{-2}y^{-4}(3y^3 - 1 + 4x^3y^2)$

Exercise Set 6.2

1. $x^2 + 7x + 6$

$(x+6)(x+1)$

3. $x^2 + 9x + 20$

$(x+5)(x+4)$

5. $x^2 - 8x + 15$

$(x-5)(x-3)$

7. $x^2 - 10x + 9$

$(x-9)(x-1)$

9. $x^2 - 15x + 5$

not factorable

11. $x^2 - 3x - 18$

$(x-6)(x+3)$

13. $x^2 + 5x + 2$

not factorable

15. $x^2 + 8xy + 15y^2$

$(x+3y)(x+5y)$

17. $x^2 - 2xy + y^2$

$(x-y)(x-y)$

$(x-y)^2$

19. $x^2 - 3xy - 4y^2$

$(x-4y)(x+y)$

21. $2x^2 + 20z + 32$; GCF = 2

$2(z^2 + 10z + 16)$

$2(z+8)(z+2)$

23. $2x^3 - 18x^2 + 40x$; GCF = 2x

$2x(x^2 - 9x + 20)$

$2x(x-5)(x-4)$

25. $7x^2 + 14xy - 21y^2$; GCF = 7

$7(x^2 + 2xy - 3y^2)$

$7(x+3y)(x-y)$

27. $x^2+15x+36$
$(x+12)(x+3)$

29. x^2-x-2
$(x-2)(x+1)$

31. $r^2-16r+48$
$(r-12)(r-4)$

33. $x^2-4x-21$
$(x-7)(x+3)$

35. $x^2+7xy+10y^2$
$(x+2y)(x+5y)$

37. r^2-3r+6
not factorable

39. $2t^2+24t+64$; GCF $=2$
$2(t^2+12t+32)$
$2(t+4)(t+8)$

41. x^3-2x^2-24x; GCF $=x$
$x(x^2-2x-24)$
$x(x-6)(x+4)$

43. $x^2-16x+63$
$(x-9)(x-7)$

45. $x^2+xy-2y^2$
$(x+2y)(x-y)$

47. $3x^2+9x-30$; GCF $=3$
$3(x^2+3x-10)$
$3(x+5)(x-2)$

49. $3x^2-60x+108$; GCF $=3$
$3(x^2-20x+36)$
$3(x-18)(x-2)$

51. $x^2-18x-144$
$(x-24)(x+6)$

53. $6x^3+54x^2+120x$; GCF $=6x$
$6x(x^2+9x+20)$
$6x(x+5)(x+4)$

55. $2t^5-14t^4+24t^3$; GCF $=2t^3$
$2t^3(t^2-7t+12)$
$2t^3(t-4)(t-3)$

57. $5x^3y-25x^2y^2-120xy^3$; GCF $=5xy$
$5xy(x^2-5xy-24y^2)$
$5xy(x-8y)(x+3y)$

59. $4x^2+4x-12$; GCF $=4$
$4(x^2+x-3)$

61. $x^2-10x+21$
$(x-3)(x-7)$

63. $2x^2y+30xy+100y$; GCF $=2y$
$2y(x^2+15x+50)$
$2y(x+5)(x+10)$

65. $-12x^2y^3-24xy^3-36y^3$; GCF $=-12y^3$
$-12y^3(x^2+2x+3)$

67. $y^2(x+1)-2y(x+1)-15(x+1)$;
GCF $=(x+1)$
$(x+1)(y^2-2y-15)$
$(x+1)(y-5)(y+3)$

69. 5^{-2}
$\frac{1}{5^2}$
$\frac{1}{25}$

71. $\frac{x^{-10}}{x^5}$
x^{-10-5}
x^{-15}
$\frac{1}{x^{15}}$

73. $F=\frac{(6.24\times10)(4\times10^4)}{2}$
$F=\frac{24.96\times10^5}{2}$
$F=12.48\times10^5$

$F = 1.248 \times 10^1 \times 10^5$

$F = 1.248 \times 10^6$

75. $(3x-2)(x+5)$

$3x^2 + 15x - 2x - 10$

$3x^2 + 13x - 10$

77. $(y-1)^2$

$y^2 + 2(y)(-1) + (-1)^2$

$y^2 - 2y + 1$

79. $(P \bullet Q)(x)$

$P(x) \bullet Q(x)$

$(5x+1)(4x-3)$

$20x^2 - 15x + 4x - 3$

$20x^2 - 11x - 3$

81. $(P \bullet P)(x)$

$P(x) \bullet P(x)$

$(5x+1)(5x+1)$

$25x^2 + 5x + 5x + 1$

$25x^2 + 10x + 1$

Exercise Set 6.3

1. $2x^2 + 13x + 15$

$(2x+3)(x+5)$

3. $2x^2 - 9x - 5$

$(2x+1)(x-5)$

5. $2y^2 - y - 6$

$(2y+3)(y-2)$

7. $16a^2 - 24a + 9$

$(4a-3)(4a-3)$

$(4a-3)^2$

9. $36r^2 - 5r - 24$

$(9r-8)(4r+3)$

11. $10x^2 + 17x + 3$

$(5x+1)(2x+3)$

13. $21x^2 - 48x - 45$; $GCF = 3$

$3(7x^2 - 16x - 15)$

$3(7x+5)(x-3)$

15. $12x^2 - 14x - 6$; $GCF = 2$

$2(6x^2 - 7x - 3)$

$2(2x-3)(3x+1)$

17. $4x^3 - 9x^2 - 9x$; $GCF = x$

$x(4x^2 - 9x - 9)$

$x(4x+3)(x-3)$

19. $x^2 + 22x + 121$

$(x+11)(x+11)$

$(x+11)^2$

21. $x^2 - 16x + 64$

$(x-8)(x-8)$

$(x-8)^2$

23. $16y^2 - 40y + 25$

$(4y-5)(4y-5)$

$(4y-5)^2$

25. $x^2y^2 - 10xy + 25$

$(xy-5)(xy-5)$

$(xy-5)^2$

27. $2x^2 - 7x - 99$

$(2x+11)(x-9)$

29. $4x^2 - 8x - 21$

$(2x-7)(2x+3)$

31. $30x^2 - 53x + 21$

$(6x-7)(5x-3)$

33. $24x^2 - 58x + 9$

$(4x-9)(6x-1)$

35. $9x^2 - 24xy + 16y^2$

$(3x-4y)(3x-4y)$

$(3x-4y)^2$

37. $x^2 - 14xy + 49y^2$

$(x-7y)(x-7y)$

$(x-7y)^2$

39. $2x^2 + 7x + 5$

$(2x+5)(x+1)$

41. $3x^2 - 5x + 1$

not factorable

43. $-2y^2 + y + 10$

$10 + y - 2y^2$

$(5-2y)(2+y)$

45. $16x^2 + 24xy + 9y^2$

$(4x+3y)(4x+3y)$

$(4x+3y)^2$

47. $8x^2y + 34xy - 84y$; GCF $= 2y$

$2y(4x^2 + 17x - 42)$

$2y(4x-7)(x+6)$

49. $3x^2 + x - 2$

$(3x-2)(x+1)$

51. $x^2y^2 + 4xy + 4$

$(xy+2)(xy+2)$

$(xy+2)^2$

53. $49y^2 + 42xy + 9x^2$

$(7y+3x)(7y+3x)$

$(7y+3x)^2$

55. $3x^2 - 42x + 63$; GCF $= 3$

$3(x^2 - 14x + 21)$

57. $42a^2 - 43a + 6$

$(7a-6)(6a-1)$

59. $18x^2 - 9x - 14$

$(6x-7)(3x+2)$

61. $25p^2 - 70pq + 49q^2$

$(5p-7q)(5p-7q)$

$(5p-7q)^2$

63. $15x^2 - 16x - 15$

$(5x+3)(3x-5)$

65. $-27t + 7t^2 - 4$

$7t^2 - 27t - 4$

$(7t+1)(t-4)$

67. $-12x^3y^2 + 3x^2y^2 + 15xy^2$; GCF $= -3xy^2$

$-3xy^2(4x^2 - x - 5)$

$-3xy^2(4x-5)(x+1)$

69. $-30p^3q + 88p^2q^2 + 6pq^3$; GCF $= -2pq$

$-2pq(15p^2 - 44pq - 3q^2)$

$-2pq(15p+q)(p-3q)$

71. $4x^2(y-1)^2 + 10x(y-1)^2 + 25(y-1)^2$;

GCF $= (y-1)^2$

$(y-1)^2(4x^2 + 10x + 25)$

73. $3x^2y - 11xy + 8y$

$y(3x^2 - 11x + 8)$

$y(3x-8)(x-1)$

75. $2x^2 + 2x - 12$

$2(x^2 + x - 6)$

$2(x+3)(x-2)$

77. $(x-4)^2 + 3(x-4) - 18$

$[(x-4)+6][(x-4)-3]$

$(x+2)(x-7)$

79. $2x^6 + 3x^3 - 9$

$(2x^3 - 3)(x^3 + 3)$

81. $72xy^4 - 24xy^2z + 2xz^2$

$2x(36y^4 - 12y^2z + z^2)$

$2x(6y^2 - z)^2$

83. $3h^3 - 2h^2 - 8h$

$h(3h^2 - 2h - 8)$

$h(3h+4)(h-2)$

85. x^2+2x+4

$x-2$

$-2x^2-4x-8$

x^3+2x^2+4x

$x^3 \qquad -8$

x^3-8

87. $(x+3)(x-3)$

$x^2-3x+3x-9$

x^2-9

89. $(5a+b)(5a-b)$

$25a^2-5ab+5ab-b^2$

$25a^2-b^2$

91. $P(0)=3(0)^2+2(0)-9=-9$

93. $P(-1)=3(-1)^2+2(-1)-9$

$P(-1)=3-2-9$

$P(-1)=-8$

95. $x+y<2$

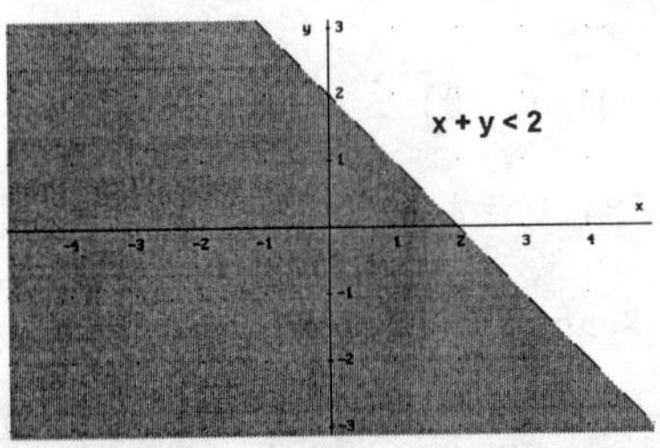

97. $y \le 2$

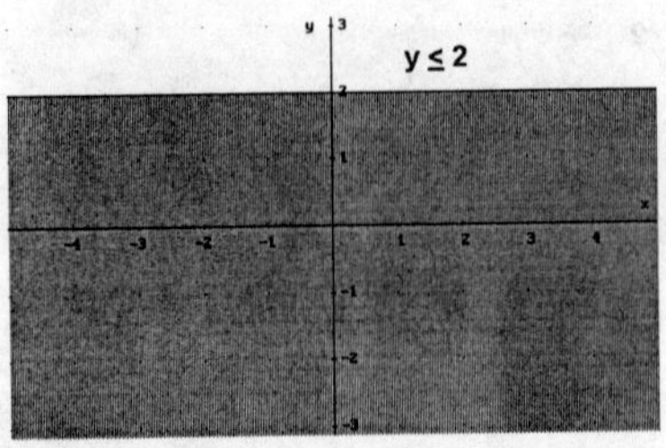

99. $x^{2n}+10x^n+16$

$(x^n+2)(x^n+8)$

101. $x^{2n}-3x^n-18$

$(x^n-6)(x^n+3)$

103. $2x^{2n}+11x^n+5$

$(2x^n+1)(x^n+5)$

105. $4x^{2n}-12x^n+9$

$(2x^n-3)^2$

Exercise Set 6.4

1. $25y^2-9$

$(5y)^2-3^2$

$(5y+3)(5y-3)$

3. $121-100x^2$

$11^2-(10x)^2$

$(11-10x)(11+10x)$

5. $12x^2-27$; $GCF=3$

$3(4x^2-9)$

$3[(2x)^2-3^2]$

$3(2x+3)(2x-3)$

7. $169a^2-49b^2$

$(13a)^2-(7b)^2$

$(13a+7b)(13a-7b)$

9. x^2y^2-1

$(xy)^2-1^2$

$(xy+1)(xy-1)$

11. a^3+27

a^3+3^3

$(a+3)(a^2-3a+9)$

13. $8a^3+1$

$(2a)^3+1^3$

$(2a+1)(4a^2-2a+1)$

15. $5k^3+40$; $GCF=5$

$5(k^3+8)$

$5(k^3+2^3)$

$5(k+2)(k^2-2k+4)$

17. x^3y^3-64
$(xy)^3-4^3$
$(xy-4)(x^2y^2+4xy+16)$

19. x^3+125
x^3+5^3
$(x+5)(x^2-5x+25)$

21. $24x^4-81xy^3$; GCF $=3x$
$3x(8x^3-27y^3)$
$3x[(2x)^3-(3y)^3]$
$3x(2x-3y)(4x^2+6xy+9y^2)$

23. x^2-4
x^2-2^2
$(x-2)(x+2)$

25. $81-p^2$
9^2-p^2
$(9-p)(9+p)$

27. $4r^2-1$
$(2r)^2-1^2$
$(2r-1)(2r+1)$

29. $9x^2-16^2$
$(3x)^2-4^2$
$(3x-4)(3x+4)$

31. $16r^2+1$
not factorable

33. $27-t^3$
3^3-t^3
$(3-t)(9+3t+t^2)$

35. $8r^3-64$; GCF $=8$
$8(r^3-8)$
$8(r^3-2^3)$
$8(r-2)(r^2+2r+4)$

37. t^3-343
t^3-7^3
$(t-7)(t^2+7t+49)$

39. x^2-169y^2
$x^2-(13y)^2$
$(x-13y)(x+13y)$

41. $x^2y^2-z^2$
$(xy)^2-z^2$
$(xy-z)(xy+z)$

43. x^3y^3+1
$(xy)^3+1^3$
$(xy+1)(x^2y^2-xy+1)$

45. s^3-64t^3
$s^3-(4t)^3$
$(s-4t)(s^2+4st+16t^2)$

47. $18r^2-8$; GCF $=2$
$2(9r^2-4)$
$2[(3r)^2-2^2]$
$2(3r-2)(3r+2)$

49. $9xy^2-4x$; GCF $=x$
$x(9y^2-4)$
$x[(3y)^2-2^2]$
$x(3y+2)(3y-2)$

51. $25y^4-100y^2$; GCF $=25y^2$
$25y^2(y^2-4)$
$25y^2(y^2-2^2)$
$25y^2(y+2)(y-2)$

53. x^3y-4xy^3; GCF $=xy$
$xy(x^2-4y^2)$
$xy[x^2-(2y)^2]$
$xy(x-2y)(x+2y)$

55. $8s^6t^3+100s^3t^6$; GCF $=4s^3t^3$
$4s^3t^3(2s^3+25t^3)$

57. $27x^2y^3 - xy^2$; $\text{GCF} = xy^2$

$xy^2(27xy - 1)$

59. $x^4 - 16$

$(x^2)^2 - 4^2$

$(x^2 + 4)(x^2 - 4)$

$(x^2 + 4)(x^2 - 2^2)$

$(x^2 + 4)(x + 2)(x - 2)$

61. $a^2 - (2 + b)^2$

$[a - (2 + b)][a + (2 + b)]$

$(a - 2 - b)(a + 2 + b)$

63. $(x^2 - 4)^2 - (x - 2)^2$

$[(x^2 - 4) + (x - 2)][(x^2 - 4) - (x - 2)]$

$[x^2 - 4 + x - 2][x^2 - 4 - x + 2]$

$(x^2 + x - 6)(x^2 - x - 2)$

$(x + 3)(x - 2)(x + 1)(x - 2)$

$(x + 3)(x + 1)(x - 2)^2$

65. $x + 6$

67. $(2x + y)$

69. $\pi R^2 - \pi r^2$

$\pi(R^2 - r^2)$

$\pi(R - r)(R + r)$

71. Area of large square $= x^2$

Area of small square $= y^2$

Area of shaded region $= x^2 - y^2$

$x^2 - y^2$

$(x + y)(x - y)$

73. $\dfrac{8x^4 + 4x^3 - 2x + 6}{2x}$

$\dfrac{8x^4}{2x} + \dfrac{4x^3}{2x} - \dfrac{2x}{2x} + \dfrac{6}{2x}$

$4x^3 + 2x^2 - 1 + \frac{3}{x}$

75.
$$\begin{array}{r} 2x + 1 \\ x - 2 \overline{\smash{)}\,2x^2 - 3x - 2} \\ \underline{2x^2 - 4x} \\ x - 2 \\ \underline{x - 2} \\ 0 \end{array}$$

$2x + 1$

77.
$$\begin{array}{r} 3x + 4 \\ x + 3 \overline{\smash{)}\,3x^2 + 13x + 10} \\ \underline{3x^2 + 9x} \\ 4x + 10 \\ \underline{4x + 12} \\ -2 \end{array}$$

$3x + 4 - \dfrac{2}{x + 3}$

79. $6 < x - 1 < 7$

$7 < x < 8$

$(7,\ 8)$

81. $0 \le \dfrac{x + 2}{6} \le 5$

$0 \le x + 2 \le 30$

$-2 \le x \le 28$

$[-2,\ 28]$

83. $x \ge -5$ or $x \ge -1$

$x \ge -5$

$[-5,\ \infty)$

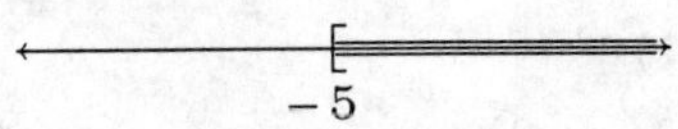

85. $x < -2$ and $x > -10$

$-10 < x < -2$

$(-10, -2)$

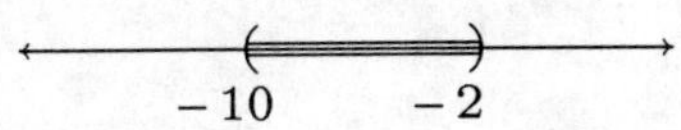

87. $x^{2n} - 25$

$(x^n + 5)(x^n - 5)$

89. $x^{2n}-9$

$(x^n+3)(x^n-3)$

91. $36x^{2n}-49$

$(6x^n+7)(6x^n-7)$

93. $x^{4n}-16$

$(x^{2n}+4)(x^{2n}-4)$

$(x^{2n}+4)(x^n+2)(x^n-2)$

Exercise Set 6.5

1. $x^2-9=(x+3)(x-3)$

3. $x^2-8x-9=(x-9)(x+1)$

5. x^2+8 is prime.

7. $x^2-8x+16-y^2$

$(x-4)^2-y^2$

$(x-4-y)(x-4+y)$

9. x^4-x

$x(x^3-1)$

$x(x-1)(x^2+x+1)$

11. $14x^2y-2xy=2xy(7x-1)$

13. $8a^2b-6ab^2=2ab(4a-3b)$

15. $x^4-x^3=x^3(x-1)$

17. x^4-4x^2

$x^2(x^2-4)$

$x^2(x+2)(x-2)$

19. $4x^2-16$

$4(x^2-4)$

$4(x+2)(x-2)$

21. $x-9x^3$

$x(1-9x^2)$

$x(1+3x)(1-3x)$

23. $3x^2-8x-11$

$(3x-11)(x+1)$

25. $4x^2+8x-12$

$4(x^2+2x-3)$

$4(x+3)(x-1)$

27. $4x^2+23x+15$

$(4x+3)(x+5)$

29. $6x^2-8+3x^2y-4y$

$2(3x^2-4)+y(3x^2-4)$

$(2+y)(3x^2-4)$

31. $2xy+6y+8x+24$

$2y(x+3)+8(x+3)$

$(2y+8)(x+3)$

$2(y+4)(x+3)$

33. $x^3+3x^2-4x-12$

$x^2(x+3)-4(x+3)$

$(x^2-4)(x+3)$

$(x+2)(x-2)(x+3)$

35. $4x^2+36x+81=(2x+9)^2$

37. $9x^2-30x+25=(3x-5)^2$

39. $16x^2+12x+9$ is prime.

41. $48x^2-24x+3$

$3(16x^2-8x+1)$

$3(4x-1)^2$

43. x^2+16 is prime.

45. $2x^4-2$

$2(x^4-1)$

$2(x^2+1)(x^2-1)$

$2(x^2+1)(x+1)(x-1)$

47. a^3-8b^3

$a^3-(2b)^3$

$(a-2b)(a^2+2ab+4b^2)$

49. $125 - x^3$

$5^3 - x^3$

$(5 - x)(25 + 5x + x^2)$

51. $8x^3 + 27y^3$

$(2x)^3 + (3y)^3$

$(2x + 3y)(4x^2 - 6xy + 9y^2)$

53. $2a^3 + 128b^3$

$2(a^3 + 64b^3)$

$2[a^3 + (4b)^3]$

$2(a + 4b)(a^2 - 4ab + 16b^2)$

55. $6a^2b^4 - 24a^4$

$6a^2(b^4 - 4a^2)$

$6a^2(b^2 + 2a)(b^2 - 2a)$

57. $8x^2y^5 - 2y^3$

$2y^3(4x^2y^2 - 1)$

$2y^3(2xy + 1)(2xy - 1)$

59. $x^2 + 6x + 9 - y^2$

$(x + 3)^2 - y^2$

$(x + 3 + y)(x + 3 - y)$

61. $2x^2 - 20x + 50 - 2y^2$

$2[(x^2 - 10x + 25) - y^2]$

$2[(x - 5)^2 - y^2]$

$2(x - 5 + y)(x - 5 - y)$

63. $3a^2 - 6a + 3 - 3b^2$

$3[(a^2 - 2a + 1) - b^2]$

$3[(a - 1)^2 - b^2]$

$3(a - 1 + b)(a - 1 - b)$

65. $27x^4 - xy^3$

$x(27x^3 - y^3)$

$x[(3x)^3 - y^3]$

$x(3x - y)(9x^2 + 3xy + y^2)$

67. $16x^3y^4 + 54y$

$2y(8x^3y^3 + 27)$

$2y[(2xy)^3 + 3^3]$

$2y(2xy + 3)(4x^2y^2 - 6xy + 9)$

69. $64x^2y^3 - 8x^2$

$8x^2(8y^3 - 1)$

$8x^2[(2y)^3 - 1]$

$8x^2(2y - 1)(4y^2 + 2y + 1)$

71. $(3x + 1)^2 + 3(3x + 1) + 2$

$[(3x + 1) + 1][(3x + 1) + 2]$

$(3x + 2)(3x + 3)$

$3(3x + 2)(x + 1)$

73. $x^4 + 6x^2 - 7$

$(x^2 + 7)(x^2 - 1)$

$(x^2 + 7)(x + 1)(x - 1)$

75. $x^6 + 4x^3 + 3$

$(x^3 + 1)(x^3 + 3)$

$(x + 1)(x^2 - x + 1)(x^3 + 3)$

77. $(x + y)^2 - 9$

$(x + y + 3)(x + y - 3)$

79. $(a - 4)^3 + 1$

$[(a - 4) + 1][(a - 4)^2 - (a - 4) + 1]$

$(a - 3)(a^2 - 8a + 16 - a + 4 + 1)$

$(a - 3)(a^2 - 9a + 21)$

81. $(x + 5)^3 + y^3$

$[(x + 5) + y][(x + 5)^2 - (x + 5)y + y^2]$

$(x + 5 + y)(x^2 + 10x + 25 - xy - 5y + y^2)$

83. $(2x + 1)^3 + 27$

$(2x + 1)^3 + 3^3$

$[(2x + 1) + 3][(2x + 1)^2 - 3(2x + 1) + 9]$

$(2x + 4)(4x^2 + 4x + 1 - 6x - 3 + 9)$

$2(x + 2)(4x^2 - 2x + 7)$

85. $27 - (x + 3)^3$

$3^3 - (x + 3)^3$

$[3 - (x + 3)][9 + 3(x + 3) + (x + 3)^2]$

$-x(9+3x+9+x^2+6x+9)$

$-x(x^2+9x+27)$

87. $A=(x+6)^2-x^2$

$(x+6+x)(x+6-x)$

$(2x+6)6$

$12(x+3)$ sq. in.

89. $4+(-5)$

-1

91. $-7-10$

-17

93. $x+7=0$

$x+7-7=0-7$

$x=-7$

$\{-7\}$

95. $5x-15=0$

$5x-15+15=0+15$

$\frac{5x}{5}=\frac{15}{5}$

$x=3$

$\{3\}$

97. $3x=0$

$\frac{3x}{3}=\frac{0}{3}$

$x=0$

$\{0\}$

99. $-4x-16=0$

$-4x-16+16=0+16$

$-4x=16$

$x=\frac{16}{-4}$

$x=-4$

$\{-4\}$

101. $A=\frac{1}{2}bh$

$25=\frac{1}{2}(10)(x)$

$2(25)=2\bullet\frac{1}{2}(10)(x)$

$50=10x$

$\frac{50}{10}=x$

$5\text{ feet}=x$

103. $x^{2n}-25=(x^n+5)(x^n-5)$

105. $x^{4n}-16$

$(x^{2n}+4)(x^{2n}-4)$

$(x^{2n}+4)(x^n+2)(x^n-2)$

107. $y^{3n}-27$

$(y^n)^3-3^3$

$(y^n-3)(y^{2n}+3y^n+9)$

Graphing Calculator Exercise 6.6

1. $x^2+3x-2=0$

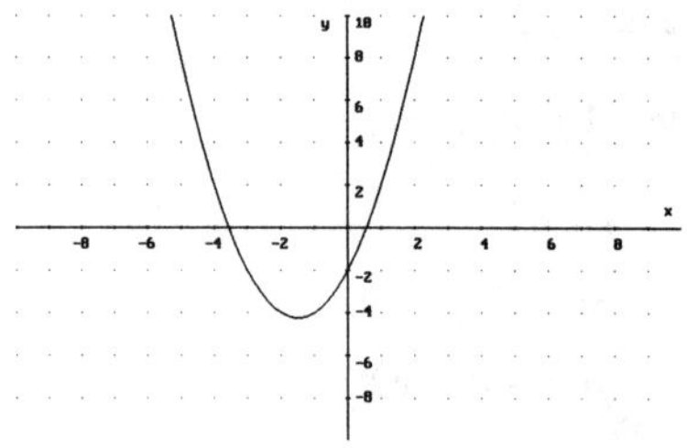

x-intercepts are -3.56 and 0.56.

3. $2.3x^2-4.4x-5.6=0$

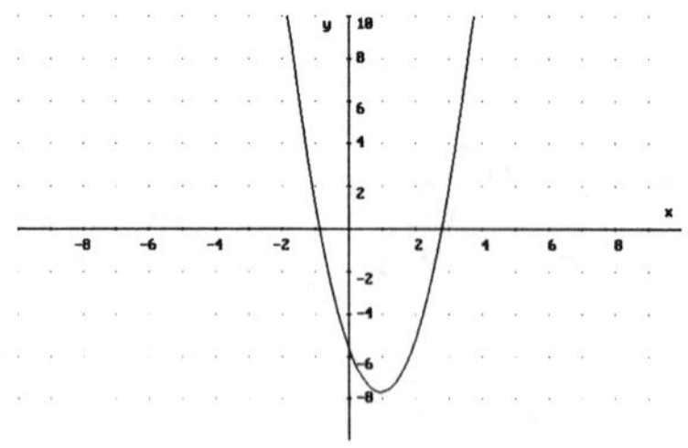

x-intercepts are -0.87 and 2.79.

5. $0.09x^2 - 0.13x - 0.08 = 0$

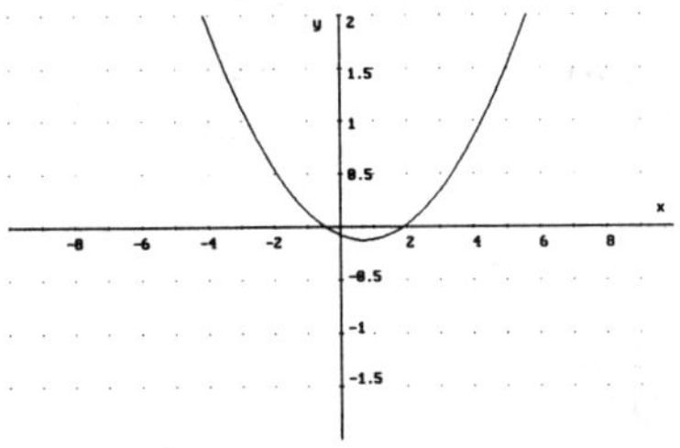

x-intercepts are -0.47 and 1.91.

Exercise Set 6.6

1. $(x+3)(3x-4) = 0$

$x+3=0$ or $3x-4=0$

$x=-3$ or $3x=4$

$x=\frac{4}{3}$

$\left\{-3, \frac{4}{3}\right\}$

3. $3(2x-5)(4x+3)=0$

$2x-5=0$ or $4x+3=0$

$2x=5$ or $4x=-3$

$x=\frac{5}{2}$ or $x=-\frac{3}{4}$

$\left\{\frac{5}{2}, -\frac{3}{4}\right\}$

5. $x^2+11x+24=0$

$(x+3)(x+8)=0$

$x+3=0$ or $x+8=0$

$x=-3$ or $x=-8$

$\{-3, -8\}$

7. $12x^2+5x-2=0$

$(4x-1)(3x+2)=0$

$4x-1=0$ or $3x+2=0$

$4x=1$ or $3x=-2$

$x=\frac{1}{4}$ or $x=-\frac{2}{3}$

$\left\{\frac{1}{4}, -\frac{2}{3}\right\}$

9. $x^2+9=10z$

$z^2-10z+9=0$

$(z-1)(z-9)=0$

$z-1=0$ or $z-9=0$

$z=1$ or $z=9$

$\{1, 9\}$

11. $x(5x+2)=3$

$5x^2+2x-3=0$

$(5x-3)(x+1)=0$

$5x-3=0$ or $x+1=0$

$5x=3$ or $x=-1$

$x=\frac{3}{5}$

$\left\{\frac{3}{5}, -1\right\}$

13. $x^2-6x=x(8+x)$

$x^2-6x=8x+x^2$

$0=14x$

$x=0$

$\{0\}$

15. $\frac{z^2}{6}-\frac{z}{2}-3=0$

$z^2-3z-18=0$

$(z-6)(z+3)=0$

$z-6=0$ or $z+3=0$

$z=6$ or $z=-3$

$\{6, -3\}$

17. $\frac{x^2}{2}+\frac{x}{20}=\frac{1}{10}$

$10x^2+x=2$

$10x^2+x-2=0$

$(5x-2)(2x+1)=0$

$5x-2=0$ or $2x+1=0$

$5x=2$ or $2x=-1$

$x=\frac{2}{5}$ or $x=-\frac{1}{2}$

$\left\{\frac{2}{5}, -\frac{1}{2}\right\}$

19. $\frac{4t^2}{5} = \frac{t}{5} + \frac{3}{10}$

$8t^2 = 2t + 3$

$8t^2 - 2t - 3 = 0$

$(4t - 3)(2t + 1) = 0$

$4t - 3 = 0$ or $2t + 1 = 0$

$4t = 3$ or $2t = -1$

$t = \frac{3}{4}$ or $t = -\frac{1}{2}$

$\left\{\frac{3}{4}, -\frac{1}{2}\right\}$

21. $(x + 2)(x - 7)(3x - 8) = 0$

$x + 2 = 0$ or $x - 7 = 0$ or $3x - 8 = 0$

$x = -2$ or $x = 7$ or $3x = 8$

$x = \frac{8}{3}$

$\left\{-2, \frac{8}{3}, 7\right\}$

23. $y^3 = 9y$

$y^3 - 9y = 0$

$y(y^2 - 9) = 0$

$y(y + 3)(y - 3) = 0$

$y = 0$ or $y + 3 = 0$ or $y - 3 = 0$

$y = -3$ or $y = 3$

$\{-3, 0, 3\}$

25. $x^3 - x = 2x^2 - 2$

$x^3 - 2x^2 - x + 2 = 0$

$x^2(x - 2) - (x - 2) = 0$

$(x^2 - 1)(x - 2) = 0$

$(x + 1)(x - 1)(x - 2) = 0$

$x + 1 = 0$ or $x - 1 = 0$ or $x - 2 = 0$

$x = -1$ or $x = 1$ or $x = 2$

$\{-1, 1, 2\}$

27. $h(t) = -16t^2 + 64t + 80$

$0 = -16t^2 + 64t + 80$

$0 = -16(t^2 - 4t - 5)$

$0 = -16(t - 5)(t + 1)$

$t - 5 = 0$ or $t + 1 = 0$

$t = 5$ or $t = -1$

The object will hit the ground when $t = 5$ seconds.

29. $N(x) = \frac{x(x - 3)}{2}$

$5 = \frac{x(x - 3)}{2}$

$2 \bullet 5 = 2 \bullet \frac{x(x - 3)}{2}$

$10 = x(x - 3)$

$10 = x^2 - 3x$

$0 = x^2 - 3x - 10$

$0 = (x - 5)(x + 2)$

$x - 5 = 0$ or $x + 2 = 0$

$x = 5$ or $x = -2$

The polygon has 5 sides.

31. short leg $= x - 10$
long leg $= x - 5$
hypotenuse $= x$

$a^2 + b^2 = c^2$

$(x - 10)^2 + (x - 5)^2 = x^2$

$x^2 - 20x + 100 + x^2 - 10x + 25 = x^2$

$x^2 - 30x + 125 = 0$

$(x - 5)(x - 25) = 0$

$x - 5 = 0$ or $x - 25 = 0$

$x = 5$ or $x = 25$

hypotenuse $= 25$ cm.
long leg $= 20$ cm.
short leg $= 15$ cm.

33. short leg $= x$
long leg $= x + 12$
hypotenuse $= 2x - 12$

$a^2 + b^2 = c^2$

$x^2 + (x + 12)^2 = (2x - 12)^2$

$x^2 + x^2 + 24x + 144 = 4x^2 - 48x + 144$

$0 = 2x^2 - 72x$

$0 = 2x(x - 36)$

$2x = 0$ or $x - 36 = 0$

$x = 0$ or $x = 36$

Short leg = 36 feet.

35. $(2x+7)(x-10) = 0$

$2x+7 = 0$ or $x-10 = 0$

$2x = -7$ or $x = 10$

$x = -\frac{7}{2}$

$\left\{-\frac{7}{2},\ 10\right\}$

37. $3x(x-5) = 0$

$3x = 0$ or $x-5 = 0$

$x = 0$ or $x = 5$

$\{0,\ 5\}$

39. $x^2 - 2x - 15 = 0$

$(x-5)(x+3) = 0$

$x-5 = 0$ or $x+3 = 0$

$x = 5$ or $x = -3$

$\{5,\ -3\}$

41. $12x^2 + 2x - 2 = 0$

$2(6x^2 + x - 1) = 0$

$2(3x-1)(2x+1) = 0$

$3x-1 = 0$ or $2x+1 = 0$

$3x = 1$ or $2x = -1$

$x = \frac{1}{3}$ or $x = -\frac{1}{2}$

$\left\{-\frac{1}{2},\ \frac{1}{3}\right\}$

43. $w^2 - 5w = 36$

$w^2 - 5w - 36 = 0$

$(w-9)(w+4) = 0$

$w-9 = 0$ or $w+4 = 0$

$w = 9$ or $w = -4$

$\{-4,\ 9\}$

45. $25x^2 - 40x + 16 = 0$

$(5x-4)^2 = 0$

$5x-4 = 0$

$5x = 4$

$x = \frac{4}{5}$

$\left\{\frac{4}{5}\right\}$

47. $2r^3 + 6r^2 = 20r$

$r^3 + 3r^2 = 10r$

$r^3 + 3r^2 - 10r = 0$

$r(r^2 + 3r - 10) = 0$

$r(r+5)(r-2) = 0$

$r = 0$ or $r+5 = 0$ or $r-2 = 0$

$r = -5$ or $r = 2$

$\{-5,\ 0,\ 2\}$

49. $z(5z-4)(z+3) = 0$

$z = 0$ or $5z-4 = 0$ or $z+3 = 0$

$5z = 4$ or $z = -3$

$z = \frac{4}{5}$

$\left\{-3,\ 0,\ \frac{4}{5}\right\}$

51. $2z(z+6) = 2z^2 + 12z - 8$

$2z^2 + 12z = 2z^2 + 12z - 8$

$0 = -8$

No solution.

$\{\ \}$

53. $(x-1)(x+4) = 24$

$x^2 + 3x - 4 = 24$

$x^2 + 3x - 28 = 0$

$(x+7)(x-4) = 0$

$x+7 = 0$ or $x-4 = 0$

$x = -7$ or $x = 4$

$\{-7,\ 4\}$

55. $\frac{x^2}{4} - \frac{5}{2}x + 6 = 0$

$x^2 - 10x + 24 = 0$

$(x-4)(x-6) = 0$

$x-4 = 0$ or $x-6 = 0$

$x = 4$ or $x = 6$

$\{4,\ 6\}$

57. $y^2+\frac{1}{4}=-y$

$4y^2+1=-4y$

$4y^2+4y+1=0$

$(2y+1)^2=0$

$2y+1=0$

$2y=-1$

$y=-\frac{1}{2}$

$\left\{-\frac{1}{2}\right\}$

59. $y^3+4y^2=9y+36$

$y^3+4y^2-9y-36=0$

$y^2(y+4)-9(y+4)=0$

$(y^2-9)(y+4)=0$

$(y+3)(y-3)(y+4)=0$

$y+3=0$ or $y-3=0$ or $y+4=0$

$y=-3$ or $y=3$ or $y=-4$

$\{-4,-3,3\}$

61. $2x^3=50x$

$x^3=25x$

$x^3-25x=0$

$x(x^2-25)=0$

$x(x+5)(x-5)=0$

$x=0$ or $x+5=0$ or $x-5=0$

$x=-5$ or $x=5$

$\{-5,0,5\}$

63. $x^2+(x+1)^2=61$

$x^2+x^2+2x+1=61$

$2x^2+2x-60=0$

$2(x^2+x-30)=0$

$2(x+6)(x-5)=0$

$x+6=0$ or $x-5=0$

$x=-6$ or $x=5$

$\{-6,5\}$

65. $m^2(3m-2)=m$

$3m^3-2m^2=m$

$3m^3-2m^2-m=0$

$m(3m^2-2m-1)=0$

$m(3m+1)(m-1)=0$

$m=0$ or $3m+1=0$ or $m-1=0$

$3m=-1$ or $m=1$

$m=-\frac{1}{3}$

$\left\{-\frac{1}{3},0,1\right\}$

67. $3x^2=-x$

$3x^2+x=0$

$x(3x+1)=0$

$x=0$ or $3x+1=0$

$3x=-1$

$x=-\frac{1}{3}$

$\left\{-\frac{1}{3},0\right\}$

69. $x(x-3)=x^2+5x+7$

$x^2-3x=x^2+5x+7$

$-7=8x$

$-\frac{7}{8}=x$

$\left\{-\frac{7}{8}\right\}$

71. $3(t-8)+2t=7+t$

$3t-24+2t=7+t$

$5t-24=7+t$

$4t=31$

$t=\frac{31}{4}$

$\left\{\frac{31}{4}\right\}$

73. $-3(x-4)+x=5(3-x)$

$-3x+12+x=15-5x$

$-2x+12=15-5x$

$3x=3$

$x=1$

$\{1\}$

75. 1st integer = x
2nd integer = x + 1

$x^2+(x+1)^2=221$

$x^2+x^2+2x+1=221$

$2x^2+2x-220=0$

$2(x^2+x-110)=0$

$(x+11)(x-10)=0$

$x+11=0$ or $x-10=0$

$x=-11$ or $x=10$

The integers are -10 and -11.

77. base = 2x
altitude = x

$100=\frac{1}{2}x(2x)$

$100=x^2$

$\pm 10=x$

altitude = 10 km.

79. $C(x)=x^2-15x+50$

$9500=x^2-15x+50$

$0=x^2-15x-9450$

$0=(x-105)(x+90)$

$x-105=0$ or $x+90=0$

$x=105$ or $x=-90$

105 units.

81.

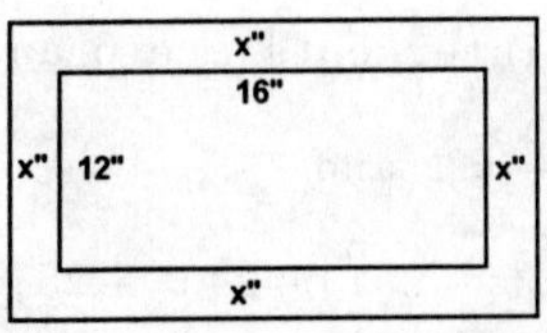

Let A = the area of the border.

$A=(12+2x)(16+2x)-12(16)=128$

$192+56x+4x^2-192=128$

$4x^2+56x-128=0$

$4(x^2+14x-32)=0$

$4(x+16)(x-2)=0$

$x+16=0$ or $x-2=0$

$x=-16$ or $x=2$

The width of the border is 2 inches.

83. $h(t)=-16t^2+80t$

$96=-16t^2+80t$

$16t^2-80t+96=0$

$16(t^2-5t+6)=0$

$16(t-3)(t-2)=0$

$t-3=0$ or $t-2=0$

$t=3$ or $t=2$

While ascending the rocket reaches a height of 96 feet in 2 seconds. After reaching the maximum height and beginning to descend the rocket will again be at a height of 96 feet in 3 seconds after launching.

85. smaller leg = x
longer leg = x + 4
hypotenuse = x + 8

$x^2+(x+4)^2=(x+8)^2$

$x^2+x^2+8x+16=x^2+16x+64$

$x^2-8x-48=0$

$(x-12)(x+4)=0$

$x-12=0$ or $x+4=0$

$x=12$ or $x=-4$

smaller leg = 12 mm.
longer leg = 16 mm.
hypotenuse = 20 mm.

87. $\frac{20}{35}=\frac{5\bullet 4}{5\bullet 7}=\frac{4}{7}$

89. $\frac{27}{18}=\frac{9\bullet 3}{9\bullet 2}=\frac{3}{2}$

91. $\frac{10x^2y}{5x^3}=\frac{2y}{x}$

93. $\frac{45a^2b}{9b^3}=\frac{5a^2}{b^2}$

95. It is not a function.

97. It is a function.

Exercise Set 6.7

1. $f(x) = 2x^2$

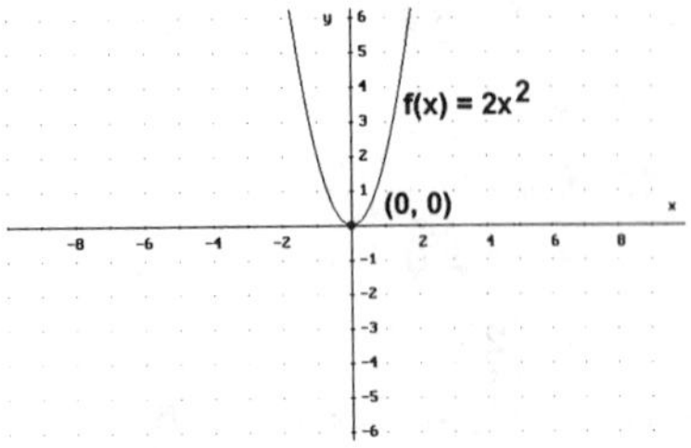

3. $f(x) = x^2 + 1$

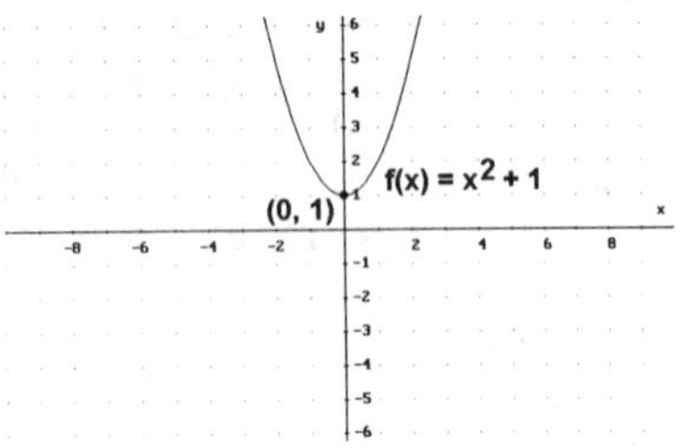

5. $f(x) = -x^2$

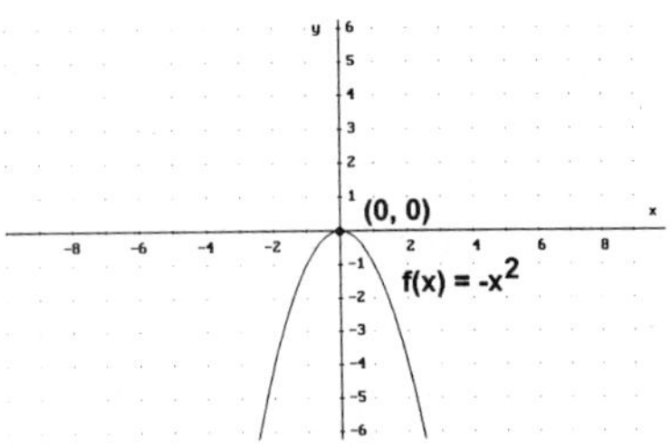

7. $f(x) = x^2 + 8x + 7$,
$a = 1$, and $b = 8$.
So, $h = \dfrac{-8}{2(1)} = -4$ and
$k = f(-4) = (-4)^2 + 8(-4) + 7 = -9$
thus, $V(-4, -9)$

9. $f(x) = 3x^2 + 6x + 4$, $a = 3$, and
$b = 6$. So, $h = -\dfrac{6}{2(3)} = -1$
and $k = f(-1)$
$= 3(-1)^2 + 6(-1) + 4 = 1$;
thus $V(-1, 1)$.

11. $f(x) = -x^2 + 10x + 5$, $a = -1$
and $b = 10$. So, $h = -\dfrac{10}{2(-1)} = 5$
and $k = f(5) = -5^2 + 10(5) + 5 = 30$;
thus $V(5, 30)$.

13. $f(x) = x^2 + 8x + 7$
$= (x+1)(x+7)$
Solve $(x+1)(x+7) = 0$
$x + 1 = 0$ or $x + 7 = 0$
$x = -1$ or $x = -7$
So the x-intercepts are -1 and -7.
$h = \dfrac{-8}{2(1)} = -4$ and
$k = f(-4) = (-4)^2 + 8(-4) + 7 = -9$;
so $V(-4, -9)$.

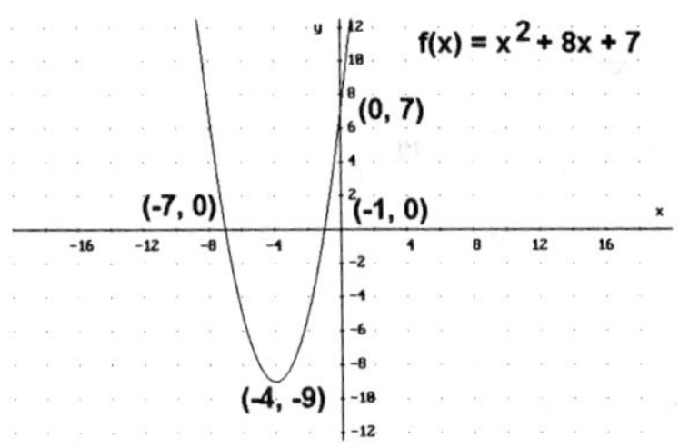

15. $f(x) = x^2 - 2x - 24$
$= (x-6)(x+4)$
Solve $(x-6)(x+4) = 0$
$x - 6 = 0$ or $x + 4 = 0$
$x = 6$ or $x = -4$
So the x-intercepts are 6 and -4.
$h = \dfrac{-(-2)}{2(1)} = 1$ and
$k = f(1) = 1^2 - 2(1) - 24 = -25$;
so $V(1, -25)$.

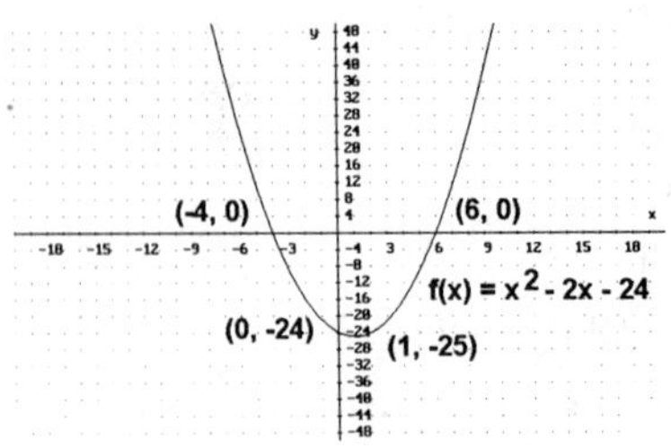

17. $f(x) = 2x^2 - 6x$

$= 2x(x-3)$

Solve $2x(x-3) = 0$

$2x = 0$ or $x - 3 = 0$

$x = 0$ or $x = 3$

So the x-intercepts are 0 and 3.

$h = \dfrac{-(-6)}{2(2)} = \dfrac{3}{2}$ and

$k = f\left(\frac{3}{2}\right) = 2\left(\frac{3}{2}\right)^2 - 6\left(\frac{3}{2}\right) = \frac{9}{2} - 9 = -\frac{9}{2}$;

so $V\left(\frac{3}{2}, -\frac{9}{2}\right)$.

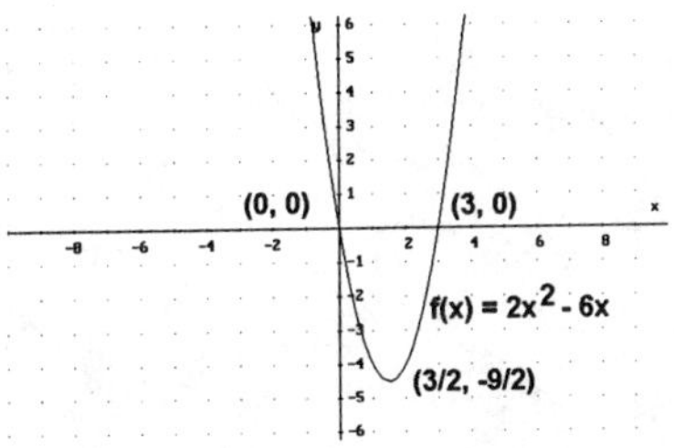

19. $f(x) = 4x^3 - 9x$

$= x(4x^2 - 9)$

$= x(2x+3)(2x-3)$

Solve $x(2x+3)(2x-3) = 0$

$x = 0$ or $2x + 3 = 0$ or $2x - 3 = 0$

$2x = -3$ or $2x = 3$

$x = -\frac{3}{2}$ or $x = \frac{3}{2}$

Therefore, the x-intercepts are $0, -\frac{3}{2}$, and $\frac{3}{2}$.

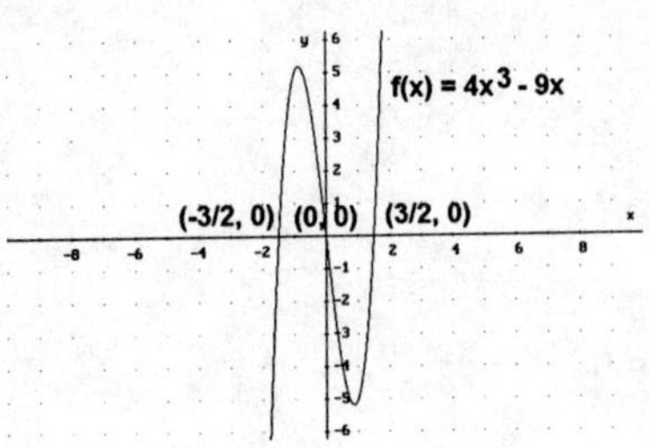

21. $f(x) = x^3 + 3x^2 - x - 3$

$= x^2(x+3) - 1(x+3)$

$= (x^2 - 1)(x+3)$

$= (x+1)(x-1)(x+3)$

Solve $(x+1)(x-1)(x+3) = 0$

$x + 1 = 0$ or $x - 1 = 0$ or $x + 3 = 0$

$x = -1$ or $x = 1$ or $x = -3$

Therefore, the x-intercepts are -1, 1, and -3.

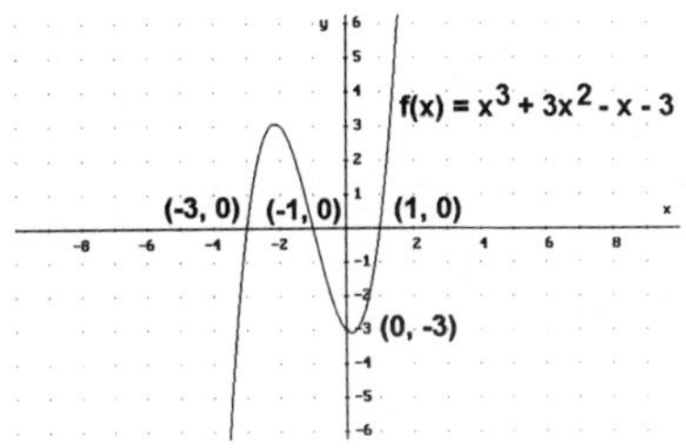

23. $f(x) = x^2 + 4x - 5$

$= (x+5)(x-1)$

Solve $(x+5)(x-1) = 0$

$x + 5 = 0$ or $x - 1 = 0$

$x = -5$ or $x = 1$

The x-intercepts are -5 and 1.

$h = \dfrac{-4}{2(1)} = -2$ and

$k = f(-2) = (-2)^2 + 4(-2) - 5 = -9$;

so $V(-2, -9)$.

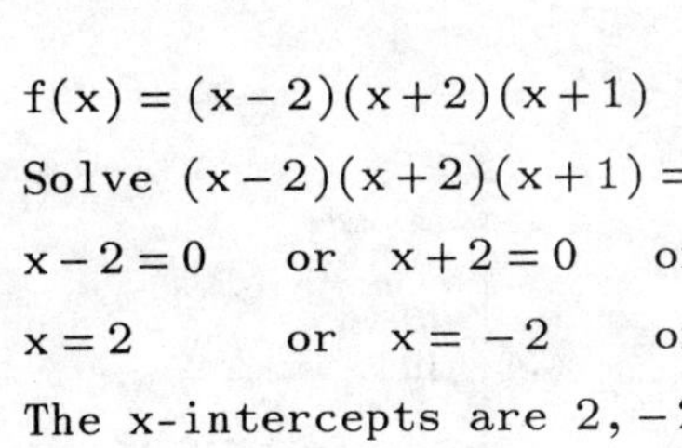

25. $f(x) = (x-2)(x+2)(x+1)$

Solve $(x-2)(x+2)(x+1) = 0$

$x - 2 = 0$ or $x + 2 = 0$ or $x + 1 = 0$

$x = 2$ or $x = -2$ or $x = -1$

The x-intercepts are $2, -2$, and -1.

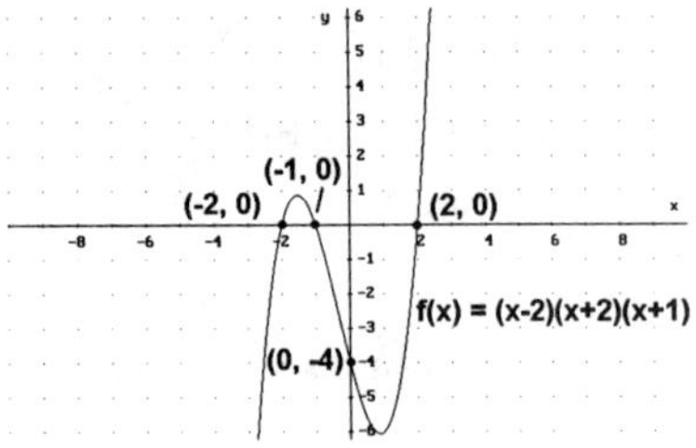

27. $f(x) = x^2 + 1 \geq 1;$

thus has no x-intercepts.

$h = -\frac{0}{2(1)} = 0$ and

$k = f(0) = 0^2 + 1 = 1,$

so $V(0,\ 1)$.

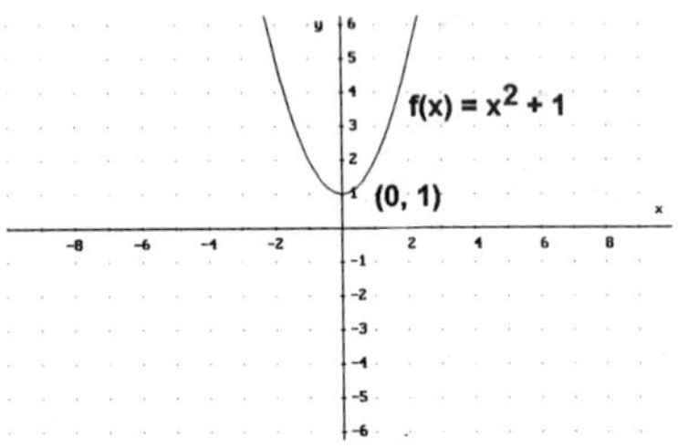

29. $f(x) = -5x^2 + 5x$

$= -5x(x-1)$

Solve $-5x(x-1) = 0$

$-5x = 0$ or $x - 1 = 0$

$x = 0$ or $x = 1$

The intercepts are 0 and 1.

$h = \frac{-5}{2(-5)} = \frac{1}{2}$ and $k = f\left(\frac{1}{2}\right)$

$= -5\left(\frac{1}{2}\right)^2 + 5\left(\frac{1}{2}\right) = \frac{-5}{4} + \frac{5}{2} = \frac{5}{4},$

so $V\left(\frac{1}{2},\ \frac{5}{4}\right)$.

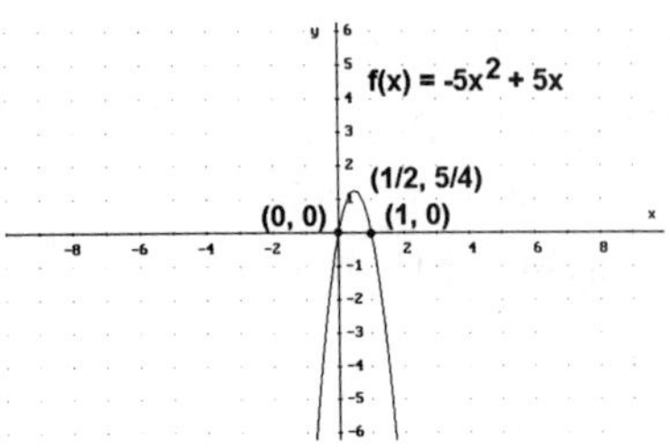

31. $f(x) = x^3 - 9x$

$= x(x^2 - 9)$

$= x(x+3)(x-3)$

Solve $x(x+3)(x-3) = 0$

$x = 0$ or $x + 3 = 0$ or $x - 3 = 0$

$x = -3$ or $x = 3$

The x-intercepts are $0, -3,$ and 3.

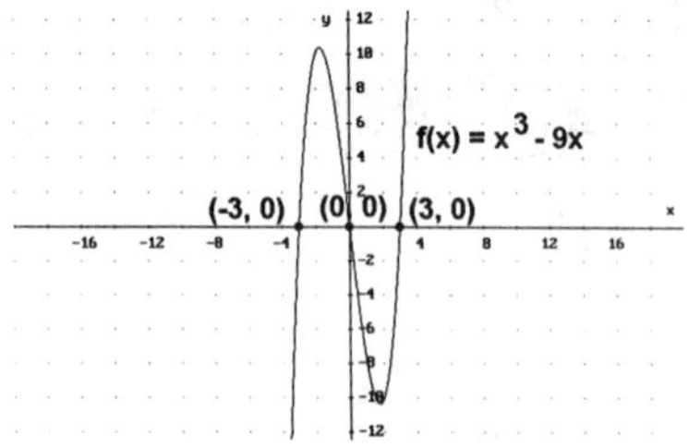

33. $f(x) = -x^3 - x^2 + 2x$

$= -x(x^2 + x - 2)$

$= -x(x+2)(x-1)$

Solve $-x(x+2)(x-1) = 0$

$-x = 0$ or $x + 2 = 0$ or $x - 1 = 0$

$x = 0$ or $x = -2$ or $x = 1$

The x-intercepts are $0, -2,$ and 1.

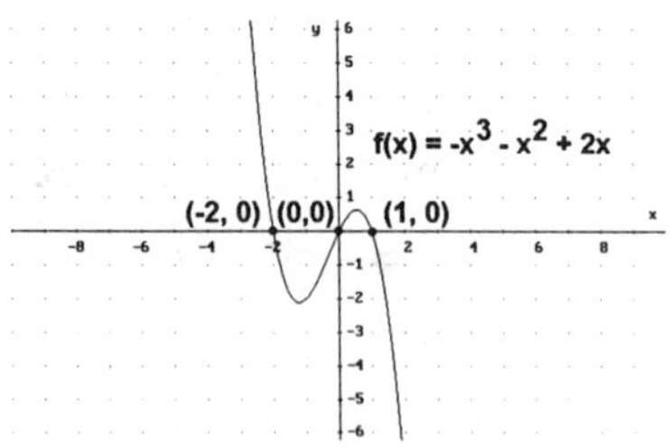

35. $f(x) = x^2 - 4x + 4$

$= (x-2)^2$

Solve $(x-2)^2 = 0$

$x - 2 = 0$

$x = 2$

The intercept is 2.

$h = \frac{-(-4)}{2(1)} = 2$ and

$k = f(2) = 0$ since 2 is an x-intercept.

Thus, V(2, 0).

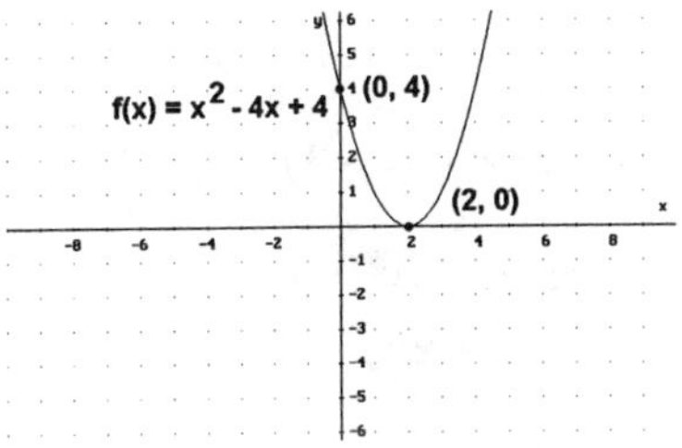

37. $f(x) = -x^3 + x$

$= -x(x^2 - 1)$

$= -x(x+1)(x-1)$

Solve $-x(x+1)(x-1) = 0$

$-x = 0$ or $x+1=0$ or $x-1=0$

$x = 0$ or $x = -1$ or $x = 1$

The x-intercepts are $0, -1$, and 1.

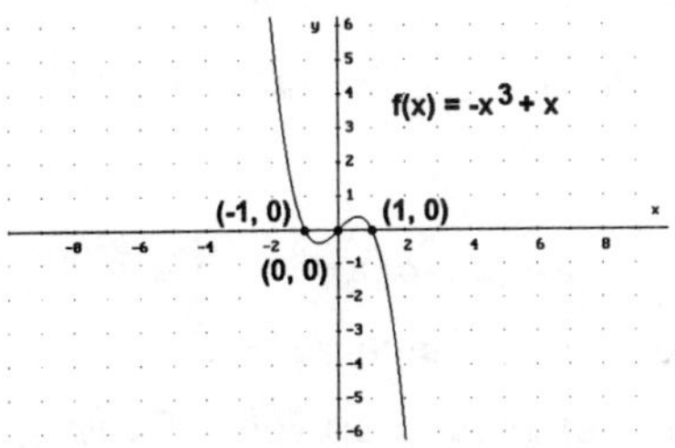

39. $f(x) = 2x^2 - x - 3$

$= (2x-3)(x+1)$

Solve $(2x-3)(x+1) = 0$

$2x - 3 = 0$ or $x + 1 = 0$

$2x = 3$ or $x = -1$

$x = \frac{3}{2}$

The x-intercepts are $\frac{3}{2}$ and -1.

$h = \frac{-(-1)}{2(2)} = \frac{1}{4}$ and $k = f\left(\frac{1}{4}\right) =$

$2\left(\frac{1}{4}\right)^2 - \left(\frac{1}{4}\right) - 3 = \frac{1}{8} - \frac{1}{4} - 3 = \frac{-25}{8}$,

so $V\left(\frac{1}{4}, -\frac{25}{8}\right)$.

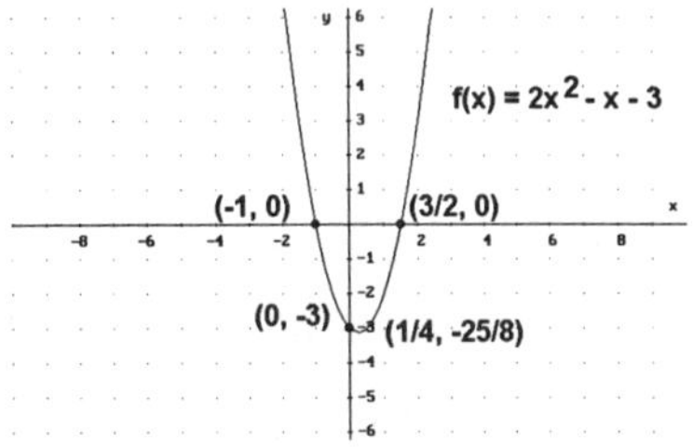

41. $f(x) = -x^3 + 3x^2 + x - 3$

$= -x^2(x-3) + (x-3)$

$= (-x^2 + 1)(x-3)$

$= -(x^2 - 1)(x-3)$

$= -(x+1)(x-1)((x-3)$

Solve $-(x+1)(x-1)(x-3) = 0$

$-(x+1) = 0$ or $x - 1 = 0$ or $x - 3 = 0$

$x + 1 = 0$ or $x = 1$ or $x = 3$

$x = -1$

The x-intercepts are -1, 1, and 3.

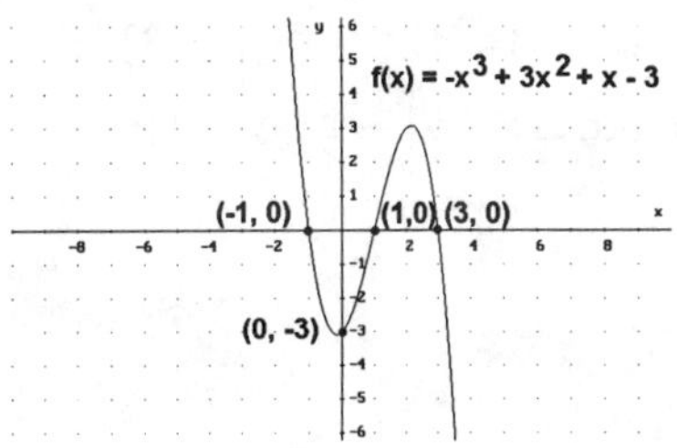

43. $f(x) = x^2 - 10x + 26$

$h = \frac{-(-10)}{2(1)} = \frac{10}{2} = 5$ and

$k = f(5) = 5^2 - 10(5) + 26 = 1$,

so V(5, 1).

f is not factorable, so the x-intercepts, if any, are unaccessible.

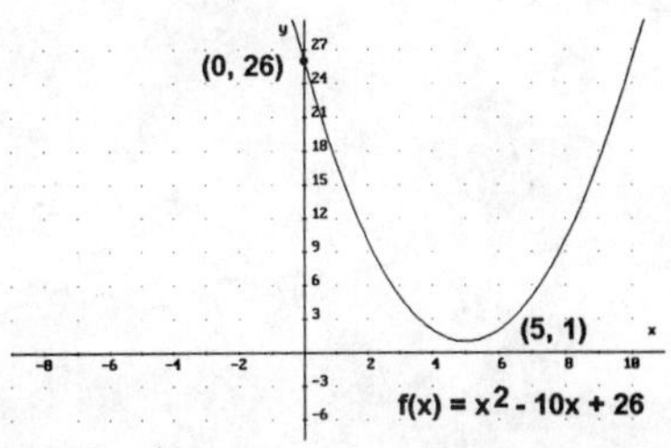

45. $f(x) = x(x-4)(x+2)$

Solve $x(x-4)(x+2) = 0$

$x = 0$ or $x - 4 = 0$ or $x + 2 = 0$

$x = 4$ or $x = -2$

The x-intercepts are 0, 4, and -2.

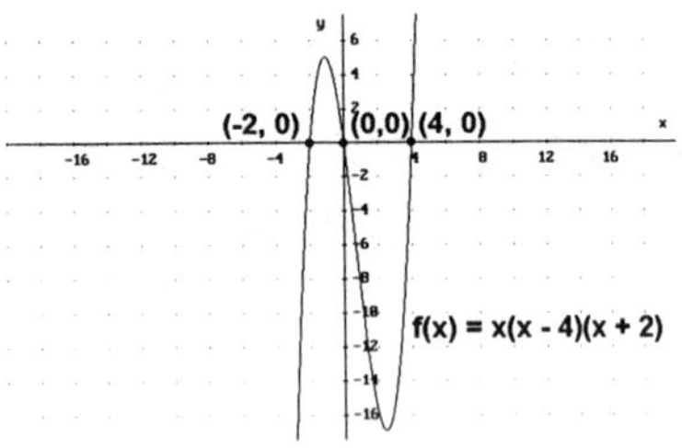

47. The domain is

$\{x | x$ is a real number$\}$.

The range is $\{y | y \geq 0\}$.

49. The domain is $\{x | -4 \leq x \leq 3\}$.

The range is $\{y | -4 \leq y \leq 4\}$.

51. $(x^2y)(3x)$

$3x^3y$

53. $(x^2y^2)(-16xy)$

$-16x^3y^3$

55. $(x+6)^2$

$(x+6)(x+6)$

$x^2 + 6x + 6x + 36$

$x^2 + 12x + 36$

57. $(2x-1)^2$

$(2x-1)(2x-1)$

$4x^2 - 2x - 2x + 1$

$4x^2 - 4x + 1$

Chapter 6 Review

1. 24, 60, 84 have GCF 12.

3. x^6, x^8, x^2, x^4 have GCF x^2.

5. $6x^2y^3$, $16xy^2$, $8x^3$ have GCF $2x$.

7. $16x^3 - 24x^2 = 8x^2(2x-3)$

9. $15x^3y^4z - 3xy^2z^2 + 6x^2y^2z$

$3xy^2z(5x^2y^2 - z + 2x)$

11. $6ab^2 + 8ab - 4a^2b^2$

$2ab(3b + 4 - 2ab)$

13. $6a(a+3b) - 5(a+3b)$

$(6a-5)(a+3b)$

15. $xy - 6y + 3x - 18$

$(x-6)(y+3)$

17. $pq - 3p - 5q + 15$

$(p-5)(q-3)$

19. $x^3 - x^2 - 2x + 2$

$(x^2-2)(x-1)$

21. Area of large square $= (x+y)^2$

Area of small square $= x^2$

Area of shaded portion $= (x+y)^2 - x^2$

$(x+y)^2 - x^2$

$[(x+y) - x][(x+y) + x]$

$[x + y - x][x + y + x]$

$[y][2x + y]$

$y(2x+y)$

23. $x^2 - 11x + 24$

$(x-8)(x-3)$

25. $x^2 - 5x - 6$

$(x-6)(x+1)$

27. $x^2 + 4xy - 12y^2$

$(x+6y)(x-2y)$

29. $3x^2y+6xy^2+3y^3$
$3y(x^2+2xy+y^2)$
$3y(x+y)(x+y)$
$3y(x+y)^2$

31. $32+12x-4x^2$
$4(8+3x-x^2)$

33. $4x^2-7x+4$
prime

35. $6x^2+5xy-4y^2$
$6x^2+8xy-3xy-4y^2$
$2x(3x+4y)-y(3x+4y)$
$(3x+4y)(2x-y)$

37. $18x^2-60x+50$
$2(9x^2-30x+25)$
$2(3x-5)(3x-5)$
$2(3x-5)^2$

39. $4x^2-28xy+49y^2$
$(2x-7y)(2x-7y)$
$(2x-7y)^2$

41. $36x^3y+24x^2y^2-45xy^3$
$3xy(12x^2+8xy-15y^2)$
$3xy(12x^2+18xy-10xy-15y^2)$
$3xy[6x(2x+3y)-5y(2x+3y)]$
$3xy(2x+3y)(6x-5y)$

43. $9t^2-25s^2$
$(3t-5s)(3t+5s)$

45. x^3-8y^3
$(x-2y)(x^2+2xy+4y^2)$

47. $2x^3+8x$
$2x(x^2+4)$

49. $9x^2-4y^2$
$(3x-2y)(3x+2y)$

51. x^4+16
prime

53. $6xy^2-3xy=3xy(2y-1)$

55. $25x^2-100$
$25(x^2-4)$
$25(x+2)(x-2)$

57. $3x^2-10x+8$
$(3x-4)(x-2)$

59. $x^2y+3x^2-4y-12$
$(x^2-4)(y+3)$
$(x+2)(x-2)(y+3)$

61. $4x^2-14x+49$ is prime.

63. $4x^2-25=(2x+5)(2x-5)$

65. $8x^3-y^3$
$(2x)^3-y^3$
$(2x-y)(4x^2+2xy+y^2)$

67. $2x^6y+54x^3y^4$
$2x^3y(x^3+27y^3)$
$2x^3y[x^3+(3y)^3]$
$2x^3y(x+3y)(x^2-3xy+9y^2)$

69. $4a^2-24a+36-4b^2$
$4(a^2-6a+9-b^2)$
$4[(a-3)^2-b^2]$
$4(a-3-b)(a-3+b)$

71. $2x^3y^8-128x^3y^5$
$2x^3y^5(y^3-64)$
$2x^3y^5(y^3-4^3)$
$2x^3y^5(y-4)(y^2+4y+16)$

73. $(3x-1)(x+7)=0$
$3x-1=0$ or $x+7=0$
$3x=1$ or $x=-7$
$x=\frac{1}{3}$

$\left\{-7, \frac{1}{3}\right\}$

75. $5x(x-4)(2x-9)=0$

$5x=0$ or $x-4=0$ or $2x-9=0$

$x=0$ or $x=4$ or $2x=9$

$x=\frac{9}{2}$

$\left\{0, \frac{9}{2}, 4\right\}$

77. $2x^2=12x$

$2x^2-12x=0$

$2x(x-6)=0$

$2x=0$ or $x-6=0$

$x=0$ or $x=6$

$\{0, 6\}$

79. $(1-x)(3x+2)=-4x$

$3x+2-3x^2-2x=-4x$

$-3x^2+x+2=-4x$

$0=3x^2-5x-2$

$0=(3x+1)(x-2)$

$3x+1=0$ or $x-2=0$

$3x=-1$ or $x=2$

$x=-\frac{1}{3}$

$\left\{-\frac{1}{3}, 2\right\}$

81. $3x^2+2x=12-7x$

$3x^2+9x-12=0$

$x^2+3x-4=0$

$(x+4)(x-1)=0$

$x+4=0$ or $x-1=0$

$x=-4$ or $x=1$

$\{-4, 1\}$

83. $x^3-18x=3x^2$

$x^3-3x^2-18x=0$

$x(x^2-3x-18)=0$

$x(x-6)(x+3)=0$

$x=0$ or $x-6=0$ or $x+3=0$

$x=6$ or $x=-3$

$\{-3, 0, 6\}$

85. $12x=6x^3+6x^2$

$6x^3+6x^2-12x=0$

$6x(x^2+x-2)=0$

$6x(x+2)(x-1)=0$

$6x=0$ or $x+2=0$ or $x-1=0$

$x=0$ or $x=-2$ or $x=1$

$\{-2, 0, 1\}$

87. base $=4x$
altitude $=x$

$162=\frac{1}{2}(x)(4x)$

$162=2x^2$

$81=x^2$

$x^2-81=0$

$(x-9)(x+9)=0$

$x-9=0$ or $x+9=0$

$x=9$ or $x=-9$

base = 36 feet

89. 1st integer $=x$
2nd integer $=x+1$

$x(x+1)=380$

$x^2+x-380=0$

$(x+20)(x-19)=0$

$x+20=0$ or $x-19=0$

$x=-20$ or $x=19$

1st integer = 19
2nd integer = 20

91. Let $x=$ width
$5x-2=$ length

$A=x(5x-2)$

$16=x(5x-2)$

$16=5x^2-2x$

$0=5x^2-2x-16$

$0=(5x+8)(x-2)$

$5x+8=0$ or $x-2=0$

$5x = -8 \quad \text{or} \quad x = 2$

$x = -\frac{8}{5}$

Disregard $-\frac{8}{5}$ since length can not be negative. Therefore, the width is 2 meters and the length is 8 meters.

93. $f(x) = x^2 - 5x + 4$

$\frac{-b}{2a} = \frac{5}{2(1)} = \frac{5}{2}$

$f\left(\frac{5}{2}\right) = \left(\frac{5}{2}\right)^2 - 5\left(\frac{5}{2}\right) + 4 = -\frac{9}{4}$

The vertex is $\left(\frac{5}{2}, -\frac{9}{4}\right)$.

$x^2 - 5x + 4 = 0$

$(x-1)(x-4) = 0$

$x - 1 = 0 \quad \text{or} \quad x - 4 = 0$

$x = 1 \quad \text{or} \quad x = 4$

The x-intercepts are 1 and 4.
If $x = 0$, then $y = f(0) = 4$.
The y-intercept is 4.

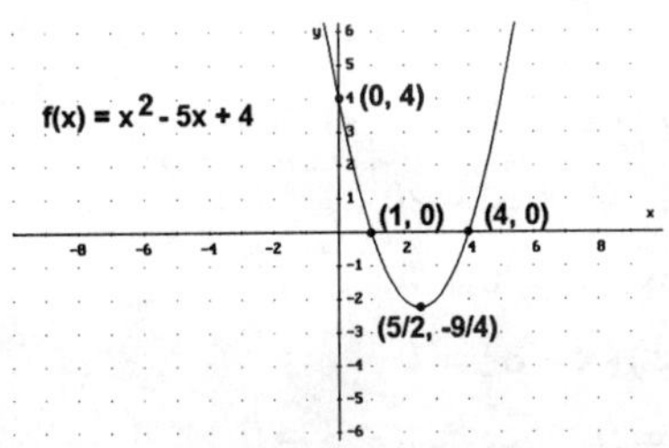

95. $f(x) = (x+3)(x^2 - 4x + 3)$

$f(x) = (x+3)(x-1)(x-3)$

$(x+3)(x-1)(x-3) = 0$

$x + 3 = 0 \quad \text{or} \quad x - 1 = 0 \quad \text{or} \quad x - 3 = 0$

$x = -3 \quad \text{or} \quad x = 1 \quad \text{or} \quad x = 3$

The x-intercepts are -3, 1, and 3.
If $x = 0$, then $y = f(0) = (3)(3) = 9$.
The y-intercept is 9.

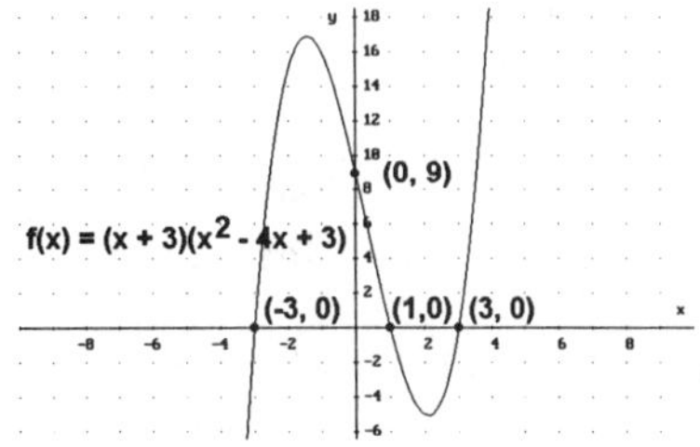

97. $f(x) = x^2 - 2x + 3$

$\frac{-b}{2a} = \frac{2}{2(1)} = 1$

$f(1) = 1 - 2 + 3 = 2$

The vertex is (1, 2).

There are no x-intercepts.
If $x = 0$, then $y = f(0) = 3$.
The y-intercept is 3.

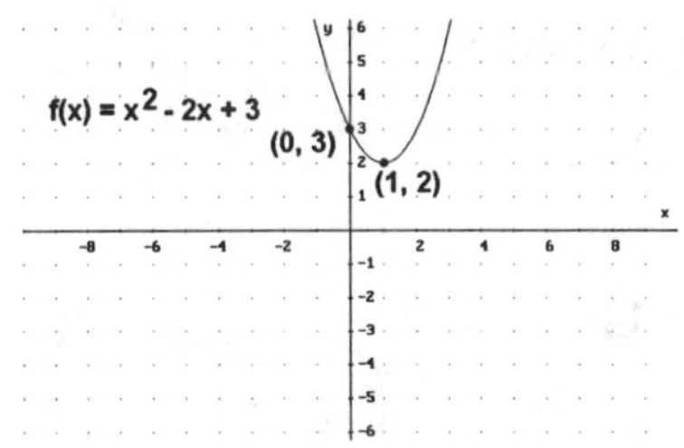

99. $f(x) = x^3 + 5x^2 + 6x$

$f(x) = x(x^2 + 5x + 6)$

$f(x) = x(x+3)(x+2)$

$x(x+3)(x+2) = 0$

$x = 0 \quad \text{or} \quad x + 3 = 0 \quad \text{or} \quad x + 2 = 0$

$x = 0 \quad \text{or} \quad x = -3 \quad \text{or} \quad x = -2$

The x-intercepts are $-3, -2$, and 0.
The y-intercept is 0.

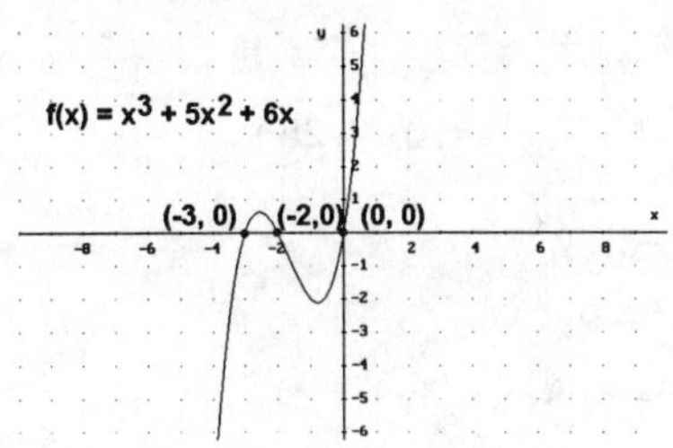

Chapter 6 Test

1. $16x^3y - 12x^2y^4 = 4x^2y(4x - 3y^3)$

2. $20a^3b^2 - 35ab^3 = 5ab^2(4a^2 - 7b)$

3. $xy - 5x + 3y - 15 = (x+3)(y-5)$

4. $x^3 + 2x^2 + 3x + 6 = (x^2+3)(x+2)$

5. $x^2 - 11x + 24 = (x-8)(x-3)$

6. $x^2 - 13x - 30 = (x-15)(x+2)$

7. $2x^2 + 17x - 9 = (2x-1)(x+9)$

8. $4y^2 + 20y + 25 = (2y+5)^2$

9. $6x^2 - 15x - 9$
   $3(2x^2 - 5x - 3)$
   $3(2x+1)(x-3)$

10. $x^5 + 3x^3 + 2x$
    $x(x^4 + 3x^2 + 2)$
    $x(x^2+1)(x^2+2)$

11. $4x^2 - 25 = (2x+5)(2x-5)$

12. $(3x+1)^2 - 4$
    $[(3x+1) - 2][(3x+1)+2]$
    $(3x-1)(3x+3)$
    $3(3x-1)(x+1)$

13. $x^3 + 64$
    $x^3 + 4^3$
    $(x+4)(x^2 - 4x + 16)$

14. $8x^3 - 125$
    $(2x)^3 - 5^3$
    $(2x-5)(4x^2 + 10x + 25)$

15. $3x^2y - 27y^3$
    $3y(x^2 - 9y^2)$
    $3y(x+3y)(x-3y)$

16. $8x^2 - 6x - 9 = (4x+3)(2x-3)$

17. $6x^2 + 24 = 6(x^2+4)$

18. $4x^6y^2 - 32y^5$
    $4y^2(x^6 - 8y^3)$
    $4y^2[(x^2)^3 - (2y)^3]$
    $4y^2(x^2 - 2y)(x^4 + 2x^2y + 4y^2)$

19. $x^2 - 2x + 1 - y^2$
    $(x-1)^2 - y^2$
    $[(x-1) + y][(x-1) - y]$
    $[x - 1 + y][x - 1 - y]$
    $(x + y - 1)(x - y - 1)$

20. $8x^2 - 44x + 20$
    $4(2x^2 - 11x + 5)$
    $4(2x-1)(x-5)$

21. $3(n-4)(7n+8) = 0$
    $3(n-4) = 0$ or $7n + 8 = 0$
    $n - 4 = 0$ or $7n = -8$
    $n = 4$ or $n = -\frac{8}{7}$
    $\left\{-\frac{8}{7},\ 4\right\}$

22. $(x-7)(x+2) = -20$
    $x^2 - 5x - 14 = -20$
    $x^2 - 5x + 6 = 0$
    $(x-2)(x-3) = 0$
    $x - 2 = 0$ or $x - 3 = 0$
    $x = 2$ or $x = 3$
    $\{2,\ 3\}$

23. $3m^3 = 12m$
    $3m^3 - 12m = 0$
    $3m(m^2 - 4) = 0$
    $3m(m+2)(m-2) = 0$
    $3m = 0$ or $m + 2 = 0$ or $m - 2 = 0$
    $m = 0$ or $m = -2$ or $m = 2$
    $\{-2,\ 0,\ 2\}$

24. $2x^3 + 5x^2 - 8x - 20 = 0$

$(2x + 5)(x^2 - 4) = 0$

$(2x + 5)(x + 2)(x - 2) = 0$

$2x + 5 = 0$ or $x + 2 = 0$ or $x - 2 = 0$

$2x = -5$ or $x = -2$ or $x = 2$

$x = -\frac{5}{2}$

$\left\{-\frac{5}{2}, -2, 2\right\}$

25. $\frac{3x^2}{5} - \frac{2x}{5} = 1$

$3x^2 - 2x - 5 = 0$

$(3x - 5)(x + 1) = 0$

$3x - 5 = 0$ or $x + 1 = 0$

$3x = 5$ or $x = -1$

$x = \frac{5}{3}$

$\left\{-1, \frac{5}{3}\right\}$

26. Let $x = \text{width}$
$x + 5 = \text{length}$

$A = x(x + 5)$

$66 = x(x + 5)$

$66 = x^2 + 5x$

$0 = x^2 + 5x - 66$

$0 = (x + 11)(x - 6)$

$x + 11 = 0$ or $x - 6 = 0$

$x = -11$ or $x = 6$

Disregard -11 since length can not be negative. Therefore, the width is 6 feet and the length is 11 feet.

27. Area of large square $= x^2$
Area of small square $= (2y)^2 = 4y^2$
Area of shaded portion $= x^2 - 4y^2$

$x^2 - 4y^2$

$(x - 2y)(x + 2y)$

28. $h(t) = -16t^2 + 96t + 880$

$0 = -16t^2 + 96t + 880$

$0 = -16(t^2 - 6t - 55)$

$0 = -16(t - 11)(t + 5)$

$t - 11 = 0$ or $t + 5 = 0$

$t = 11$ or $t = -5$

Disregard -5 since time can not be negative. Therefore, the pebble will hit the ground when $t = 11$ seconds.

29. $f(x) = x^2 - 4x - 5$

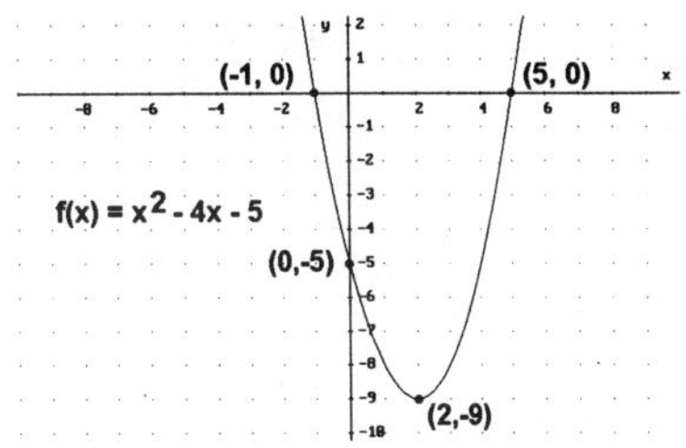

30. $f(x) = x^3 - 1$

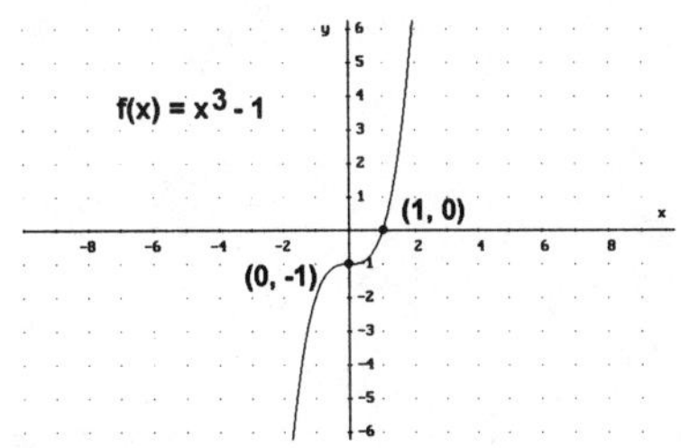

Chapter 6 Cumulative Review

1. $\frac{2}{5} \bullet \frac{4}{4} = \frac{8}{20}$

3a. $(a + b) + c = a + (b + c)$

$[(-3) + (2)] + (4) = 4 + [2 + (-3)]$

$(-1) + 4 = 4 + (-1)$

$3 = 3$

b. $(a \bullet b) \bullet c = a \bullet (b \bullet c)$

$[(-3)(2)] \bullet (4) = (-3) \bullet [(2)(4)]$

$[-6](4) = (-3)(8)$

$-24 = -24$

5. $\frac{y}{7} = 20$

$7\left(\frac{y}{7}\right) = 7(20)$

$y = 140$

$\{140\}$

7. $\$7.03 - \$5.80 = \$1.23$

The amount of increase is $1.23

$\frac{1.23}{5.80} = 0.212 = 21.2\%$

9. $x - 2y = 6$

a. $6 - 2(0) \stackrel{?}{=} 6$

$6 - 0 \stackrel{?}{=} 6$

$6 = 6$

Yes, it is a solution.

b. $0 - 2(3) \stackrel{?}{=} 6$

$-6 \neq 6$

No, it is not a solution.

c. $2 - (-2) \stackrel{?}{=} 6$

$2 + 4 \stackrel{?}{=} 6$

$6 = 6$

Yes, it is a solution.

11. y-int is -3, $m = \frac{1}{4}$

$y = mx + b$

$y = \frac{1}{4}x - 3$

13a. $(2x^3)(5x)^{-2}$

$(2x^3)(5^{-2}x^{-2})$

$(2)(5^{-2})(x)$

$\frac{2x}{5^2} = \frac{2x}{25}$

b. $\left(\frac{3a^2}{b}\right)^{-3} = \frac{3^{-3}a^{-6}}{b^{-3}} = \frac{b^3}{3^3a^6} = \frac{b^3}{27a^6}$

c. $\frac{4^{-1}x^{-3}y}{4^{-3}x^2y^{-6}} = 4^{-1-(-3)}x^{-3-2}y^{1-(-6)}$

$4^{-1+3}x^{-5}y^{1+6} = 4^2x^{-5}y^7 = \frac{16y^7}{x^5}$

d. $(y^{-3}z^6)^{-6} = y^{18}z^{-36} = \frac{y^{18}}{z^{36}}$

e. $\left(\frac{-2x^3y}{xy^{-1}}\right)^3 = (-2x^{3-1}y^{1-(-1)})^3$

$(-2x^2y^2)^3 = (-2)^3x^6y^6 = -8x^6y^6$

15.

$$\begin{array}{r@{}l} & 2x - 3 \\ 3x - 5 \,\big) & \overline{6x^2 - 19x + 12} \\ & \underline{6x^2 - 10x} \\ & -9x + 12 \\ & \underline{-9x + 15} \\ & -3 \end{array}$$

$2x - 3 + \frac{-3}{3x - 5}$

17. $20x^3y$, $10x^2y^2$, and $35x^3$

The GCF is $5x^2$.

19a. $8a^2b - 4ab$

$4ab(2a - 1)$

b. $36x^2 - 9$

$9(4x^2 - 1)$

$9(2x + 1)(2x - 1)$

c. $2x^2 - 5x - 7$

$(2x - 7)(x + 1)$

21. $h(t) = -16t^2 + 256$

$0 = -16t^2 + 256$

$0 = -16(t + 4)(t - 4)$

$t + 4 = 0$ or $t - 4 = 0$

$t = -4$ or $t = 4$

Disregard -4 since time can not be negative. The luggage will hit the ground when $t = 4$ seconds.

Exercise Set 7.1

1. $f(x) = \frac{x + 8}{2x - 1}$

$f(2) = \frac{2 + 8}{2(2) - 1} = \frac{10}{4 - 1} = \frac{10}{3}$

$f(0) = \frac{0 + 8}{2(0) - 1} = \frac{8}{-1} = -8$

$f(-1)=\frac{-1+8}{2(-1)-1}=\frac{7}{-3}=-\frac{7}{3}$

3. $g(x)=\frac{x^2+8}{x^3-25x}$

$g(3)=\frac{3^2+8}{3^3-25(3)}=\frac{9+8}{27-75}=\frac{17}{-48}=-\frac{17}{48}$

$g(-2)=\frac{(-2)^2+8}{(-2)^3-25(-2)}=\frac{4+8}{-8+50}=\frac{12}{42}=\frac{2}{7}$

$g(1)=\frac{1^2+8}{1^3-25(1)}=\frac{1+8}{1-25}=\frac{9}{-24}=-\frac{3}{8}$

5. $f(x)=\frac{5x-7}{4}$

Domain $\{x|x$ is a real number$\}$

7. $s(t)=\frac{t^2+1}{2t}$

Undefined values when

$2t=0$

$t=\frac{0}{2}=0$

Domain $\{t|t$ is a real number and $t\neq 0\}$

9. $C(x)=\frac{x+3}{x^2-4}$

Undefined values when

$x^2-4=0$

$(x+2)(x-2)=0$

$x+2=0$ or $x-2=0$

$x=-2$ or $x=2$

Domain $\{x|x$ is a real number and $x\neq 2,\ x\neq -2\}$

11. $\frac{10x^3}{18x}=\frac{5x^{3-1}}{9}=\frac{5x^2}{9}$

13. $\frac{9x^6y^3}{18x^2y^5}=\frac{x^{6-2}}{2y^{5-3}}=\frac{x^4}{2y^2}$

15. $\frac{8q^2}{16q^3-16q^2}=\frac{8q^2}{16q^2(q-1)}=\frac{1}{2(q-1)}$

17. $\frac{x+5}{5+x}=1$

19. $\frac{x-1}{1-x^2}=\frac{-(1-x)}{(1+x)(1-x)}=\frac{-1}{1+x}$

21. $\frac{7-x}{x^2-14x+49}=\frac{-(x-7)}{(x-7)^2}=\frac{-1}{x-7}$

23. $\frac{x+3}{x^3+27}=\frac{x+3}{x^3+3^3}$

$\frac{x+3}{(x+3)(x^2-3x+9)}$

$\frac{1}{x^2-3x+9}$

25. $\frac{2x^3-16}{3x-6}=\frac{2(x^3-8)}{3(x-2)}$

$\frac{2(x^3-2^3)}{3(x-2)}$

$\frac{2(x-2)(x^2+2x+4)}{3(x-2)}$

$\frac{2(x^2+2x+4)}{3}$

27. $\frac{xy-3y+2x-6}{x^2-6x+9}$

$\frac{(x-3)(y+2)}{(x-3)^2}$

$\frac{y+2}{x-3}$

29. First note $4y^3z=2y(2y^2z)$

$\frac{5}{2y}=\frac{5(2y^2z)}{2y(2y^2z)}=\frac{10y^2z}{4y^3z}$

31. First note

$2x^2+9x-5=(2x-1)(x+5)$

$\frac{3x}{2x-1}=\frac{3x}{2x-1}\bullet\frac{x+5}{x+5}=\frac{3x^2+15x}{2x^2+9x-5}$

33. $\frac{x-1}{1}=\frac{(x-2)(x+2)}{1\bullet(x+2)}=\frac{x^2-4}{x+2}$

35. $f(x)=\frac{3x}{7-x}$

Undefined value when

$7-x=0$

$7=x$

Domain $\{x|x$ is a real number and $x\neq 7\}$

37. $g(x) = \frac{2-3x^2}{3x^2+9x}$

Undefined values when

$3x^2+9x=0$

$3x(x+3)=0$

$3x=0$ or $x+3=0$

$x=0$ or $x=-3$

Domain $\{x \mid x$ is a real number and $x \neq 0,\ x \neq -3\}$.

39. $R(x) = \frac{3+2x}{x^3+x^2-2x}$

Undefined values when

$x^3+x^2-2x=0$

$x(x^2+x-2)=0$

$x(x+2)(x-1)=0$

$x=0$ or $x+2=0$ or $x-1=0$

$x=-2$ or $x=1$

Domain $\{x \mid x$ is a real number and $x \neq 0,\ x \neq -2,\ x \neq 1\}$.

41. $R(x) = \frac{200x^2}{x^2+5}$

a. $R(1) = \frac{200(1)^2}{1^2+5} = \frac{200(1)}{1+5} = \frac{200}{6} = 33.33$

b. $R(2) = \frac{200(2)^2}{2^2+5} = \frac{200(4)}{4+5} = \frac{800}{9} = 88.89$

c. $R(3) = \frac{200(3)^2}{3^2+5} = \frac{200(9)}{9+5} = \frac{1800}{14} = 128.57$

d. $R(2\text{ only}) = R(2) - R(1)$

$= 88.89 - 33.33$

$= 55.56$

43. $\frac{6x^3}{27x^3} = \frac{2}{9}$

45. $\frac{6a^2b^3}{3a^2b^2} = 2b^{3-2} = 2b$

47. $\frac{7-y}{y-7} = \frac{-(y-7)}{y-7} = -1$

49. $\frac{4x-8}{3x-6} = \frac{4(x-2)}{3(x-2)} = \frac{4}{3}$

51. $\frac{2x-14}{7-x} = \frac{2(x-7)}{-(x-7)} = -2$

53. $\frac{x^2-2x-3}{x^2-6x+9} = \frac{(x-3)(x+1)}{(x-3)^2} = \frac{x+1}{x-3}$

55. $\frac{2x^2+12x+18}{x^2-9}$

$\frac{2(x^2+6x+9)}{x^2-3^2}$

$\frac{2(x+3)^2}{(x+3)(x-3)}$

$\frac{2(x+3)}{x-3}$

57. $\frac{3x+6}{x^2+2x} = \frac{3(x+2)}{x(x+2)} = \frac{3}{x}$

59. $\frac{x+2}{x^2-4} = \frac{x+2}{(x+2)(x-2)} = \frac{1}{x-2}$

61. $\frac{2x^2-x-3}{2x^3-3x^2+2x-3}$

$\frac{(2x-3)(x+1)}{(2x-3)(x^2+1)}$

$\frac{x+1}{x^2+1}$

63. $\frac{x^4-16}{x^2+4} = \frac{(x^2+4)(x^2-4)}{x^2+4} = x^2-4$

65. $\frac{x^2+6x-40}{10+x} = \frac{(x+10)(x-4)}{x+10} = x-4$

67. $\frac{2x^2-7x-4}{x^2-5x+4} = \frac{(2x+1)(x-4)}{(x-1)(x-4)} = \frac{2x+1}{x-1}$

69. $\frac{x^3-125}{5-x} = \frac{x^3-5^3}{-(x-5)}$

$\frac{(x-5)(x^2+5x+25)}{-(x-5)}$

$-(x^2+5x+25)$

$-x^2-5x-25$

71. $\frac{8x^3-27}{4x-6} = \frac{(2x)^3-3^3}{2(2x-3)}$

$\frac{(2x-3)(4x^2+6x+9)}{2(2x-3)}$

$\frac{4x^2+6x+9}{2}$

73. $\frac{x+5}{x^2+5}$ is in lowest terms.

75. First note $6m^3 = m(6m^2)$

$\frac{5}{m} = \frac{5(6m^2)}{m(6m^2)} = \frac{30m^2}{6m^3}$

77. First note $5m-10 = 5(m-2)$

$\frac{7}{m-2} = \frac{7(5)}{(m-2)5} = \frac{35}{5m-10}$

79. First note $y^2-16 = (y-4)(y+4)$

$\frac{y+4}{y-4} = \frac{(y+4)(y+4)}{(y-4)(y+4)} = \frac{y^2+8y+16}{y^2-16}$

81. First note $x^2+4x+4 = (x+2)(x+2)$

$\frac{12x}{x+2} = \frac{12x(x+2)}{(x+2)(x+2)} = \frac{12x^2+24x}{x^2+4x+4}$

83. First note $x^3+8 = x^3+2^3$
$= (x+2)(x^2-2x+4)$

$\frac{1}{x+2} = \frac{1\bullet(x^2-2x+4)}{(x+2)(x^2-2x+4)} = \frac{x^2-2x+4}{x^3+8}$

85. First note
$ab-3a+2b-6 = (a+2)(b-3)$
$\frac{a}{a+2} = \frac{a(b-3)}{(a+2)(b-3)} = \frac{ab-3a}{ab-3a+2b-6}$

87. $\frac{6}{35}\bullet\frac{28}{9} = \frac{(3\bullet 2)(4\bullet 7)}{(5\bullet 7)(3\bullet 3)} = \frac{(21)(8)}{(21)(15)} = \frac{8}{15}$

89. $\frac{8}{35}\div\frac{4}{5} = \frac{8}{35}\bullet\frac{5}{4} = \frac{(4\bullet 2)(5)}{(5\bullet 7)(4)} = \frac{(20)(2)}{(20)(7)} = \frac{2}{7}$

91. $\left(\frac{1}{2}\bullet\frac{1}{4}\right)\div\frac{3}{8}$

$\frac{1}{8}\div\frac{3}{8}$

$\frac{1}{8}\bullet\frac{8}{3}$

$\frac{1}{3}$

93.

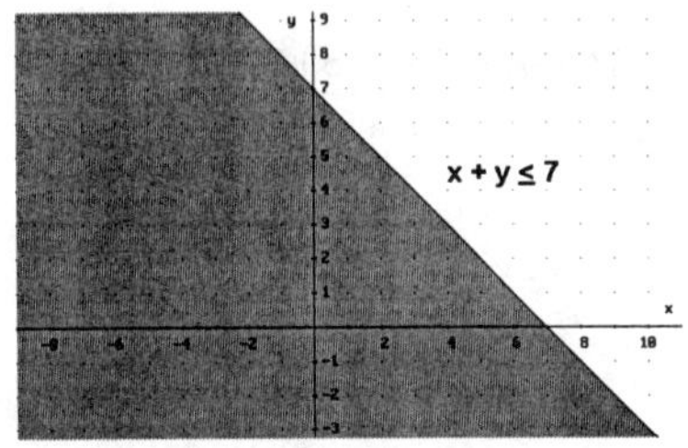

95. 14%

97. 28.9% + 20.9%

49.8%

99. $\frac{3+q^n}{q^n+3} = 1$

101. $\frac{x^{2k}-9}{3+x^k} = \frac{(x^k-3)(x^k+3)}{3+x^k} = x^k-3$

103. $\frac{4x^k-12}{x^{2k}+4}$ is irreducible.

Exercise Set 7.2

1. $\frac{4}{x}\bullet\frac{x^2}{8} = \frac{1}{1}\bullet\frac{x}{2} = \frac{x}{2}$

3. $\frac{2a^2b}{6ac}\bullet\frac{3c^2}{4ab} = \frac{6a^2bc^2}{24a^2bc} = \frac{c}{4}$

5. $\frac{2x}{5}\bullet\frac{5x+10}{6(x+2)}$

$\frac{(2x)\bullet 5(x+2)}{30(x+2)} = \frac{10x}{30} = \frac{x}{3}$

7. $\frac{2x-4}{15}\bullet\frac{6}{2-x}$

$\frac{2(x-2)\bullet 6}{15[-(x-2)]} = \frac{12}{-15} = -\frac{4}{5}$

9. $\frac{18a-12a^2}{4a^2+4a+1}\bullet\frac{4a^2+8a+3}{4a^2-9}$

$\frac{6a(3-2a)(2a+3)(2a+1)}{(2a+1)^2(2a+3)(2a-3)}$

$\frac{(6a)[-(2a-3)]}{(2a+1)(2a-3)} = \frac{-6a}{2a+1}$

11. $\frac{x^2-6x-16}{2x^2-128}\bullet\frac{x^2+16x+64}{3x^2+30x+48}$

$$\frac{(x-8)(x+2)(x+8)^2}{2(x^2-64)[3(x^2+10x+16)]}$$

$$\frac{(x-8)(x+2)(x+8)^2}{2(x+8)(x-8)3(x+8)(x+2)}$$

$$\frac{1}{6}$$

13. $\frac{4x+8}{x+1} \bullet \frac{2-x}{3x-15} \bullet \frac{2x^2-8x-10}{x^2-4}$

$$\frac{4(x+2)[-(x-2)] \bullet 2(x^2-4x-5)}{(x+1)[3(x-5)](x+2)(x-2)}$$

$$\frac{-8(x-5)(x+1)}{3(x+1)(x-5)}$$

$$-\frac{8}{3}$$

15. $\frac{4}{x} \div \frac{8}{x^2} = \frac{4}{x} \bullet \frac{x^2}{8} = \frac{1}{1} \bullet \frac{x}{2} = \frac{x}{2}$

17. $\frac{4ab}{3c^2} \div \frac{2a^2b}{6ac} = \frac{4ab}{3c^2} \bullet \frac{6ac}{2a^2b}$

$$\frac{24a^2bc}{6a^2bc^2} = \frac{4}{c}$$

19. $\frac{2x}{5} \div \frac{6x+12}{5x+10} = \frac{2x}{5} \bullet \frac{5x+10}{6x+12}$

$$\frac{2x[5(x+2)]}{5[6(x+2)]} = \frac{2x}{6} = \frac{x}{3}$$

21. $\frac{2(x+y)}{5} \div \frac{6(x+y)}{25}$

$$\frac{2(x+y)}{5} \bullet \frac{25}{6(x+y)}$$

$$\frac{50(x+y)}{30(x+y)} = \frac{50}{30} = \frac{5}{3}$$

23. $\frac{x^2-6x+9}{x^2-x-6} \div \frac{x^2-9}{4}$

$$\frac{(x-3)^2}{(x-3)(x+2)} \bullet \frac{4}{(x+3)(x-3)}$$

$$\frac{4}{(x+2)(x+3)} = \frac{4}{x^2+5x+6}$$

25. $\frac{x^2-6x-16}{2x^2-128} \div \frac{x^2+10x+16}{x^2+16x+64}$

$$\frac{(x-8)(x+2)}{2(x^2-64)} \bullet \frac{(x+8)^2}{(x+2)(x+8)}$$

$$\frac{(x-8)(x+8)}{2(x+8)(x-8)} = \frac{1}{2}$$

27. $\frac{14x^4}{y^5} \div \frac{2x^2}{y^7} \div \frac{2x^4}{7y^5}$

$$\frac{14x^4}{y^5} \bullet \frac{y^7}{2x^2} \bullet \frac{7y^5}{2x^4}$$

$$\frac{98x^4y^{12}}{4x^6y^5} = \frac{49y^7}{2x^2}$$

29. $\frac{3xy^3}{4x^3y^2} \bullet \frac{-8x^3y^4}{9x^4y^7}$

$$\frac{-24x^4y^7}{36x^7y^9} = \frac{-2}{3x^3y^2}$$

31. $\frac{8a}{3a^4b^2} \div \frac{4b^5}{6a^2b} = \frac{8a}{3a^4b^2} \bullet \frac{6a^2b}{4b^5}$

$$\frac{48a^3b}{12a^4b^7} = \frac{4}{ab^6}$$

33. $\frac{a^2b}{a^2-b^2} \bullet \frac{a+b}{4a^3b}$

$$\frac{a^2b(a+b)}{4a^3b(a+b)(a-b)}$$

$$\frac{1}{4a(a-b)}$$

35. $\frac{x^2-9}{4} \div \frac{x^2-6x+9}{x^2-x-6}$

$$\frac{(x+3)(x-3)}{4} \bullet \frac{(x-3)(x+2)}{(x-3)^2}$$

$$\frac{(x+3)(x+2)}{4} = \frac{x^2+5x+6}{4}$$

37. $\frac{9x+9}{4x+8} \bullet \frac{2x+4}{3x^2-3}$

$$\frac{9(x+1) \bullet 2(x+2)}{4(x+2) \bullet 3(x^2-1)}$$

$$\frac{18(x+1)}{12(x+1)(x-1)}$$

$$\frac{3}{2(x-1)}$$

39. $\frac{a+b}{ab} \div \frac{a^2-b^2}{4a^3b}$

$$\frac{a+b}{ab} \bullet \frac{4a^3b}{(a+b)(a-b)}$$

$\frac{4a^2}{a-b}$

41. $\frac{2x^2-4x-30}{5x^2-40x-75} \div \frac{x^2-8x+15}{x^2-6x+9}$

$\frac{2(x^2-2x-15)}{5(x^2-8x-15)} \bullet \frac{(x-3)^2}{(x-5)(x-3)}$

$\frac{2(x-5)(x+3)(x-3)}{5(x^2-8x-15)(x-5)}$

$\frac{2(x+3)(x-3)}{5(x^2-8x-15)}$

43. $\frac{2x^3-16}{6x^2+6x-36} \bullet \frac{9x+18}{3x^2+6x+12}$

$\frac{2(x^3-8) \bullet 9(x+2)}{6(x^2+x-6) \bullet 3(x^2+2x+4)}$

$\frac{18(x-2)(x^2+2x+4)(x+2)}{18(x+3)(x-2)(x^2+2x+4)}$

$\frac{x+2}{x+3}$

45. $\frac{15b-3a}{b^2-a^2} \div \frac{a-5b}{ab+b^2}$

$\frac{3(5b-a)}{(b+a)(b-a)} \bullet \frac{b(a+b)}{-(5b-a)}$

$\frac{3}{b-a} \bullet \frac{b}{-1}$

$\frac{3b}{a-b}$

47. $\frac{a^3+a^2b+a+b}{a^3+a} \bullet \frac{6a^2}{2a^2-2b^2}$

$\frac{(a^2+1)(a+b)}{a(a^2+1)} \bullet \frac{6a^2}{2(a^2-b^2)}$

$\frac{a+b}{1} \bullet \frac{3a}{(a+b)(a-b)} = \frac{3a}{a-b}$

49. $\frac{5a}{12} \bullet \frac{2}{25a^2} \bullet \frac{15a}{2} = \frac{1}{6} \bullet \frac{1}{5a} \bullet \frac{15a}{2}$

$\frac{1}{6} \bullet \frac{1}{1} \bullet \frac{3}{2} = \frac{3}{12} = \frac{1}{4}$

51. $\frac{3x-x^2}{x^3-27} \div \frac{x}{x^2+3x+9}$

$\frac{x(3-x)}{(x-3)(x^2+3x+9)} \bullet \frac{x^2+3x+9}{x}$

$\frac{3-x}{x-3} = \frac{-(x-3)}{x-3} = -1$

53. $\frac{4a}{7} \div \left(\frac{a^2}{14} \bullet \frac{3}{a}\right) = \frac{4a}{7} \div \frac{3a}{14}$

$\frac{4a}{7} \bullet \frac{14}{3a} = \frac{4}{1} \bullet \frac{2}{3} = \frac{8}{3}$

55. $\frac{8b+24}{3a+6} \div \frac{ab-2b+3a-6}{a^2-4a+4}$

$\frac{8(b+3)}{3(a+2)} \bullet \frac{(a-2)^2}{(a-2)(b+3)}$

$\frac{8(a-2)}{3(a+2)}$

57. $\frac{4}{x} \div \frac{3xy}{x^2} \bullet \frac{6x^2}{x^4} = \frac{4}{x} \bullet \frac{x^2}{3xy} \bullet \frac{6}{x^2}$

$\frac{4}{3y} \bullet \frac{6}{x^2} = \frac{4}{y} \bullet \frac{2}{x^2} = \frac{8}{x^2y}$

59. $\frac{3x^2-5x-2}{y^2+y-2} \bullet \frac{y^2+4y-5}{12x^2+7x+1} \div \frac{5x^2-9x-2}{8x^2-2x-1}$

$\frac{(3x+1)(x-2)(y+5)(y-1)(4x+1)(2x-1)}{(y+2)(y-1)(4x+1)(3x+1)(5x+1)(x-2)}$

$\frac{(y+5)(2x-1)}{(y+2)(5x+1)}$

61. $\frac{5a^2-20}{3a^2-12a} \div \frac{a^3+2a^2}{2a^2-8a} \bullet \frac{9a^3+6a^2}{2a^2-4a}$

$\frac{5(a^2-4)}{3a(a-4)} \bullet \frac{2a(a-4)}{a^2(a+2)} \bullet \frac{3a^2(3a+2)}{2a(a-2)}$

$\frac{5(a+2)(a-2)(3a+2)}{a(a+2)(a-2)}$

$\frac{5(3a+2)}{a}$

63. $\frac{5x^4+3x^2-2}{x-1} \bullet \frac{x+1}{x^4-1}$

$\frac{(5x^2-2)(x^2+1)(x+1)}{(x-1)(x^2+1)(x^2-1)}$

$\frac{(5x^2-2)(x+1)}{(x-1)(x+1)(x-1)}$

$\frac{5x^2-2}{(x-1)^2}$

65. Recall that $A = l \bullet w$. So,

$A = \frac{x+2}{x} \bullet \frac{5x}{x^2-4}$

$\frac{(x+2)5}{(x+2)(x-2)}$

$\frac{5}{x-2}$ sq. m.

67. Since $A = b \bullet h$, $b = \frac{A}{h}$. Now,

$$b = \frac{\frac{x^2+x-2}{x^3}}{\frac{x^2}{x-1}}$$

$$b = \frac{(x+2)(x-1)}{x^3} \bullet \frac{(x-1)}{x^2}$$

$$b = \frac{(x+2)(x-1)^2}{x^5} \text{ ft.}$$

69. $\frac{4}{5} + \frac{3}{5}$

$\frac{7}{5}$

71. $\frac{5}{28} - \frac{2}{21}$

The LCD is 84.

$\frac{5}{28} \bullet \frac{3}{3} - \frac{2}{21} \bullet \frac{4}{4}$

$\frac{15}{84} - \frac{8}{84}$

$\frac{7}{84} = \frac{7 \bullet 1}{7 \bullet 12} = \frac{1}{12}$

73. $\frac{3}{8} + \frac{1}{2} - \frac{3}{16}$

The LCD is 16.

$\frac{3}{8} \bullet \frac{2}{2} + \frac{1}{2} \bullet \frac{8}{8} - \frac{3}{16}$

$\frac{6}{16} + \frac{8}{16} - \frac{3}{16}$

$\frac{14}{16} - \frac{3}{16}$

$\frac{11}{16}$

75.
$$\begin{array}{r|rrrr} 1 & 1 & -6 & 3 & -4 \\ & & 1 & -5 & -2 \\ \hline & 1 & -5 & -2 & -6 \end{array}$$

The quotient is

$x^2 - 5x - 2 + \frac{-6}{x-1}$

77. 5 people

79. $5 + 9$

14 people

81. Total number of people =

$5 + 9 + 5 + 6 + 2 + 3 = 30$

$\frac{5}{30} = 0.167 = 16.7\%$

83. $\frac{x^{2n}-4}{7x} \bullet \frac{14x^3}{x^n-2}$

$\frac{(x^n+2)(x^n-2)2x^2}{x^n-2}$

$2x^2(x^n+2)$

85. $\frac{y^{2n}+9}{10y} \bullet \frac{y^n-3}{y^{4n}-81}$

$\frac{(y^{2n}+9)(y^n-3)}{10y(y^{2n}+9)(y^{2n}-9)}$

$\frac{y^n-3}{10y(y^n+3)(y^n-3)}$

$\frac{1}{10y(y^n+3)}$

87. $\frac{y^{2n}-y^n-2}{2y^n-4} \div \frac{y^{2n}-1}{1+y^n}$

$\frac{(y^n-2)(y^n+1)}{2(y^n-2)} \bullet \frac{y^n+1}{(y^n+1)(y^n-1)}$

$\frac{y^n+1}{2(y^n-1)}$

Exercise Set 7.3

1. $\frac{2}{x} - \frac{5}{x} = \frac{2-5}{x} = \frac{-3}{x}$

3. $\frac{2}{x-2} + \frac{x}{x-2} = \frac{2+x}{x-2}$

5. $\frac{x^2}{x+2} - \frac{4}{x+2} = \frac{x^2-4}{x+2}$

$\frac{(x+2)(x-2)}{x+2} = x - 2$

7. $\frac{2x-6}{x^2+x-6} + \frac{3-3x}{x^2+x-6}$

$\frac{-x-3}{x^2+x-6}$

$$\frac{-(x+3)}{(x+3)(x-2)}$$

$$\frac{-1}{x-2}$$

9. The LCD of 7 and 5x is $7(5x) = 35x$.

11. The LCD of x and $x+1$ is $x(x+1)$.

13. The LCD of $x+7$ and $x-7$ is $(x+7)(x-7)$

15. The LCD of $3x+6 = 3(x+2)$ and $2x-4 = 2(x-2)$ is

$[3(x+2)][2(x-2)]$

$6(x+2)(x-2)$

17. The LCD of $a^2 - b^2 = (a+b)(a-b)$ and $a^2 - 2ab + b^2 = (a-b)^2$ is:

$(a+b)(a-b)^2$

19. $\frac{4}{3x} + \frac{3}{2x} = \frac{(4)2}{(3x)2} + \frac{(3)3}{(2x)3}$

$\frac{8+9}{6x} = \frac{17}{6x}$

21. $\frac{5}{2y^2} - \frac{2}{7y} = \frac{(5)7}{(2y^2)7} - \frac{2(2y)}{(7y)2y}$

$\frac{35-4y}{14y^2}$

23. $\frac{x-3}{x+4} - \frac{x+2}{x-4}$

$$\frac{(x-3)(x-4)}{(x+4)(x-4)} - \frac{(x+2)(x+4)}{(x-4)(x+4)}$$

$$\frac{(x^2-7x+12)-(x^2+6x+8)}{(x+4)(x-4)}$$

$$\frac{x^2-7x+12-x^2-6x-8}{(x+4)(x-4)}$$

$$\frac{-13x+4}{(x+4)(x-4)}$$

25. $\frac{1}{x-5} + \frac{x}{(x-5)(x+4)}$

$$\frac{1(x+4)}{(x-5)(x+4)} + \frac{x}{(x-5)(x+4)}$$

$$\frac{x+4+x}{(x-5)(x+4)} = \frac{2x+4}{(x-5)(x+4)}$$

27. $\frac{1}{a-b} + \frac{1}{b-a} = \frac{1}{a-b} + \frac{1}{-(a-b)}$

$\frac{1}{a-b} - \frac{1}{a-b} = 0$

29. $x+1+\frac{1}{x-1}$

$$\frac{(x+1)(x-1)}{x-1} + \frac{1}{x-1}$$

$$\frac{x^2-1+1}{x-1} = \frac{x^2}{x-1}$$

31. $\frac{5}{x-2} + \frac{x+4}{2-x} = \frac{5}{x-2} + \frac{x+4}{-(x-2)}$

$$\frac{5}{x-2} - \frac{x+4}{x-2} = \frac{5-(x+4)}{x-2}$$

$$\frac{5-x-4}{x-2} = \frac{1-x}{x-2}$$

33. $\frac{y+1}{y^2-6y+8} - \frac{3}{y^2-16}$

$$\frac{y+1}{(y-2)(y-4)} - \frac{3}{(y+4)(y-4)}$$

$$\frac{(y+1)(y+4)}{(y-2)(y-4)(y+4)} - \frac{3(y-2)}{(y-2)(y-4)(y+4)}$$

$$\frac{y^2+5y+4-(3y-6)}{(y-2)(y-4)(y+4)}$$

$$\frac{y^2+5y+4-3y+6}{(y-2)(y-4)(y+4)}$$

$$\frac{y^2+2y+10}{(y-2)(y-4)(y+4)}$$

35. $\frac{x+4}{3x^2+11x+6} + \frac{x}{2x^2+x-15}$

$$\frac{x+4}{(3x+2)(x+3)} + \frac{x}{(2x-5)(x+3)}$$

$$\frac{(x+4)(2x-5)}{(3x+2)(x+3)(2x-5)} + \frac{x(3x+2)}{(2x-5)(x+3)(3x+2)}$$

$$\frac{2x^2+3x-20+3x^2+2x}{(3x+2)(x+3)(2x-5)}$$

$$\frac{5x^2+5x-20}{(3x+2)(x+3)(2x-5)}$$

$$\frac{5(x^2+x-4)}{(3x+2)(x+3)(2x-5)}$$

37. $\frac{7}{x^2-x-2} + \frac{x}{x^2+4x+3}$

$$\frac{7}{(x-2)(x+1)} + \frac{x}{(x+1)(x+3)}$$

$$\frac{7(x+3)}{(x-2)(x+1)(x+3)}+\frac{x(x-2)}{(x+1)(x+3)(x-2)}$$
$$\frac{7x+21+x^2-2x}{(x-2)(x+1)(x+3)}$$
$$\frac{x^2+5x+21}{(x-2)(x+1)(x+3)}$$

39. $\frac{2}{x+1}-\frac{3x}{3x+3}+\frac{1}{2x+2}$
$$\frac{2}{x+1}-\frac{3x}{3(x+1)}+\frac{1}{2(x+1)}$$
$$\frac{2}{x+1}-\frac{x}{x+1}+\frac{1}{2(x+1)}$$
$$\frac{2-x}{x+1}+\frac{1}{2(x+1)}$$
$$\frac{2(2-x)}{2(x+1)}+\frac{1}{2(x+1)}$$
$$\frac{4-2x+1}{2(x+1)}=\frac{5-2x}{2(x+1)}$$

41. $\frac{3}{x+3}+\frac{5}{x^2+6x+9}-\frac{x}{x^2-9}$
$$\frac{3}{x+3}+\frac{5}{(x+3)^2}-\frac{x}{(x+3)(x-3)}$$
$$\frac{3(x+3)(x-3)}{(x+3)^2(x-3)}+\frac{5(x-3)}{(x+3)^2(x-3)}-\frac{x(x+3)}{(x+3)^2(x-3)}$$
$$\frac{3x^2-27+5x-15-x^2-3x}{(x+3)^2(x-3)}$$
$$\frac{2x^2+2x-42}{(x+3)^2(x-3)}$$
$$\frac{2(x^2+x-21)}{(x+3)^2(x-3)}$$

43. $\frac{4}{3x^2y^3}+\frac{5}{3x^2y^3}=\frac{4+5}{3x^2y^3}=\frac{9}{3x^2y^3}=\frac{3}{x^2y^3}$

45. $\frac{x-5}{2x}-\frac{x+5}{2x}=\frac{x-5-x-5}{2x}=\frac{-10}{2x}=-\frac{5}{x}$

47. $\frac{3}{2x+10}+\frac{8}{3x+15}$
$$\frac{3}{2(x+5)}+\frac{8}{3(x+5)}$$
$$\frac{9}{6(x+5)}+\frac{16}{6(x+5)}$$
$$\frac{9+16}{6(x+5)}=\frac{25}{6(x+5)}$$

49. $\frac{-2}{x^2-3x}-\frac{1}{x^3-3x^2}$
$$\frac{-2}{x(x-3)}-\frac{1}{x^2(x-3)}$$
$$\frac{-2x}{x^2(x-3)}-\frac{1}{x^2(x-3)}$$
$$\frac{-2x-1}{x^2(x-3)}$$

51. $\frac{ab}{a^2-b^2}+\frac{b}{a+b}$
$$\frac{ab}{(a+b)(a-b)}+\frac{b}{a+b}$$
$$\frac{ab}{(a+b)(a-b)}+\frac{b(a-b)}{(a+b)(a-b)}$$
$$\frac{ab+ab-b^2}{(a+b)(a-b)}$$
$$\frac{2ab-b^2}{(a+b)(a-b)}$$

53. $\frac{5}{x^2-4}-\frac{3}{x^2+4x+4}$
$$\frac{5}{(x+2)(x-2)}-\frac{3}{(x+2)^2}$$
$$\frac{5(x+2)}{(x+2)^2(x-2)}-\frac{3(x-2)}{(x+2)^2(x-2)}$$
$$\frac{5x+10-3x+6}{(x+2)^2(x-2)}$$
$$\frac{2x+16}{(x+2)^2(x-2)}$$

55. $\frac{2}{a^2+2a+1}+\frac{3}{a^2-1}$
$$\frac{2}{(a+1)^2}+\frac{3}{(a+1)(a-1)}$$
$$\frac{2(a-1)}{(a+1)^2(a-1)}+\frac{3(a+1)}{(a+1)^2(a-1)}$$
$$\frac{2a-2+3a+3}{(a+1)^2(a-1)}$$
$$\frac{5a+1}{(a+1)^2(a-1)}$$

57. $\left(\frac{2}{3}-\frac{1}{x}\right)\bullet\left(\frac{3}{x}+\frac{1}{2}\right)$
$$\left(\frac{2x}{3x}-\frac{3}{3x}\right)\bullet\left(\frac{6}{2x}+\frac{x}{2x}\right)$$
$$\frac{2x-3}{3x}\bullet\frac{x+6}{2x}$$
$$\frac{2x^2+9x-18}{6x^2}$$

59. $\left(\frac{1}{x}+\frac{2}{3}\right)-\left(\frac{1}{x}-\frac{2}{3}\right)$

$\frac{1}{x}+\frac{2}{3}-\frac{1}{x}+\frac{2}{3}=\frac{4}{3}$

61. $\left(\frac{2a}{3}\right)^2 \div \left(\frac{a^2}{a+1}-\frac{1}{a+1}\right)$

$\frac{4a^2}{9} \div \frac{a^2-1}{a+1}$

$\frac{4a^2}{9} \bullet \frac{a+1}{(a+1)(a-1)}$

$\frac{4a^2}{9} \bullet \frac{1}{a-1}$

$\frac{4a^2}{9(a-1)}$

63. $\left(\frac{2x}{3}\right)^2 \div \left(\frac{x}{3}\right)^2 = \left(\frac{\frac{2x}{3}}{\frac{x}{3}}\right)^2 = 2^2 = 4$

65. $\frac{x}{x^2-9}+\frac{3}{x^2-6x+9}-\frac{1}{x+3}$

$\frac{x}{(x+3)(x-3)}+\frac{3}{(x-3)^2}-\frac{1}{(x+3)}$

$\frac{x(x-3)+3(x+3)-(x-3)^2}{(x+3)(x-3)^2}$

$\frac{x^2-3x+3x+9-x^2+6x-9}{(x-3)(x-3)^2}$

$\frac{6x}{(x+3)(x-3)^2}$

67. $\left(\frac{x}{x+1}-\frac{x}{x-1}\right) \div \frac{x}{2x+2}$

$\frac{x(x-1)-x(x+1)}{(x-1)(x+1)} \bullet \frac{2(x+1)}{x}$

$\frac{x^2-x-x^2-x}{(x+1)(x-1)} \bullet \frac{2(x+1)}{x}$

$\frac{-2x}{(x+1)(x-1)} \bullet \frac{2(x+1)}{x}$

$\frac{-4}{x-1}$

69. $\frac{4}{x} \bullet \left(\frac{2}{x+2}-\frac{2}{x-2}\right)$

$\frac{4 \bullet 2}{x}\left(\frac{1}{x+2}-\frac{1}{x-2}\right)$

$\frac{8}{x}\left(\frac{x-2-(x+2)}{(x+2)(x-2)}\right)$

$\frac{8}{x} \bullet \frac{x-2-x-2}{(x+2)(x-2)}$

$\frac{8}{x} \bullet \frac{-4}{(x+2)(x-2)}$

$\frac{-32}{x(x+2)(x-2)}$

71. Recall that $P = 4 \bullet s$

$P = 4\left(\frac{x}{x+5}\right) = \left(\frac{4x}{x+5}\right)$ feet

Recall that $A = s^2$

$A = \left(\frac{x}{x+5}\right)^2 = \frac{x^2}{(x+5)^2}$

$A = \left(\frac{x^2}{x^2+10x+25}\right)$ sq. ft.

73. $f(x) = \frac{3x}{x^2-4}$ $\quad g(x) = \frac{6}{x^2+2x}$

$(f+g)(x) = \frac{3x}{x^2-4}+\frac{6}{x^2+2x}$

$(f+g)(x) = \frac{3x}{(x+2)(x-2)}+\frac{6}{x(x+2)}$

The LCD is $x(x+2)(x-2)$.

$(f+g)(x) = \frac{3x}{(x+2)(x-2)} \bullet \frac{x}{x} + \frac{6}{x(x+2)} \bullet \frac{(x-2)}{(x-2)}$

$(f+g)(x) = \frac{3x^2}{x(x+2)(x-2)}+\frac{6(x-2)}{x(x+2)(x-2)}$

$(f+g)(x) = \frac{3x^2+6(x-2)}{x(x+2)(x-2)}$

$(f+g)(x) = \frac{3x^2+6x-12}{x(x+2)(x-2)}$

75. $\left(\frac{f}{g}\right)(x) = \frac{\frac{3}{x^2-4}}{\frac{6}{x^2+2x}}$

$\left(\frac{f}{g}\right)(x) = \frac{\frac{3}{(x+2)(x-2)}}{\frac{6}{x(x+2)}}$

$\left(\frac{f}{g}\right)(x) = \frac{\overset{1}{\cancel{3}}}{(x+2)(x-2)} \bullet \frac{x(x+2)}{\underset{2}{\cancel{6}}}$

$\left(\frac{f}{g}\right)(x) = \frac{x}{2(x-2)}$

77. $12\left(\frac{2}{3}+\frac{1}{6}\right) = \frac{24}{3}+\frac{12}{6} = 8+2 = 10$

79. $x^2\left(\frac{4}{x^2}+1\right)=x^2\bullet\frac{4}{x^2}+x^2\bullet 1=4+x^2$

81. $\sqrt{100}=10$

83. $\sqrt[3]{8}$

2

85. $\sqrt[4]{81}=3$

87. $a^2+b^2=c^2$

$3^2+4^2=c^2$

$9+16=c^2$

$25=c^2$

$5\text{ meters}=c$

89. $x^{-1}+(2x)^{-1}=\frac{1}{x}+\frac{1}{2x}$

$\frac{2}{2x}+\frac{1}{2x}=\frac{3}{2x}$

91. $4x^{-2}-3x^{-1}=\frac{4}{x^2}-\frac{3}{x}$

$\frac{4}{x^2}-\frac{3x}{x^2}=\frac{4-3x}{x^2}$

93. $x^{-3}(2x+1)-5x^{-2}$

$\frac{2x+1}{x^3}-\frac{5}{x^2}$

$\frac{2x+1}{x^3}-\frac{5x}{x^3}$

$\frac{2x+1-5x}{x^3}$

$\frac{1-3x}{x^3}$

Exercise Set 7.4

1. $\dfrac{\frac{1}{3}}{\frac{2}{5}}=\frac{1}{3}\bullet\frac{5}{2}=\frac{5}{6}$

3. $\dfrac{\frac{4}{x}}{\frac{5}{2x}}=\frac{4}{x}\bullet\frac{2x}{5}=\frac{4}{1}\bullet\frac{2}{5}=\frac{8}{5}$

5. $\dfrac{\frac{10}{3x}}{\frac{5}{6x}}=\frac{10}{3x}\bullet\frac{6x}{5}=\frac{2}{1}\bullet\frac{2}{1}=4$

7. $\dfrac{1+\frac{2}{5}}{2+\frac{3}{5}}=\dfrac{\left(1+\frac{2}{5}\right)5}{\left(2+\frac{3}{5}\right)5}=\dfrac{5+2}{10+3}=\dfrac{7}{13}$

9. $\dfrac{\frac{4}{x-1}}{\frac{x}{x-1}}=\frac{4}{x-1}\bullet\frac{x-1}{x}=\frac{4}{x}$

11. $\dfrac{1-\frac{2}{x}}{x-\frac{4}{9x}}=\dfrac{\left(1-\frac{2}{x}\right)9x}{\left(x-\frac{4}{9x}\right)9x}=\dfrac{9x-18}{9x^2-4}$

13. $\dfrac{\frac{1}{x+1}-1}{\frac{1}{x-1}+1}=\dfrac{\left(\frac{1}{x+1}-1\right)(x+1)(x-1)}{\left(\frac{1}{x-1}+1\right)(x-1)(x+1)}$

$\dfrac{[1-(x+1)](x-1)}{[1+(x-1)](x+1)}=\dfrac{(1-x-1)(x-1)}{(1+x-1)(x+1)}$

$\dfrac{-x(x-1)}{x(x+1)}=\dfrac{-(x-1)}{x+1}=\dfrac{1-x}{x+1}$

15. $\dfrac{x^{-1}}{x^{-2}+y^{-2}}=\dfrac{x^{-1}(x^2y^2)}{(x^{-2}+y^{-2})(x^2y^2)}$

$\dfrac{x^1y^2}{x^0y^2+x^2y^0}=\dfrac{xy^2}{y^2+x^2}$

17. $\dfrac{2a^{-1}+3b^{-2}}{a^{-1}-b^{-1}}=\dfrac{(2a^{-1}+3b^{-2})ab^2}{(a^{-1}-b^{-1})ab^2}$

$\dfrac{2a^0b^2+3ab^0}{a^0b^2-ab^1}=\dfrac{2b^2+3a}{b^2-ab}$

19. $\dfrac{1}{x-x^{-1}}=\dfrac{1\bullet x}{(x-x^{-1})x}=\dfrac{x}{x^2-x^0}=\dfrac{x}{x^2-1}$

21. $\dfrac{\frac{x+1}{7}}{\frac{x+2}{7}}=\frac{x+1}{7}\bullet\frac{7}{x+2}=\frac{x+1}{x+2}$

23. $\dfrac{\frac{1}{2}-\frac{1}{3}}{\frac{3}{4}+\frac{2}{5}}=\dfrac{\left(\frac{1}{2}-\frac{1}{3}\right)60}{\left(\frac{3}{4}+\frac{2}{5}\right)60}=\dfrac{30-20}{45+24}=\dfrac{10}{69}$

25. $\dfrac{\frac{x+1}{3}}{\frac{2x-1}{6}}=\frac{x+1}{3}\bullet\frac{6}{2x-1}$

$\frac{x+1}{1}\bullet\frac{2}{2x-1}$

$$\frac{2(x+1)}{2x-1}$$

27. $\dfrac{\frac{x}{3}}{\frac{2}{x+1}} = \frac{x}{3} \bullet \frac{x+1}{2} = \frac{x(x+1)}{6}$

29. $\dfrac{\frac{2}{x}+3}{\frac{4}{x^2}-9} = \dfrac{\left(\frac{2}{x}+3\right)x^2}{\left(\frac{4}{x^2}-9\right)x^2} = \dfrac{2x+3x^2}{4-9x^2}$

$$\frac{x(2+3x)}{(2-3x)(2+3x)} = \frac{x}{2-3x}$$

31. $\dfrac{1-\frac{x}{y}}{\frac{x^2}{y^2}-1} = \dfrac{\left(1-\frac{x}{y}\right)y^2}{\left(\frac{x^2}{y^2}-1\right)y^2} = \dfrac{y^2-xy}{x^2-y^2}$

$$\frac{y(y-x)}{(x+y)(x-y)} = \frac{y(-1)}{x+y} = \frac{-y}{x+y}$$

33. $\dfrac{\frac{-2x}{x-y}}{\frac{y}{x^2}} = \frac{-2x}{x-y} \bullet \frac{x^2}{y} = \frac{-2x^3}{(x-y)y}$

35. $\dfrac{\frac{2}{x}+\frac{1}{x^2}}{\frac{y}{x^2}} = \dfrac{\left(\frac{2}{x}+\frac{1}{x^2}\right)x^2}{\left(\frac{y}{x^2}\right)x^2} = \dfrac{2x+1}{y}$

37. $\dfrac{\frac{x}{9}-\frac{1}{x}}{1+\frac{3}{x}} = \dfrac{\left(\frac{x}{9}-\frac{1}{x}\right)9x}{\left(1+\frac{3}{x}\right)9x} = \dfrac{x^2-9}{9x+27}$

$$\frac{(x+3)(x-3)}{9(x+3)} = \frac{x-3}{9}$$

39. $\dfrac{\frac{x-1}{x^2-4}}{1+\frac{1}{x-2}}$

$$\frac{\frac{x-1}{(x+2)(x-2)}(x+2)(x-2)}{\left(1+\frac{1}{x-2}\right)(x-2)(x+2)}$$

$$\frac{x-1}{(x-2+1)(x+2)}$$

$$\frac{x-1}{(x-1)(x+2)} = \frac{1}{x+2}$$

41. $\dfrac{\frac{4}{5-x}+\frac{5}{x-5}}{\frac{2}{x}+\frac{3}{x-5}} = \dfrac{-\frac{4}{x-5}+\frac{5}{x-5}}{\frac{2(x-5)+3x}{x(x-5)}}$

$$\frac{\frac{1}{x-5}}{\frac{2x-10+3x}{x(x-5)}} = \frac{1}{x-5} \bullet \frac{x(x-5)}{5x-10}$$

$$\frac{x}{5x-10}$$

43. $\dfrac{\frac{x+2}{x}-\frac{2}{x-1}}{\frac{x+1}{x}+\frac{x+1}{x-1}}$

$$\frac{\frac{(x+2)(x-1)-2x}{x(x-1)}}{\frac{(x+1)(x-1)+(x+1)x}{x(x-1)}}$$

$$\frac{x^2+x-2-2x}{x^2-1+x^2+x}$$

$$\frac{x^2-x-2}{2x^2+x-1}$$

$$\frac{(x-2)(x+1)}{(2x-1)(x+1)} = \frac{x-2}{2x-1}$$

45. $\dfrac{\frac{x-2}{x+2}+\frac{x+2}{x-2}}{\frac{x-2}{x+2}-\frac{x+2}{x-2}}$

$$\frac{\frac{(x-2)(x-2)+(x+2)(x+2)}{(x+2)(x-2)}}{\frac{(x-2)(x-2)-(x+2)(x+2)}{(x+2)(x-2)}}$$

$$\frac{x^2-4x+4+x^2+4x+4}{x^2-4x+4-x^2-4x-4}$$

$$\frac{2x^2+8}{-8x} = -\frac{x^2+4}{4x}$$

47. $\dfrac{\frac{2}{y^2}-\frac{5}{xy}-\frac{3}{x^2}}{\frac{2}{y^2}+\frac{7}{xy}+\frac{3}{x^2}} = \dfrac{\frac{2x^2-5xy-3y^2}{x^2y^2}}{\frac{2x^2+7xy+3y^2}{x^2y^2}}$

$$\frac{(2x+y)(x-3y)}{(2x+y)(x+3y)} = \frac{x-3y}{x+3y}$$

49. $\dfrac{a^{-1}+1}{a^{-1}-1} = \dfrac{a(a^{-1}+1)}{a(a^{-1}-1)} = \dfrac{1+a}{1-a}$

51. $\dfrac{3x^{-1}+(2y)^{-1}}{x^{-2}}=\dfrac{2x^2y}{2x^2y}\bullet\dfrac{[3x^{-1}+(2y)^{-1}]}{x^{-2}}$

$\dfrac{6xy+x^2}{2y}$

53. $\dfrac{2a^{-1}+(2a)^{-1}}{a^{-1}+2a^{-2}}=\dfrac{2a^2[2a^{-1}+(2a)^{-1}]}{2a^2(a^{-1}+2a^{-2})}$

$\dfrac{4a+a}{2a+4}=\dfrac{5a}{2a+4}$

55. $\dfrac{5x^{-1}+2y^{-1}}{x^{-2}y^{-2}}=\dfrac{x^2y^2(5x^{-1}+2y^{-1})}{x^2y^2(x^{-2}y^{-2})}$

$\dfrac{5xy^2+2x^2y}{1}=5xy^2+2x^2y$

57. $\dfrac{5x^{-1}-2y^{-1}}{25x^{-2}-4y^{-2}}=\dfrac{5x^{-1}-2y^{-1}}{(5x^{-1}-2y^{-1})(5x^{-1}+2y^{-1})}$

$\dfrac{1}{5x^{-1}+2y^{-1}}\bullet\dfrac{xy}{xy}=\dfrac{xy}{5y+2x}$

59. $(x^{-1}+y^{-1})^{-1}=\dfrac{1}{x^{-1}+y^{-1}}\bullet\dfrac{xy}{xy}=\dfrac{xy}{y+x}$

61. $\dfrac{x}{1-\dfrac{1}{1+\frac{1}{x}}}=\dfrac{x}{1-\dfrac{x}{x+1}}=\dfrac{x}{\dfrac{x+1-x}{x+1}}$

$x\bullet\dfrac{x+1}{1}=x^2+x$

63. $f(x)=\frac{1}{x}$

a. $f(a+h)=\dfrac{1}{a+h}$

b. $f(a)=\frac{1}{a}$

c. $\dfrac{f(a+h)-f(a)}{h}=\dfrac{\frac{1}{a+h}-\frac{1}{a}}{h}$

d. $\dfrac{f(a+h)-f(a)}{h}=\dfrac{\frac{1}{a+h}\bullet\frac{a}{a}-\frac{1}{a}\bullet\frac{(a+h)}{(a+h)}}{h}$

$\dfrac{f(a+h)-f(a)}{h}=\dfrac{\frac{a}{a(a+h)}-\frac{a+h}{a(a+h)}}{h}$

$\dfrac{f(a+h)-f(a)}{h}=\dfrac{\frac{a-(a+h)}{a(a+h)}}{h}$

$\dfrac{f(a+h)-f(a)}{h}=\dfrac{\frac{a-a-h}{a(a+h)}}{h}$

$\dfrac{f(a+h)-f(a)}{h}=\dfrac{\frac{-h}{a(a+h)}}{h}$

$\dfrac{f(a+h)-f(a)}{h}=\dfrac{-h}{a(a+h)}\bullet\dfrac{1}{h}$

$\dfrac{f(a+h)-f(a)}{h}=\dfrac{-1}{a(a+h)}$

65. $f(x)=\dfrac{3}{x+1}$

a. $f(a+h)=\dfrac{3}{a+h+1}$

b. $f(a)=\dfrac{3}{a+1}$

c. $\dfrac{f(a+h)-f(a)}{h}=\dfrac{\frac{3}{a+h+1}-\frac{3}{a+1}}{h}$

d. $\dfrac{f(a+h)-f(a)}{h}=\dfrac{h(a+h+1)(a+1)\left[\frac{3}{(a+h+1)}-\frac{3}{(a+1)}\right]}{h(a+h+1)(a+1)\bullet[h]}$

$\dfrac{f(a+h)-f(a)}{h}=\dfrac{3h(a+1)-3h(a+h+1)}{h^2(a+h+1)(a+1)}$

$\dfrac{f(a+h)-f(a)}{h}=\dfrac{3ah+3h-3ah-3h^2-3h}{h^2(a+h+1)(a+1)}$

$\dfrac{f(a+h)-f(a)}{h}=\dfrac{-3h^2}{h^2(a+h+1)(a+1)}$

$\dfrac{f(a+h)-f(a)}{h}=\dfrac{-3}{(a+h+1)(a+1)}$

67. $\dfrac{1}{\frac{1}{R_1}+\frac{1}{R_2}}$

$\dfrac{R_1R_2}{R_1R_2}\bullet\dfrac{[1]}{\left[\frac{1}{R_1}+\frac{1}{R_2}\right]}$

$\dfrac{R_1R_2}{R_1R_2\left(\frac{1}{R_1}\right)+R_1R_2\left(\frac{1}{R_2}\right)}$

$\dfrac{R_1R_2}{R_2+R_1}$

69. $4-2x=17-5x$

$3x=13$

$x=\dfrac{13}{3}$

$\left\{\dfrac{13}{3}\right\}$

71. $5x^2 + 10x = 15$

$5(x^2 + 2x - 3) = 0$

$5(x-1)(x+3) = 0$

$x - 1 = 0$ or $x + 3 = 0$

$x = 1$ or $x = -3$

$\{-3,\ 1\}$

73. $\frac{2x}{9} + 1 = \frac{7}{9}$

$\frac{2x}{9} = \frac{-2}{9}$

$2x = -2$

$x = -1$

$\{-1\}$

75. $8y^3 + 1$

$(2y+1)(4y^2 - 2y + 1)$

77. $a^3 - 27$

$(a-3)(a^2 + 3a + 9)$

79. $x^2 - x + xy - y$

$x(x-1) + y(x-1)$

$(x-1)(x+y)$

81. $2x^3 - 32x$

$2x(x^2 - 16)$

$2x(x+4)(x-4)$

83. $\frac{1}{1 + (1+x)^{-1}} = \frac{(1) \bullet (1+x)}{\left(1 + \frac{1}{1+x}\right) \bullet (1+x)}$

$\frac{1+x}{1+x+1} = \frac{1+x}{2+x}$

85. $\frac{(y-1)^{-1} - (y+4)^{-1}}{(y^2 + 3y - 4)^{-1}}$

$$\frac{\left(\frac{1}{y-1} - \frac{1}{y+4}\right) \bullet (y-1)(y+4)}{\left(\frac{1}{y^2+3y-4}\right) \bullet (y-1)(y+4)}$$

$y + 4 - (y-1) = 5$

87. $\frac{9x^{-1} - 5(x-y)^{-1}}{4(x-y)^{-1}}$

$$\frac{\left(\frac{9}{x} - \frac{5}{x-y}\right) \bullet x(x-y)}{\left(\frac{4}{x-y}\right) \bullet x(x-y)}$$

$\frac{9(x-y) - 5x}{4x} = \frac{4x - 9y}{4x}$

Exercise Set 7.5

1. $\frac{x}{2} - \frac{x}{3} = 12$

$3x - 2x = 72$

$x = 72$

$\{72\}$

3. $\frac{x}{3} = \frac{1}{6} + \frac{x}{4}$

$4x = 2 + 3x$

$x = 2$

$\{2\}$

5. $\frac{2}{x} + \frac{1}{2} = \frac{5}{x}$

$\frac{1}{2} = \frac{3}{x}$

$x = 6$

$\{6\}$

7. $\frac{x+3}{x} = \frac{5}{x}$

$x + 3 = 5$

$x = 2$

$\{2\}$

9. $\frac{x+5}{x+3} = \frac{8}{x+3}$

$(x+3) \bullet \frac{x+5}{x+3} = (x+3) \bullet \frac{8}{x+3}$

$x + 5 = 8$

$x = 3$

$\{3\}$

11. $\frac{1}{x-1}+\frac{1}{x+1}=\frac{2}{x^2-1}$

$\frac{x+1+x-1}{(x-1)(x+1)}=\frac{2}{(x+1)(x-1)}$

$2x=2$

$x=1$

which we discard as extraneous.

No solution.

{ }

13. $\frac{6}{x+3}=\frac{4}{x-3}$

$6(x-3)=4(x+3)$

$6x-18=4x+12$

$2x=30$

$x=15$

$\{15\}$

15. $\frac{3}{2x+3}-\frac{1}{2x-3}=\frac{4}{4x^2-9}$

$\frac{3(2x-3)-(2x+3)\bullet 1}{(2x+3)(2x-3)}=\frac{4}{(2x+3)(2x-3)}$

$6x-9-2x-3=4$

$4x-12=4$

$4x=16$

$x=4$

$\{4\}$

17. $\frac{2}{x^2-4}=\frac{1}{2x-4}$

$\frac{4}{2(x+2)(x-2)}=\frac{x+2}{2(x-2)(x+2)}$

$4=x+2$

$x=2$

which we discard as extraneous.

No solution.

{ }

19. $\frac{12}{3x^2+12x}=1-\frac{1}{x+4}$

$\frac{12}{3x(x+4)}=\frac{3x(x+4)-3x}{3x(x+4)}$

$12=3x^2+12x-3x$

$12=3x^2+9x$

$4=x^2+3x$

$x^2+3x-4=0$

$(x+4)(x-1)=0$

$x+4=0$ or $x-1=0$

$x=-4$ or $x=1$

We discard -4 as extraneous.

$x=1$

$\{1\}$

21. $\frac{2}{x}=\frac{10}{5}$

$10=10x$

$x=1$

$\{1\}$

23. $7+\frac{6}{a}=5$

$\frac{6}{a}=-2$

$6=-2a$

$a=-3$

$\{-3\}$

25. $\frac{2}{x-5}+\frac{1}{2x}=\frac{5}{3x^2-15x}$

$\frac{2(2x)+x-5}{2x(x-5)}=\frac{5}{3x(x-5)}$

$\frac{3(4x+x-5)}{6x(x-5)}=\frac{2(5)}{6x(x-5)}$

$12x+3x-15=10$

$15x=25$

$x=\frac{25}{15}=\frac{5}{3}$

$\left\{\frac{5}{3}\right\}$

27. $\frac{x}{4}+\frac{5}{x}=3$

$\frac{x^2+20}{4x}=3$

$x^2+20=12x$

$x^2-12x+20=0$

$(x-10)(x-2)=0$

$x-10=0$ or $x-2=0$

$x = 10 \quad \text{or} \quad x = 2$

$\{2, 10\}$

29. $1 - \frac{5}{y+7} = \frac{4}{y+7}$

$1 = \frac{9}{y+7}$

$y + 7 = 9$

$y = 2$

$\{2\}$

31. $\frac{6x+7}{2x+9} = \frac{5}{3}$

$3(6x+7) = 5(2x+9)$

$18x + 21 = 10x + 45$

$8x = 24$

$x = 3$

$\{3\}$

33. $\frac{2x+1}{4-x} = \frac{9}{4-x}$

$2x + 1 = 9$

$2x = 8$

$x = 4$

which we discard as extraneous.

No solution.

$\{\ \}$

35. $\frac{12}{9-a^2} + \frac{3}{3+a} = \frac{2}{3-a}$

$\frac{12}{(3+a)(3-a)} + \frac{3(3-a)}{(3+a)(3-a)} = \frac{2(3+a)}{(3-a)(3+a)}$

$12 + 9 - 3a = 6 + 2a$

$21 - 3a = 6 + 2a$

$15 = 5a$

$3 = a$

which we discard as extraneous.

No solution.

$\{\ \}$

37. $2 + \frac{3}{x} = \frac{2x}{x+3}$

$\frac{2x+3}{x} = \frac{2x}{x+3}$

$(2x+3)(x+3) = 2x \bullet x$

$2x^2 + 9x + 9 = 2x^2$

$9x + 9 = 0$

$9x = -9$

$x = -1$

$\{-1\}$

39. $\frac{36}{x^2-9} + 1 = \frac{2x}{x+3}$

$\frac{36 + x^2 - 9}{(x+3)(x-3)} = \frac{2x(x-3)}{(x+3)(x-3)}$

$x^2 + 27 = 2x^2 - 6x$

$x^2 - 6x - 27 = 0$

$(x-9)(x+3) = 0$

$x - 9 = 0 \quad \text{or} \quad x + 3 = 0$

$x = 9 \quad \text{or} \quad x = -3$

We discard -3 as extraneous.

$x = 9$

$\{9\}$

41. $\frac{x^2-20}{x^2-7x+12} = \frac{3}{x-3} + \frac{5}{x-4}$

$\frac{x^2-20}{(x-3)(x-4)} = \frac{3(x-4)+5(x-3)}{(x-3)(x-4)}$

$x^2 - 20 = 3x - 12 + 5x - 15$

$x^2 - 20 = 8x - 27$

$x^2 - 8x + 7 = 0$

$(x-1)(x-7) = 0$

$x - 1 = 0 \quad \text{or} \quad x - 7 = 0$

$x = 1 \quad \text{or} \quad x = 7$

$\{1, 7\}$

43. $\frac{3}{2x-5} + \frac{2}{2x+3} = 0$

$\frac{3(2x+3) + 2(2x-5)}{(2x-5)(2x+3)} = 0$

$6x + 9 + 4x - 10 = 0$

$10x - 1 = 0$

$10x = 1$

$x = \frac{1}{10}$

$\left\{\frac{1}{10}\right\}$

45. $\frac{3}{x^2-25} = \frac{1}{x+5} + \frac{2}{x-5}$

$\frac{3}{(x+5)(x-5)} = \frac{x-5+2(x+5)}{(x+5)(x-5)}$

$3 = x - 5 + 2x + 10$

$3 = 3x + 5$

$3x = -2$

$x = -\frac{2}{3}$

$\left\{-\frac{2}{3}\right\}$

47. $\frac{5}{x^2-3x} \div \frac{4}{2x-6}$

$\frac{5}{x(x-3)} \bullet \frac{2(x-3)}{4}$

$\frac{5}{x} \bullet \frac{1}{2} = \frac{5}{2x}$

49. $\left(1-\frac{y}{x}\right) \div \left(1-\frac{x}{y}\right)$

$\frac{x-y}{x} \div \frac{y-x}{y}$

$\frac{x-y}{x} \bullet \frac{y}{-(x-y)}$

$\frac{1}{x} \bullet \frac{y}{-1} = \frac{-y}{x}$

51. $\frac{2}{a-6} + \frac{3a}{a^2-5a-6} - \frac{a}{5a+5}$

$\frac{2}{a-6} + \frac{3a}{(a-6)(a+1)} - \frac{a}{5(a+1)}$

$\frac{2[5(a+1)] + 3a(5) - a(a-6)}{5(a-6)(a+1)}$

$\frac{10a + 10 + 15a - a^2 + 6a}{5(a-6)(a+1)}$

$\frac{-a^2 + 31a + 10}{5(a-6)(a+1)}$

53. $\frac{5x-3}{2x} = \frac{10x+3}{4x+1}$

$(5x-3)(4x+1) = 2x(10x+3)$

$20x^2 - 7x - 3 = 20x^2 + 6x$

$-7x - 3 = 6x$

$-3 = 13x$

$x = -\frac{3}{13}$

$\left\{-\frac{3}{13}\right\}$

55. $\frac{3}{4a-8} - \frac{a+2}{a^2-2a}$

$\frac{3}{4(a-2)} - \frac{a+2}{a(a-2)}$

$\frac{3a}{4a(a-2)} - \frac{4(a+2)}{4a(a-2)}$

$\frac{3a-4a-8}{4a(a-2)}$

$\frac{-a-8}{4a(a-2)}$

57. $\frac{x}{2x+6} + \frac{5}{x^2-9}$

$\frac{x}{2(x+3)} + \frac{5}{(x+3)(x-3)}$

$\frac{x(x-3)}{2(x+3)(x-3)} + \frac{2(5)}{2(x+3)(x-3)}$

$\frac{x^2-3x+10}{2(x+3)(x-3)}$

59. $\frac{x-8}{x^2-x-2} + \frac{2}{x-2} = \frac{3}{x+1}$

$\frac{x-8}{(x-2)(x+1)} + \frac{2(x+1)}{(x-2)(x+1)} = \frac{3(x-2)}{(x+1)(x-2)}$

$x - 8 + 2x + 2 = 3x - 6$

$3x - 6 = 3x - 6$

$-6 = -6$

All real numbers except 2 and -1.

$\{x|x$ is a real number and

$x \neq -1,\ x \neq 2\}$

61. $\frac{7}{3z-9} + \frac{5}{z} = \frac{7}{3(z-3)} + \frac{5}{z}$

$\frac{7z + 5[3(z-3)]}{3z(z-3)}$

$\frac{7z + 15z - 45}{3z(z-3)}$

$\frac{22z-45}{3z(z-3)}$

63. $x^{-2}-5x^{-1}-36=0$

$\frac{1}{x^2}-\frac{5}{x}-36=0$

$1-5x-36x^2=0$

$36x^2+5x-1=0$

$(9x-1)(4x+1)=0$

$9x-1=0$ or $4x+1=0$

$9x=1$ or $4x=-1$

$x=\frac{1}{9}$ or $x=-\frac{1}{4}$

$\left\{-\frac{1}{4}, \frac{1}{9}\right\}$

65. $6p^{-2}-5p^{-1}+1=0$

$\frac{6}{p^2}-\frac{5}{p}+1=0$

$6-5p+p^2=0$

$p^2-5p+6=0$

$(p-3)(p-2)=0$

$p-3=0$ or $p-2=0$

$p=3$ or $p=2$

$\{2, 3\}$

67. Let $n=$ 1st integer
$n+1=$ 2nd integer.

$n+(n+1)=147$

$2n+1=147$

$2n=146$

$n=73$

The integers are 73 and 74.

69. Let $x=$ the number.

$\frac{1}{x}=$ the reciprocal of the number.

$x+\frac{1}{x}=\frac{5}{2}$

$\frac{x^2+1}{x}=\frac{5}{2}$

$2x^2+2=5x$

$2x^2-5x+2=0$

$(2x-1)(x-2)=0$

$2x-1=0$ or $x-2=0$

$2x=1$ or $x=2$

$x=\frac{1}{2}$

The reciprocal pair is 2 and $\frac{1}{2}$.

71. $\sqrt{49}-(10-6)^2=7-4^2=7-16=-9$

73. $(-4)^2-5^2=16-25=-9$

75. 1%

77. 21% + 46%

67%

79. $(x-1)^2+3(x-1)+2=0$

Let $u=x-1$

$u^2+3u+2=0$

$(u+1)(u+2)=0$

$u+1=0$ or $u+2=0$

$u=-1$ or $u=-2$

Substituting $x-1$ for u,

$x-1=-1$ or $x-1=-2$

$x=0$ or $x=-1$

$\{-1, 0\}$

81. $\left(\frac{3}{x-1}\right)^2+2\left(\frac{3}{x-1}\right)+1=0$

Let $u=\frac{3}{x-1}$

$u^2+2u+1=0$

$(u+1)^2=0$

$u+1=0$

$u=-1$

Substituting $\frac{3}{x-1}$ for u,

$\frac{3}{x-1}=-1$

$(x-1)\left(\frac{3}{x-1}\right)=-1(x-1)$

$3=-x+1$

$x=-2$

$\{-2\}$

Exercise Set 7.6

1. $F = \frac{9}{5}C + 32$

$F - 32 = \frac{9}{5}C$

$C = \frac{5}{9}(F - 32)$

3. $\frac{1}{R} = \frac{1}{R_1} + \frac{1}{R_2}$

$\frac{1}{R} = \frac{R_2 + R_1}{R_1 R_2}$

$R = \frac{R_1 R_2}{R_1 + R_2}$

5. $S = \frac{n(a + L)}{2}$

$2S = n(a + L)$

$n = \frac{2S}{a + L}$

7. Let $n =$ the number.

$\frac{1}{n} =$ reciprocal of the number.

$n + 5\left(\frac{1}{n}\right) = 6$

$n + \frac{5}{n} = 6$

$\frac{n^2 + 5}{n} = 6$

$n^2 + 5 = 6n$

$n^2 - 6n + 5 = 0$

$(n - 1)(n - 5) = 0$

$n - 1 = 0$ or $n - 5 = 0$

$n = 1$ or $n = 5$

The number is either 1 or 5.

9. Let $x =$ the number.

$\frac{12 + x}{41 + 2x} = \frac{1}{3}$

$3(12 + x) = (41 + 2x) \bullet 1$

$36 + 3x = 41 + 2x$

$x = 5$

The number is 5.

11. $r = 2$ ohms and $r_1 = 3$ ohms.

$\frac{1}{r} = \frac{1}{r_1} + \frac{1}{r_2}$

$\frac{1}{2} = \frac{1}{3} + \frac{1}{r_2}$

$\frac{1}{2} = \frac{r_2 + 3}{3r_2}$

$3r_2 = 2(r_2 + 3)$

$3r_2 = 2r_2 + 6$

$r_2 = 6$

The other resistance is 6 ohms.

13. For three resistance r_1, r_2, and r_3 wired in a parallel circuit, the combined resistance r is given by

$\frac{1}{r} = \frac{1}{r_1} + \frac{1}{r_2} + \frac{1}{r_3}$

$\frac{1}{r} = \frac{1}{5} + \frac{1}{6} + \frac{1}{2}$

$\frac{1}{r} = \frac{6 + 5 + 15}{30}$

$\frac{1}{r} = \frac{26}{30} = \frac{13}{15}$

$r = \frac{15}{13}$

The combined resistance is $\frac{15}{13}$ ohms.

15. Let $x =$ the number of hours needed to roof the house when two roofers are working together. Convert times to rates.

$\frac{1 \text{ roof}}{26 \text{ hrs}} = \frac{1}{26} \frac{\text{roof}}{\text{hr}}$

$\frac{1 \text{ roof}}{39 \text{ hrs}} = \frac{1}{39} \frac{\text{roof}}{\text{hr}}$

$\frac{1 \text{ roof}}{x \text{ hrs}} = \frac{1}{x} \frac{\text{roof}}{\text{hr}}$

Now, their combined rate can be expressed in two different but equivalent ways.

$\frac{1}{26} + \frac{1}{36} = \frac{1}{x}$

$\frac{3 + 2}{78} = \frac{1}{x}$

$\frac{5}{78} = \frac{1}{x}$ so $x = \frac{78}{5} = 15.6$

The roofers together can roof a house in 15.6 hrs.

17. Convert each time to a rate.

$\frac{1 \text{ task}}{20 \text{ min}} = \frac{1}{20} \frac{\text{task}}{\text{min}}$

$\frac{1\text{ task}}{30\text{ min}} = \frac{1}{30}\frac{\text{task}}{\text{min}}$

$\frac{1\text{ task}}{60\text{ min}} = \frac{1}{60}\frac{\text{task}}{\text{min}}$

Let $x =$ amount of time required for all three computers to complete the task. So

$\frac{1\text{ task}}{x\text{ min}} = \frac{1}{x}\frac{\text{task}}{\text{min}}$. Summing we get,

$\frac{1}{20} + \frac{1}{30} + \frac{1}{60} = \frac{1}{x}$

$\frac{3+2+1}{60} = \frac{1}{x}$

$\frac{6}{60} = \frac{1}{x}$

$\frac{1}{10} = \frac{1}{x}$ so $x = 10$ min.

It takes 10 minutes for the three computers to complete the task.

19. Let $r =$ the speed of the plane and $r - 150 =$ the speed of the car. Recall that $d = rt$ or $t = \frac{d}{r}$. Then using that latter formula we get:

$\frac{150}{r - 150} = \frac{600}{r}$ or

$\frac{1}{r - 150} = \frac{4}{r}$

$r = 4(r - 150)$

$r = 4r - 600$

$600 = 3r$

$r = 200$

The speed of the plane is 200 mph.

21. Let $r =$ the speed of the boat in still water. Recall that $d = rt$ or $t = \frac{d}{r}$. Using the latter equation we get: $\frac{20}{r+5} = \frac{10}{r-5}$ where $r + 5$ is the rate of the boat traveling downstream and $r - 5$ is the rate of the boat traveling upstream. Now,

$\frac{2}{r+5} = \frac{1}{r-5}$

$2(r-5) = r+5$

$2r - 10 = r + 5$

$r = 15$

Thus, the speed of the boat in still water is 15 mph.

23. $A = \frac{h(a+b)}{2}$

$2A = h(a+b)$

$h = \frac{2A}{a+b}$

25. $H = \frac{kA(T_1 - T_2)}{L}$

$LH = kA(T_1 - T_2)$

$\frac{LH}{kA} = T_1 - T_2$

$T_2 = T_1 - \frac{LH}{kA}$

27. $I = \frac{E}{R+r}$

$R + r = \frac{E}{I}$

$r = \frac{E}{I} - R$

29. $S = \frac{a_1 - a_n r}{1 - r}$

$S(1 - r) = a_1 - a_n r$

$a_1 = S(1 - r) + a_n r$

31. $F = \frac{-GMm}{r^2}$

$r^2F = -GMm$

$M = \frac{r^2F}{-Gm} = -\frac{r^2F}{Gm}$

33. Let $n =$ an integer and $n + 1 =$ the next integer.

$\frac{1}{n} + \frac{1}{n+1} = -\frac{15}{56}$

$\frac{(n+1)+n}{n(n+1)} = \frac{-15}{56}$

$\frac{2n+1}{n^2+n} = \frac{-15}{56}$

$56(2n+1) = -15(n^2+n)$

$112n + 56 = -15n^2 - 15n$

$15n^2+127n+56=0$

$(15n+7)(n+8)=0$

$15n+7=0$ or $n+8=0$

$15n=-7$ or $n=-8$

$n=-\frac{7}{15}$

Discarding the noninteger solution, we find that -8 and -7 are the integers.

35. Convert times to rates.

$\frac{1 \text{ pond}}{45 \text{ min}}=\frac{1}{45} \frac{\text{pond}}{\text{min}}$

$\frac{1 \text{ pond}}{20 \text{ min}}=\frac{1}{20} \frac{\text{pond}}{\text{min}}$

Let $x=$ the number of minutes required for the second hose to fill the pond. Then,

$\frac{1 \text{ pond}}{x \text{ min}}=\frac{1}{x} \frac{\text{pond}}{\text{min}}$ Now,

$\frac{1}{20}=\frac{1}{45}+\frac{1}{x}$

$\frac{1}{20}=\frac{x+45}{45x}$

$45x=20(x+45)$

$45x=20x+900$

$25x=900$

$x=\frac{900}{25}=36$

Thus, the second hose alone can fill the pond in 36 minutes.

37. Let $r=$ the rate of one train so $r+15=$ the rate of the other train. Note that the trains are moving apart at $r+(r+15)=2r+15$. Recall that $d=rt$ or $r=\frac{d}{t}$. Therefore,

$2r+15=\frac{630}{6}$

$2r+15=105$

$2r=90$

$r=45$

Thus, one train travels at 45 mph and the other train at 60 mph.

39.

	distance	= rate	• time
First part	20	r	$\frac{20}{r}$
Cooldown	16	$r-2$	$\frac{16}{r-2}$

$\frac{20}{r}=\frac{16}{r-2}$

$20(r-2)=16r$

$20r-40=16r$

$20r-16r=40$

$4r=40$

$r=\frac{40}{4}=10$

The first part is at 10 mph, and the cooldown at 8 mph.

41.

	Hours to complete	Part of job completed in one hour
Machine #1	5	$\frac{1}{5}$
Machine #2	6	$\frac{1}{6}$
Machine #3	7.5	$\frac{1}{7.5}$
Together	t	$\frac{1}{t}$

$\frac{1}{5}+\frac{1}{6}+\frac{1}{7.5}=\frac{1}{t}$

$(225t)\left(\frac{1}{5}+\frac{1}{6}+\frac{1}{7.5}\right)=\frac{1}{t}(225t)$

$45t+37.5t+30t=225$

$112.5t=225$

$t=2$ hrs.

43.

	distance	= rate	• time
with wind	465	$x+20$	$\frac{465}{x+20}$
against wind	345	$x-20$	$\frac{345}{x-20}$

$\frac{465}{x+20}=\frac{345}{x-20}$

$465(x-20)=345(x+20)$

$465x-9300=345x+6900$

$120x=16200$

$x=135$ mph.

45.

	distance	= rate	• time
jogger 1	x	8	$\frac{x}{8}$
jogger 2	x	6	$\frac{x}{6}$

$\frac{x}{8}=\frac{x}{6}-\frac{1}{2}$

$24\left(\frac{x}{8}\right)=\left(\frac{x}{6}-\frac{1}{2}\right)(24)$

$3x=4x-12$

12 miles = x

47.

	Time	In one hour
Experienced	4	$\frac{1}{4}$
Apprentice	5	$\frac{1}{5}$
Together	x	$\frac{1}{x}$

$\frac{1}{4}+\frac{1}{5}=\frac{1}{x}$

$20x\left(\frac{1}{4}+\frac{1}{5}\right)=20x\left(\frac{1}{x}\right)$

$20x\left(\frac{1}{4}\right)+20x\left(\frac{1}{5}\right)=20$

$5x+4x=20$

$9x=20$

$x=\frac{20}{9}=2\frac{2}{9}$ hours

49.

	distance	= rate	• time
Car	240	$\frac{240}{x+1}$	x + 1
Jet	1080	$\frac{1080}{x}$	x

$\frac{1080}{x}=6\left(\frac{240}{x+1}\right)$

$\frac{1080}{x}=\frac{1440}{x+1}$

$1080x+1080=1440x$

$1080=360x$

$\frac{360x}{360}=\frac{1080}{360}$

$x=3$

Jet = 3 hrs.
Car = 4 hrs.

51.

	Time	In one minute
Belt	2	$\frac{1}{2}$
Smaller	6	$\frac{1}{6}$
Together	x	$\frac{1}{x}$

$\frac{1}{2}+\frac{1}{6}=\frac{1}{x}$

$6x\left(\frac{1}{2}+\frac{1}{6}\right)=6x\left(\frac{1}{x}\right)$

$6x\left(\frac{1}{2}\right)+6x\left(\frac{1}{6}\right)=6$

$3x+x=6$

$4x=6$

$x=\frac{6}{4}=\frac{3}{2}=1\frac{1}{2}$ minutes

53. Let x = speed of car in still air

	distance	= rate	• time
Into wind	10	x − 3	$\frac{10}{x-3}$
With the wind	11	x + 3	$\frac{11}{x+3}$

$\frac{10}{x-3}=\frac{11}{x+3}$

$10\bullet(x+3)=11\bullet(x-3)$

$10x+30=11x-33$

$30+33=11x-10x$

63 mph = x

55. $\frac{x}{5}=\frac{x+2}{3}$

$3x=5(x+2)$

$3x=5x+10$

$-10=2x$

$x=-5$

$\{-5\}$

57. $\frac{x-3}{2}=\frac{x-5}{6}$

$6(x-3)=2(x-5)$

$6x-18=2x-10$

$4x=8$

$x=2$

$\{2\}$

59. $2x^3 - 9x^2 - 18x$

$x(2x^2 - 9x - 18)$

$x(2x+3)(x-6)$

61. $x^3 + 8 = x^3 + 2^3$

$(x+2)(x^2 - 2x + 4)$

63. 25%

65. 25% + 59%

84%

67. answers vary

Exercise Set 7.7

1. $A = kB$

3. $X = \frac{k}{Z}$

5. $N = kP^2$

7. $T = \frac{k}{R}$

9. $P = kR$

11. $A = kB$

$60 = k(12)$

$k = 5$

$A = 5B$

$A = 5(9)$

$A = 45$

13. $V = kT$

$20 = k(300)$

$k = \frac{20}{300} = \frac{1}{15}$

$V = \frac{1}{15}T$

$V = \frac{1}{15}(360)$

$V = 24m^3$

15. $H = \frac{k}{J}$

$4 = \frac{k}{5}$

$k = 20$

$H = \frac{20}{J}$

$H = \frac{20}{2}$

$H = 10$

17. $I = \frac{k}{R}$

$40 = \frac{k}{270}$

$k = 10{,}800$

$I = \frac{10{,}800}{R}$

$I = \frac{10{,}800}{150}$

$I = 72$ amps.

19. $x = kyz$

21. $r = kst^3$

23. $Q = kR$

$4 = k(20)$

$k = \frac{1}{5}$

$Q = \frac{1}{5}R = \frac{1}{5}(35) = 7$

25. $M = kP$

$8 = k(20)$

$k = \frac{8}{20} = \frac{2}{5}$

$M = \frac{2}{5}P = \frac{2}{5}(24) = \frac{48}{5}$

27. $B = \frac{k}{C}$

$12 = \frac{k}{3}$

$k = 36$

$B = \frac{36}{C} = \frac{36}{18} = 2$

29. $W = \frac{k}{X}$

$18 = \frac{k}{6}$

$k = 108$

$W = \frac{108}{X} = \frac{108}{40} = \frac{27}{10} = 2.7$

31. $W = kr^3$

$1.2 = k \bullet 2^3$

$k = \frac{1.2}{8} = 0.15$

$W = 0.15r^3 = 0.15(3)^3$

$W = 0.15(27) = 4.05$ lbs.

33. $C = \frac{k}{n}$

$1.20 = \frac{k}{4000}$

$k = 1.20(4000) = 4800$

$C = \frac{4800}{n} = \frac{4800}{6000} = \$0.80$

35. $C = kWt$

$60 = k(200)(2)$

$60 = 400k$

$k = \frac{60}{400} = \frac{3}{20} = 0.15$

$C = 0.15Wt = 0.15(240)(3) = 108$ cars

37. $F = kAv$

$20 = k(12)(10)$

$20 = 120k$

$k = \frac{1}{6}$

$F = \frac{1}{6}Av = \frac{1}{6}(8)12 = 16$ lbs.

39. $L = \frac{kd^4}{l^2}$

$16 = \frac{k(8^4)}{10^2}$

$16 = \frac{4096k}{100}$

$k = \frac{1600}{4096} = \frac{25}{64}$

$L = \frac{25d^4}{641^2}$

$L = \frac{25(6^4)}{64(8^2)}$

$L = \frac{2025}{256}$ tons

$L = 7.91$ tons

41. $A_1 = kr^2$

Replace r by 3r.

$A_2 = k(3r)^2$

$A_2 = k(9r^2)$

$A_2 = 9(kr^2)$

$A_2 = 9A_1$

Thus, the area is multiplied by 9.

43. $I_1 = \frac{k}{d^2}$

Replace d by 2d.

$I_2 = \frac{k}{(2d)^2} = \frac{k}{4d^2} = \frac{1}{4}I_1$

Thus, the intensity is divided by 4.

45. $r = 4$ in.

$C = 2\pi(4) = 8\pi$ in.

$A = \pi(4^2) = 16\pi$ in.^{2}

47. $r = 9$ cm.

$C = 2\pi(9) = 18\pi$ cm.

$A = 2\pi(9^2) = 81\pi$ cm^2.

49. $(-5, -2)$, $(0, 7)$

$m = \frac{7-(-2)}{0-(-5)} = \frac{7+2}{5} = \frac{9}{5}$

51. $(2, 1)$, $(2-3)$

$m = \frac{-3-1}{2-2} = \frac{-4}{0}$

The slope is undefined.

53.

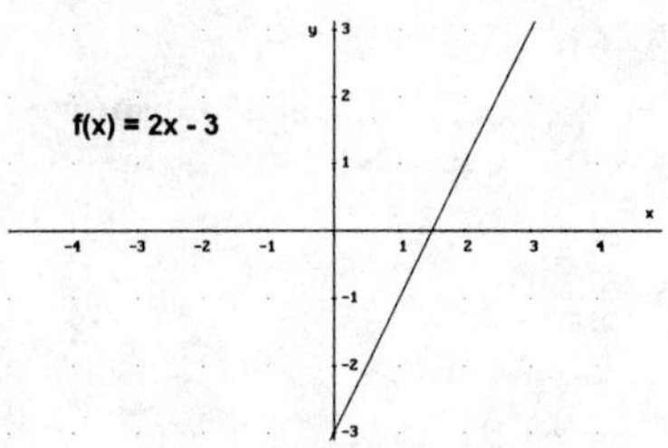

55.

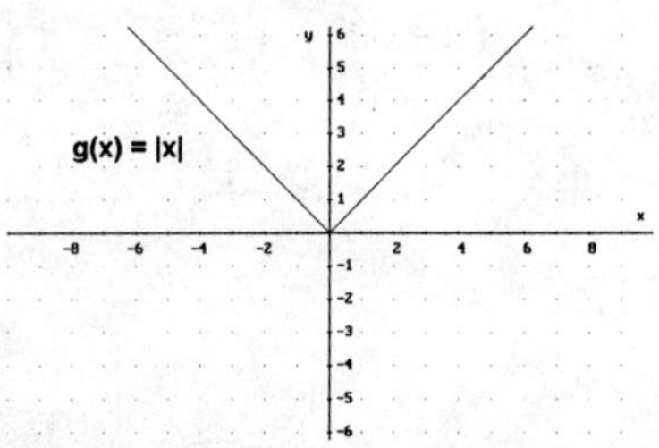

57.

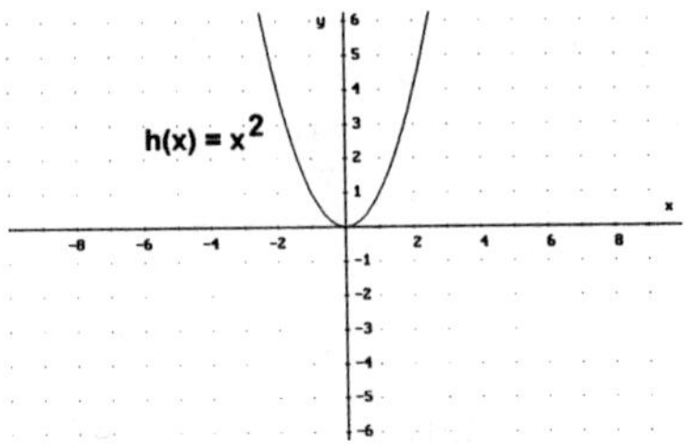

Chapter 7 - Review

1. $f(x) = \frac{3-5x}{7}$

   Domain $\{x|x \text{ is a real number}\}$

3. $F(x) = \frac{-3x^2}{x-5}$

   Undefined value when

   $x - 5 = 0$

   $x = 5$

   Domain $\{x|x \text{ is a real number and } x \neq 5\}$

5. $f(x) = \frac{x^3+2}{x^2+8x}$

   Undefined values when

   $x^2 + 8x = 0$

   $x(x+8) = 0$

   $x = 0 \quad \text{or} \quad x + 8 = 0$

   $x = -8$

   Domain $\{x|x \text{ is a real number and } x \neq 0,\ x \neq -8\}$

7. $\frac{15x^4}{45x^2} = \frac{x^2}{3}$

9. $\frac{18m^6p^2}{10m^4p} = \frac{9m^2p}{5}$

11. $\frac{5x-15}{25x-75} = \frac{5(x-3)}{25(x-3)} = \frac{1}{5}$

13. $\frac{2x}{2x^2-2x} = \frac{2x}{2x(x-1)} = \frac{1}{x-1}$

15. $\frac{2x^2+4x-30}{x^2+x-20} = \frac{2(x^2+2x-15)}{x^2+x-20}$

    $\frac{2(x-3)(x+5)}{(x-4)(x+5)} = \frac{2(x-3)}{x-4}$

17. $C(x) = \frac{35x+4200}{x}$

    $C(50) = \frac{35(50)+4200}{50}$

    $C(50) = \frac{1750+4200}{50}$

    $C(50) = \frac{5950}{50}$

    $C(50) = 119$

    $C(1000) = \frac{35(1000)+4200}{50}$

    $C(1000) = \frac{35000+4200}{50}$

    $C(1000) = \frac{39200}{50}$

    $C(1000) = 784$

19. $\frac{3x^4yz^3}{15x^2y^2} \bullet \frac{10xy}{z^6}$

    $\frac{30x^{4+1}y^{1+1}z^3}{15x^2y^2z^6}$

    $\frac{30x^5y^2z^3}{15x^2y^2z^6}$

    $\frac{2x^{5-2}}{z^{6-3}} = \frac{2x^3}{z^3}$

21. $\frac{x^2-6x+9}{2x^2-18} \bullet \frac{4x+12}{5x-15}$

    $\frac{(x-3)^2}{2(x^2-9)} \bullet \frac{4(x+3)}{5(x-3)}$

    $\frac{x-3}{(x+3)(x-3)} \bullet \frac{2(x+3)}{5}$

    $\frac{1}{1} \bullet \frac{2}{5} = \frac{2}{5}$

23. $\frac{x^2-x-12}{2x^2-32} \bullet \frac{x^2+8x+16}{3x^2+21x+36}$

    $\frac{(x-4)(x+3)}{2(x^2-16)} \bullet \frac{(x+4)^2}{3(x^2+7x+12)}$

    $\frac{(x-4)(x+3)(x+4)^2}{6(x+4)(x-4)(x+3)(x+4)}$

$\frac{1}{6}$

25. $\frac{3}{4x} \div \frac{8}{2x^2} = \frac{3}{4x} \bullet \frac{2x^2}{8} = \frac{6x^2}{32x} = \frac{3x}{16}$

27. $\frac{5ab}{14c^3} \div \frac{10a^4b^2}{6ac^5}$

$\frac{5ab}{14c^3} \bullet \frac{6ac^5}{10a^4b^2}$

$\frac{30a^2bc^5}{140a^4b^2c^3}$

$\frac{3c^{5-3}}{14a^{4-2}b^{2-1}}$

$\frac{3c^2}{14a^2b}$

29. $\frac{x^2-25}{3} \div \frac{x^2-10x+25}{x^2-x-20}$

$\frac{(x+5)(x-5)}{3} \bullet \frac{(x-5)(x+4)}{(x-5)^2}$

$\frac{(x+5)(x+4)}{3} = \frac{x^2+9x+20}{3}$

31. $\frac{7x+28}{2x+4} \div \frac{x^2+2x-8}{x^2-2x-8}$

$\frac{7(x+4)}{2(x+2)} \bullet \frac{(x-4)(x+2)}{(x+4)(x-2)}$

$\frac{7(x-4)}{2(x-2)} = \frac{7x-28}{2(x-2)}$

33. $\frac{2x-x^2}{x^3-8} \div \frac{x^2}{x^2+2x+4}$

$\frac{x(2-x)}{(x-2)(x^2+2x+4)} \bullet \frac{x^2+2x+4}{x^2}$

$\frac{-(x-2)}{x-2} \bullet \frac{1}{x} = -1 \bullet \frac{1}{x} = -\frac{1}{x}$

35. $\frac{2a}{21} \div \frac{3a^2}{7} \bullet \frac{4}{a} = \frac{2a}{21} \bullet \frac{7}{3a^2} \bullet \frac{4}{a} = \frac{56a}{63a^3} = \frac{8}{9a^2}$

37. $\frac{4a+8}{5a^2-20} \bullet \frac{3a^2-6a}{a+3} \div \frac{2a^2}{5a+15}$

$\frac{4(a+2)}{5(a^2-4)} \bullet \frac{3a(a-2)}{a+3} \bullet \frac{5(a+3)}{2a^2}$

$\frac{60a(a+2)(a-2)(a+3)}{10a^2(a+2)(a-2)(a+3)}$

$\frac{6}{a}$

39. $\frac{5}{4x^2y^5}, \frac{3}{10x^2y^4}, \frac{x}{6y^4}$

The LCD is $60x^2y^5$.

41. $\frac{3}{5x}, \frac{2}{x-5}$

The LCD is $5x(x-5)$.

43. $\frac{2}{15} + \frac{4}{15} = \frac{2+4}{15} = \frac{6}{15} = \frac{2}{5}$

45. $\frac{4}{3x^2} + \frac{2}{3x^2} = \frac{4+2}{3x^2} = \frac{6}{3x^2} = \frac{2}{x^2}$

47. $\frac{2x+1}{x^2+x-6} + \frac{2-x}{x^2+x-6}$

$\frac{2x+1+2-x}{x^2+x-6}$

$\frac{x+3}{(x+3)(x-2)}$

$\frac{1}{x-2}$

49. $\frac{1}{3x^2y^3} - \frac{1}{5x^4y} = \frac{5x^2}{15x^4y^3} - \frac{3y^2}{15x^4y^3} = \frac{5x^2-3y^2}{15x^4y^3}$

51. $\frac{x-2}{x+1} - \frac{x-3}{x-1}$

$\frac{(x-2)(x-1)-(x-3)(x+1)}{(x+1)(x-1)}$

$\frac{x^2-3x+2-(x^2-2x-3)}{(x+1)(x-1)}$

$\frac{x^2-3x+2-x^2+2x+3}{(x+1)(x-1)}$

$\frac{-x+5}{x^2-1}$

53. $2x+1-\frac{1}{x-3}$

$\frac{(2x+1)(x-3)-1}{x-3}$

$\frac{2x^2-5x-3-1}{x-3}$

$\frac{2x^2-5x-4}{x-3}$

55. $\frac{x}{9x^2+12x+16} - \frac{3x+4}{27x^3-64}$

$\frac{x}{9x^2+12x+16} - \frac{3x+4}{(3x-4)(9x^2+12x+16)}$

$$\frac{(3x-4)x-(3x+4)}{(3x-4)(9x^2+12x+16)}$$

$$\frac{3x^2-4x-3x-4}{(3x-4)(9x^2+12x+16)}$$

$$\frac{3x^2-7x-4}{27x^3-64}$$

57. $\frac{3}{2x}\left(\frac{2}{x+1}-\frac{2}{x-3}\right)$

$$\frac{3}{x}\left(\frac{1}{x+1}-\frac{1}{x-3}\right)$$

$$\frac{3}{x}\left[\frac{x-3-(x+1)}{(x+1)(x-3)}\right]$$

$$\frac{3}{x}\bullet\frac{x-3-x-1}{(x+1)(x-3)}$$

$$\frac{3(-4)}{x(x+1)(x-3)}$$

$$\frac{-12}{x(x+1)(x-3)}$$

59. $\left(\frac{2}{x}-\frac{1}{5}\right)\left(\frac{2}{x}+\frac{1}{3}\right)$

$$\frac{10-x}{5x}\bullet\frac{6+x}{3x}$$

$$\frac{60+4x-x^2}{15x^2}$$

61. $\left(\frac{x}{x+5}\right)^2-1$

$$\frac{x^2-(x+5)^2}{(x+5)^2}$$

$$\frac{x^2-(x^2+10x+25)}{(x+5)^2}$$

$$\frac{x^2-x^2-10x-25}{(x+5)^2}$$

$$\frac{-10x-25}{(x+5)^2}$$

63. $\frac{\frac{2}{5}}{\frac{3}{5}}=\frac{2}{5}\bullet\frac{5}{3}=\frac{2}{1}\bullet\frac{1}{3}=\frac{2}{3}$

65. $\frac{\frac{1}{x}-\frac{2}{3x}}{\frac{5}{2x}-\frac{1}{3}}=\frac{\frac{3x-2x}{3x^2}}{\frac{15-2x}{6x}}$

$$\frac{x}{3x^2}\bullet\frac{6x}{15-2x}$$

$$\frac{6x^2}{3x^2(15-2x)}$$

$$\frac{2}{15-2x}$$

67. $\frac{\frac{3}{y^2}}{\frac{6}{y^3}}=\frac{3}{y^2}\bullet\frac{y^3}{6}=\frac{y}{2}$

69. $\frac{2-\frac{3}{2x}}{x-\frac{2}{5x}}=\frac{\frac{4x-3}{2x}}{\frac{5x^2-2}{5x}}$

$$\frac{4x-3}{2x}\bullet\frac{5x}{5x^2-2}$$

$$\frac{5(4x-3)}{2(5x^2-2)}=\frac{20x-15}{2(5x^2-2)}$$

71. $\frac{\frac{5}{x}+\frac{1}{xy}}{\frac{3}{x^2}}=\frac{5y+1}{xy}\bullet\frac{x^3}{3}$

$$\frac{x^2(5y+1)}{3y}=\frac{5x^2y+x^2}{3y}$$

73. $\frac{\frac{1}{x-1}+1}{\frac{1}{x+1}-1}=\frac{\frac{1+x-1}{x-1}}{\frac{1-(x+1)}{x+1}}$

$$\frac{x}{x-1}\bullet\frac{x+1}{1-x-1}$$

$$\frac{x(x+1)}{-x(x-1)}$$

$$\frac{x+1}{-(x-1)}$$

$$\frac{1+x}{1-x}$$

75. $\frac{1}{1+\frac{2}{1-\frac{1}{x}}}=\frac{1}{1+\frac{2x}{x-1}}$

$$\frac{1}{\frac{x-1+2x}{x-1}}=\frac{x-1}{3x-1}$$

77. $$\frac{\frac{x-3}{x+3}+\frac{x+3}{x-3}}{\frac{x-3}{x+3}-\frac{x+3}{x-3}}$$

$$\frac{\frac{(x-3)^2+(x+3)^2}{(x+3)(x-3)}}{\frac{(x-3)^2-(x+3)^2}{(x+3)(x-3)}}$$

$$\frac{x^2-6x+9+x^2+6x+9}{x^2-6x+9-(x^2+6x+9)}$$

$$\frac{2x^2+18}{x^2-6x+9-x^2-6x-9}$$

$$\frac{2x^2+18}{-12x}=-\frac{x^2+9}{6x}$$

79. $f(x)=\frac{3}{x}$

a. $f(a+h)=\frac{3}{a+h}$

b. $f(a)=\frac{3}{a}$

c. $$\frac{f(a+h)-f(a)}{h}=\frac{\frac{3}{a+h}-\frac{3}{a}}{h}$$

d. $$\frac{f(a+h)-f(a)}{h}=\frac{\frac{3}{(a+h)}\bullet\frac{a}{a}-\frac{3}{a}\bullet\frac{(a+h)}{(a+h)}}{h}$$

$$\frac{f(a+h)-f(a)}{h}=\frac{\frac{3a}{a(a+h)}-\frac{3(a+h)}{a(a+h)}}{h}$$

$$\frac{f(a+h)-f(a)}{h}=\frac{\frac{3a-3(a+h)}{a(a+h)}}{h}$$

$$\frac{f(a+h)-f(a)}{h}=\frac{\frac{3a-3a-3h}{a(a+h)}}{h}$$

$$\frac{f(a+h)-f(a)}{h}=\frac{\frac{-3h}{a(a+h)}}{h}$$

$$\frac{f(a+h)-f(a)}{h}=\frac{-3h}{a(a+h)}\bullet\frac{1}{h}$$

$$\frac{f(a+h)-f(a)}{h}=\frac{-3}{a(a+h)}$$

81. $\frac{3}{x}+\frac{1}{3}=\frac{5}{x}$

$3x\left(\frac{3}{x}+\frac{1}{3}\right)=\left(\frac{5}{x}\right)(3x)$

$9+x=15$

$x=6$

$\{6\}$

83. $\frac{2x+3}{5x-9}=\frac{3}{2}$

$2(5x-9)\left(\frac{2x+3}{5x-9}\right)=\left(\frac{3}{2}\right)(2)(5x-9)$

$4x+6=15x-27$

$33=11x$

$3=x$

$\{3\}$

85. $\frac{7}{x}-\frac{x}{7}=0$

$7x\left(\frac{7}{x}-\frac{x}{7}\right)=0(7x)$

$49-x^2=0$

$(7-x)(7+x)=0$

$7-x=0$ or $7+x=0$

$7=x$ or $x=-7$

$\{-7,\ 7\}$

87. $$\frac{5}{x^2-7x}+\frac{4}{2x-14}$$

$$\frac{5}{x(x-7)}+\frac{4}{2(x-7)}$$

$$\frac{10}{2x(x-7)}+\frac{4x}{2x(x-7)}$$

$$\frac{4x+10}{2x(x-7)}=\frac{2(2x+5)}{2x(x-7)}$$

$$\frac{2x+5}{x(x-7)}$$

89. $$\frac{4}{3-x}-\frac{7}{2x-6}+\frac{5}{x}$$

$$\frac{-4}{x-3}-\frac{7}{2(x-3)}+\frac{5}{x}$$

$$\frac{-8x}{2x(x-3)}-\frac{7x}{2x(x-3)}+\frac{10(x-3)}{2x(x-3)}$$

$$\frac{-5x-30}{2x(x-3)}$$

91. $\frac{1}{R}=\frac{1}{R_1}+\frac{1}{R_2}$

$(RR_1R_2)\frac{1}{R}=\left(\frac{1}{R_1}+\frac{1}{R_2}\right)(RR_1R_2)$

$R_1R_2 = RR_2 + RR_1$

$R_1R_2 - RR_2 = RR_1$

$R_2(R_1 - R) = RR_1$

$R_2 = \frac{RR_1}{R_1 - R}$

93. $A = P + Prt$

$A - P = Prt$

$\frac{A-P}{Pt} = r$

95. $x + 2\left(\frac{1}{x}\right) = 3$

$x\left(x + \frac{2}{x}\right) = 3(x)$

$x^2 + 2 = 3x$

$x^2 - 3x + 2 = 0$

$(x-1)(x-2) = 0$

$x - 1 = 0$ or $x - 2 = 0$

$x = 1$ or $x = 2$

97. Let $x =$ Mary's age
$42 - x =$ Mark's age

$x = \frac{3}{4}(42 - x)$

$(4)(x) = \frac{3}{4}(42 - x)(4)$

$4x = 126 - 3x$

$7x = 126$

$x = 18$

Mary's age is 18.
Mark's age is 24.

99. $\frac{1}{x} + \frac{1}{x+1} = \frac{29}{210}$

$210x(x+1)\left[\frac{1}{x} + \frac{1}{x+1}\right] = \left(\frac{29}{210}\right)x(x+1)(210)$

$210(x+1) + 210x = 29x(x+1)$

$420x + 210 = 29x^2 + 29x$

$29x^2 - 391x - 210 = 0$

$(29x + 15)(x - 14) = 0$

$29x + 15 = 0$ or $x - 14 = 0$

$x = -\frac{15}{29}$ or $x = 14$

not an integer $\quad x + 1 = 15$

101. $\frac{1}{4} + \frac{1}{5} + \frac{1}{6} = \frac{1}{t}$

$120t\left[\frac{1}{4} + \frac{1}{5} + \frac{1}{6}\right] = \left(\frac{1}{t}\right)(120t)$

$30t + 24t + 20t = 120$

$74t = 120$

$t = \frac{120}{74} = 1\frac{23}{37}$ hrs.

103. $\frac{1}{2} - \frac{1}{2.5} = \frac{1}{t}$

$10t\left[\frac{1}{2} - \frac{1}{2.5}\right] = \frac{1}{t}(10t)$

$5t - 4t = 10$

$t = 10$ hours

105. $\frac{1}{R} = \frac{1}{r_1} + \frac{1}{r_2}$

$\frac{1}{\frac{30}{11}} = \frac{1}{5} + \frac{1}{r_2}$

$\frac{11}{30} = \frac{1}{5} + \frac{1}{r_2}$

$30r_2\left(\frac{11}{30}\right) = \left(\frac{1}{5} + \frac{1}{r_2}\right)(30r_2)$

$11r_2 = 6r_2 + 30$

$5r_2 = 30$

$r_2 = 6$ ohms

107.

	distance	= rate	• time
with wind	445	$400 + x$	$\frac{445}{400+x}$
against wind	355	$400 - x$	$\frac{355}{400-x}$

$\frac{445}{400+x} = \frac{355}{400-x}$

$445(400 - x) = 355(400 + x)$

$178000 - 445x = 142000 + 355x$

$36000 = 800x$

45 mph $= x$

109.

	distance	= rate	• time
train 1	382	$\frac{382}{6}$	6
train 2	$382 - 112 = 270$	$\frac{270}{6}$	6

The first train is traveling at the rate of $\frac{382}{6} = 63\frac{2}{3}$ mph.
The second train is traveling at the rate of $\frac{270}{6} = 45$ mph.

111. $C = \frac{k}{D}$

$12 = \frac{k}{8}$

$96 = k$

$C = \frac{96}{24} = 4$

113. $A = kr^2$

$36 = k(3)^2$

$4 = k$

$A = 4(4)^2 = 64$ sq. in.

Chapter 7 - Test

1. $f(x) = \frac{5x^2}{1-x}$

Undefined value when

$1 - x = 0$

$1 = x$

Domain $\{x|x$ is a real number and $x \neq 1\}$

2. $g(x) = \frac{9x^2 - 9}{x^2 + 4x + 3}$

Undefined values when

$x^2 + 4x + 3 = 0$

$(x+3)(x+1) = 0$

$x + 3 = 0$ or $x + 1 = 0$

$x = -3$ or $x = -1$

Domain $\{x|x$ is a real number and $x \neq -3,\ x \neq -1\}$

3. $\frac{5x^7}{3x^4} = \frac{5x^{7-4}}{3} = \frac{5x^3}{3}$

4. $\frac{7x-21}{24-8x} = \frac{7(x-3)}{8(3-x)} = \frac{7(-1)}{8} = \frac{-7}{8}$

5. $\frac{2x+6}{x^2-9} = \frac{2(x+3)}{(x+3)(x-3)} = \frac{2}{x-3}$

6. $\frac{x^2-4x}{x^2+5x-36} = \frac{x(x-4)}{(x+9)(x-4)} = \frac{x}{x+9}$

7. $\frac{x}{x-2} \bullet \frac{x^2-4}{5x}$

$\frac{1}{x-2} \bullet \frac{(x-2)(x+2)}{5}$

$\frac{1}{1} \bullet \frac{x+2}{5} = \frac{x+2}{5}$

8. $\frac{2x^2-x-3}{5x+10} \bullet \frac{3x+6}{4x-6}$

$\frac{(2x-3)(x+1) \bullet 3(x+2)}{5(x+2) \bullet 2(2x-3)}$

$\frac{3(x+1)}{10} = \frac{3x+3}{10}$

9. $\frac{2x^3+16}{6x^2+12x} \bullet \frac{5}{x^2-2x+4}$

$\frac{2(x^3+8) \bullet 5}{6x(x+2)(x^2-2x+4)}$

$\frac{5(x+2)(x^2-2x+4)}{3x(x+2)(x^2-2x+4)}$

$\frac{5}{3x}$

10. $\frac{26ab}{7c} \div \frac{13a^2c^5}{14a^4b^3} = \frac{26ab}{7c} \bullet \frac{14a^4b^3}{13a^2c^5}$

$\frac{2ab}{c} \bullet \frac{2a^4b^3}{a^2c^5} = \frac{4a^5b^4}{a^2c^6} = \frac{4a^3b^4}{c^6}$

11. $\frac{3x^2-12}{x^2+2x-8} \div \frac{6x+18}{x+4}$

$\frac{3(x^2-4)}{(x+4)(x-2)} \bullet \frac{x+4}{6(x+3)}$

$\frac{(x+2)(x-2)}{x-2} \bullet \frac{1}{2(x+3)}$

$\frac{x+2}{2(x+3)}$

12. $\frac{4x-12}{2x-9} \div \frac{3-x}{4x^2-81} \bullet \frac{x+3}{5x+15}$

$\frac{4(x-3)}{2x-9} \bullet \frac{(2x+9)(2x-9)}{-(x-3)} \bullet \frac{x+3}{5(x+3)}$

$\frac{4}{1} \bullet \frac{2x+9}{-1} \bullet \frac{1}{5} = \frac{8x+36}{-5} = -\frac{8x+36}{5}$

13. $\frac{2}{25x}, \frac{3}{15x^3}$ has LCD $75x^3$.

14. $\frac{5}{4x^3}+\frac{7}{4x^3}=\frac{5+7}{4x^3}=\frac{12}{4x^3}=\frac{3}{x^3}$

15. $\frac{3+2x}{10-x}+\frac{13+x}{x-10}$

$\frac{3+2x-(13+x)}{10-x}$

$\frac{3+2x-13-x}{10-x}$

$\frac{-10+x}{-(-10+x)}$

$\frac{1}{-1}=-1$

16. $\frac{3}{x^2-x-6}+\frac{2}{x^2-5x+6}$

$\frac{3}{(x-3)(x+2)}+\frac{2}{(x-3)(x-2)}$

$\frac{3(x-2)+2(x+2)}{(x-3)(x+2)(x-2)}$

$\frac{3x-6+2x+4}{(x-3)(x+2)(x-2)}$

$\frac{5x-2}{(x-3)(x+2)(x-2)}$

17. $\frac{x}{4x^2-2x+1}-\frac{2x+1}{8x^3+1}$

$\frac{x}{4x^2-2x+1}-\frac{2x+1}{(2x+1)(4x^2-2x+1)}$

$\frac{x(2x+1)-(2x+1)}{(2x+1)(4x^2-2x+1)}$

$\frac{2x^2-x-1}{(2x+1)(4x^2-2x+1)}$

$\frac{(2x+1)(x-1)}{(2x+1)(4x^2-2x+1)}$

$\frac{x-1}{4x^2-2x+1}$

18. $\frac{5}{x-7}-\frac{2x}{3x-21}+\frac{x}{2x-14}$

$\frac{5}{x-7}-\frac{2x}{3(x-7)}+\frac{x}{2(x-7)}$

$\frac{6\bullet 5-2\bullet 2x+3\bullet x}{6(x-7)}$

$\frac{30-4x+3x}{6(x-7)}=\frac{30-x}{6(x-7)}$

19. $\frac{3x}{5}\left(\frac{5}{x}-\frac{5}{2x}\right)=3x\left(\frac{1}{x}-\frac{1}{2x}\right)$

$3x\bullet\frac{2-1}{2x}=3x\left(\frac{1}{2x}\right)=\frac{3}{2}$

20. $\frac{5x+3y}{x^2-y^2}\left(\frac{x}{y}-\frac{y}{x}\right)$

$\frac{5x+3y}{x^2-y^2}\bullet\frac{x^2-y^2}{xy}$

$\frac{5x+3y}{xy}$

21. $\frac{3}{x+y}+\frac{2x^2-2xy+4x-4y}{4x+8}\div\frac{y^2-x^2}{2y}$

$\frac{3}{x+y}+\frac{(2x+4)(x-y)}{4(x+2)}\bullet\frac{2y}{(y+x)(y-x)}$

$\frac{3}{x+y}+\frac{x-y}{2}\bullet\frac{2y}{(x+y)\bullet -(x-y)}$

$\frac{3}{x+y}-\frac{y}{x+y}=\frac{3-y}{x+y}$

22. $\frac{\frac{4x}{13}}{\frac{20x}{13}}=\frac{4x}{20x}=\frac{1}{5}$

23. $\frac{\frac{5}{x}-\frac{7}{3x}}{\frac{9}{8x}-\frac{1}{x}}=\frac{\frac{15-7}{3x}}{\frac{9-8}{8x}}$

$\frac{8}{3x}\bullet\frac{8x}{1}=\frac{64}{3}$

24. $\frac{\frac{7}{2x}+\frac{2}{xy}}{\frac{3}{xy^2}}$

$\left(\frac{7}{2x}+\frac{2}{xy}\right)\left(\frac{xy^2}{3}\right)$

$\left(\frac{7y+4}{2xy}\right)\left(\frac{xy^2}{3}\right)$

$\frac{7y^2+4y}{6}$

25. $\frac{\frac{x^2-5x+6}{x+3}}{\frac{x^2-4x+4}{x^2-9}}$

$$\frac{(x-3)(x-2)}{x+3} \bullet \frac{(x-3)(x+3)}{(x-2)(x-2)}$$

$$\frac{(x-3)^2}{x-2} = \frac{x^2-6x+9}{x-2}$$

26. Let $x =$ the number.

$(x+1)\frac{2}{x} = \frac{12}{5}$

$\frac{2(x+1)}{x} = \frac{12}{5}$

$12x = 10(x+1)$

$12x = 10x + 10$

$2x = 10$

$x = 5$

The number is 5.

27.

	Hours to complete	Part of job completed in one hour
Jan	2	$\frac{1}{2}$
Husband	1.5	$\frac{1}{1.5}$
Together	x	$\frac{1}{x}$

$\frac{1}{2} + \frac{1}{1.5} = \frac{1}{x}$

$6x\left(\frac{1}{2} + \frac{1}{1.5}\right) = 6x\left(\frac{1}{x}\right)$

$3x + 4x = 6$

$7x = 6$

$x = \frac{6}{7}$

Together they weeded the garden in $\frac{6}{7}$ hour.

28. $W = \frac{k}{V}$

$20 = \frac{k}{12}$

$240 = k$

$W = \frac{240}{15}$

$W = 16$

29. $Q = kRS^2$

$24 = k(3)(4)^2$

$24 = k(48)$

$\frac{24}{48} = k$

$\frac{1}{2} = k$

$Q = \frac{1}{2}(2)(3)^2$

$Q = 9$

30. $S = k\sqrt{D}$

$160 = k\sqrt{400}$

$160 = k(20)$

$8 = k$

$128 = 8\sqrt{D}$

$16 = \sqrt{D}$

$256 = D$

Height of cliff is 256 feet.

Chapter 7 - Cumulative Review

1a. $5(x+2)$

$5x + 10$

b. $-2(y + 0.3z - 1)$

$-2y - 0.6z + 2$

c. $-(x + y - 2z + 6)$

$-x - y + 2z - 6$

3. $3(x-4) = 3x - 12$

$3x - 12 = 3x - 12$

$3x = 3x$

$0 = 0$

Identity true for all real numbers.

$\{x \mid x \text{ is a real number}\}$

5. $\frac{x}{x-2} = \frac{x-3}{x+1}$

Undefined values $x = 2$, $x = -1$.

$x(x+1) = (x-2)(x-3)$

$x^2 + x = x^2 - 5x + 6$

$x = -5x + 6$

$6x = 6$

$x = 1$

$\{1\}$

7. $|g| = -1$

No Solution.

Absolute value never equals a negative.

$\{\ \}$

9. $g(x) = x^2 - 3$

a. $g(2) = 2^2 - 3$

$g(2) = 4 - 3$

$g(2) = 1$

b. $g(-2) = (-2)^2 - 3$

$g(-2) = 4 - 3$

$g(-2) = 1$

c. $g(0) = 0^2 - 3$

$g(0) = -3$

11.

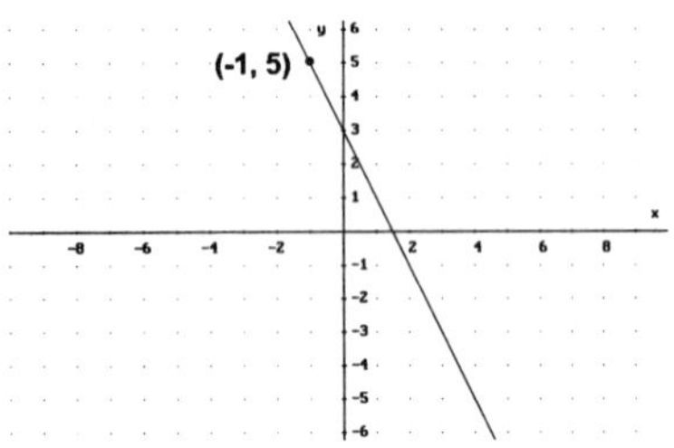

13a. $3^{-2} = \frac{1}{3^2} = \frac{1}{9}$

b. $2x^{-3} = \frac{2}{x^3}$

c. $\frac{1}{2^{-5}} = 2^5$

15.

$$\begin{array}{r|l} & 2x - 5 \\ \hline x+2 & 2x^2 - x - 10 \\ & \underline{2x^2 + 4x} \\ & -5x - 10 \\ & \underline{-5x - 10} \\ & 0 \end{array}$$

$2x - 5$

17. $2x^2 = \frac{17}{3}x + 1$

$3(2x^2) = 3\left(\frac{17}{3}x\right) + 3(1)$

$6x^2 = 17x + 3$

$6x^2 - 17x - 3 = 0$

$(6x + 1)(x - 3) = 0$

$6x + 1 = 0$ or $x - 3 = 0$

$6x = -1$ or $x = 3$

$x = -\frac{1}{6}$

$\left\{-\frac{1}{6},\ 3\right\}$

19a. $\frac{2x^2 + 3x - 2}{-4x - 8} \bullet \frac{16x^2}{4x^2 - 1}$

$\frac{(2x - 1)(x + 2)}{-4(x + 2)} \bullet \frac{16x^2}{(2x + 1)(2x - 1)} = \frac{-4x^2}{2x + 1}$

b. $(ac - ad + bc - bd) \bullet \frac{a + b}{d - c}$

$[a(c - d) + b(c - d)] \bullet \frac{a + b}{d - c}$

$(c - d)(a + b) \bullet \frac{(a + b)}{(d - c)}$

$-1(d - c)(a + b) \bullet \frac{(a + b)}{(d - c)}$

$-(a + b)^2$

21. $\frac{3}{x} - \frac{x + 21}{3x} = \frac{5}{3}$

Undefined values, $x = 0$.

$3x\left(\frac{3}{x}\right) - 3x\left(\frac{x + 21}{3x}\right) = 3x\left(\frac{5}{3}\right)$

$9 - (x + 21) = x(5)$

$9 - x - 21 = 5x$

$-12 - x = 5x$

$-12 = 6x$

$-2 = x$

$\{-2\}$

23. $y = kx$

$5 = k(30)$

$\frac{5}{30} = k$

$\frac{1}{6} = k$

$y = \frac{1}{6}x$

$y = \frac{1}{6}(90)$

$y = 15$

Exercise Set 8.1

1. $\sqrt{16}$

   4

3. $\sqrt{81}$

   9

5. $\sqrt{\frac{1}{25}}$

   $\frac{1}{5}$

7. $-\sqrt{100}$

   $-(10)$

   -10

9. $f(x) = \sqrt{x} + 2$

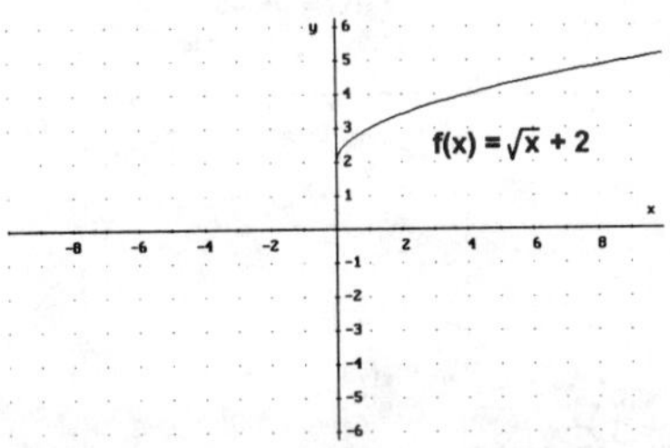

11. $f(x) = \sqrt{x - 3}$

x	f(x)
3	$\sqrt{3-3} = \sqrt{0} = 0$
4	$\sqrt{4-3} = \sqrt{1} = 1$
7	$\sqrt{7-3} = \sqrt{4} = 2$
12	$\sqrt{12-3} = \sqrt{9} = 3$

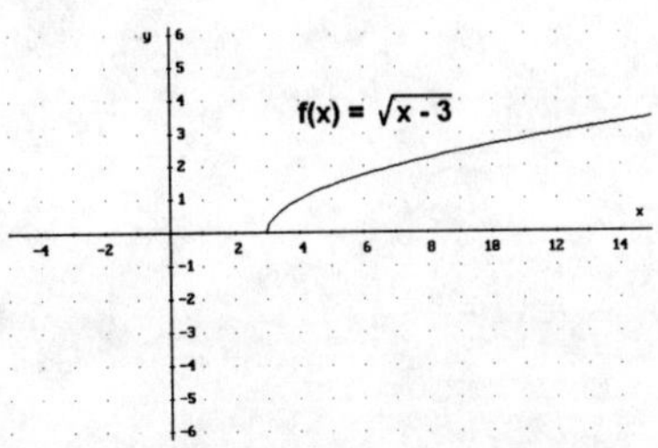

13. $\sqrt[3]{64}$

    4

15. $-\sqrt[3]{27}$

    $-(3)$

    -3

17. $\sqrt[3]{\frac{1}{8}}$

    $\frac{1}{2}$

19. $\sqrt[3]{-125}$

    -5

21. $f(x) = \sqrt[3]{x} + 1$

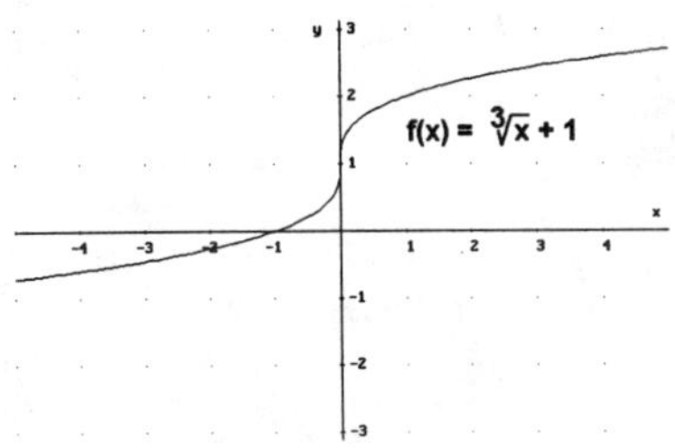

23. $g(x) = \sqrt[3]{x - 1}$

x	f(x)
1	$\sqrt[3]{1-1} = \sqrt[3]{0} = 0$
2	$\sqrt[3]{2-1} = \sqrt[3]{1} = 1$
0	$\sqrt[3]{0-1} = \sqrt[3]{-1} = -1$
9	$\sqrt[3]{9-1} = \sqrt[3]{8} = 2$
-7	$\sqrt[3]{-7-1} = \sqrt[3]{-8} = -2$

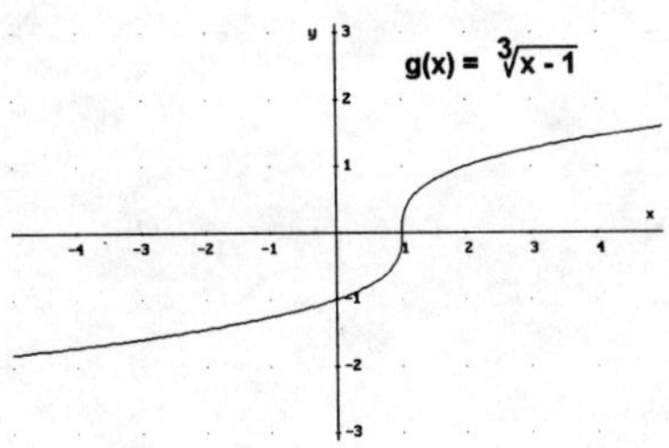

25. $\sqrt[5]{32}$

2

27. $\sqrt[4]{81}$

3

29. $\sqrt{-4}$

not a real number

31. $\sqrt[3]{\frac{1}{27}}$

$\frac{1}{3}$

33. $\sqrt{\frac{9}{25}}$

$\frac{3}{5}$

35. $-\sqrt{49}$

$-(7)$

-7

37. $\sqrt{z^2}$

$|z|$

39. $\sqrt[3]{x^3}$

x

41. $\sqrt{(x+5)^2}$

$|x+5|$

43. $\sqrt[4]{(2z)^4}$

$|2z|$

45. $\sqrt{0}$

0

47. $-\sqrt[5]{\frac{1}{32}}$

$-\left(\frac{1}{2}\right)$

$-\frac{1}{2}$

49. $\sqrt{-64}$

not a real number

51. $-\sqrt{64}$

$-(8)$

-8

53. $-\sqrt{169}$

$-(13)$

-13

55. $\sqrt{1}$

1

57. $\sqrt{\frac{25}{64}}$

$\frac{5}{8}$

59. $-\sqrt[3]{-8}$

$-(-2)$

2

61. $f(x) = \sqrt{x} - 3$

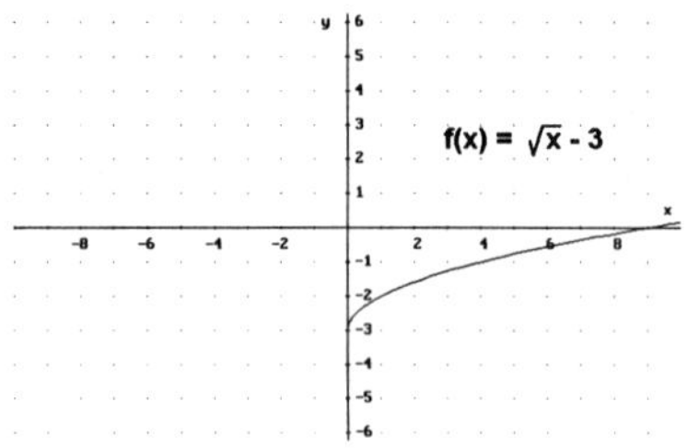

63. $g(x) = \sqrt[3]{x} - 3$

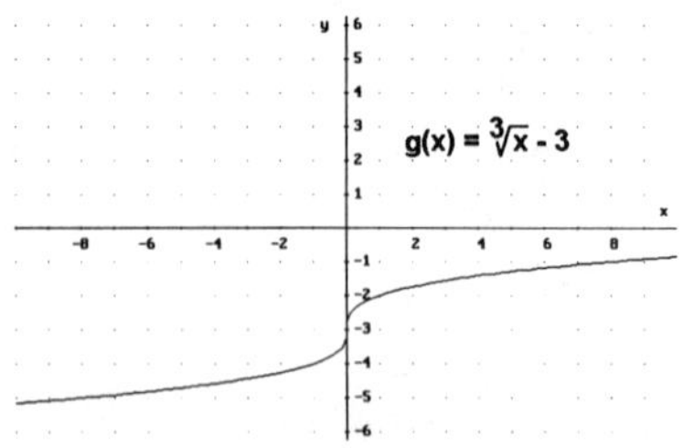

65. $f(x) = \sqrt{x-2}$

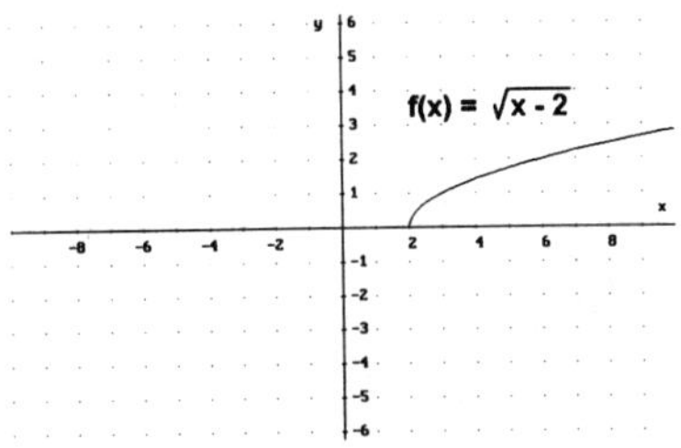

67. $h(x) = \sqrt[3]{x+4}$

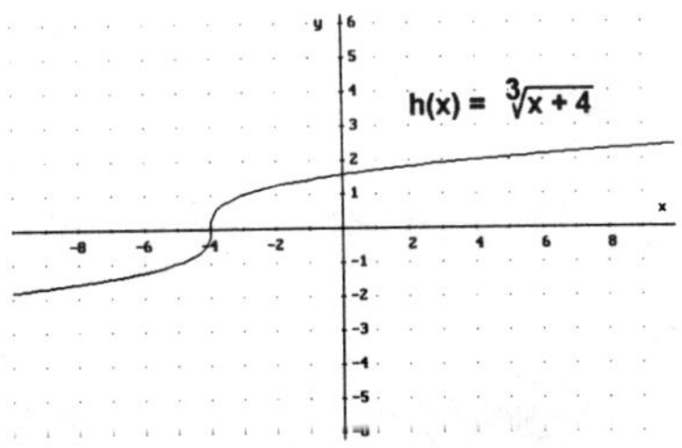

69. $\sqrt{9}$
rational, 3

71. $\sqrt{37}$
irrational, 6.083

73. $\sqrt{169}$
rational, 13

75. $\sqrt{4}$
rational, 2

77. $\sqrt[3]{x^{15}}$
x^5

79. $\sqrt{x^{12}}$
x^6

81. $\sqrt{81x^2}$
$|9x|$

83. $-\sqrt{144y^{14}}$
$-(12y^7)$
$-|12y^7|$

85. $\sqrt{x^2+4x+4}$
$\sqrt{(x+2)^2}$
$|x+2|$

87. $\sqrt{324}$
18.0

89. $240\sqrt{41}$
240(6.403)
1537 sq. ft.

91. $8 = 4 \bullet 2$

93. $75 = 25 \bullet 3$

95. $44 = 4 \bullet 11$

97. $90 = 9 \bullet 10$

99. $56 = 8 \bullet 7$

101. $270 = 27 \bullet 10$

Exercise Set 8.2

1. $\sqrt{20}$
$\sqrt{4}\sqrt{5}$
$2\sqrt{5}$

3. $\sqrt{18}$
$\sqrt{9}\sqrt{2}$
$3\sqrt{2}$

5. $\sqrt{50}$
$\sqrt{25}\sqrt{2}$
$5\sqrt{2}$

7. $\sqrt{33}$
can not be simplified

9. $\sqrt{\frac{8}{25}} = \frac{\sqrt{8}}{\sqrt{25}} = \frac{\sqrt{4}\sqrt{2}}{5} = \frac{2\sqrt{2}}{5}$

11. $\sqrt{\frac{27}{121}} = \frac{\sqrt{27}}{\sqrt{121}} = \frac{\sqrt{9}\sqrt{3}}{\sqrt{121}} = \frac{3\sqrt{3}}{11}$

13. $\sqrt{\frac{9}{4}} = \frac{\sqrt{9}}{\sqrt{4}} = \frac{3}{2}$

15. $\sqrt{\frac{125}{9}} = \frac{\sqrt{25}\sqrt{5}}{\sqrt{9}} = \frac{5\sqrt{5}}{3}$

17. $\sqrt{x^7}$

$\sqrt{x^6}\sqrt{x}$

$x^3\sqrt{x}$

19. $\sqrt{\frac{88}{x^4}} = \frac{\sqrt{88}}{\sqrt{x^4}} = \frac{\sqrt{4}\sqrt{22}}{\sqrt{x^4}} = \frac{2\sqrt{22}}{x^2}$

21. $\sqrt[3]{24}$

$\sqrt[3]{8}\sqrt[3]{3}$

$2\sqrt[3]{3}$

23. $\sqrt[3]{\frac{5}{64}}$

$\frac{\sqrt[3]{5}}{\sqrt[3]{64}}$

$\frac{\sqrt[3]{5}}{4}$

25. $\sqrt{\frac{3}{25}} = \frac{\sqrt{3}}{\sqrt{25}} = \frac{\sqrt{3}}{5}$

27. $\sqrt{\frac{49}{4x^2}} = \frac{\sqrt{49}}{\sqrt{4x^2}} = \frac{7}{\sqrt{4}\sqrt{x^2}} = \frac{7}{2x}$

29. $\sqrt[3]{\frac{y^7}{8x^6}} = \frac{\sqrt[3]{y^7}}{\sqrt[3]{8x^6}} = \frac{\sqrt[3]{y^6 y}}{\sqrt[3]{8}\ \sqrt[3]{x^6}} = \frac{\sqrt[3]{y^6}\ \sqrt[3]{y}}{2x^2} = \frac{y^2\ \sqrt[3]{y}}{2x^2}$

31. $\sqrt{52}$

$\sqrt{4}\sqrt{13}$

$2\sqrt{13}$

33. $\sqrt{\frac{11}{36}} = \frac{\sqrt{11}}{\sqrt{36}} = \frac{\sqrt{11}}{6}$

35. $-\sqrt{\frac{27}{144}} = -\frac{\sqrt{27}}{\sqrt{144}} = -\frac{\sqrt{9}\sqrt{3}}{12} = -\frac{3\sqrt{3}}{12} = -\frac{\sqrt{3}}{4}$

37. $\sqrt[3]{\frac{15}{64}} = \frac{\sqrt[3]{15}}{\sqrt[3]{64}} = \frac{\sqrt[3]{15}}{4}$

39. $\sqrt[3]{80}$

$\sqrt[3]{8}\ \sqrt[3]{10}$

$2\ \sqrt[3]{10}$

41. $\sqrt[4]{48}$

$\sqrt[4]{16}\ \sqrt[4]{3}$

$2\ \sqrt[4]{3}$

43. $\sqrt{121} = 11$

45. $\sqrt[3]{8x^3} = \sqrt[3]{8}\ \sqrt[3]{x^3} = 2x$

47. $\sqrt{y^5} = \sqrt{y^4 y} = y^2\sqrt{y}$

49. $\sqrt{20} = \sqrt{4(5)} = \sqrt{4}\sqrt{5} = 2\sqrt{5}$

51. $\sqrt{25a^2b^3} = \sqrt{25}\sqrt{a^2}\sqrt{b^3}$

$5a\sqrt{b^2b} = 5a\sqrt{b^2}\sqrt{b} = 5ab\sqrt{b}$

53. $\sqrt[3]{-27x^9} = \sqrt[3]{-27}\ \sqrt[3]{x^9} = -3x^3$

55. $\sqrt[4]{a^{16}b^4} = \sqrt[4]{a^{16}}\ \sqrt[4]{b^4} = a^4b$

57. $\sqrt[3]{50x^{14}} = \sqrt[3]{x^{12}(50x^2)}$

$\sqrt[3]{x^{12}}\ \sqrt[3]{50x^2} = x^4\ \sqrt[3]{50x^2}$

59. $\sqrt[5]{-32x^{10}y} = \sqrt[5]{-32}\ \sqrt[5]{x^{10}}\ \sqrt[5]{y} = -2x^2\ \sqrt[5]{y}$

61. $-\sqrt{32a^8b^7} = -\sqrt{16a^8b^6(2b)}$

$-\sqrt{16}\sqrt{a^8}\sqrt{b^6}\sqrt{2b} = -4a^4b^3\sqrt{2b}$

63. $\sqrt{\frac{6}{49}} = \frac{\sqrt{6}}{\sqrt{49}} = \frac{\sqrt{6}}{7}$

65. $\sqrt{\frac{5x^2}{4y^2}} = \frac{\sqrt{5x^2}}{\sqrt{4y^2}} = \frac{\sqrt{5}\sqrt{x^2}}{\sqrt{4}\sqrt{y^2}} = \frac{x\sqrt{5}}{2y}$

67. $-\sqrt[3]{\frac{z^7}{27x^3}} = \frac{-\sqrt[3]{z^7}}{\sqrt[3]{27x^3}} = \frac{-\sqrt[3]{z^6 z}}{\sqrt[3]{27}\ \sqrt[3]{x^3}}$

$\frac{-\sqrt[3]{z^6}\ \sqrt[3]{z}}{3x} = \frac{-z^2\ \sqrt[3]{z}}{3x}$

69. $\sqrt[4]{\frac{x^7}{16}} = \frac{\sqrt[4]{x^7}}{\sqrt[4]{16}} = \frac{\sqrt[4]{x^4x^3}}{2} = \frac{\sqrt[4]{x^4}\sqrt[4]{x^3}}{2} = \frac{x\sqrt[4]{x^3}}{2}$

71. $\sqrt[3]{80} = \sqrt[3]{8}\sqrt[3]{10} = 2\sqrt[3]{10}$ in.

73. $\sqrt{a^2+b^2} \neq a+b$

Let $a=2$ and $b=3$

$\sqrt{2^2+3^2} \neq 2+3$

$\sqrt{4+9} \neq 2+3$

$\sqrt{13} \neq 5$

$3.61 \neq 5$

75. $(6x)(8x)$

$48x^2$

77. $(2x+3)+(x-5)$

$3x-2$

79. $(9y^2)(-8y^2)$

$-72y^4$

81. $4x^2-7x+4$

not factorable

83. $6x^2+5xy-4y^2$

$(3x+4y)(2x-y)$

85. $18x^2-60x+50$

$2(9x^2-30x+25)$

$2(3x-5)(3x-5)$

$2(3x-5)^2$

87. $4x^2-28xy+49y^2$

$(2x-7y)(2x-7y)$

$(2x-7y)^2$

Exercise Set 8.3

1. $\sqrt{8}-\sqrt{32}$

$\sqrt{4(2)}-\sqrt{(16)(2)}$

$\sqrt{4}\sqrt{2}-\sqrt{16}\sqrt{2}$

$2\sqrt{2}-4\sqrt{2}$

$-2\sqrt{2}$

3. $2\sqrt{2x^3}+4x\sqrt{8x}$

$2\sqrt{x^2(2x)}+4x\sqrt{4(2x)}$

$2\sqrt{x^2}\sqrt{2x}+4x\sqrt{4}\sqrt{2x}$

$2x\sqrt{2x}+4x(2)\sqrt{2x}$

$2x\sqrt{2x}+8x\sqrt{2x}$

$10x\sqrt{2x}$

5. $2\sqrt{50}-3\sqrt{125}+\sqrt{98}$

$2\sqrt{25(2)}-3\sqrt{25(5)}+\sqrt{49(2)}$

$2\sqrt{25}\sqrt{2}-3\sqrt{25}\sqrt{5}+\sqrt{49}\sqrt{2}$

$2(5)\sqrt{2}-3(5)\sqrt{5}+7\sqrt{2}$

$10\sqrt{2}-15\sqrt{5}+7\sqrt{2}$

$17\sqrt{2}-15\sqrt{5}$

7. $\sqrt[3]{16x}-\sqrt[3]{54x}$

$\sqrt[3]{8(2x)}-\sqrt[3]{27(2x)}$

$\sqrt[3]{8}\sqrt[3]{2x}-\sqrt[3]{27}\sqrt[3]{2x}$

$2\sqrt[3]{2x}-3\sqrt[3]{2x}$

$-\sqrt[3]{2x}$

9. $\sqrt{9b^3}-\sqrt{25b^3}+\sqrt{49b^3}$

$\sqrt{9b^2(b)}-\sqrt{25b^2(b)}+\sqrt{49b^2(b)}$

$\sqrt{9b^2}\sqrt{b}-\sqrt{25b^2}\sqrt{b}+\sqrt{49b^2}\sqrt{b}$

$3b\sqrt{b}-5b\sqrt{b}+7b\sqrt{b}$

$-2b\sqrt{b}+7b\sqrt{b}$

$5b\sqrt{b}$

11. $\frac{5\sqrt{2}}{3}+\frac{2\sqrt{2}}{5} = \frac{5(5\sqrt{2})+3(2\sqrt{2})}{3(5)}$

$\frac{25\sqrt{2}+6\sqrt{2}}{15} = \frac{31\sqrt{2}}{15}$

13. $\sqrt[3]{\frac{11}{8}}-\frac{\sqrt[3]{11}}{6} = \frac{\sqrt[3]{11}}{\sqrt[3]{8}}-\frac{\sqrt[3]{11}}{6} = \frac{\sqrt[3]{11}}{2}-\frac{\sqrt[3]{11}}{6}$

$\frac{3\sqrt[3]{11}-\sqrt[3]{11}}{6} = \frac{2\sqrt[3]{11}}{6} = \frac{\sqrt[3]{11}}{3}$

15. $\frac{\sqrt{20x}}{9}+\sqrt{\frac{5x}{9}} = \frac{\sqrt{4(5x)}}{9}+\frac{\sqrt{5x}}{\sqrt{9}}$

$$\frac{\sqrt{4}\sqrt{5x}}{9}+\frac{\sqrt{5x}}{3}=\frac{2\sqrt{5x}+3\sqrt{5x}}{9}=\frac{5\sqrt{5x}}{9}$$

17. $7\sqrt{9}-7+\sqrt{3}=7(3)-7+\sqrt{3}$
$21-7+\sqrt{3}=14+\sqrt{3}$

19. $2+3\sqrt{y^2}-6\sqrt{y^2}+5$
$7-3\sqrt{y^2}=7-3y$

21. $3\sqrt{108}-2\sqrt{18}-3\sqrt{48}$
$3\sqrt{36}\sqrt{3}-2\sqrt{9}\sqrt{2}-3\sqrt{16}\sqrt{3}$
$3(6)\sqrt{3}-2(3)\sqrt{2}-3(4)\sqrt{3}$
$18\sqrt{3}-6\sqrt{2}-12\sqrt{3}$
$6\sqrt{3}-6\sqrt{2}$

23. $-5\sqrt[3]{625}+\sqrt[3]{40}=-5\sqrt[3]{125}\sqrt[3]{5}+\sqrt[3]{8}\sqrt[3]{5}$
$-5(5)\sqrt[3]{5}+2\sqrt[3]{5}=-25\sqrt[3]{5}+2\sqrt[3]{5}=-23\sqrt[3]{5}$

25. $\sqrt{9b^3}-\sqrt{25b^3}+\sqrt{16b^3}=\sqrt{9b^2}\sqrt{b}-\sqrt{25b^2}\sqrt{b}+\sqrt{16b^2}\sqrt{b}$
$3b\sqrt{b}-5b\sqrt{b}+4b\sqrt{b}=(3-5+4)b\sqrt{b}=2b\sqrt{b}$

27. $5y\sqrt{8y}+2\sqrt{50y^3}=5y\sqrt{4}\sqrt{2y}+2\sqrt{25y^2}\sqrt{2y}$
$5y(2)\sqrt{2y}+2(5y)\sqrt{2y}=10y\sqrt{2y}+10y\sqrt{2y}$
$20y\sqrt{2y}$

29. $\sqrt[3]{54xy^3}-5\sqrt[3]{2xy^3}+y\sqrt[3]{128x}$
$\sqrt[3]{27y^3}\sqrt[3]{2x}-5\sqrt[3]{y^3}\sqrt[3]{2x}+y\sqrt[3]{64}\sqrt[3]{2x}$
$3y\sqrt[3]{2x}-5y\sqrt[3]{2x}+y(4)\sqrt[3]{2x}$
$-2y\sqrt[3]{2x}+4y\sqrt[3]{2x}=2y\sqrt[3]{2x}$

31. $6\sqrt[3]{11}+8\sqrt{11}-12\sqrt{11}=6\sqrt[3]{11}-4\sqrt{11}$

33. $-2\sqrt[4]{x^7}+3\sqrt[4]{16x^7}$
$-2\sqrt[4]{x^4}\sqrt[4]{x^3}+3\sqrt[4]{16x^4}\sqrt[4]{x^3}$
$-2x\sqrt[4]{x^3}+3(2x)\sqrt[4]{x^3}$
$-2x\sqrt[4]{x^3}+6x\sqrt[4]{x^3}$
$4x\sqrt[4]{x^3}$

35. $\frac{4\sqrt{3}}{3}-\frac{\sqrt{12}}{3}=\frac{4\sqrt{3}}{3}-\frac{\sqrt{4}\sqrt{3}}{3}$
$\frac{4\sqrt{3}-2\sqrt{3}}{3}=\frac{2\sqrt{3}}{3}$

37. $\frac{\sqrt[3]{8x^4}}{7}+\frac{3x\sqrt[3]{x}}{7}=\frac{\sqrt[3]{8x^3}\sqrt[3]{x}+3x\sqrt[3]{x}}{7}$
$\frac{2x\sqrt[3]{x}+3x\sqrt[3]{x}}{7}=\frac{5x\sqrt[3]{x}}{7}$

39. $\sqrt{\frac{28}{x^2}}+\sqrt{\frac{7}{4x^2}}=\frac{\sqrt{28}}{\sqrt{x^2}}+\frac{\sqrt{7}}{\sqrt{4x^2}}$
$\frac{\sqrt{4}\sqrt{7}}{x}+\frac{\sqrt{7}}{2x}=\frac{2\sqrt{7}}{x}+\frac{\sqrt{7}}{2x}$
$\frac{4\sqrt{7}+\sqrt{7}}{2x}=\frac{5\sqrt{7}}{2x}$

41. $\sqrt[3]{\frac{16}{27}}-\frac{\sqrt[3]{54}}{6}=\frac{\sqrt[3]{16}}{\sqrt[3]{27}}-\frac{\sqrt[3]{27}\sqrt[3]{2}}{6}$
$\frac{\sqrt[3]{8}\sqrt[3]{2}}{3}-\frac{3\sqrt[3]{2}}{6}=\frac{2(2)\sqrt[3]{2}}{6}-\frac{3\sqrt[3]{2}}{6}$
$\frac{4\sqrt[3]{2}-3\sqrt[3]{2}}{6}=\frac{\sqrt[3]{2}}{6}$

43. $-\frac{\sqrt[3]{2x^4}}{9}+\sqrt[3]{\frac{250x^4}{27}}=\frac{-\sqrt[3]{x^3}\sqrt[3]{2x}}{9}+\frac{\sqrt[3]{250x^4}}{\sqrt[3]{27}}$
$\frac{-x\sqrt[3]{2x}}{9}+\frac{\sqrt[3]{125x^3}\sqrt[3]{2x}}{3}=\frac{-x\sqrt[3]{2x}}{9}+\frac{5x\sqrt[3]{2x}}{3}$
$\frac{-x\sqrt[3]{2x}+15x\sqrt[3]{2x}}{9}=\frac{14x\sqrt[3]{2x}}{9}$

45. $P=2\sqrt{12}+\sqrt{12}+2\sqrt{27}+3\sqrt{3}$
$P=2\sqrt{4}\sqrt{3}+\sqrt{4}\sqrt{3}+2\sqrt{9}\sqrt{3}+3\sqrt{3}$
$P=2\bullet 2\sqrt{3}+2\sqrt{3}+2\bullet 3\sqrt{3}+3\sqrt{3}$
$P=(4+2+6+3)\sqrt{3}=15\sqrt{3}$
The perimeter of the trapezoid is $15\sqrt{3}$ inches.

47. $P=2(3\sqrt{20})+2\sqrt{125}$
$P=6\sqrt{4}\sqrt{5}+2\sqrt{25}\sqrt{5}$
$P=6(2)\sqrt{5}+2(5)\sqrt{5}$
$P=12\sqrt{5}+10\sqrt{5}=22\sqrt{5}$ feet.

49. $3\sqrt{5}+3\sqrt{5}+\sqrt{5}+\sqrt{5}=8\sqrt{5}$ inches

51. $2(3\bullet 8)+2\left(\frac{3\sqrt{27}}{4}\right)$

$2(24)+\frac{3\sqrt{27}}{2}$

$48+3\frac{\sqrt{9\bullet 3}}{2}$

$48+\frac{9\sqrt{3}}{2}$

$\left(48+\frac{9\sqrt{3}}{2}\right)$ sq. ft.

53. $(x+4)(x-4)$

$x^2-4x+4x-16$

x^2-16

55. $(2x+5)^2$

$(2x)^2+2(2x)(5)+(5)^2$

$4x^2+20x+25$

57. $f(x)=\frac{1}{x}$

Undefined value when $x=0$.

Domain: $\{x|x$ is a real number and $x\neq 0\}$

59. $h(x)=\sqrt{x-1}$

Defined only when

$x-1\geq 0$

$x\geq 1$

Domain: $\{x|x\geq 1\}$

61. $f(x)=\sqrt[3]{x}$

Always defined.

Domain: $\{x|x$ is a real number$\}$

63. $h(x)=\frac{-2x}{x(x-3)}$

Undefined values when

$x(x-3)=0$

$x=0$ or $x-3=0$

$x=3$

Domain: $\{x|x$ is a real number and $x\neq 0,\ x\neq 3\}$

65. $f(x)=2x-6$

Always defined.

Domain: $\{x|x$ is a real number$\}$

Exercise Set 8.4

1. $\sqrt{7}(\sqrt{5}+\sqrt{3})=\sqrt{7}\sqrt{5}+\sqrt{7}\sqrt{3}=\sqrt{35}+\sqrt{21}$

3. $(\sqrt{5}-\sqrt{2})^2=\sqrt{5}^2-2\sqrt{5}\sqrt{2}+\sqrt{2}^2$

$5-2\sqrt{10}+2=7-2\sqrt{10}$

5. $\sqrt{3x}(\sqrt{3}-\sqrt{x})=\sqrt{3x}\sqrt{3}-\sqrt{3x}\sqrt{x}$

$\sqrt{3}\sqrt{x}\sqrt{3}-\sqrt{3}\sqrt{x}\sqrt{x}=3\sqrt{x}-x\sqrt{3}$

7. $(2\sqrt{x}-5)(3\sqrt{x}+1)$

$(2\sqrt{x})(3\sqrt{x})+(2\sqrt{x})1-5(3\sqrt{x})-5\bullet 1$

$6x+2\sqrt{x}-15\sqrt{x}-5=6x-13\sqrt{x}-5$

9. $(\sqrt[3]{a}-4)(\sqrt[3]{a}+5)$

$(\sqrt[3]{a})^2+5\sqrt[3]{a}-4\sqrt[3]{a}-4\bullet 5$

$\sqrt[3]{a^2}+\sqrt[3]{a}-20$

11. $\frac{1}{\sqrt{3}}=\frac{1}{\sqrt{3}}\bullet\frac{\sqrt{3}}{\sqrt{3}}=\frac{\sqrt{3}}{3}$

13. $\sqrt{\frac{1}{5}}=\sqrt{\frac{1}{5}\bullet\frac{5}{5}}=\sqrt{\frac{5}{25}}=\frac{\sqrt{5}}{\sqrt{25}}=\frac{\sqrt{5}}{5}$

15. $\frac{4}{\sqrt[3]{3}}\bullet\frac{\sqrt[3]{9}}{\sqrt[3]{9}}=\frac{4\sqrt[3]{9}}{\sqrt[3]{27}}=\frac{4\sqrt[3]{9}}{3}$

17. $\frac{3}{\sqrt{8x}}=\frac{3}{\sqrt{8x}}\bullet\frac{\sqrt{2x}}{\sqrt{2x}}=\frac{3\sqrt{2x}}{\sqrt{16x^2}}=\frac{3\sqrt{2x}}{4x}$

19. $\frac{3}{\sqrt[3]{4x^2}}=\frac{3}{\sqrt[3]{4x^2}}\bullet\frac{\sqrt[3]{2x}}{\sqrt[3]{2x}}=\frac{3\sqrt[3]{2x}}{\sqrt[3]{8x^3}}=\frac{3\sqrt[3]{2x}}{2x}$

21. $\frac{5}{2-\sqrt{7}}=\frac{5}{2-\sqrt{7}}\bullet\frac{2+\sqrt{7}}{2+\sqrt{7}}=\frac{5(2+\sqrt{7})}{2^2-\sqrt{7}^2}$

$\frac{5(2+\sqrt{7})}{4-7}=-\frac{5(2+\sqrt{7})}{3}$

23. $\frac{-7}{\sqrt{x}-3}=\frac{-7}{\sqrt{x}-3}\bullet\frac{\sqrt{x}+3}{\sqrt{x}+3}$

$$\frac{-7(\sqrt{x}+3)}{\sqrt{x^2}-3^2}=\frac{-7(\sqrt{x}+3)}{x-9}$$

25. $$\frac{\sqrt{2}-\sqrt{3}}{\sqrt{2}+\sqrt{3}}=\frac{\sqrt{2}-\sqrt{3}}{\sqrt{2}+\sqrt{3}}\bullet\frac{\sqrt{2}-\sqrt{3}}{\sqrt{2}-\sqrt{3}}$$
$$\frac{\sqrt{2}^2-2\sqrt{2}\sqrt{3}+\sqrt{3}^2}{\sqrt{2}^2-\sqrt{3}^2}=\frac{2-2\sqrt{6}+3}{2-3}$$
$$\frac{5-2\sqrt{6}}{-1}=-5+2\sqrt{6}$$

27. $$\frac{\sqrt{a}+1}{2\sqrt{a}-\sqrt{b}}=\frac{\sqrt{a}+1}{2\sqrt{a}-\sqrt{b}}\bullet\frac{2\sqrt{a}+\sqrt{b}}{2\sqrt{a}+\sqrt{b}}$$
$$\frac{\sqrt{a}(2\sqrt{a})+\sqrt{a}\sqrt{b}+1(2\sqrt{a})+1\sqrt{b}}{(2\sqrt{a})^2-(\sqrt{b})^2}$$
$$\frac{2a+\sqrt{ab}+2\sqrt{a}+\sqrt{b}}{4a-b}$$

29. $$\sqrt{\frac{5}{3}}=\frac{\sqrt{5}}{\sqrt{3}}\bullet\frac{\sqrt{5}}{\sqrt{5}}=\frac{\sqrt{25}}{\sqrt{15}}=\frac{5}{\sqrt{15}}$$

31. $$\sqrt{\frac{18}{5}}=\frac{\sqrt{18}}{\sqrt{5}}=\frac{\sqrt{9}\sqrt{2}}{\sqrt{5}}=\frac{3\sqrt{2}}{\sqrt{5}}$$
$$\frac{3\sqrt{2}}{\sqrt{5}}\bullet\frac{\sqrt{2}}{\sqrt{2}}=\frac{3\sqrt{4}}{\sqrt{10}}=\frac{3(2)}{\sqrt{10}}=\frac{6}{\sqrt{10}}$$

33. $$\frac{\sqrt{4x}}{7}\bullet\frac{\sqrt{4x}}{\sqrt{4x}}=\frac{\sqrt{16x^2}}{7\sqrt{4x}}=\frac{4x}{7\sqrt{4x}}$$

35. $$\frac{\sqrt[3]{5y^2}}{\sqrt[3]{4x}}\bullet\frac{\sqrt[3]{5^2y}}{\sqrt[3]{5^2y}}=\frac{\sqrt[3]{5^3y^3}}{\sqrt[3]{4(5^2)xy}}=\frac{5y}{\sqrt[3]{100xy}}$$

37. $$\frac{(2-\sqrt{7})}{-5}\bullet\frac{(2+\sqrt{7})}{(2+\sqrt{7})}=\frac{(2-\sqrt{7})(2+\sqrt{7})}{-5(2+\sqrt{7})}$$
$$\frac{4-\sqrt{49}}{-10-5\sqrt{7}}=\frac{4-7}{-10-5\sqrt{7}}=\frac{-3}{-10-5\sqrt{7}}$$
$$\frac{-1(3)}{-1(10+5\sqrt{7})}=\frac{3}{10+5\sqrt{7}}$$

39. $$\frac{(\sqrt{x}+3)}{\sqrt{x}}\bullet\frac{(\sqrt{x}-3)}{(\sqrt{x}-3)}=\frac{(\sqrt{x}+3)(\sqrt{x}-3)}{\sqrt{x}(\sqrt{x}-3)}$$
$$\frac{\sqrt{x^2}-9}{\sqrt{x^2}-3\sqrt{x}}=\frac{x-9}{x-3\sqrt{x}}$$

41. $6(\sqrt{2}-2)=6\sqrt{2}-6\bullet 2=6\sqrt{2}-12$

43. $\sqrt{2}(\sqrt{2}+x\sqrt{6})=\sqrt{2}^2+\sqrt{2}(x\sqrt{6})$
$2+\sqrt{2}(x\sqrt{2}\sqrt{3})=2+2x\sqrt{3}$

45. $(2\sqrt{7}+3\sqrt{5})(\sqrt{7}-2\sqrt{5})$
$2\sqrt{7}^2-(2\sqrt{7})(2\sqrt{5})+(3\sqrt{5})\sqrt{7}-3\bullet 2\sqrt{5}^2$
$2\bullet 7-4\sqrt{35}+3\sqrt{35}-6\bullet 5$
$14-\sqrt{35}-30=-16-\sqrt{35}$

47. $(\sqrt{x}-y)(\sqrt{x}+y)=\sqrt{x}^2-y^2=x-y^2$

49. $(\sqrt{3}+x)^2=\sqrt{3}^2+2\sqrt{3}x+x^2=3+2\sqrt{3}x+x^2$

51. $(\sqrt{5x}-3\sqrt{2})(\sqrt{5x}-3\sqrt{3})$
$(\sqrt{5x})^2-3\sqrt{3}\sqrt{5x}-3\sqrt{2}\sqrt{5x}+(3\sqrt{2})(3\sqrt{3})$
$5x-3\sqrt{15x}-3\sqrt{10x}+9\sqrt{6}$

53. $(\sqrt[3]{4}+2)(\sqrt[3]{2}-1)$
$\sqrt[3]{4}\ \sqrt[3]{2}-\sqrt[3]{4}\bullet 1+2\sqrt[3]{2}-2\bullet 1$
$\sqrt[3]{8}-\sqrt[3]{4}+2\sqrt[3]{2}-2$
$2-\sqrt[3]{4}+2\sqrt[3]{2}-2$
$-\sqrt[3]{4}+2\sqrt[3]{2}$

55. $(\sqrt[3]{x}+1)(\sqrt[3]{x}-4\sqrt{x}+7)$
$\sqrt[3]{x}(\sqrt[3]{x}-4\sqrt{x}+7)+1(\sqrt[3]{x}-4\sqrt{x}+7)$
$\sqrt[3]{x}^2-\sqrt[3]{x}(4\sqrt{x})+\sqrt[3]{x}(7)+\sqrt[3]{x}-4\sqrt{x}+7$
$\sqrt[3]{x}^2-4\sqrt[3]{\sqrt{x}^2}\ \sqrt{\sqrt[3]{x^3}}+8\sqrt[3]{x}-4\sqrt{x}+7$
$\sqrt[3]{x^2}-4\sqrt[6]{x^5}+8\sqrt[3]{x}-4\sqrt{x}+7$

57. $$\sqrt{\frac{2}{5}}=\sqrt{\frac{2}{5}\bullet\frac{5}{5}}=\sqrt{\frac{10}{25}}=\frac{\sqrt{10}}{\sqrt{25}}=\frac{\sqrt{10}}{5}$$

59. $$\frac{9}{\sqrt{3a}}=\frac{9}{\sqrt{3a}}\bullet\frac{\sqrt{3a}}{\sqrt{3a}}=\frac{9\sqrt{3a}}{3a}=\frac{3\sqrt{3a}}{a}$$

61. $$\frac{3}{\sqrt[3]{2}}=\frac{3}{\sqrt[3]{2}}\bullet\frac{\sqrt[3]{4}}{\sqrt[3]{4}}=\frac{3\sqrt[3]{4}}{\sqrt[3]{8}}=\frac{3\sqrt[3]{4}}{2}$$

63. $\dfrac{8}{1+\sqrt{10}} \bullet \dfrac{1-\sqrt{10}}{1-\sqrt{10}} = \dfrac{8(1-\sqrt{10})}{1^2-\sqrt{10^2}}$

$\dfrac{8(1-\sqrt{10})}{1-10} = \dfrac{-8(1-\sqrt{10})}{9}$

65. $\dfrac{x}{\sqrt[3]{16x^2}} = \dfrac{x\sqrt[3]{4x}}{\sqrt[3]{16x^2}\ \sqrt[3]{4x}}$

$\dfrac{x\sqrt[3]{4x}}{\sqrt[3]{64x^3}} = \dfrac{x\sqrt[3]{4x}}{4x} = \dfrac{\sqrt[3]{4x}}{4}$

67. $\sqrt{\dfrac{18x^4y^6}{3z}} = \sqrt{\dfrac{6x^4y^6z}{z^2}}$

$\dfrac{\sqrt{x^4}\sqrt{y^6}\sqrt{6z}}{\sqrt{z^2}} = \dfrac{x^2y^3\sqrt{6z}}{z}$

69. $\dfrac{\sqrt{2}-1}{\sqrt{2}+1} = \dfrac{\sqrt{2}-1}{\sqrt{2}+1} \bullet \dfrac{\sqrt{2}-1}{\sqrt{2}-1}$

$\dfrac{\sqrt{2}^2-2\sqrt{2}\bullet 1+1^2}{\sqrt{2}^2-1^2}$

$\dfrac{2-2\sqrt{2}+1}{2-1} = 3-2\sqrt{2}$

71. $\dfrac{\sqrt{x}+1}{\sqrt{x}-1} = \dfrac{\sqrt{x}+1}{\sqrt{x}-1} \bullet \dfrac{\sqrt{x}+1}{\sqrt{x}+1}$

$\dfrac{\sqrt{x}^2+2\sqrt{x}\bullet 1+1^2}{\sqrt{x}^2-1^2}$

$\dfrac{x+2\sqrt{x}+1}{x-1}$

73. $\sqrt{\dfrac{2}{5}} = \dfrac{\sqrt{2}}{\sqrt{5}} \bullet \dfrac{\sqrt{2}}{\sqrt{2}} = \dfrac{\sqrt{4}}{\sqrt{10}} = \dfrac{2}{\sqrt{10}}$

75. $\dfrac{\sqrt{2x}}{11} \bullet \dfrac{\sqrt{2x}}{\sqrt{2x}} = \dfrac{\sqrt{4x^2}}{11\sqrt{2x}} = \dfrac{2x}{11\sqrt{2x}}$

77. $\sqrt[3]{\dfrac{7}{8}} = \dfrac{\sqrt[3]{7}}{\sqrt[3]{8}} = \dfrac{\sqrt[3]{7}}{2} = \dfrac{\sqrt[3]{7}}{2} \bullet \dfrac{\sqrt[3]{7^2}}{\sqrt[3]{7^2}} = \dfrac{\sqrt[3]{7^3}}{2\sqrt[3]{7^2}} = \dfrac{7}{2\sqrt[3]{7^2}}$

79. $\dfrac{(2-\sqrt{11})}{6} \bullet \dfrac{(2+\sqrt{11})}{(2+\sqrt{11})} = \dfrac{(2-\sqrt{11})(2+\sqrt{11})}{6(2+\sqrt{11})}$

$\dfrac{4-\sqrt{121}}{12+6\sqrt{11}} = \dfrac{4-11}{12+6\sqrt{11}} = \dfrac{-7}{12+6\sqrt{11}}$

81. $\dfrac{\sqrt[3]{3x^5}}{10} \bullet \dfrac{\sqrt[3]{3^2x}}{\sqrt[3]{3^2x}} = \dfrac{\sqrt[3]{3^3x^6}}{10\sqrt[3]{3^2x}} = \dfrac{3x^2}{10\sqrt[3]{9x}}$

83. $\sqrt{\dfrac{18x^4y^6}{3z}} = \sqrt{\dfrac{6x^4y^6}{z}} = \dfrac{x^2y^3\sqrt{6}}{\sqrt{z}}$

$\dfrac{x^2y^3\sqrt{6}}{\sqrt{z}} \bullet \dfrac{\sqrt{6}}{\sqrt{6}} = \dfrac{x^2y^3\sqrt{36}}{\sqrt{6z}} = \dfrac{6x^2y^3}{\sqrt{6z}}$

85. $\dfrac{(\sqrt{2}-1)}{(\sqrt{2}+1)} \bullet \dfrac{(\sqrt{2}+1)}{(\sqrt{2}+1)} = \dfrac{(\sqrt{2}-1)(\sqrt{2}+1)}{(\sqrt{2}+1)(\sqrt{2}+1)}$

$\dfrac{\sqrt{4}-1}{\sqrt{4}-2\sqrt{2}+1} = \dfrac{2-1}{2-2\sqrt{2}+1} = \dfrac{1}{3-2\sqrt{2}}$

87. $\dfrac{(\sqrt{x}+1)}{(\sqrt{x}-1)} \bullet \dfrac{(\sqrt{x}-1)}{(\sqrt{x}-1)} = \dfrac{(\sqrt{x}+1)(\sqrt{x}-1)}{(\sqrt{x}-1)(\sqrt{x}-1)}$

$\dfrac{\sqrt{x^2}-1}{\sqrt{x^2}-2\sqrt{x}+1} = \dfrac{x-1}{x-2\sqrt{x}+1}$

89. $V = \sqrt{3}(\sqrt{2})(\sqrt{5}+\sqrt{2})$

$V = \sqrt{6}(\sqrt{5}+\sqrt{2})$

$V = \sqrt{6}\sqrt{5}+\sqrt{6}\sqrt{2}$

$V = \sqrt{30}+\sqrt{3}\sqrt{2}\sqrt{2}$

$V = (\sqrt{30}+2\sqrt{3})\ \text{cm}^3.$

91. $5^{-1} = \frac{1}{5}$

93. $-2^{-3} = -\dfrac{1}{2^3} = -\dfrac{1}{8}$

95. $x^{-2}x^{-3} = x^{-5} = \dfrac{1}{x^5}$

97. $\dfrac{a^{-2}}{a^{-3}} = a^{-2-(-3)} = a^{-2+3} = a^1 = a$

99. $\dfrac{(xy^3)^5}{(xy)^{-4}} = \dfrac{x^5y^{15}}{x^{-4}y^{-4}} = x^{5-(-4)}\ y^{15-(-4)}$

$x^{5+4}\ y^{15+4} = x^9y^{19}$

101. $\left(\dfrac{3x^2}{x^{-4}}\right)^{-2} = \dfrac{3^{-2}x^{-4}}{x^8} = 3^{-2}x^{-4-8}$

$3^{-2}x^{-12} = \dfrac{1}{3^2x^{12}} = \dfrac{1}{9x^{12}}$

103. $\frac{(c^2)^4c^{-5}}{c^{-10}} = \frac{c^8c^{-15}}{c^{-10}} = \frac{c^{-7}}{c^{-10}}$

$c^{-7-(-10)} = c^{-7+10} = c^3$

Exercise Set 8.5

1. $8^{\frac{1}{3}} = \sqrt[3]{8} = 2$

3. $9^{\frac{1}{2}} = \sqrt{9} = 3$

5. $16^{\frac{3}{4}} = \left(\sqrt[4]{16}\right)^3 = 2^3 = 8$

7. $32^{\frac{2}{5}} = \left(\sqrt[5]{32}\right)^2 = 2^2 = 4$

9. $-16^{-\frac{1}{4}} = -\frac{1}{16^{\frac{1}{4}}} = -\frac{1}{\sqrt[4]{16}} = -\frac{1}{2}$

11. $16^{-\frac{3}{2}} = \frac{1}{16^{\frac{3}{2}}} = \frac{1}{(\sqrt{16})^3} = \frac{1}{4^3} = \frac{1}{64}$

13. $81^{-\frac{3}{2}} = \frac{1}{81^{\frac{3}{2}}} = \frac{1}{(\sqrt{81})^3} = \frac{1}{9^3} = \frac{1}{729}$

15. $\left(\frac{4}{25}\right)^{-\frac{1}{2}} = \frac{4^{-\frac{1}{2}}}{25^{-\frac{1}{2}}} = \frac{25^{\frac{1}{2}}}{4^{\frac{1}{2}}} = \frac{\sqrt{25}}{\sqrt{4}} = \frac{5}{2}$

17. $a^{\frac{3}{7}} = \sqrt[7]{a^3}$

19. $2x^{\frac{5}{3}} = 2\sqrt[3]{x^5}$

21. $(4t)^{-\frac{5}{6}} = \frac{1}{(4t)^{\frac{5}{6}}} = \frac{1}{\sqrt[6]{(4t)^5}}$

23. $(4x-1)^{\frac{3}{5}} = \sqrt[5]{(4x-1)^3}$

25. $\sqrt{3} = 3^{\frac{1}{2}}$

27. $\sqrt[3]{y^5} = (y^5)^{\frac{1}{3}} = y^{\frac{5}{3}}$

29. $\sqrt[5]{4y^7} = (4y^7)^{\frac{1}{5}} = 4^{\frac{1}{5}}(y^7)^{\frac{1}{5}} = 4^{\frac{1}{5}}y^{\frac{7}{5}}$

31. $\sqrt{(y+1)^3} = [(y+1)^3]^{\frac{1}{2}} = (y+1)^{\frac{3}{2}}$

33. $2\sqrt{x} - 3\sqrt{y} = 2x^{\frac{1}{2}} - 3y^{\frac{1}{2}}$

35. $\sqrt[6]{x^3} = x^{\frac{3}{6}} = x^{\frac{1}{2}}$

37. $\sqrt[4]{16x^2} = 16^{\frac{1}{4}}x^{\frac{2}{4}} = 2x^{\frac{1}{2}}$

39. $\sqrt[4]{(x+3)^2} = (x+3)^{\frac{2}{4}} = (x+3)^{\frac{1}{2}}$

41. $\sqrt[8]{x^4y^4} = x^{\frac{4}{8}}y^{\frac{4}{8}} = x^{\frac{1}{2}}y^{\frac{1}{2}}$

43. $a^{\frac{2}{3}}a^{\frac{5}{3}} = a^{\frac{2}{3}+\frac{5}{3}} = a^{\frac{7}{3}}$

45. $(4u^2v^{-6})^{\frac{3}{2}} = 4^{\frac{3}{2}}(u^2)^{\frac{3}{2}}(v^{-6})^{\frac{3}{2}}$

$(4^{\frac{1}{2}})^3u^3v^{-9} = \frac{2^3u^3}{v^9} = \frac{8u^3}{v^9}$

47. $\frac{b^{\frac{1}{2}}b^{\frac{3}{4}}}{-b^{\frac{1}{4}}} = -b^{\frac{1}{2}+\frac{3}{4}-\frac{1}{4}} = -b^{\frac{1}{2}+\frac{1}{2}} = -b^1 = -b$

49. $y^{\frac{1}{2}}(y^{\frac{1}{2}} - y^{\frac{2}{3}}) = y^{\frac{1}{2}}y^{\frac{1}{2}} - y^{\frac{1}{2}}y^{\frac{2}{3}}$

$y^{\frac{1}{2}+\frac{1}{2}} - y^{\frac{1}{2}+\frac{2}{3}} = y^1 - y^{\frac{7}{6}} = y - y^{\frac{7}{6}}$

51. $x^{\frac{2}{3}}(2x-2) = 2x^1x^{\frac{2}{3}} - 2x^{\frac{2}{3}} = 2x^{\frac{5}{3}} - 2x^{\frac{2}{3}}$

53. $(2x^{\frac{1}{3}}+3)(2x^{\frac{1}{3}}-3) = (2x^{\frac{1}{3}})^2 - 3^2$

$2^2(x^{\frac{1}{3}})^2 - 9 = 4x^{\frac{2}{3}} - 9$

55. $81^{\frac{1}{2}} = \sqrt{81} = 9$

57. $(-8)^{\frac{1}{3}} = \sqrt[3]{-8} = -2$

59. $-81^{\frac{1}{4}} = -(81^{\frac{1}{4}}) = -\left(\sqrt[4]{81}\right) = -(3) = -3$

61. $\left(\frac{1}{81}\right)^{\frac{1}{2}} = \frac{1^{\frac{1}{2}}}{81^{\frac{1}{2}}} = \frac{\sqrt{1}}{\sqrt{81}} = \frac{1}{9}$

63. $\left(\frac{27}{64}\right)^{\frac{1}{3}} = \frac{27^{\frac{1}{3}}}{64^{\frac{1}{3}}} = \frac{\sqrt[3]{27}}{\sqrt[3]{64}} = \frac{3}{4}$

65. $9^{\frac{3}{2}} = (\sqrt{9})^3 = (3)^3 = 27$

67. $64^{\frac{3}{2}} = (\sqrt{64})^3 = (8)^3 = 512$

69. $-8^{\frac{2}{3}} = -(8^{\frac{2}{3}}) = -(\sqrt[3]{8})^2 = -(2)^2 = -(4) = -4$

71. $4^{\frac{5}{2}} = (\sqrt{4})^5 = (2)^5 = 32$

73. $\left(\frac{4}{9}\right)^{\frac{3}{2}} = \frac{4^{\frac{3}{2}}}{9^{\frac{3}{2}}} = \frac{(\sqrt{4})^3}{(\sqrt{9})^3} = \frac{2^3}{3^3} = \frac{8}{27}$

75. $\left(\frac{1}{81}\right)^{\frac{3}{4}} = \frac{1^{\frac{3}{4}}}{81^{\frac{3}{4}}} = \frac{(\sqrt[4]{1})^3}{(\sqrt[4]{81})^3} = \frac{1^3}{3^3} = \frac{1}{27}$

77. $4^{-\frac{1}{2}} = \frac{1}{4^{\frac{1}{2}}} = \frac{1}{\sqrt{4}} = \frac{1}{2}$

79. $125^{-\frac{1}{3}} = \frac{1}{125^{\frac{1}{3}}} = \frac{1}{\sqrt[3]{125}} = \frac{1}{5}$

81. $625^{-\frac{3}{4}} = \frac{1}{625^{\frac{3}{4}}} = \frac{1}{(\sqrt[4]{625})^3} = \frac{1}{5^3} = \frac{1}{125}$

83. $x^{-\frac{5}{3}}x^{\frac{1}{2}} = x^{-\frac{5}{3}+\frac{1}{2}} = x^{-\frac{7}{6}} = \frac{1}{x^{\frac{7}{6}}}$

85. $\frac{w^{\frac{3}{4}}}{w^{\frac{1}{4}}} = w^{\frac{3}{4}-\frac{1}{4}} = w^{\frac{1}{2}}$

87. $(x^{-\frac{1}{5}}y^{\frac{1}{12}})^3 = (x^{-\frac{1}{5}})^3(y^{\frac{1}{12}})^3$

$x^{-\frac{3}{5}}y^{\frac{3}{12}} = \frac{y^{\frac{1}{4}}}{x^{\frac{3}{5}}}$

89. $(a^3b^9)^{-\frac{2}{3}}a^{\frac{2}{3}} = (a^3)^{-\frac{2}{3}} \bullet (b^9)^{-\frac{2}{3}} \bullet a^{\frac{2}{3}}$

$a^{-2} \bullet b^{-6} \bullet a^{\frac{2}{3}} = \frac{a^{-\frac{4}{3}}}{b^6} = \frac{1}{a^{\frac{4}{3}}b^6}$

91. $(16x^4y^2)^{\frac{1}{2}} = 16^{\frac{1}{2}}(x^4)^{\frac{1}{2}}(y^2)^{\frac{1}{2}} = 4x^2y^1 = 4x^2y$

93. $4x^{\frac{2}{3}}(6x^{\frac{5}{2}} - y^{\frac{2}{3}}) = 4x^{\frac{2}{3}}(6x^{\frac{5}{2}}) - 4x^{\frac{2}{3}}(y^{\frac{2}{3}})$

$24x^{\frac{19}{6}} - 4x^{\frac{2}{3}}y^{\frac{2}{3}}$

95. $(x^{\frac{1}{2}}+2)(x^{\frac{1}{2}}-3)$

$x^{\frac{1}{2}} \bullet x^{\frac{1}{2}} + 2x^{\frac{1}{2}} - 3x^{\frac{1}{2}} - 6$

$x - x^{\frac{1}{2}} - 6$

97. $(x^{\frac{1}{2}} - 2x)^2$

$(x^{\frac{1}{2}})^2 - 2x^{\frac{1}{2}}(2x) + (2x)^2$

$x - 4x^{\frac{3}{2}} + 4x^2$

99. $9x^{\frac{3}{4}} - x^{\frac{7}{4}} = x^{\frac{3}{4}}(9 - x^1) = x^{\frac{3}{4}}(9 - x)$

101. $9x^{\frac{5}{3}} + 15x^{\frac{7}{3}} = 3x^{\frac{5}{3}}(3 + 5x^{\frac{2}{3}})$

103. $P = P_0(1.08)^N$

$P = 10,000(1.08)^{\frac{3}{2}}$

$P = 10,000(\sqrt{1.08})^3$

$P = 10,000(1.0392)^3$

$P = 10,000(1.1224)$

$P = 11,224$

105. $(\sqrt{y})^2 = \sqrt{y}\sqrt{y} = \sqrt{y^2} = y$

107. $(\sqrt{z+2})^2$

$\sqrt{z+2}\sqrt{z+2}$

$\sqrt{(z+2)^2}$

$z+2$

109. $y-2=5^2$

$y-2=25$

$y=27$

$\{27\}$

111. $x^2+2x=8$

$x^2+2x-8=0$

$(x+4)(x-2)=0$

$x+4=0$ or $x-2=0$

$x=-4$ or $x=2$

$\{-4, 2\}$

113. $3x^2+x-2=0$

$(3x-2)(x+1)=0$

$3x-2=0$ or $x+1=0$

$3x=2$ or $x=-1$

$x=\frac{2}{3}$

$\left\{-1, \frac{2}{3}\right\}$

115. $x+7=(x+5)^2$

$x+7=x^2+10x+25$

$0=x^2+9x+18$

$0=(x+6)(x+3)$

$x+6=0$ or $x+3=0$

$x=-6$ or $x=-3$

$\{-6, -3\}$

Graphing Calculator Exercise 8.6

1. $\sqrt{x+7}=x$

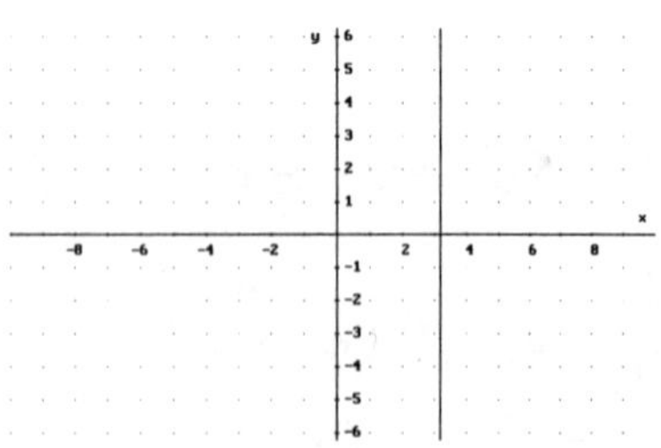

$x=3.19$

$\{3.19\}$

3. $\sqrt{2x+1}=\sqrt{2x+2}$

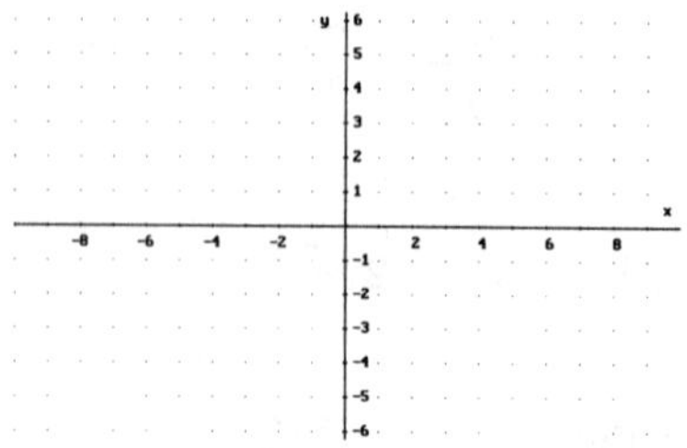

No solution.

$\{\ \}$

5. $1.2x=\sqrt{3.1x+5}$

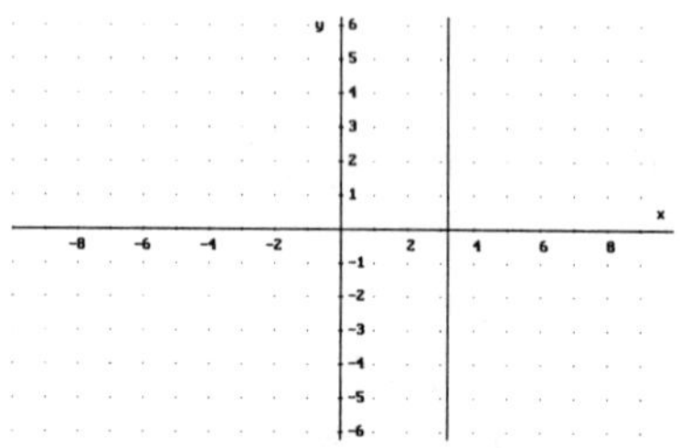

$x=3.23$

$\{3.23\}$

Exercise Set 8.6

1. $\sqrt{2x}=4$

$2x=4^2$

$2x=16$

$x=8$

$\{8\}$

3. $\sqrt{x-3}=2$

$x-3=2^2$

$x-3=4$

$x=7$

$\{7\}$

5. $\sqrt{2x}=-4$

No solution since a principal square root does not yield a

negative number.

{ }

7. $\sqrt{4x-3}-5=0$

$\sqrt{4x-3}=5$

$4x-3=5^2$

$4x-3=25$

$4x=28$

$x=7$

$\{7\}$

9. $\sqrt{2x-3}-2=1$

$\sqrt{2x-3}=3$

$2x-3=3^2$

$2x-3=9$

$2x=12$

$x=6$

$\{6\}$

11. $\sqrt[3]{6x}=-3$

$6x=(-3)^3$

$6x=-27$

$x=\frac{-27}{6}=-\frac{9}{2}$

$\left\{-\frac{9}{2}\right\}$

13. $\sqrt[3]{x-2}-3=0$

$\sqrt[3]{x-2}=3$

$x-2=3^3$

$x-2=27$

$x=29$

$\{29\}$

15. $\sqrt{13-x}=x-1$

$13-x=(x-1)^2$

$13-x=x^2-2x+1$

$0=x^2-x-12$

$0=(x-4)(x+3)$

$x-4=0$ or $x+3=0$

$x=4$ or $x=-3$

We discard the -3 as extraneous, leaving $x=4$ as the only solution.

$\{4\}$

17. $x-\sqrt{4-3x}=-8$

$x+8=\sqrt{4-3x}$

$(x+8)^2=4-3x$

$x^2+16x+64=4-3x$

$x^2+19x+60=0$

$(x+4)(x+15)=0$

$x+4=0$ or $x+15=0$

$x=-4$ or $x=-15$

We discard the -15 as extraneous, leaving $x=-4$ as the only solution.

$\{-4\}$

19. $\sqrt{y+5}=2-\sqrt{y-4}$

$y+5=(2-\sqrt{y-4})^2$

$y+5=4-4\sqrt{y-4}+y-4$

$y+5=y-4\sqrt{y-4}$

$5=-4\sqrt{y-4}$

$25=16(y-4)$

$\frac{25}{16}=y-4$

$y=\frac{89}{16}=5\frac{9}{16}$

which we discard as extraneous. No solution.

{ }

21. $\sqrt{x-3}+\sqrt{x+2}=5$

$\sqrt{x-3}=5-\sqrt{x+2}$

$x-3=25-10\sqrt{x+2}+x+2$

$-3=27-10\sqrt{x+2}$

$-30=-10\sqrt{x+2}$

$3=\sqrt{x+2}$

$9=x+2$

$7 = x$

$\{7\}$

23. Let $c =$ the length of the hypotenuse of the right triangle. By the Pythagorean theorem,

$c^2 = 6^2 + 3^2$

$c^2 = 36 + 9$

$c^2 = 45$

$c = \sqrt{45} = \sqrt{9}\sqrt{5} = 3\sqrt{5}$ ft.

25. Let $b =$ the length of the unknown leg of the right triangle. By the Pythagorean theorem,

$7^2 = 3^2 + b^2$

$49 = 9 + b^2$

$b^2 = 40$

$b = \sqrt{40} = \sqrt{4}\sqrt{10} = 2\sqrt{10}$ m.

27. $\sqrt{3x-2} = 5$

$3x - 2 = 5^2$

$3x - 2 = 25$

$3x = 27$

$x = 9$

$\{9\}$

29. $-\sqrt{2x} + 4 = -6$

$10 = \sqrt{2x}$

$10^2 = 2x$

$100 = 2x$

$x = 50$

$\{50\}$

31. $\sqrt{3x+1} + 2 = 0$

$\sqrt{3x+1} = -2$

No solution since a principal square root does not yield a negative number.

$\{\ \}$

33. $\sqrt[4]{4x+1} - 2 = 0$

$\sqrt[4]{4x+1} = 2$

$4x + 1 = 2^4$

$4x + 1 = 16$

$4x = 15$

$x = \frac{15}{4}$

$\left\{\frac{15}{4}\right\}$

35. $\sqrt{4x-3} = 5$

$4x - 3 = 5^2$

$4x - 3 = 25$

$4x = 28$

$x = 7$

$\{7\}$

37. $\sqrt[3]{6x-3} - 3 = 0$

$\sqrt[3]{6x-3} = 3$

$6x - 3 = 3^3$

$6x - 3 = 27$

$6x = 30$

$x = 5$

$\{5\}$

39. $\sqrt[3]{2x-3} - 2 = -5$

$\sqrt[3]{2x-3} = -3$

$2x - 3 = (-3)^3$

$2x - 3 = -27$

$2x = -24$

$x = -12$

$\{-12\}$

41. $\sqrt{x+4} = \sqrt{2x-5}$

$x + 4 = 2x - 5$

$9 = x$

$\{9\}$

43. $x-\sqrt{1-x}=-5$

$x+5=\sqrt{1-x}$

$(x+5)^2=1-x$

$x^2+10x+25=1-x$

$x^2+11x+24=0$

$(x+3)(x+8)=0$

$x+3=0$ or $x+8=0$

$x=-3$ or $x=-8$

We discard -8 as extraneous.

$x=-3$

$\{-3\}$

45. $\sqrt[3]{-6x-1}=\sqrt[3]{-2x-5}$

$-6x-1=-2x-5$

$4=4x$

$x=1$

$\{1\}$

47. $\sqrt{5x-1}-\sqrt{x}+2=3$

$\sqrt{5x-1}=\sqrt{x}+1$

$5x-1=x+2\sqrt{x}+1$

$4x-2=2\sqrt{x}$

$2x-1=\sqrt{x}$

$4x^2-4x+1=x$

$4x^2-5x+1=0$

$(4x-1)(x-1)=0$

$4x-1=0$ or $x-1=0$

$4x=1$ or $x=1$

$x=\frac{1}{4}$

Discard $\frac{1}{4}$ as extraneous.

$x=1$

$\{1\}$

49. $\sqrt{2x-1}=\sqrt{1-2x}$

$\sqrt{2x-1}=\sqrt{-(2x-1)}$

It follows that $2x-1=0$ (otherwise one of the radicands would be negative).

So, $2x=1$

$x=\frac{1}{2}$

$\left\{\frac{1}{2}\right\}$

51. We need to solve the equation:

$80\sqrt[3]{x}+500=1620$

$80\sqrt[3]{x}=1120$

$\sqrt[3]{x}=14$

$x=14^3$

$x=2744$

Thus, the company needs to make fewer than 2744 deliveries per day.

53. We are given $R=\sqrt{A^2+B^2}$ with $A=600$ and $R=850$.
Substituting, we get

$850=\sqrt{600^2+B^2}$

$850^2=600^2+B^2$

$B^2=850^2-600^2$

$B^2=722{,}500-360{,}000$

$B^2=362{,}500$

$B=\sqrt{362{,}500}$

$B=50\sqrt{145}\approx 602$ lbs.

Thus, tractor B is exerting approximately 602 lbs. of force.

55. $x^2=5^2+10^2$

$x^2=25+100$

$x^2=125$

$x=\pm\sqrt{125}=\pm\sqrt{25\bullet 5}=\pm 5\sqrt{5}$

$5\sqrt{5}$ cm.

57. $x^2=2^2+2^2$

$x^2=4+4$

$x^2=8$

$x=\pm\sqrt{8}=\pm\sqrt{4\bullet 2}=\pm 2\sqrt{2}$

$2\sqrt{2}$ inches.

59. $x^2=(5)^2+(12)^2$

$x^2=25+144$

$x^2 = 169$

$x = \pm 13$

The ladder is 13 ft.

61. $h^2 + (15)^2 = (28)^2$

$h^2 + 225 = 784$

$h^2 = 559$

$h = \pm\sqrt{559} \approx \pm 23.6$

Wire is attached 23.6 ft. from the base of the pole.

63. $S(x) = \sqrt{10.5x}$

$S(280) = \sqrt{10.5(280)}$

$S(280) = \sqrt{2940}$

$S(280) = 54.22$ mph.

65. $b = \sqrt{\frac{3V}{H}}$

$6 = \sqrt{\frac{3V}{2}}$

$6^2 = \left(\sqrt{\frac{3V}{2}}\right)^2$

$36 = \frac{3V}{2}$

$\frac{2}{3} \bullet 36 = \frac{2}{3} \bullet \frac{3V}{2}$

$24 \text{ ft}^3 = V$

67. $(-1, 5), (0, 2)$

$m = \frac{2-5}{0-(-1)} = \frac{-3}{1} = -3$

69. $(4, 7), (-1, 5)$

$m = \frac{5-7}{-1-4} = \frac{-2}{-5} = \frac{2}{5}$

71. It is a function.

73. It is a function.

75. It is not a function.

77. $\dfrac{\frac{x}{6}}{\frac{2x}{3} + \frac{1}{2}} = \dfrac{\left(\frac{x}{6}\right) \bullet 6}{\left(\frac{2x}{3} + \frac{1}{2}\right) \bullet 6} = \dfrac{x}{4x+3}$

79. $\dfrac{\frac{z}{5} + \frac{1}{10}}{\frac{z}{20} - \frac{z}{5}} = \dfrac{\left(\frac{z}{5} + \frac{1}{10}\right) \bullet 20}{\left(\frac{z}{20} - \frac{z}{5}\right) \bullet 20}$

$\frac{4z+2}{z-4z} = -\frac{4z+2}{3z}$

81. $3\sqrt{x^2 - 8x} = x^2 - 8x$

Let $u = x^2 - 8x$

$3\sqrt{u} = u$

$9u = u^2$

$0 = u^2 - 9u$

$0 = u(u-9)$

$u = 0$ or $u - 9 = 0$

$u = 9$

Substitute $x^2 - 8x$ for u.

$x^2 - 8x = 0$ or $x^2 - 8x = 9$

$x(x-8) = 0$ or $x^2 - 8x - 9 = 0$

$x = 0$ or $x = 8$ or $x - 9 = 0$ or $x + 1 = 0$

$x = 0$ or $x = 8$ or $x = 9$ or $x = -1$

All solutions check.

$\{-1, 0, 8, 9\}$

83. $7 - (x^2 - 3x) = \sqrt{(x^2 - 3x) + 5}$

Let $u = x^2 - 3x$

$7 - u = \sqrt{u + 5}$

$49 - 14u + u^2 = u + 5$

$44 - 15u + u^2 = 0$

$(u-4)(u-11) = 0$

$u - 4 = 0$ or $u - 11 = 0$

$u = 4$ or $u = 11$

Substitute $x^2 - 3x$ for u.

$x^2 - 3x = 4$ or $x^2 - 3x = 11$

$x^2 - 3x - 4 = 0$ or $x^2 - 3x - 11 = 0$

$(x-4)(x+1) = 0$ or can't factor

$x - 4 = 0$ or $x + 1 = 0$

$x = 4$ or $x = -1$

Both solutions check.

$\{-1, 4\}$

Exercise Set 8.7

1. $\sqrt{-24} = \sqrt{4}\sqrt{6}\sqrt{-1} = 2i\sqrt{6}$

3. $-\sqrt{-36} = -\sqrt{36}\sqrt{-1} = -6i$

5. $8\sqrt{-63} = 8\sqrt{9}\sqrt{7}\sqrt{-1}$

$8 \bullet 3\sqrt{7}i = 24i\sqrt{7}$

7. $-\sqrt{54} = -\sqrt{9}\sqrt{6} = -3\sqrt{6}$

9. $(4-7i)+(2+3i)$

$(4+2)+(-7+3)i$

$6-4i$

11. $(6+5i)-(8-i)$

$(6-8)+[5-(-1)]i$

$-2+6i$

13. $6-(8+4i)$

$6-8-4i$

$-2-4i$

15. $6i(2-3i)$

$6i(2)-6i(3i)$

$12i-18i^2$

$12i-18(-1)$

$18+12i$

17. $(\sqrt{3}+2i)(\sqrt{3}-2i)$

$(\sqrt{3})^2-(2i)^2$

$\sqrt{3^2}+2^2 = 3+4 = 7$

19. $(4-2i)^2$

$16-16i+4i^2$

$16-16i+4(-1)$

$16-4-16i$

$12-16i$

21. $\frac{4}{i} \bullet \frac{-i}{-i} = \frac{-4i}{-i^2} = \frac{-4i}{-(-1)} = \frac{-4i}{1} = -4i$

23. $\frac{7}{4+3i} = \frac{7}{4+3i} \bullet \frac{4-3i}{4-3i} = \frac{28-21i}{4^2+3^2}$

$\frac{28-21i}{16+9} = \frac{28-21i}{25} = \frac{28}{25} - \frac{21}{25}i$

25. $\frac{3+5i}{1+i} = \frac{3+5i}{1+i} \bullet \frac{1-i}{1-i} = \frac{3+5i-3i-5i^2}{1^2+1^2}$

$\frac{3+2i-5(-1)}{1+1} = \frac{3+5+2i}{2} = \frac{8+2i}{2} = 4+i$

27. $\sqrt{-2}\sqrt{-7} = (\sqrt{2}i)(\sqrt{7}i) = \sqrt{14}i^2$

$\sqrt{14}(-1) = -\sqrt{14}$

29. $\sqrt{-5}\sqrt{-10} = (\sqrt{5}i)(\sqrt{10}i) = \sqrt{5}\sqrt{5}\sqrt{2}i^2$

$5\sqrt{2}(-1) = -5\sqrt{2}$

31. $\sqrt{16}\sqrt{-1} = 4i$

33. $\frac{\sqrt{-9}}{\sqrt{3}} = \frac{3i}{\sqrt{3}} = i\sqrt{3}$

35. $\frac{\sqrt{-80}}{\sqrt{-10}} = \frac{\sqrt{80}i}{\sqrt{10}i} = \sqrt{\frac{80}{10}} = \sqrt{8} = \sqrt{4}\sqrt{2} = 2\sqrt{2}$

37. $i^8 = (i^4)^2 = 1^2 = 1$

39. $i^{21} = i^{20}i = (i^4)^5 i = 1^5 i = 1i = i$

41. $i^{11} = i^{10}i = (i^2)^5 i = (-1)^5 i = (-1)i = -i$

43. $i^{-6} = (i^2)^{-3} = (-1)^{-3} = \frac{1}{(-1)^3} = \frac{1}{-1} = -1$

45. $(7i)(-9i) = -63i^2 = -63(-1) = 63$

47. $(6-3i)-(4-2i) = 6-3i-4+2i = 2-i$

49. $(6-2i)(3+i) = 2(3-i)(3+i)$

$2(3^2+1^2) = 2(9+1) = 2(10) = 20$

51. $(8-\sqrt{-3})-(2+\sqrt{-12})$

$8-i\sqrt{3}-2-i\sqrt{4}\sqrt{3}$

$6-i\sqrt{3}-2i\sqrt{3} = 6-3i\sqrt{3}$

53. $(1-i)(1+i) = 1^2-i^2 = 1^2+1^2 = 1+1 = 2$

55. $\frac{16+15i}{-3i} = \frac{(16+15i)i}{-3i^2} = \frac{16i+15i^2}{-3(-1)}$

$\frac{16i+15(-1)}{3} = \frac{-15}{3} + \frac{16}{3}i = -5 + \frac{16}{3}i$

57. $(9+8i)^2 = 81+144i+64i^2$

$81+144i+64(-1)$

$81-64+144i = 17+144i$

59. $\frac{2}{3+i} = \frac{2}{3+i} \bullet \frac{3-i}{3-i} = \frac{2(3-i)}{3^2+1^2}$

$\frac{6-2i}{9+1} = \frac{6}{10} - \frac{2}{10}i = \frac{3}{5} - \frac{1}{5}i$

61. $(5-6i)-4i = 5-6i-4i = 5-10i$

63. $\frac{2-3i}{2+i} = \frac{(2-3i)(2-i)}{(2+i)(2-i)} = \frac{4-6i-2i+3i^2}{2^2+1^2}$

$\frac{4-8i+3(-1)}{4+1} = \frac{4-3-8i}{5} = \frac{1}{5} - \frac{8}{5}i$

65. $(2+4i)+(6-5i)$

$(2+6)+(4-5)i$

$8-i$

67. Since the unknown angle is the complement of the 50° angle, it must have measure $90°-50° = 40°$.

69. Since the measures of the three interior angles of the triangle must sum to 180°, the unknown angle must have measure $180°-(36°+61°) = 180°-97° = 83°$

71. $8 < x-7 < 12$

$8+7 < x-7+7 < 12+7$

$15 < x < 19$

$(15, 19)$

73. $-9 \le 2x+3 \le 7$

$-9-3 \le 2x+3-3 \le 7-3$

$-12 \le 2x \le 4$

$-\frac{12}{2} \le \frac{2x}{2} \le \frac{4}{2}$

$-6 \le x \le 2$

$[-6, 2]$

75. $\frac{15x}{x+8} \bullet \frac{2x+16}{3x}$

$\frac{15x}{x+8} \bullet \frac{2(x+8)}{3x}$

10

77. $\frac{5a+10}{18} \div \frac{a^2-4}{10a}$

$\frac{5(a+2)}{18} \bullet \frac{10a}{(a+2)(a-2)}$

$\frac{5(10a)}{18(a-2)}$

$\frac{25a}{9(a-2)}$

79. $\frac{5}{x^2-3x+2} + \frac{1}{x-2}$

$\frac{5}{(x-1)(x-2)} + \frac{1(x-1)}{(x-2)(x-1)}$

$\frac{5+x-1}{(x-2)(x-1)}$

$\frac{4+x}{(x-2)(x-1)}$

Chapter 8 Review

1. $\sqrt{81} = 9$

3. $\sqrt[3]{27} = 3$

5. $-\sqrt{\frac{9}{64}} = -\frac{3}{8}$

7. $\sqrt[4]{-\frac{16}{81}}$

Not a real number.

9. $\sqrt{76} = 8.718$, irrational

11. $\sqrt{x^{12}} = x^6$

13. $\sqrt{9x^6y^2} = |3x^3y|$

15. $-\sqrt[3]{8x^6} = -2x^2$

17. $f(x) = \sqrt{x} + 3$

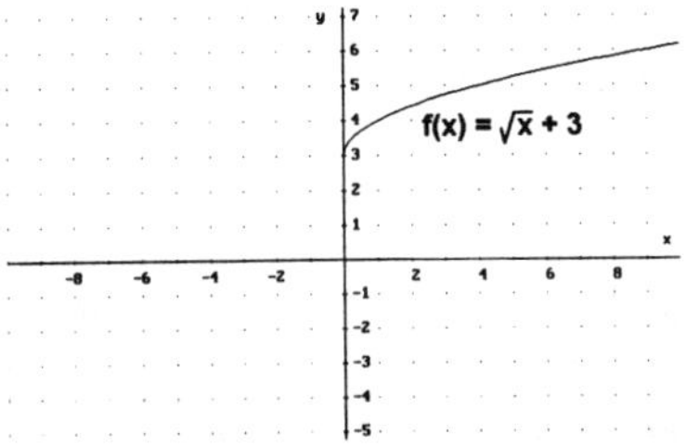

19. $F(x) = \sqrt[3]{x} - 1$

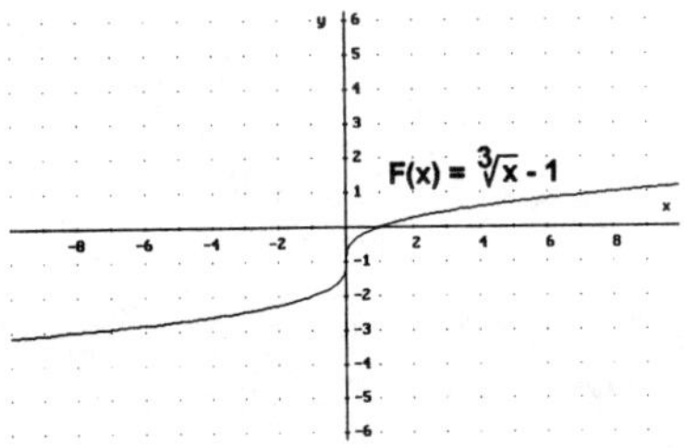

21. $\sqrt{54}$

$\sqrt{9}\sqrt{6}$

$3\sqrt{6}$

23. $\sqrt{150x^3y^6}$

$\sqrt{25x^2y^6}\sqrt{6x}$

$5xy^3\sqrt{6x}$

25. $\sqrt[3]{54}$

$\sqrt[3]{27}\,\sqrt[3]{2}$

$3\sqrt[3]{2}$

27. $\sqrt[4]{48x^3y^6}$

$\sqrt[4]{16y^4}\ \ \sqrt[4]{3x^3y^2}$

$2y\sqrt[4]{3x^3y^2}$

29. $\sqrt{\frac{18}{25}} = \frac{\sqrt{18}}{\sqrt{25}} = \frac{\sqrt{9}\sqrt{2}}{5} = \frac{3\sqrt{2}}{5}$

31. $\sqrt{\frac{45x^2y^2}{4x^2}} = \frac{\sqrt{45x^2y^2}}{\sqrt{4x^6}} = \frac{\sqrt{9x^2y^2}\sqrt{5}}{2x^3}$

$\frac{3xy\sqrt{5}}{2x^3} = \frac{3y\sqrt{5}}{2x^2}$

33. $\sqrt[4]{\frac{9}{16}} = \frac{\sqrt[4]{9}}{\sqrt[4]{16}} = \frac{\sqrt[4]{9}}{2}$

35. $\sqrt[3]{\frac{3y^6}{8x^3}} = \frac{\sqrt[3]{3y^6}}{\sqrt[3]{8x^3}} = \frac{\sqrt[3]{y^6}\ \sqrt[3]{3}}{2x} = \frac{y^2\ \sqrt[3]{3}}{2x}$

37. $3\sqrt[3]{2} + 2\sqrt[3]{3} - 4\sqrt[3]{2}$

$-\sqrt[3]{2} + 2\sqrt[3]{3}$

39. $\sqrt{6} + 2\sqrt[3]{6} - 4\sqrt[3]{6} + 5\sqrt{6}$

$6\sqrt{6} - 2\sqrt[3]{6}$

41. $\sqrt{28} + \sqrt{63} + \sqrt[3]{56}$

$\sqrt{4}\sqrt{7} + \sqrt{9}\sqrt{7} + \sqrt[3]{8}\sqrt[3]{7}$

$2\sqrt{7} + 3\sqrt{7} + 2\sqrt[3]{7}$

$5\sqrt{7} + 2\sqrt[3]{7}$

43. $\sqrt{\frac{5}{9}} - \sqrt{\frac{5}{36}}$

$\frac{\sqrt{5}}{\sqrt{9}} - \frac{\sqrt{5}}{\sqrt{36}}$

$\frac{\sqrt{5}}{3} - \frac{\sqrt{5}}{6}$

$\frac{2}{2} \bullet \frac{\sqrt{5}}{3} - \frac{\sqrt{5}}{6}$

$\frac{2\sqrt{5}}{6} - \frac{\sqrt{5}}{6}$

$\frac{\sqrt{5}}{6}$

45. $2\sqrt[3]{125x^3} - 5x\sqrt[3]{8}$

$2(5x) - 5x(2)$

$10x - 10x$

0

47. $3\sqrt{10} \bullet 2\sqrt{5}$

$6\sqrt{50}$

$6\sqrt{25}\sqrt{2}$

$6(5)\sqrt{2}$

$30\sqrt{2}$

49. $\sqrt{3}(2\sqrt{6}-3\sqrt{12})$

$2\sqrt{18}-3\sqrt{36}$

$2\sqrt{9}\sqrt{2}-3(6)$

$2(3)\sqrt{2}-18$

$6\sqrt{2}-18$

51. $(\sqrt{3}+2)(\sqrt{6}-5)$

$\sqrt{18}-5\sqrt{3}+2\sqrt{6}-10$

$\sqrt{9}\sqrt{2}-5\sqrt{3}+2\sqrt{6}-10$

$3\sqrt{2}-5\sqrt{3}+2\sqrt{6}-10$

53. $\dfrac{\sqrt{96}}{\sqrt{3}}=\sqrt{\dfrac{96}{3}}=\sqrt{32}=\sqrt{16}\sqrt{2}=4\sqrt{2}$

55. $\dfrac{\sqrt{15x^6y}}{\sqrt{12x^3y^9}}=\sqrt{\dfrac{15x^6y}{12x^3y^9}}=\sqrt{\dfrac{5x^3}{4y^8}}=\dfrac{\sqrt{5x^3}}{\sqrt{4y^8}}=$

$\dfrac{\sqrt{x^2}\sqrt{5x}}{2y^4}=\dfrac{x\sqrt{5x}}{2y^4}$

57. $\sqrt{\dfrac{5}{6}}=\dfrac{\sqrt{5}}{\sqrt{6}}\bullet\dfrac{\sqrt{6}}{\sqrt{6}}=\dfrac{\sqrt{30}}{6}$

59. $\sqrt[3]{\dfrac{3}{2x}}=\dfrac{\sqrt[3]{3}}{\sqrt[3]{2x}}\bullet\dfrac{\sqrt[3]{4x^2}}{\sqrt[3]{4x^2}}=\dfrac{\sqrt[3]{12x^2}}{\sqrt[3]{8x^3}}=\dfrac{\sqrt[3]{12x^2}}{2x}$

61. $\dfrac{3x}{\sqrt{5}-2}$

$\dfrac{3x}{(\sqrt{5}-2)}\bullet\dfrac{(\sqrt{5}+2)}{(\sqrt{5}+2)}$

$\dfrac{3x\sqrt{5}+6x}{\sqrt{25}-4}$

$\dfrac{3x\sqrt{5}+6x}{5-4}$

$\dfrac{3x\sqrt{5}+6x}{1}$

$3x\sqrt{5}+6x$

63. $\dfrac{\sqrt{2}}{4+\sqrt{x}}$

$\dfrac{\sqrt{2}}{(4+\sqrt{x})}\bullet\dfrac{(4-\sqrt{x})}{(4-\sqrt{x})}$

$\dfrac{4\sqrt{2}-\sqrt{2}\sqrt{x}}{16-\sqrt{x^2}}$

$\dfrac{4\sqrt{2}-\sqrt{2x}}{16-x}$

65. $\sqrt{\dfrac{7}{20y^2}}$

$\dfrac{\sqrt{7}}{\sqrt{20y^2}}=\dfrac{\sqrt{7}}{\sqrt{4y^2}\sqrt{5}}=\dfrac{\sqrt{7}}{2y\sqrt{5}}$

$\dfrac{\sqrt{7}}{2y\sqrt{5}}\bullet\dfrac{\sqrt{7}}{\sqrt{7}}$

$\dfrac{\sqrt{49}}{2y\sqrt{35}}$

$\dfrac{7}{2y\sqrt{35}}$

67. $\sqrt[3]{\dfrac{7}{9}}=\dfrac{\sqrt[3]{7}}{\sqrt[3]{9}}$

$\dfrac{\sqrt[3]{7}}{\sqrt[3]{9}}\bullet\dfrac{\sqrt[3]{49}}{\sqrt[3]{49}}$

$\dfrac{\sqrt[3]{343}}{\sqrt[3]{441}}$

$\dfrac{7}{\sqrt[3]{441}}$

69. $\dfrac{\sqrt{6}+2}{12}$

$\dfrac{(\sqrt{6}+2)(\sqrt{6}-2)}{12(\sqrt{6}-2)}$

$\dfrac{\sqrt{36}-4}{12\sqrt{6}-24}$

$\dfrac{2}{12\sqrt{6}-24}$

$\dfrac{1}{6\sqrt{6}-12}$

71. $\dfrac{\sqrt{x}-5}{2\sqrt{3}}$

$\dfrac{(\sqrt{x}-5)(\sqrt{x}+5)}{2\sqrt{3}(\sqrt{x}+5)}$

$$\frac{\sqrt{x^2}-25}{2\sqrt{3x}+10\sqrt{3}}$$

$$\frac{x-25}{2\sqrt{3x}+10\sqrt{3}}$$

73. $\left(\frac{1}{81}\right)^{\frac{1}{4}}=\frac{1}{3}$

75. $(-27)^{-\frac{1}{3}}=\frac{1}{(-27)^{\frac{1}{3}}}=\frac{1}{-3}=-\frac{1}{3}$

77. $-9^{\frac{3}{2}}=-(9^{\frac{1}{2}})^3=-3^3=-27$

79. $(-25)^{\frac{5}{2}}=[(-25)^{\frac{1}{2}}]^5$ is not a real number, since the square of no real number is negative.

81. $\left(\frac{8}{27}\right)^{-\frac{2}{3}}=\frac{1}{\left(\frac{8}{27}\right)^{\frac{2}{3}}}=\frac{1}{\left[\left(\frac{8}{27}\right)^{\frac{1}{3}}\right]^2}$

$$\frac{1}{\left(\frac{2}{3}\right)^2}=\frac{1}{\frac{4}{9}}=\frac{9}{4}$$

83. $a^{\frac{1}{3}}a^{\frac{4}{3}}a^{\frac{1}{2}}=a^{\frac{1}{3}+\frac{4}{3}+\frac{1}{2}}=a^{\frac{5}{3}+\frac{1}{2}}$

$$a^{\frac{10}{6}+\frac{3}{6}}=a^{\frac{13}{6}}$$

85. $(a^{-\frac{1}{2}})^{-2}=a^1=a$

87. $(a^{\frac{1}{2}}a^{-2})^3=(a^{\frac{1}{2}-2})^3=(a^{-\frac{3}{2}})^3$

$$a^{-\frac{9}{2}}=\frac{1}{a^{\frac{9}{2}}}$$

89. $(x^{-3}y^6)^{\frac{1}{3}}=(x^{-3})^{\frac{1}{3}}(y^6)^{\frac{1}{3}}=x^{-1}y^2=\frac{y^2}{x}$

91. $\frac{x^{\frac{1}{4}}x^{-\frac{1}{2}}}{x^{\frac{2}{3}}}=\frac{x^{\frac{1}{4}-\frac{1}{2}}}{x^{\frac{2}{3}}}=\frac{x^{-\frac{1}{4}}}{x^{\frac{2}{3}}}=x^{-\frac{1}{4}-\frac{2}{3}}=x^{-\frac{11}{12}}=\frac{1}{x^{\frac{11}{12}}}$

93. $4x\sqrt[3]{(3x)^5}=4x(3x)^{\frac{5}{3}}$

95. $7x(3^{\frac{1}{3}}y^{\frac{2}{3}})=7x\sqrt[3]{3y^2}$

97. $\sqrt[3]{4x}=-2$

$4x=(-2)^3$

$4x=-8$

$x=-2$

$\{-2\}$

99. $\sqrt[3]{x-2}=3$

$x-2=3^3$

$x-2=27$

$x=29$

$\{29\}$

101. $\sqrt{2x}+1=-4$

$\sqrt{2x}=-5$

No solution exists since the principal square root of a number is not negative.

$\{\ \}$

103. $\sqrt[3]{3x-9}-\sqrt[3]{2x+12}=0$

$\sqrt[3]{3x-9}=\sqrt[3]{2x+12}$

$3x-9=2x+12$

$x=21$

$\{21\}$

105. $\sqrt{x+6}=\sqrt{x+2}$

$x+6=x+2$

$6=2$

Since the last equation is never satisfied, there is no solution.

$\{\ \}$

107. Let $c=$ the length of the hypotenuse of the right triangle. By the Pythagorean theorem,

$c^2=3^2+3^2$

$c^2=9+9$

$c^2=9(2)$

$c=\sqrt{9(2)}$

$c = \sqrt{9}\sqrt{2}$

$c = 3\sqrt{2}$

109. $a^2 + b^2 = c^2$

$40^2 + b^2 = 65^2$

$1600 + b^2 = 4225$

$b^2 = 2625$

$b = \sqrt{2625}$

$b = 51.2$ ft.

111. $\sqrt{-8} = \sqrt{4}\sqrt{2}\sqrt{-1} = 2i\sqrt{2}$

113. $\sqrt{-4} + \sqrt{-16} = 2i + 4i = 6i$

115. $(12 - 6i) + (3 + 2i)$

$(12 + 3) + (-6 + 2)i$

$15 - 4i$

117. $(\sqrt{3} + \sqrt{2}) + (3\sqrt{2} - \sqrt{-8})$

$\sqrt{3} + \sqrt{2} + 3\sqrt{2} - \sqrt{4}\sqrt{2}\sqrt{-1}$

$(\sqrt{3} + 4\sqrt{2}) - 2i\sqrt{2}$

119. $2i(2 - 5i) = 4i - 10i^2$

$4i - 10(-1) = 10 + 4i$

121. $(3 + 2i)(1 + i)$

$3 + 2i + 3i + 2i^2$

$3 + 5i + 2(-1)$

$(3 - 2) + 5i$

$1 + 5i$

123. $\frac{2+3i}{2i} = \frac{(2+3i)i}{2i^2} = \frac{2i+3i^2}{2(-1)}$

$\frac{2i+3(-1)}{-2} = \frac{-3+2i}{-2} = \frac{3}{2} - i$

Chapter 8 Test

1. $\sqrt{16} = 4$

2. $\sqrt[3]{125} = 5$

3. $16^{\frac{3}{4}} = (\sqrt[4]{16})^3 = 2^3 = 8$

4. $\left(\frac{9}{16}\right)^{\frac{1}{2}} = \frac{9^{\frac{1}{2}}}{16^{\frac{1}{2}}} = \frac{\sqrt{9}}{\sqrt{16}} = \frac{3}{4}$

5. $\sqrt[4]{-81}$ not a real number

6. $27^{-\frac{2}{3}} = \frac{1}{27^{\frac{2}{3}}} = \frac{1}{(\sqrt[3]{27})^2} = \frac{1}{3^2} = \frac{1}{9}$

7. $\sqrt{54} = \sqrt{9}\sqrt{6} = 3\sqrt{6}$

8. $\sqrt{92} = \sqrt{4}\sqrt{23} = 2\sqrt{23}$

9. $\sqrt{3x^6} = \sqrt{x^6}\sqrt{3} = x^3\sqrt{3}$

10. $\sqrt{8x^4y^7} = \sqrt{4x^4y^6}\sqrt{2y} = 2x^2y^3\sqrt{2y}$

11. $\sqrt{9x^9} = \sqrt{9x^8}\sqrt{x} = 3x^4\sqrt{x}$

12. $\sqrt[3]{40} = \sqrt[3]{8}\,\sqrt[3]{5} = 2\sqrt[3]{5}$

13. $\sqrt[3]{8x^6y^{10}} = \sqrt[3]{8x^6y^9}\,\sqrt[3]{y} = 2x^2y^3\,\sqrt[3]{y}$

14. $\sqrt{12} - 2\sqrt{75}$

$\sqrt{4}\sqrt{3} - 2\sqrt{25}\sqrt{3}$

$2\sqrt{3} - 2(5)\sqrt{3}$

$2\sqrt{3} - 10\sqrt{3}$

$-8\sqrt{3}$

15. $\sqrt{2x^2} + \sqrt[3]{54} - x\sqrt{18}$

$\sqrt{x^2}\sqrt{2} + \sqrt[3]{27}\,\sqrt[3]{2} - x\sqrt{9}\sqrt{2}$

$x\sqrt{2} + 3\sqrt[3]{2} - x(3)\sqrt{2}$

$x\sqrt{2} + 3\sqrt[3]{2} - 3x\sqrt{2}$

$-2x\sqrt{2} + 3\sqrt[3]{2}$

16. $\sqrt{\frac{5}{16}} = \frac{\sqrt{5}}{\sqrt{16}} = \frac{\sqrt{5}}{4}$

17. $\sqrt[3]{\frac{2x^3}{27}} = \frac{\sqrt[3]{2x^3}}{\sqrt[3]{27}} = \frac{\sqrt[3]{x^3}\sqrt[3]{2}}{\sqrt[3]{27}} = \frac{x\sqrt[3]{2}}{3}$

18. $\sqrt[3]{\frac{3}{2x^2}} = \frac{\sqrt[3]{3}}{\sqrt[3]{2x^2}}$

$\frac{\sqrt[3]{3}}{\sqrt[3]{2x^2}} \bullet \frac{\sqrt[3]{4x}}{\sqrt[3]{4x}}$

$\frac{\sqrt[3]{12x}}{\sqrt[3]{8x^3}} = \frac{\sqrt[3]{12x}}{2x}$

19. $\frac{\sqrt{6}+x}{8}$

$\frac{(\sqrt{6}+x)(\sqrt{6}-x)}{8(\sqrt{6}-x)}$

$\frac{\sqrt{36}-x^2}{8\sqrt{6}-8x}$

$\frac{6-x^2}{8\sqrt{6}-8x}$

20. $\sqrt{x}+8=11$

$\sqrt{x}=11-8$

$\sqrt{x}=3$

$(\sqrt{x})^2=(3)^2$

$x=9$

check

$\sqrt{9}+8=11$

$3+8=11$

$11=11$ True

The solution is 9.

{9}

21. $\sqrt{3x-6}=\sqrt{x+4}$

$(\sqrt{3x-6})^2=(\sqrt{x+4})^2$

$3x-6=x+4$

$3x-x-6=4$

$2x-6=4$

$2x=4+6$

$2x=10$

$x=\frac{10}{2}=5$

check

$\sqrt{3(5)-6}=\sqrt{5+4}$

$\sqrt{15-6}=\sqrt{9}$

$\sqrt{9}=\sqrt{9}$ True

The solution is 5.

{5}

22. $\sqrt{2x-2}+5=x$

$\sqrt{2x-2}=x-5$

$(\sqrt{2x-2})^2=(x-5)^2$

$2x-2=x^2-10x+25$

$0=x^2-12x=27$

$0=(x-9)(x-3)$

$x-9=0$ or $x-3=0$

$x=9$ or $x=3$

check $x=9$

$\sqrt{2(9)-2}+5=9$

$\sqrt{18-2}+5=9$

$\sqrt{16}+5=9$

$4+5=9$

$9=9$ True

check $x=3$

$\sqrt{2(3)-2}+5=9$

$\sqrt{6-2}+5=9$

$\sqrt{4}+5=9$

$2+5=9$

$7=9$ False

Therefore $x=9$ is the solution.

{9}

23. $\sqrt{-20}$

$\sqrt{20}\sqrt{-1}$

$\sqrt{4}\sqrt{5}\sqrt{-1}$

$2i\sqrt{5}$

24. $(12-6i)-(12-3i)$

$12-6i-12+3i$

$-3i$

25. $(4-5i)^2$

$(4-5i)(4-5i)$

$16-20i-20i+25i^2$

$16-40i+25(-1)$

$16-40i-25$

$-9-40i$

26. $\frac{1+4i}{1-i}$

$\frac{(1+4i)}{(1-i)} \bullet \frac{(1+i)}{(1+i)}$

$\frac{1+i+4i+4i^2}{1-i^2}$

$\frac{1+5i+4i^2}{1-i^2}$

$\frac{1+5i+4(-1)}{-(-1)}$

$\frac{1+5i-4}{1+1}$

$\frac{-3+5i}{2}$

$-\frac{3}{2}+\frac{5}{2}i$

27. $a^2+b^2=c^2$

$4^2+b^2=9^2$

$16+b^2=81$

$b^2=65$

$b=\sqrt{65}$

28. $a^2+b^2=c^2$

$10^2+12^2=c^2$

$100+144=c^2$

$244=c^2$

$\sqrt{244}=c$

$\sqrt{4}\sqrt{61}=c$

$2\sqrt{61}=c$

29. $V(r)=\sqrt{2.5r}$

$V(300)=\sqrt{2.5(300)}$

$V(300)=\sqrt{750}$

$V(300)=\sqrt{25}\sqrt{30}$

$V(300)=5\sqrt{30}$

Velocity is 27 mph.

30. $V(r)=\sqrt{2.5r}$

$30=\sqrt{2.5r}$

$(30)^2=(\sqrt{2.5r})^2$

$900=2.5r$

$360\text{ ft.}=r$

Chapter 8 Cumulative Review

1a. $-13-(+4)$

$-13-4$

-17

b. $5-(-6)$

$5+6$

11

c. $3-6$

-3

d. $-1-(-7)$

$-1+7$

6

3. $-2(x-5)+10=-3(x+2)+x$

$-2x+10+10=-3x-6+x$

$-2x+20=-2x-6$

$-2x+2x+20=-2x+2x-6$

$20=-6$ Contradiction

No solution.

{ }

5. Let $x=$ liters of 40% solution
then $12-x=$ liters of 70% solution.

$0.40x+0.70(12-x)=0.50(12)$

$0.40x+8.4-0.70x=6$

$-0.3x+8.4=6$

$-0.3x=-2.4$

$x=\frac{-2.4}{-0.3}=8$

So 8 liters of 40% solution and
4 liters of 70% solution are needed.

7. $5x - 3 \le 10$ or $x + 1 \ge 5$

$5x \le 13$ or $x \ge 4$

$x \le \frac{13}{5}$

$\left(-\infty, \frac{13}{5}\right] \cup [4, \infty)$

9. $y = -3$

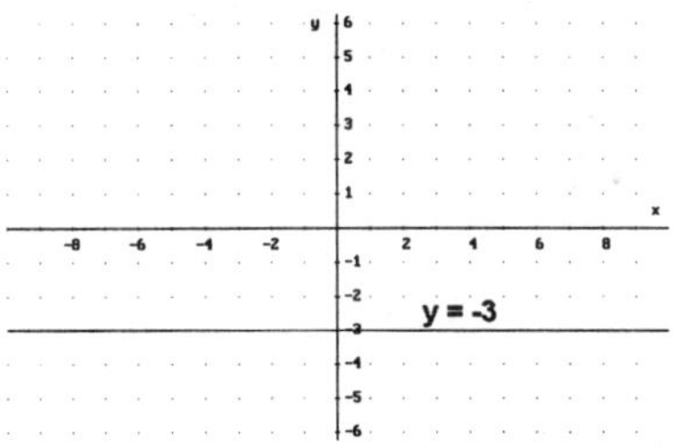

11a. $-12x^2 + 7x^2 - 6x$

$-5x^2 - 6x$

b. $3xy - 2x + 5xy - x$

$8xy - 3x$

13. $P(x) = 4x^6 - 25x^5 + 35x^4 + 17x^2$

$$\begin{array}{r|rrrrrrr} 4 & 4 & -25 & 35 & 0 & 17 & 0 & 0 \\ & & 16 & -36 & -4 & -16 & 4 & 16 \\ \hline & 4 & -9 & -1 & -4 & 1 & 4 & 16 \end{array}$$

$P(4) = 16$

15. $2x^2 + 9x - 5 = 0$

$(2x - 1)(x + 5) = 0$

$2x - 1 = 0$ or $x = -5$

$x = \frac{1}{2}$

$\left\{-5, \frac{1}{2}\right\}$

17. $\frac{x+6}{x-2} = \frac{2(x+2)}{x-2}$

Restricted value; $x \neq 2$.

$(x-2)\frac{(x+6)}{(x-2)} = \frac{2(x+2)}{(x-2)}(x-2)$

$x + 6 = 2(x + 2)$

$x + 6 = 2x + 4$

$2 = x$

No solution.

{ }

19a. $\sqrt{54} = \sqrt{9}\sqrt{6} = 3\sqrt{6}$

b. $\sqrt{12} = \sqrt{4}\sqrt{3} = 2\sqrt{3}$

c. $\sqrt{200} = \sqrt{100}\sqrt{2} = 10\sqrt{2}$

d. $\sqrt{35}$ can not be simplified.

21a. $25^{\frac{1}{2}} = 5$

b. $8^{\frac{1}{3}} = 2$

c. $-16^{\frac{1}{4}} = -1(16^{\frac{1}{4}}) = -1(2) = -2$

d. $(-27)^{\frac{1}{3}} = -3$

e. $\left(\frac{1}{9}\right)^{\frac{1}{2}} = \frac{1}{3}$

23. $a^2 + b^2 = c^2$

$240^2 + b^2 = 320^2$

$57{,}600 + b^2 = 102{,}400$

$b^2 = 44{,}800$

$b = \sqrt{44{,}800}$

$b = 80\sqrt{7}$

$b = 212$ ft.

Graphing Calculator Exercise 9.1

1. $x(x - 5) = 8$

$Y_1 = x(x - 5)$

$Y_2 = 8$

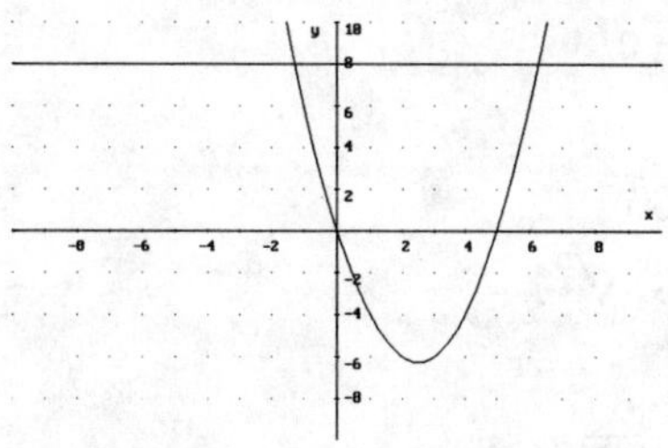

Solutions are -1.27 and 6.27.

3. $x^2 + 0.5x = 0.3x + 1$

$Y_1 = x^2 + 0.5x$

$Y_2 = 0.3x + 1$

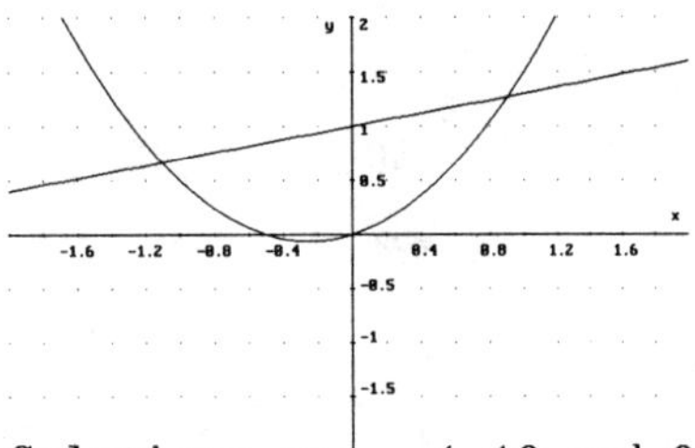

Solutions are -1.10 and 0.90.

5. $(2x-5)^2 = -16$

$Y_1 = (2x-5)^2$

$Y_2 = -16$

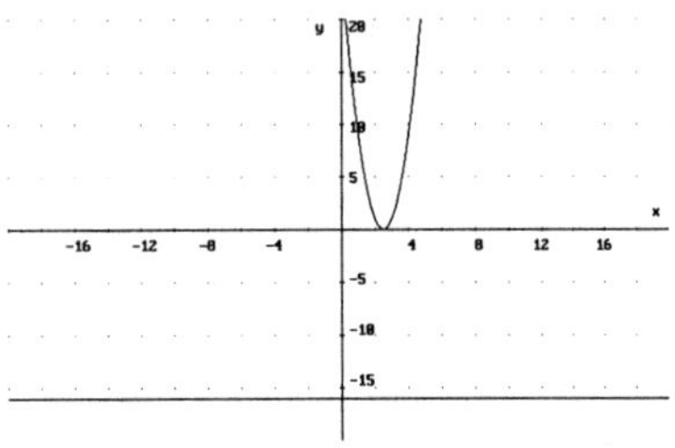

There are no real solutions since the graphs do not intersect.

Exercise Set 9.1

1. $x^2 = 16$

$x = \pm\sqrt{16}$

$x = \pm 4$

$\{-4,\ 4\}$

3. $x^2 - 7 = 0$

$x^2 = 7$

$x = \pm\sqrt{7}$

$\{-\sqrt{7},\ \sqrt{7}\}$

5. $x^2 = 18$

$x = \pm\sqrt{18}$

$x = \pm\sqrt{9}\sqrt{2}$

$x = \pm 3\sqrt{2}$

$\{-3\sqrt{2},\ 3\sqrt{2}\}$

7. $3z^2 - 30 = 0$

$3z^2 = 30$

$z^2 = 10$

$z = \pm\sqrt{10}$

$\{-\sqrt{10},\ \sqrt{10}\}$

9. $x^2 + 9 = 0$

$x^2 = -9$

$x = \pm\sqrt{-9}$

$x = \pm 3i$

$\{-3i,\ 3i\}$

11. $x^2 - 6 = 0$

$x^2 = 6$

$x = \pm\sqrt{6}$

$\{-\sqrt{6},\ \sqrt{6}\}$

13. $2z^2 + 16 = 0$

$2z^2 = -16$

$z^2 = -8$

$z = \pm\sqrt{-8}$

$z = \pm\sqrt{4}\sqrt{2}\sqrt{-1}$

$z = \pm 2i\sqrt{2}$

$\{-2i\sqrt{2},\ 2i\sqrt{2}\}$

15. $(x+5)^2 = 9$

$x + 5 = \pm\sqrt{9}$

$x + 5 = \pm 3$

$x = -5 \pm 3$

$x = -8, -2$

$\{-8, -2\}$

17. $(z-6)^2 = 18$

$z - 6 = \pm\sqrt{18}$

$z - 6 = \pm\sqrt{9}\sqrt{2}$

$z - 6 = \pm 3\sqrt{2}$

$\{6 - 3\sqrt{2},\ 6 + 3\sqrt{2}\}$

19. $(2x-3)^2 = 8$

$2x-3 = \pm\sqrt{8}$

$2x-3 = \pm\sqrt{4}\sqrt{2}$

$2x-3 = \pm 2\sqrt{2}$

$2x = 3 \pm 2\sqrt{2}$

$x = \frac{3}{2} \pm \sqrt{2}$

$\left\{\frac{3}{2} - \sqrt{2},\ \frac{3}{2} + \sqrt{2}\right\}$

21. $(x-1)^2 = -16$

$x-1 = \pm\sqrt{-16}$

$x-1 = \pm 4i$

$x = 1 \pm 4i$

$\{1-4i,\ 1+4i\}$

23. $(z+7)^2 = 5$

$z+7 = \pm\sqrt{5}$

$z = -7 \pm \sqrt{5}$

$\{-7-\sqrt{5}, -7+\sqrt{5}\}$

25. $(x+3)^2 = -8$

$x+3 = \pm\sqrt{-8}$

$x+3 = \pm\sqrt{4}\sqrt{2}\sqrt{-1}$

$x+3 = \pm 2i\sqrt{2}$

$x = -3 \pm 2i\sqrt{2}$

$\{-3-2i\sqrt{2}, -3+2i\sqrt{2}\}$

27. $x^2 + 16x + \left(\frac{16}{2}\right)^2$

$x^2 + 16x + 64$

$(x+8)^2$

29. $z^2 - 12z + \left(\frac{12}{2}\right)^2$

$z^2 - 12z + 36$

$(z-6)^2$

31. $p^2 + 9p + \left(\frac{9}{2}\right)^2$

$p^2 + 9p + \frac{81}{4}$

$\left(p + \frac{9}{2}\right)^2$

33. $x^2 + x + \left(\frac{1}{2}\right)^2$

$x^2 + x + \frac{1}{4}$

$\left(x + \frac{1}{2}\right)^2$

35. $x^2 + 8x = -15$

$x^2 + 8x + \left(\frac{8}{2}\right)^2 = -15 + 16$

$(x+4)^2 = 1$

$x+4 = \pm\sqrt{1}$

$x = -4 \pm 1$

$x = -5,\ \ -3$

$\{-5, -3\}$

37. $x^2 + 6x + 2 = 0$

$x^2 + 6x + \left(\frac{6}{2}\right)^2 = -2 + 9$

$(x+3)^2 = 7$

$x+3 = \pm\sqrt{7}$

$x = -3 \pm \sqrt{7}$

$\{-3-\sqrt{7}, -3+\sqrt{7}\}$

39. $x^2 + x - 1 = 0$

$x^2 + x + \left(\frac{1}{2}\right)^2 = 1 + \frac{1}{4}$

$\left(x + \frac{1}{2}\right)^2 = \frac{5}{4}$

$x + \frac{1}{2} = \pm\sqrt{\frac{5}{4}}$

$x + \frac{1}{2} = \pm\frac{\sqrt{5}}{2}$

$x = -\frac{1}{2} \pm \frac{\sqrt{5}}{2}$

$\left\{-\frac{1}{2} - \frac{\sqrt{5}}{2}, -\frac{1}{2} + \frac{\sqrt{5}}{2}\right\}$

41. $y^2 + 2y + 2 = 0$

$y^2 + 2y + \left(\frac{2}{2}\right)^2 = -2 + 1$

$(y+1)^2 = -1$

$y+1 = \pm\sqrt{-1}$

$y+1 = \pm i$

$y = -1 \pm i$

$\{-1-i, -1+i\}$

43. $x^2 - 6x + 3 = 0$

$x^2 - 6x + \left(\frac{6}{2}\right)^2 = -3 + 9$

$(x-3)^2 = 6$

$x - 3 = \pm\sqrt{6}$

$x = 3 \pm \sqrt{6}$

$\{3-\sqrt{6},\ 3+\sqrt{6}\}$

45. $x^2 + x - 1 = 0$

$x^2 + x + \left(\frac{1}{2}\right)^2 = 1 + \left(\frac{1}{2}\right)^2$

$x^2 + x + \frac{1}{4} = 1 + \frac{1}{4}$

$\left(x + \frac{1}{2}\right)^2 = \frac{5}{4}$

$x + \frac{1}{2} = \pm\sqrt{\frac{5}{4}}$

$x = -\frac{1}{2} \pm \frac{\sqrt{5}}{2}$

$x = \frac{-1 \pm \sqrt{5}}{2}$

$\left\{\frac{-1-\sqrt{5}}{2}, \frac{-1+\sqrt{5}}{2}\right\}$

47. $3p^2 - 12p + 2 = 0$

$3p^2 - 12p = -2$

$p^2 - 4p = -\frac{2}{3}$

$p^2 - 4p + \left(\frac{4}{2}\right)^2 = -\frac{2}{3} + 4$

$(p-2)^2 = \frac{10}{3}$

$p - 2 = \pm\sqrt{\frac{10}{3}}$

$p - 2 = \pm\sqrt{\frac{10 \bullet 3}{3^2}}$

$p - 2 = \pm\frac{\sqrt{30}}{3}$

$p = 2 \pm \frac{\sqrt{30}}{3}$

$\left\{2 - \frac{\sqrt{30}}{3},\ 2 + \frac{\sqrt{30}}{3}\right\}$

49. $4y^2 - 12y - 2 = 0$

$4y^2 - 12y = 2$

$y^2 - 3y = \frac{1}{2}$

$y^2 - 3y + \left(\frac{3}{2}\right)^2 = \frac{1}{2} + \frac{9}{4}$

$\left(y - \frac{3}{2}\right)^2 = \frac{11}{4}$

$y - \frac{3}{2} = \pm\sqrt{\frac{11}{4}}$

$y - \frac{3}{2} = \pm\frac{\sqrt{11}}{2}$

$y = \frac{3}{2} \pm \frac{\sqrt{11}}{2}$

$\left\{\frac{3}{2} - \frac{\sqrt{11}}{2},\ \frac{3}{2} + \frac{\sqrt{11}}{2}\right\}$

51. $2x^2 + 7x = 4$

$x^2 + \frac{7}{2}x = 2$

$x^2 + \frac{7}{2}x + \left(\frac{7/2}{2}\right)^2 = 2 + \frac{49}{16}$

$\left(x + \frac{7}{4}\right)^2 = \frac{81}{16}$

$x + \frac{7}{4} = \pm\sqrt{\frac{81}{16}}$

$x = -\frac{7}{4} \pm \frac{9}{4}$

$x = -4,\ \frac{1}{2}$

$\left\{-4,\ \frac{1}{2}\right\}$

53. $2a^2 + 8a = -12$

$a^2 + 4a = -6$

$a^2 + 4a + \left(\frac{4}{2}\right)^2 = -6 + 4$

$(a+2)^2 = -2$

$a + 2 = \pm\sqrt{-2}$

$a + 2 = \pm i\sqrt{2}$

$a = -2 \pm i\sqrt{2}$

$\{-2-i\sqrt{2}, -2+i\sqrt{2}\}$

55. $5x^2+15x-1=0$

$5x^2+15x=1$

$x^2+3x=\frac{1}{5}$

$x^2+3x+\left(\frac{3}{2}\right)^2=\frac{1}{5}+\frac{9}{4}$

$\left(x+\frac{3}{2}\right)^2=\frac{49}{20}$

$x+\frac{3}{2}=\pm\sqrt{\frac{49}{20}}$

$x+\frac{3}{2}=\pm\frac{\sqrt{49}}{\sqrt{4}\sqrt{5}}=\pm\frac{7}{2\sqrt{5}}$

$x+\frac{3}{2}=\pm\frac{7\sqrt{5}}{2\bullet\sqrt{5^2}}=\pm\frac{7\sqrt{5}}{2\bullet 5}$

$x+\frac{3}{2}=\pm\frac{7\sqrt{5}}{10}$

$x=-\frac{3}{2}\pm\frac{7\sqrt{5}}{10}$

$\left\{-\frac{3}{2}-\frac{7\sqrt{5}}{10},-\frac{3}{2}+\frac{7\sqrt{5}}{10}\right\}$

57. $2x^2-x+6=0$

$2x^2-x=-6$

$x^2-\frac{1}{2}x=-3$

$x^2-\frac{1}{2}x+\left(\frac{1/2}{2}\right)^2=-3+\frac{1}{16}$

$\left(x-\frac{1}{4}\right)^2=-\frac{47}{16}$

$x-\frac{1}{4}=\pm\sqrt{\frac{-47}{16}}=\pm\frac{\sqrt{47}\sqrt{-1}}{\sqrt{16}}$

$x-\frac{1}{4}=\pm\frac{i\sqrt{47}}{4}$

$x=\frac{1}{4}\pm i\frac{\sqrt{47}}{4}$

$x=\frac{1\pm i\sqrt{47}}{4}$

$\left\{\frac{1-i\sqrt{47}}{4},\ \frac{1+i\sqrt{47}}{4}\right\}$

59. $A=P(1+r)^t$

$4320=3000(1+r)^2$

$\frac{4320}{3000}=(1+r)^2$

$1.44=(1+r)^2$

$\pm\sqrt{1.44}=1+r$

$\pm 1.2=1+r$

$-1\pm 1.2=r$

$r=-1+1.2$ or $r=-1-1.2$

$r=0.2$ or $r=-2.2$

Rate can not be negative, the return $r=0.2=20\%$.

61. $s(t)=16t^2$

$954=16t^2$

$\frac{954}{16}=t^2$

$\pm\sqrt{59.625}=t$

$\pm 7.72\approx t$

Time can not be negative, therefore $t\approx 7.72$ seconds.

63. $s(t)=16t^2$

$1127=16t^2$

$\frac{1127}{16}=t^2$

$70.4375=t^2$

$\pm\sqrt{70.4375}=t$

$\pm 8.39\approx t$

Time can not be negative, therefore $t=8.39$ seconds.

65. $x^2-4x-5=0$

$x^2-4x=5$

$x^2-4x+\left(\frac{4}{2}\right)^2=5+4$

$(x-2)^2=9$

$x-2=\pm\sqrt{9}$

$x-2=\pm 3$

$x=2\pm 3$

$x=-1,\ 5$

$\{-1,\ 5\}$

67. $x^2+8x+1=0$

$x^2+8x=-1$

$x^2+8x+\left(\frac{8}{2}\right)^2=-1+16$

$(x+4)^2=15$

$x+4=\pm\sqrt{15}$

$x=-4\pm\sqrt{15}$

$\{-4-\sqrt{15}, -4+\sqrt{15}\}$

69. $3y^2+6y-4=0$

$3y^2+6y=4$

$y^2+2y=\frac{4}{3}$

$y^2+2y+\left(\frac{2}{2}\right)^2=\frac{4}{3}+1$

$(y+1)^2=\frac{7}{3}$

$y+1=\pm\sqrt{\frac{7}{3}}$

$y+1=\pm\frac{\sqrt{7}}{\sqrt{3}}\bullet\frac{\sqrt{3}}{\sqrt{3}}$

$y+1=\pm\frac{\sqrt{21}}{3}$

$y=-1\pm\frac{\sqrt{21}}{3}$

$\left\{-1-\frac{\sqrt{21}}{3}, -1+\frac{\sqrt{21}}{3}\right\}$

71. $2x^2-3x-5=0$

$2x^2-3x=5$

$x^2-\frac{3}{2}x=\frac{5}{2}$

$x^2-\frac{3}{2}x+\left(\frac{3/2}{2}\right)^2=\frac{5}{2}+\frac{9}{16}$

$\left(x-\frac{3}{4}\right)^2=\frac{49}{16}$

$x-\frac{3}{4}=\pm\frac{7}{4}$

$x=\frac{3}{4}\pm\frac{7}{4}$

$x=-1, \frac{5}{2}$

$\left\{-1, \frac{5}{2}\right\}$

73. $x^2+10x+28=0$

$x^2+10x=-28$

$x^2+10x+\left(\frac{10}{2}\right)^2=-28+25$

$(x+5)^2=-3$

$x+5=\pm\sqrt{-3}$

$x+5=\pm i\sqrt{3}$

$x=-5\pm i\sqrt{3}$

$\{-5-i\sqrt{3}, -5+i\sqrt{3}\}$

75. $z^2+3z-4=0$

$z^2+3z=4$

$z^2+3z+\left(\frac{3}{2}\right)^2=4+\left(\frac{3}{2}\right)^2$

$\left(z+\frac{3}{2}\right)^2=\frac{25}{4}$

$z+\frac{3}{2}=\pm\sqrt{\frac{25}{4}}$

$z+\frac{3}{2}=\pm\frac{5}{2}$

$z=-\frac{3}{2}\pm\frac{5}{2}$

$z=-4, 1$

$\{-4, 1\}$

77. $2x^2-4x+3=0$

$2x^2-4x=-3$

$x^2-2x=-\frac{3}{2}$

$x^2-2x+\left(\frac{2}{2}\right)^2=-\frac{3}{2}+1$

$(x-1)^2=-\frac{1}{2}$

$x-1=\pm\sqrt{-\frac{1}{2}}$

$x-1=\pm\frac{\sqrt{-1}}{\sqrt{2}}$

$x-1=\pm\frac{i}{\sqrt{2}}\bullet\frac{\sqrt{2}}{\sqrt{2}}$

$x-1=\pm\frac{\sqrt{2}}{2}i$

$x=1\pm\frac{\sqrt{2}}{2}i$

$\left\{1-\frac{\sqrt{2}}{2}i, 1+\frac{\sqrt{2}}{2}i\right\}$

79. $3x^2+3x=5$

$x^2+x=\frac{5}{3}$

$x^2+x+\left(\frac{1}{2}\right)^2=\frac{5}{3}+\frac{1}{4}$

$\left(x+\frac{1}{2}\right)^2=\frac{23}{12}$

$x+\frac{1}{2}=\pm\sqrt{\frac{23}{12}}=\pm\frac{\sqrt{23}}{\sqrt{4}\sqrt{3}}$

$x+\frac{1}{2} = \pm\frac{\sqrt{23}}{2\sqrt{3}} = \pm\frac{\sqrt{23}\sqrt{3}}{2\sqrt{3^2}} = \pm\frac{\sqrt{69}}{2\bullet 3}$

$x+\frac{1}{2} = \pm\frac{\sqrt{69}}{6}$

$x = -\frac{1}{2}\pm\frac{\sqrt{69}}{6}$

$\left\{-\frac{1}{2}-\frac{\sqrt{69}}{6}, -\frac{1}{2}+\frac{\sqrt{69}}{6}\right\}$

81. $x^2 = 225$

$x = \sqrt{225}$

$x = 15$ ft.

Dimensions are 15 ft. by 15 ft.

83.

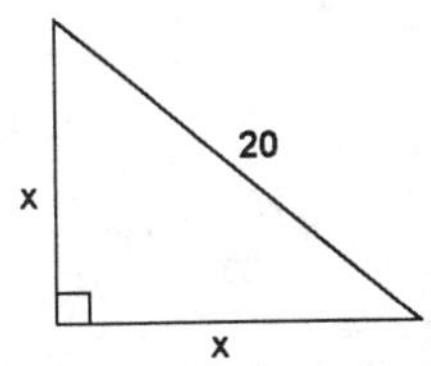

$a^2 + b^2 = c^2$

$x^2 + x^2 = 20^2$

$2x^2 = 400$

$x^2 = 200$

$x = \sqrt{200}$

$x = \sqrt{100}\sqrt{2}$

$x = 10\sqrt{2}$ cm.

85. $p = -x^2 + 47$

$11 = -x^2 + 47$

$11 - 47 = -x^2$

$-36 = -x^2$

$36 = x^2$

$\pm\sqrt{36} = x$

$\pm 6 = x$

Demand can not be negative, therefore the demand is 6000 units.

87. $A = P(1+r)^t$

$1000 = 810(1+r)^2$

$\frac{1000}{810} = (1+r)^2$

$1.2346 = (1+r)^2$

$\pm\sqrt{1.2346} = 1 + r$

$\pm 1.11 = 1 + r$

$-1 \pm 1.11 = r$

$r = -1 + 1.11$ or $r = -1 - 1.11$

$r = 0.11$ or $r = -2.11$

Rate can not be negative, therefore $r = 0.11 = 11\%$.

89. $\frac{3}{4} - \sqrt{\frac{25}{16}}$

$\frac{3}{4} - \frac{5}{4} = -\frac{2}{4} = -\frac{1}{2}$

91. $\frac{1}{2} - \sqrt{\frac{9}{4}}$

$\frac{1}{2} - \frac{3}{2} = -\frac{2}{2} = -1$

93. $\frac{6+4\sqrt{5}}{2} = \frac{6}{2} + \frac{4\sqrt{5}}{2} = 3 + 2\sqrt{5}$

95. $\frac{3-9\sqrt{2}}{6} = \frac{3}{6} - \frac{9\sqrt{2}}{6}$

$\frac{1}{2} - \frac{3\sqrt{2}}{2} = \frac{1-3\sqrt{2}}{2}$

97. $\sqrt{b^2 - 4ac}$

$a = 2,\ b = 4,\ c = -1$

$\sqrt{(4)^2 - 4(2)(-1)} = \sqrt{16+8}$

$\sqrt{24} = \sqrt{4}\sqrt{6} = 2\sqrt{6}$

99. $\sqrt{b^2 - 4ac}$

$a = 3,\ b = -1,\ c = -2$

$\sqrt{(-1)^2 - 4(3)(-2)} = \sqrt{1+24}$

$\sqrt{25} = 5$

Exercise Set 9.2

1. $m^2 + 5m - 6 = 0$

$a = 1,\ b = 5,\ c = -6.$

$$x=\frac{-5\pm\sqrt{5^2-4(1)(-6)}}{2(1)}$$

$$x=\frac{-5\pm\sqrt{25+24}}{2}=\frac{-5\pm\sqrt{49}}{2}$$

$$x=\frac{-5\pm7}{2}=-6,\ 1$$

$\{-6,\ 1\}$

3. $2y=5y^2-3$

$5y^2-2y-3=0$

$a=5,\ b=-2,\ c=-3.$

$$x=\frac{2\pm\sqrt{(-2)^2-4(5)(-3)}}{2(5)}$$

$$x=\frac{2\pm\sqrt{4+60}}{10}=\frac{2\pm\sqrt{64}}{10}$$

$$x=\frac{2\pm8}{10}=-\frac{3}{5},\ 1$$

$\left\{-\frac{3}{5},\ 1\right\}$

5. $x^2-6x+9=0$

$a=1,\ b=-6,\ c=9.$

$$x=\frac{6\pm\sqrt{(-6)^2-4(1)(9)}}{2(1)}$$

$$x=\frac{6\pm\sqrt{36-36}}{2}=\frac{6\pm\sqrt{0}}{2}=\frac{6}{2}=3$$

$\{3\}$

7. $x^2+7x+4=0$

$a=1,\ b=7,\ c=4.$

$$x=\frac{-7\pm\sqrt{7^2-4(1)(4)}}{2(1)}$$

$$x=\frac{-7\pm\sqrt{49-16}}{2}=\frac{-7\pm\sqrt{33}}{2}$$

$$x=-\frac{7}{2}\pm\frac{\sqrt{33}}{2}$$

$\left\{-\frac{7}{2}-\frac{\sqrt{33}}{2},\ -\frac{7}{2}+\frac{\sqrt{33}}{2}\right\}$

9. $8m^2-2m=7$

$8m^2-2m-7=0$

$a=8,\ b=-2,\ c=-7$

$$x=\frac{2\pm\sqrt{(-2)^2-4(8)(-7)}}{2(8)}$$

$$x=\frac{2\pm\sqrt{4+224}}{16}=\frac{2\pm\sqrt{228}}{16}$$

$$x=\frac{2\pm\sqrt{4}\sqrt{57}}{16}=\frac{2\pm2\sqrt{57}}{16}$$

$$x=\frac{1\pm\sqrt{57}}{8}=\frac{1}{8}\pm\frac{\sqrt{57}}{8}$$

$\left\{\frac{1}{8}-\frac{\sqrt{57}}{8},\ \frac{1}{8}+\frac{\sqrt{57}}{8}\right\}$

11. $3m^2-7m=3$

$3m^2-7m-3=0$

$a=3,\ b=-7,\ c=-3$

$$x=\frac{7\pm\sqrt{(-7)^2-4(3)(-3)}}{2(3)}$$

$$x=\frac{7\pm\sqrt{49+36}}{6}=\frac{7\pm\sqrt{85}}{6}$$

$$x=\frac{7}{6}\pm\frac{\sqrt{85}}{6}$$

$\left\{\frac{7}{6}-\frac{\sqrt{85}}{6},\ \frac{7}{6}+\frac{\sqrt{85}}{6}\right\}$

13. $\frac{1}{2}x^2-x-1=0$

$x^2-2x-2=0$

$a=1,\ b=-2,\ c=-2.$

$$x=\frac{2\pm\sqrt{(-2)^2-4(1)(-2)}}{2(1)}$$

$$x=\frac{2\pm\sqrt{4+8}}{2}=\frac{2\pm\sqrt{12}}{2}$$

$$x=\frac{2\pm\sqrt{4}\sqrt{3}}{2}=\frac{2\pm2\sqrt{3}}{2}$$

$x=1\pm\sqrt{3}$

$\{1-\sqrt{3},\ 1+\sqrt{3}\}$

15. $\frac{2}{5}y^2+\frac{1}{5}y=\frac{3}{5}$

$2y^2+y=3$

$2y^2+y-3=0$

$a=2,\ b=1,\ c=-3.$

$$x=\frac{-1\pm\sqrt{1^2-4(2)(-3)}}{2(2)}$$

$$x=\frac{-1\pm\sqrt{1+24}}{4}=\frac{-1\pm\sqrt{25}}{4}$$

$$x=\frac{-1\pm5}{4}=-\frac{3}{2},\ 1$$

$\left\{-\frac{3}{2},\ 1\right\}$

17. $\frac{1}{3}y^2-y-\frac{1}{6}=0$

$2y^2-6y-1=0$

$a=2,\ b=-6,\ c=-1.$

$$y=\frac{6\pm\sqrt{(-6)^2-4(2)(-1)}}{2(2)}$$

$$y=\frac{6\pm\sqrt{36+8}}{4}=\frac{6\pm\sqrt{44}}{4}$$

$$y=\frac{6\pm\sqrt{4}\sqrt{11}}{4}=\frac{6\pm2\sqrt{11}}{4}$$

$$y=\frac{3\pm\sqrt{11}}{2}=\frac{3}{2}\pm\frac{\sqrt{11}}{2}$$

$\left\{\frac{3}{2}-\frac{\sqrt{11}}{2},\ \frac{3}{2}+\frac{\sqrt{11}}{2}\right\}$

19. $6=-4x^2+3x$

$4x^2-3x+6=0$

$a=4,\ b=-3,\ c=6.$

$$x=\frac{3\pm\sqrt{3^2-4(4)(6)}}{2(4)}$$

$$x=\frac{3\pm\sqrt{9-96}}{8}=\frac{3\pm\sqrt{-87}}{8}$$

$$x=\frac{3\pm\sqrt{87}i}{8}=\frac{3\pm i\sqrt{87}}{8}$$

$\left\{\frac{3-i\sqrt{87}}{8},\ \frac{3+i\sqrt{87}}{8}\right\}$

21. $(x+5)(x-1)=2$

$x^2+4x-5=2$

$x^2+4x-7=0$

$a=1,\ b=4,\ c=-7$

$$x=\frac{-4\pm\sqrt{4^2-4(1)(-7)}}{2(1)}$$

$$x=\frac{-4\pm\sqrt{16+28}}{2}=\frac{-4\pm\sqrt{44}}{2}$$

$$x=\frac{-4\pm\sqrt{4}\sqrt{11}}{2}=\frac{-4\pm2\sqrt{11}}{2}$$

$x=-2\pm\sqrt{11}$

$\{-2-\sqrt{11},-2+\sqrt{11}\}$

23. $10y^2+10y+3=0$

$a=10,\ b=10,\ c=3$

$$y=\frac{-10\pm\sqrt{10^2-4(10)(3)}}{2(10)}$$

$$y=\frac{-10\pm\sqrt{100-120}}{20}$$

$$y=\frac{-10\pm\sqrt{-20}}{20}=\frac{-10\pm\sqrt{4}\sqrt{5}\sqrt{-1}}{20}$$

$$y=\frac{-10\pm2i\sqrt{5}}{20}=\frac{-5\pm i\sqrt{5}}{10}$$

$\left\{\frac{-5-i\sqrt{5}}{10},\ \frac{-5+i\sqrt{5}}{10}\right\}$

25. $3x=-2x^2+7$

$2x^2+3x-7=0$

$a=2,\ b=3,\ c=-7.$

$b^2-4ac=3^2-4(2)(-7)$

$b^2-4ac=9+56$

$b^2-4ac=65>0$

Therefore, there are 2 distinct real solutions.

27. $6=4x-5x^2$

$5x^2-4x+6=0$

$a=5,\ b=-4,\ c=6.$

$b^2-4ac=(-4)^2-4(5)(6)$

$b^2-4ac=16-120$

$b^2-4ac=-104<0$

Therefore, there are 2 distinct complex solutions.

29. $5-4x+12x^2=0$

$12x^2-4x+5=0$

$a=12,\ b=-4,\ c=5.$

$b^2-4ac=(-4)^2-4(12)(5)$

$b^2-4ac=16-240$

$b^2-4ac=-224<0$

Therefore, there are 2 distinct complex solutions.

31. $4x^2+12x=-9$

$4x^2+12x+9=0$

$a=4,\ b=12,\ c=9.$

$b^2-4ac=12^2-4(4)(9)$

$b^2-4ac=144-144=0$

Therefore, there is 1 real solution.

33. Let $x=$ the number of hours required for Bill to clean the house so $x+1=$ the number of hours required for Billy to clean the house. Now convert the times to rates:

$\frac{1 \text{ task}}{x \text{ hours}}=\frac{1}{x}\ \frac{\text{task}}{\text{hr}}$

$\frac{1 \text{ task}}{x+1 \text{ hrs}}=\frac{1}{x+1}\ \frac{\text{task}}{\text{hr}}$

$\frac{1 \text{ task}}{4 \text{ hrs}}=\frac{1}{4}\ \frac{\text{task}}{\text{hrs}}$

Now, expressing their combined rate in two ways we get:

$\frac{1}{x}+\frac{1}{x+1}=\frac{1}{4}$

$\frac{x+1+x}{x(x+1)}=\frac{1}{4}$

$\frac{2x+1}{x^2+x}=\frac{1}{4}$

$8x+4=x^2+x$

$x^2-7x-4=0$

$a=1,\ b=-7,\ c=-4.$

$$x=\frac{7\pm\sqrt{(-7)^2-4(1)(-4)}}{2(1)}$$

$$x=\frac{7\pm\sqrt{49+16}}{2}=\frac{7\pm\sqrt{65}}{2}$$

$$x=\frac{7}{2}\pm\frac{\sqrt{65}}{2}$$

We discard the negative solution leaving $x=\frac{7}{2}+\frac{\sqrt{65}}{2}$

so $x+1=\frac{9}{2}+\frac{\sqrt{65}}{2}\approx 8.53.$

Therefore, Billy could clean the house by himself in approximately 8.53 hours.

35. $h(t)=-16t^2+120t+80$

$30=-16t^2+120t+80$

$16t^2-120t-80+30=0$

$16t^2-120t-50=0$

$2(8t^2-60t-25)=0$

$8t^2-60t-25=\frac{0}{2}$

$8t^2-60t-25=0$

$$t=\frac{-(-60)\pm\sqrt{(-60)^2-4(8)(-25)}}{2(8)}$$

$$t=\frac{60\pm\sqrt{3600+800}}{16}=\frac{60\pm\sqrt{4400}}{16}$$

$$t\approx\frac{60\pm 66.33}{16}$$

$t\approx\frac{60+66.33}{16}$ or $t\approx\frac{60-66.33}{16}$

$t\approx 7.89$ $\qquad$ $t\approx-\frac{6.33}{16}$

Time can not be negative, therefore $t\approx 7.89$ seconds.

37. $x^2+5x=-2$

$x^2+5x+2=0$

$a=1,\ b=5,\ c=2.$

$$x=\frac{-5\pm\sqrt{5^2-4(1)(2)}}{2(1)}$$

$$x = \frac{-5 \pm \sqrt{25-8}}{2} = \frac{-5 \pm \sqrt{17}}{2}$$

$$x = -\frac{5}{2} \pm \frac{\sqrt{17}}{2}$$

$$\left\{-\frac{5}{2} - \frac{\sqrt{17}}{2}, -\frac{5}{2} + \frac{\sqrt{17}}{2}\right\}$$

39. $2m^2 - 7m + 5 = 0$

$a = 2, \; b = -7, \; c = 5$

$$x = \frac{7 \pm \sqrt{(-7)^2 - 4(2)(5)}}{2(2)}$$

$$x = \frac{7 \pm \sqrt{49-40}}{4} = \frac{7 \pm \sqrt{9}}{4}$$

$$x = \frac{7 \pm 3}{4} = 1, \; \frac{5}{2}$$

$$\left\{\frac{5}{2}, \; 1\right\}$$

41. $\frac{x^2}{3} - x = \frac{5}{3}$

$x^2 - 3x = 5$

$x^2 - 3x - 5 = 0$

$a = 1, \; b = -3, \; c = -5.$

$$x = \frac{3 \pm \sqrt{(-3)^2 - 4(1)(-5)}}{2(1)}$$

$$x = \frac{3 \pm \sqrt{9+20}}{2} = \frac{3 \pm \sqrt{29}}{2}$$

$$x = \frac{3}{2} \pm \frac{\sqrt{29}}{2}$$

$$\left\{\frac{3}{2} - \frac{\sqrt{29}}{2}, \; \frac{3}{2} + \frac{\sqrt{29}}{2}\right\}$$

43. $6x^2 + 2x - 3 = 0$

$a = 6, \; b = 2, \; c = -3.$

$$x = \frac{-2 \pm \sqrt{2^2 - 4(6)(-3)}}{2(6)}$$

$$x = \frac{-2 \pm \sqrt{4+72}}{12} = \frac{-2 \pm \sqrt{76}}{12}$$

$$x = \frac{-2 \pm \sqrt{4}\sqrt{19}}{12} = \frac{-2 \pm 2\sqrt{19}}{12}$$

$$x = \frac{-1 \pm \sqrt{19}}{6} = -\frac{1}{6} \pm \frac{\sqrt{19}}{6}$$

$$\left\{-\frac{1}{6} - \frac{\sqrt{19}}{6}, -\frac{1}{6} + \frac{\sqrt{19}}{6}\right\}$$

45. $x^2 + 6x + 13 = 0$

$a = 1, \; b = 6, \; c = 13.$

$$x = \frac{-6 \pm \sqrt{6^2 - 4(1)(13)}}{2(1)}$$

$$x = \frac{-6 \pm \sqrt{36-52}}{2} = \frac{-6 \pm \sqrt{-16}}{2}$$

$$x = \frac{-6 \pm 4i}{2} = -3 \pm 2i$$

$$\{-3-2i, -3+2i\}$$

47. $\frac{2}{5}y^2 + \frac{1}{5}y + \frac{3}{5} = 0$

$2y^2 + y + 3 = 0$

$a = 2, \; b = 1, \; c = 3.$

$$y = \frac{-1 \pm \sqrt{1^2 - 4(2)(3)}}{2(2)}$$

$$y = \frac{-1 \pm \sqrt{1-24}}{4} = \frac{-1 \pm \sqrt{-23}}{4}$$

$$y = \frac{-1 \pm i\sqrt{23}}{4}$$

$$\left\{\frac{-1 - i\sqrt{23}}{4}, \; \frac{-1 + i\sqrt{23}}{4}\right\}$$

49. $\frac{1}{2}y^2 = y - \frac{1}{2}$

$y^2 = 2y - 1$

$y^2 - 2y + 1 = 0$

$a = 1, \; b = -2, \; c = 1.$

$$y = \frac{2 \pm \sqrt{(-2)^2 - 4(1)(1)}}{2(1)}$$

$$y = \frac{2 \pm \sqrt{4-4}}{2} = \frac{2 \pm \sqrt{0}}{2} = 1$$

$$\{1\}$$

51. $(n-2)^2 = 15n$

$n^2 - 4n + 4 = 15n$

$n^2 - 19n + 4 = 0$

$a=1,\ b=-19,\ c=4.$

$$n=\frac{19\pm\sqrt{(-19)^2-4(1)(4)}}{2(1)}$$

$$n=\frac{19\pm\sqrt{361-16}}{2}=\frac{19\pm\sqrt{345}}{2}$$

$$n=\frac{19}{2}\pm\frac{\sqrt{345}}{2}$$

$$\left\{\frac{19}{2}-\frac{\sqrt{345}}{2},\ \frac{19}{2}+\frac{\sqrt{345}}{2}\right\}$$

53. Let $n=$ the first number.
$n-4=$ the second number.

$n(n-4)=96$

$n^2-4n-96=0$

$(n-12)(n+8)=0$

$n-12=0$ or $n+8=0$

$n=12$ or $n=-8$

Therefore, the number is either 12 or -8.

55.

	Time for entire job in hours.	Rate, in one hour.
IBM	$x-1$	$\frac{1}{x-1}$
Toshiba	x	$\frac{1}{x}$
Together	8	$\frac{1}{8}$

$$\frac{1}{x-1}+\frac{1}{x}=\frac{1}{8}$$

$$8x(x-1)\bullet\frac{1}{x-1}+8x(x-1)\bullet\frac{1}{x}=8x(x-1)\bullet\frac{1}{8}$$

$8x+8(x-1)=x(x-1)$

$8x+8x-8=x^2-x$

$16x-8=x^2-x$

$0=x^2-x-16x+8$

$0=x^2-17x+8$

$$x=\frac{-(-17)\pm\sqrt{(-17)^2-4(1)(8)}}{2(1)}$$

$$x=\frac{17\pm\sqrt{289-32}}{2}=\frac{17\pm\sqrt{257}}{2}$$

$$x\approx\frac{17\pm16.03}{2}$$

$x\approx\frac{17+16.03}{2}$ or $x\approx\frac{17-16.03}{2}$

$x\approx16.5$ hours or $x\approx0.485$ hours

Time could not be 0.485 hours for the Toshiba because than the IBM computer's time would be negative. Therefore it takes the Toshiba 16.5 hours alone and the IBM 15.5 hours alone.

57. $h(t)=-16t^2-20t+180$

$0=-16t^2-20t+180$

$0=-4(4t^2+5t-45)$

$0=4t^2+5t-45$

$$t=\frac{-(5)\pm\sqrt{5^2-4(4)(-45)}}{2(4)}$$

$$t=\frac{-5\pm\sqrt{25+720}}{8}=\frac{-5\pm\sqrt{745}}{8}$$

$$t\approx\frac{-5\pm27.3}{8}$$

$t\approx\frac{-5+27.3}{8}$ or $t\approx\frac{-5-27.3}{8}$

$t\approx2.8$ or $t\approx-4.0$

Time can not be negative, therefore the time until it strikes the ground is 2.8 seconds.

59. From Sunday to Monday

61. Wednesday

63. $f(x)=3x^2-18x+57$

$x=4$ days from Sunday

$f(4)=3(4)^2-18(4)+57$

$f(4)=3(16)-18(4)+57$

$f(4)=48-72+57$

$f(4)=33^\circ F$

It does agree with the graph.

65. $\sqrt{5x-2}=3$

$(\sqrt{5x-2})^2=3^2$

$5x-2=9$

$5x=11$

$x=\frac{11}{5}$

Checking

$\sqrt{5\left(\frac{11}{5}\right)-2}\stackrel{?}{=}3$

$\sqrt{11-2}\stackrel{?}{=}3$

$\sqrt{9}\stackrel{?}{=}3$

$3=3$

The solution is $\frac{11}{5}$.

$\left\{\frac{11}{5}\right\}$

67. $\frac{1}{x}+\frac{2}{5}-\frac{7}{x}$

$5x\bullet\frac{1}{x}+5x\bullet\frac{2}{5}=5x\bullet\frac{7}{x}$

$5+2x=35$

$2x=30$

$x=15$

$\{15\}$

69. $\sqrt{5}+4\sqrt{5}-7\sqrt{5}=-2\sqrt{5}$

71. $\sqrt{12x}+\sqrt{27x}$

$\sqrt{4}\sqrt{3x}+\sqrt{9}\sqrt{3x}$

$2\sqrt{3x}+3\sqrt{3x}$

$5\sqrt{3x}$

73. x^4+x^2-20

$(x^2+5)(x^2-4)$

$(x^2+5)(x+2)(x-2)$

75. z^4-13z^2+36

$(z^2-9)(z^2-4)$

$(z+3)(z-3)(z+2)(z-2)$

77. $3x^2-\sqrt{12x}+1=0$

$a=3,\ b=-\sqrt{12},\ c=1.$

$x=\frac{\sqrt{12}\pm\sqrt{(-\sqrt{12})^2-4(3)(1)}}{2(3)}$

$x=\frac{\sqrt{12}\pm\sqrt{12-12}}{6}=\frac{\sqrt{4}\sqrt{3}\pm\sqrt{0}}{6}$

$x=\frac{2\sqrt{3}}{6}=\frac{\sqrt{3}}{3}$

$\left\{\frac{\sqrt{3}}{3}\right\}$

79. $x^2+\sqrt{2}x+1=0$

$a=1,\ b=\sqrt{2},\ c=1$

$x=\frac{-\sqrt{2}\pm\sqrt{(\sqrt{2})^2-4(1)(1)}}{2(1)}$

$x=\frac{-\sqrt{2}\pm\sqrt{2-4}}{2}=\frac{-\sqrt{2}\pm\sqrt{-2}}{2}$

$x=\frac{-\sqrt{2}\pm i\sqrt{2}}{2}$

$\left\{\frac{-\sqrt{2}-i\sqrt{2}}{2},\ \frac{-\sqrt{2}+i\sqrt{2}}{2}\right\}$

81. $2x^2-\sqrt{3}x-1=0$

$a=2,\ b=-\sqrt{3},\ c=-1.$

$x=\frac{\sqrt{3}\pm\sqrt{(-\sqrt{3})^2-4(2)(-1)}}{2(2)}$

$x=\frac{\sqrt{3}\pm\sqrt{3+8}}{4}=\frac{\sqrt{3}\pm\sqrt{11}}{4}$

$\left\{\frac{\sqrt{3}-\sqrt{11}}{4},\ \frac{\sqrt{3}+\sqrt{11}}{4}\right\}$

Exercise Set 9.3

1. $\frac{2}{x}+\frac{3}{x-1}=1$

$\frac{2(x-1)+3x}{x(x-1)}=1$

$\frac{2x-2+3x}{x^2-x}=1$

$5x-2=x^2-x$

$x^2-6x+2=0$

$a = 1,\ b = -6,\ c = 2.$

$$x = \frac{6 \pm \sqrt{(-6)^2 - 4(1)(2)}}{2(1)}$$

$$x = \frac{6 \pm \sqrt{36 - 8}}{2} = \frac{6 \pm \sqrt{28}}{2}$$

$$x = \frac{6 \pm \sqrt{4}\sqrt{7}}{2} = \frac{6 \pm 2\sqrt{7}}{2}$$

$x = 3 \pm \sqrt{7}$

$\{3 - \sqrt{7},\ 3 + \sqrt{7}\}$

3. $\frac{3}{x} + \frac{4}{x+2} = 2$

$$\frac{3(x+2) + 4x}{x(x+2)} = 2$$

$$\frac{3x + 6 + 4x}{x^2 + 2x} = 2$$

$7x + 6 = 2(x^2 + 2x)$

$7x + 6 = 2x^2 + 4x$

$2x^2 - 3x - 6 = 0$

$a = 2,\ b = -3,\ c = -6.$

$$x = \frac{3 \pm \sqrt{(-3)^2 - 4(2)(-6)}}{2(2)}$$

$$x = \frac{3 \pm \sqrt{9 + 48}}{4} = \frac{3 \pm \sqrt{57}}{4}$$

$$\left\{\frac{3 - \sqrt{57}}{4},\ \frac{3 + \sqrt{47}}{4}\right\}$$

5. $\frac{7}{x^2 - 5x + 6} = \frac{2x}{x-3} - \frac{x}{x-2}$

$$\frac{7}{(x-3)(x-2)} = \frac{2x(x-2) - x(x-3)}{(x-3)(x-2)}$$

$7 = 2x^2 - 4x - x^2 + 3x$

$7 = x^2 - x$

$0 = x^2 - x - 7$

$a = 1,\ b = -1,\ c = -7$

$$x = \frac{1 \pm \sqrt{(-1)^2 - 4(1)(-7)}}{2(1)}$$

$$x = \frac{1 \pm \sqrt{1 + 28}}{2} = \frac{1 \pm \sqrt{29}}{2}$$

$$\left\{\frac{1 - \sqrt{29}}{2},\ \frac{1 + \sqrt{29}}{2}\right\}$$

7. $y^3 - 1 = 0$

$(y-1)(y^2 + y + 1) = 0$

$y - 1 = 0 \quad \text{or} \quad y^2 + y + 1 = 0$

$y = 1$

$a = 1,\ b = 1,\ c = 1$

$$y = \frac{-1 \pm \sqrt{1^2 - 4(1)(1)}}{2(1)}$$

$$y = \frac{-1 \pm \sqrt{1 - 4}}{2} = \frac{-1 \pm \sqrt{-3}}{2}$$

$$y = \frac{-1 \pm i\sqrt{3}}{2}$$

$$\left\{\frac{-1 - i\sqrt{3}}{2},\ \frac{-1 + i\sqrt{3}}{2},\ 1\right\}$$

9. $x^4 + 27x = 0$

$x(x^3 + 27) = 0$

$x(x+3)(x^2 - 3x + 9) = 0$

$x = 0 \quad \text{or} \quad x + 3 = 0 \quad \text{or} \quad x^2 - 3x + 9 = 0$

$x = -3$

$a = 1,\ b = -3,\ c = 9.$

$$x = \frac{3 \pm \sqrt{(-3)^2 - 4(1)(9)}}{2(1)}$$

$$x = \frac{3 \pm \sqrt{9 - 36}}{2} = \frac{3 \pm \sqrt{-27}}{2}$$

$$x = \frac{3 \pm \sqrt{9}\sqrt{3}\sqrt{-1}}{2} = \frac{3 \pm 3\sqrt{3}i}{2}$$

$$\left\{-3,\ 0,\ \frac{3 - 3i\sqrt{3}}{2},\ \frac{3 + 3i\sqrt{3}}{2}\right\}$$

11. $z^3 = 64$

$z^3 - 64 = 0$

$(z-4)(z^2 + 4z + 16) = 0$

$z - 4 = 0 \quad \text{or} \quad z^2 + 4z + 16 = 0$

$z = 4$

$a = 1,\ b = 4,\ c = 16.$

$$z = \frac{-4 \pm \sqrt{4^2 - 4(1)(16)}}{2(1)}$$

$z = \frac{-4 \pm \sqrt{16-64}}{2} = \frac{-4 \pm \sqrt{-48}}{2}$

$z = \frac{-4 \pm \sqrt{16}\sqrt{3}\sqrt{-1}}{2} = \frac{-4 \pm 4i\sqrt{3}}{2}$

$z = -2 \pm 2i\sqrt{3}$

$\{4, -2-2i\sqrt{3}, -2+2i\sqrt{3}\}$

13. $p^4 - 16 = 0$

$(p^2+4)(p^2-4) = 0$

$(p+2i)(p-2i)(p+2)(p-2) = 0$

$p+2i=0$ or $p-2i=0$ or $p+2=0$ or $p-2=0$

$p = -2i$ or $p = 2i$ or $p = -2$ or $p = 2$

$\{-2i, 2i, -2, 2\}$

15. $4x^4 + 11x^2 - 3 = 0$

$(4x^2-1)(x^2+3) = 0$

$(2x+1)(2x-1)(x+i\sqrt{3})(x-i\sqrt{3}) = 0$

$2x+1=0$ or $2x-1=0$ or $x+i\sqrt{3}=0$ or $x-i\sqrt{3}=0$

$2x = -1$ or $2x = 1$ or $x=-i\sqrt{3}$ or $x = i\sqrt{3}$

$x = -\frac{1}{2}$ or $x = \frac{1}{2}$

$\left\{-\frac{1}{2}, \frac{1}{2}, -i\sqrt{3}, i\sqrt{3}\right\}$

17. $z^4 - 13z^2 + 36 = 0$

$(z^2-9)(z^2-4) = 0$

$(z+3)(z-3)(z+2)(z-2) = 0$

$z+3=0$ or $z-3=0$ or $z+2=0$ or $z-2=0$

$z = -3$ or $z = 3$ or $z = -2$ or $z = 2$

$\{-3, -2, 2, 3\}$

19. $x^{\frac{2}{3}} - 3x^{\frac{1}{3}} - 10 = 0$

$(x^{\frac{1}{3}}-5)(x^{\frac{1}{3}}+2) = 0$

$x^{\frac{1}{3}} - 5 = 0$ or $x^{\frac{1}{3}} + 2 = 0$

$x^{\frac{1}{3}} = 5$ or $x^{\frac{1}{3}} = -2$

$x = 5^3$ or $x = (-2)^3$

$x = 125$ or $x = -8$

$\{-8, 125\}$

21. $2x^{\frac{2}{3}} - 5x^{\frac{1}{3}} = 3$

$2x^{\frac{2}{3}} - 5x^{\frac{1}{3}} - 3 = 0$

$(2x^{\frac{1}{3}}+1)(x^{\frac{1}{3}}-3) = 0$

$2x^{\frac{1}{3}} + 1 = 0$ or $x^{\frac{1}{3}} - 3 = 0$

$2x^{\frac{1}{3}} = -1$ or $x^{\frac{1}{3}} = 3$

$x^{\frac{1}{3}} = -\frac{1}{2}$ or $x = 3^3$

$x = \left(-\frac{1}{2}\right)^3$ or $x = 27$

$x = -\frac{1}{8}$

$\left\{-\frac{1}{8}, 27\right\}$

23. $20x^{\frac{2}{3}} - 6x^{\frac{1}{3}} - 2 = 0$

$(5x^{\frac{1}{3}}+1)(4x^{\frac{1}{3}}-2) = 0$

$5x^{\frac{1}{3}} + 1 = 0$ or $4x^{\frac{1}{3}} - 2 = 0$

$5x^{\frac{1}{3}} = -1$ or $4x^{\frac{1}{3}} = 2$

$x^{\frac{1}{3}} = -\frac{1}{5}$ or $x^{\frac{1}{3}} = \frac{1}{2}$

$x = \left(-\frac{1}{5}\right)^3$ or $x = \left(\frac{1}{2}\right)^3$

$x = -\frac{1}{125}$ or $x = \frac{1}{8}$

$\left\{-\frac{1}{125}, \frac{1}{8}\right\}$

25. We are given $A = 400$. Let $w =$ the width of the pen. So $\frac{5}{2}w =$ the length of the the pen. Then since $A = l \bullet w$ we have:

$400 = \left(\frac{5}{2}w\right)w$

$400 = \frac{5}{2}w^2$

$800 = 5w^2$

$w^2 = 160$

$w = \sqrt{160} = \sqrt{16}\sqrt{10} = 4\sqrt{10}$

so $\frac{5}{2}w = \frac{5}{2}(4\sqrt{10}) = 5(2\sqrt{10}) = 10\sqrt{10}$.

The pen is $4\sqrt{10}$ ft. by $10\sqrt{10}$ ft.

27. $a^4 - 5a^2 + 6 = 0$

$(a^2 - 3)(a^2 - 2) = 0$

$a^2 - 3 = 0$ or $a^2 - 2 = 0$

$a^2 = 3$ or $a^2 = 2$

$a = \pm\sqrt{3}$ or $a = \pm\sqrt{2}$

$\{-\sqrt{3}, -\sqrt{2}, \sqrt{2}, \sqrt{3}\}$

29. $\frac{2x}{x-2} + \frac{x}{x+3} = \frac{-5}{x+3}$

$\frac{2x}{x-2} = \frac{-x}{x+3} - \frac{5}{x+3}$

$\frac{2x}{x-2} = \frac{-x-5}{x+3}$

$2x(x+3) = (x-2)(-x-5)$

$2x^2 + 6x = -x^2 + 2x - 5x + 10$

$2x^2 + 6x = -x^2 - 3x + 10$

$3x^2 + 9x - 10 = 0$

$a = 3$, $b = 9$, $c = -10$.

$$x = \frac{-9 \pm \sqrt{9^2 - 4(3)(-10)}}{2(3)}$$

$$x = \frac{-9 \pm \sqrt{81 + 120}}{6} = \frac{-9 \pm \sqrt{201}}{6}$$

$$\left\{\frac{-9-\sqrt{201}}{6}, \frac{-9+\sqrt{201}}{6}\right\}$$

31. $x^3 + 64 = 0$

$(x+4)(x^2 - 4x + 16) = 0$

$x + 4 = 0$ or $x^2 - 4x + 16 = 0$

$x = -4$

$a = 1$, $b = -4$, $c = 16$.

$$x = \frac{4 \pm \sqrt{(-4)^2 - 4(1)(16)}}{2(1)}$$

$$x = \frac{4 \pm \sqrt{16 - 64}}{2} = \frac{4 \pm \sqrt{-48}}{2}$$

$$x = \frac{4 \pm \sqrt{16}\sqrt{3}\sqrt{-1}}{2} = \frac{4 \pm 4i\sqrt{3}}{2}$$

$x = 2 \pm 2i\sqrt{3}$

$\{-4, 2 - 2i\sqrt{3}, 2 + 2i\sqrt{3}\}$

33. $x^{\frac{2}{3}} - 8x^{\frac{1}{3}} + 15 = 0$

$(x^{\frac{1}{3}} - 5)(x^{\frac{1}{3}} - 3) = 0$

$x^{\frac{1}{3}} - 5 = 0$ or $x^{\frac{1}{3}} - 3 = 0$

$x^{\frac{1}{3}} = 5$ or $x^{\frac{1}{3}} = 3$

$x = 5^3$ or $x = 3^3$

$x = 125$ or $x = 27$

$\{27, 125\}$

35. $y^3 + 9y - y^2 - 9 = 0$

$y(y^2 + 9) - (y^2 + 9) = 0$

$(y^2 + 9)(y - 1) = 0$

$(y + 3i)(y - 3i)(y - 1) = 0$

$y + 3i = 0$ or $y - 3i = 0$ or $y - 1 = 0$

$y = -3i$ or $y = 3i$ or $y = 1$

$\{-3i, 3i, 1\}$

37. $2x^{\frac{2}{3}} + 3x^{\frac{1}{3}} - 2 = 0$

$(2x^{\frac{1}{3}} - 1)(x^{\frac{1}{3}} + 2) = 0$

$2x^{\frac{1}{3}} - 1 = 0$ or $x^{\frac{1}{3}} + 2 = 0$

$2x^{\frac{1}{3}} = 1$ or $x^{\frac{1}{3}} = -2$

$x^{\frac{1}{3}} = \frac{1}{2}$ or $x = (-2)^3$

$x = \left(\frac{1}{2}\right)^3$ or $x = -8$

$x = \frac{1}{8}$

$\left\{-8, \frac{1}{8}\right\}$

39. $2x^3 - 250 = 0$

$x^3 - 125 = 0$

$(x - 5)(x^2 + 5x + 25) = 0$

$x - 5 = 0$ or $x^2 + 5x + 25 = 0$

$x = 5$

$a = 1$, $b = 5$, $c = 25$.

$$x=\frac{-5\pm\sqrt{5^2-4(1)(25)}}{2(1)}$$

$$x=\frac{-5\pm\sqrt{25-100}}{2}$$

$$x=\frac{-5\pm\sqrt{-75}}{2}=\frac{-5\pm\sqrt{25}\sqrt{3}\sqrt{-1}}{2}$$

$$x=\frac{-5\pm 5i\sqrt{3}}{2}$$

$$\left\{5,\ \frac{-5-5i\sqrt{3}}{2},\ \frac{-5+5i\sqrt{3}}{2}\right\}$$

41. $\frac{x}{x-1}+\frac{1}{x+1}=\frac{2}{x^2-1}$

$\frac{x(x+1)+x-1}{(x-1)(x+1)}=\frac{2}{(x+1)(x-1)}$

$x^2+x+x-1=2$

$x^2+2x-1=2$

$x^2+2x-3=0$

$(x+3)(x-1)=0$

$x+3=0$ or $x-1=0$

$x=-3$ or $x=1$

We discard 1 as extraneous.

$\{-3\}$

43. $p^4-p^2-20=0$

$(p^2-5)(p^2+4)=0$

$p^2-5=0$ or $p^2+4=0$

$p^2=5$ or $(p+2i)(p-2i)=0$

$p=\pm\sqrt{5}$ or $p+2i=0$ or $p-2i=0$

$p=-2i$ or $p=2i$

$\{-\sqrt{5},\ \sqrt{5},\ -2i,\ 2i\}$

45. $2x^3=-54$

$x^3=-27$

$x^3+27=0$

$(x+3)(x^2-3x+9)=0$

$x+3=0$ or $x^2-3x+9=0$

$x=-3$

$a=1,\ b=-3,\ c=9.$

$$x=\frac{3\pm\sqrt{(-3)^2-4(1)(9)}}{2(1)}$$

$$x=\frac{3\pm\sqrt{9-36}}{2}=\frac{3\pm\sqrt{-27}}{2}$$

$$x=\frac{3\pm\sqrt{9}\sqrt{3}\sqrt{-1}}{2}=\frac{3\pm 3\sqrt{3}i}{2}$$

$$x=\frac{3}{2}\pm\frac{3i\sqrt{3}}{2}$$

$$\left\{-3,\ \frac{3-3i\sqrt{3}}{2},\ \frac{3+3i\sqrt{3}}{2}\right\}$$

47. $27y^4+15y^2=2$

$27y^4+15y^2-2=0$

$(9y^2-1)(3y^2+2)=0$

$(3y+1)(3y-1)(3y^2+2)=0$

$3y+1=0$ or $3y-1=0$ or $3y^2+2=0$

$3y=-1$ or $3y=1$ or $3y^2=-2$

$y=-\frac{1}{3}$ or $y=\frac{1}{3}$ or $y^2=-\frac{2}{3}$

$y=\pm\sqrt{-\frac{2}{3}}$

$y=\pm\frac{\sqrt{-2}}{\sqrt{3}}$

$y=\pm\frac{i\sqrt{2}}{\sqrt{3}}\bullet\frac{\sqrt{3}}{\sqrt{3}}$

$y=\pm\frac{i\sqrt{6}}{3}$

$$\left\{-\frac{1}{3},\ \frac{1}{3},\ -\frac{i\sqrt{6}}{3},\ \frac{i\sqrt{6}}{3}\right\}$$

49. We are given that $A=42$. Let $h=$ the height of the triangle so $2h=$ the base of the triangle. The since $A=\frac{1}{2}bh$ we get:

$42=\frac{1}{2}(2h)(h)$

$42=h^2$

$h=\pm\sqrt{42}$

but we discard $-\sqrt{42}$ as meaningless. Then $2h=2\sqrt{42}$. The base of the triangle is $2\sqrt{42}$ cm. and its height is $\sqrt{42}$ cm.

51. We are given that $A = 1200$.

Let $w =$ the width of the poster, so $\frac{3}{2}w =$ the length of the poster. Then since $A = l \bullet w$, we have

$1200 = \left(\frac{3}{2}w\right)w$

$1200 = \frac{3}{2}w^2$

$2400 = 3w^2$

$w^2 = 800$

$w = \sqrt{800} = \sqrt{400}\sqrt{2} = 20\sqrt{2}$

So, $\frac{3}{2}w = \frac{3}{2}(20\sqrt{2}) = 3(10\sqrt{2}) = 30\sqrt{2}$

The width must be $20\sqrt{2}$ in. and the length must be $30\sqrt{2}$ in.

53. Let $w =$ the width of the rectangle so $3w =$ the length of the rectangle. By the Pythagorean theorem,

a. $50^2 = w^2 + (3w)^2$

$2500 = w^2 + 9w^2$

$2500 = 10w^2$

$w^2 = 250$

$w = \sqrt{250} = \sqrt{25}\sqrt{10} = 5\sqrt{10}$

so $3w = 3(5\sqrt{10}) = 15\sqrt{10}$

The dimensions of the rectangle are $5\sqrt{10}$ cm. by $15\sqrt{10}$ cm.

b. Recall that

$P = 2l + 2w$

$P = 2(15\sqrt{10}) + 2(5\sqrt{10})$

$P = 30\sqrt{10} + 10\sqrt{10}$

$P = 40\sqrt{10}$

The perimeter of the rectangle is $40\sqrt{10}$ cm.

55. $\frac{5x}{3} + 2 \le 7$

$\frac{5x}{3} \le 5$

$\frac{3}{5}\left(\frac{5x}{3}\right) \le \frac{3}{5}(5)$

$x \le 3$

$(-\infty, 3]$

57. $\frac{y-1}{15} > -\frac{2}{5}$

$15\left(\frac{y-1}{15}\right) > 15\left(-\frac{2}{5}\right)$

$y - 1 > -6$

$y > -5$

$(-5, \infty)$

59. Domain $\{x \mid x \text{ is a real number}\}$

Range $\{y \mid y \text{ is a real number}\}$

It is a function.

61. Domain $\{x \mid x \text{ is a real number}\}$

Range $\{y \mid y \ge -1\}$

It is a function.

63. $f(x) = x^2$

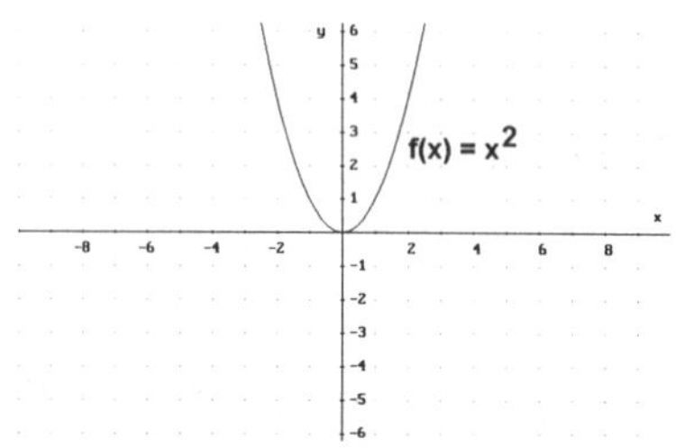

Exercise Set 9.4

1. $(x+1)(x+5) > 0$

$(x+1)(x+5) = 0$

$x + 1 = 0$ or $x + 5 = 0$

$x = -1$ or $x = -5$

Region	Interval	Test Point
A	$(-\infty, -5)$	-6
B	$(-5, -1)$	-2
C	$(-1, \infty)$	0

$x = -6$: $(-6+1)(-6+5) > 0$ True

$x = -2$:	$(-2+1)(-2+5) > 0$	False
$x = 0$:	$(0+1)(0+5) > 0$	True

The solution is $(-\infty, -5) \cup (-1, \infty)$.

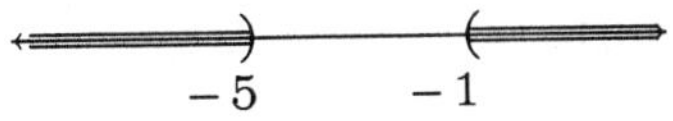

3. $(x-3)(x+4) \le 0$

$(x-3)(x+4) = 0$

$x-3=0$ or $x+4=0$

$x=3$ or $x=-4$

Region	Interval	Test Point
A	$(-\infty, -4)$	-5
B	$(-4, 3)$	0
C	$(3, \infty)$	4

$x = -5$:	$(-5-3)(-5+4) \le 0$	False
$x = 0$:	$(0-3)(0+4) \le 0$	True
$x = 4$:	$(4-3)(4+4) \le 0$	False

The solution is $[-4, 3]$.

5. $x^2 - 7x + 10 \le 0$

$(x-5)(x-2) \le 0$

$(x-5)(x-2) = 0$

$x-5=0$ or $x-2=0$

$x=5$ or $x=2$

Region	Interval	Test Point
A	$(-\infty, 2)$	0
B	$(2, 5)$	3
C	$(5, \infty)$	6

$x = 0$:	$(0-5)(0-2) \le 0$	False
$x = 3$:	$(3-5)(3-2) \le 0$	True
$x = 6$:	$(6-5)(6-2) \le 0$	False

The solution is $[2, 5]$.

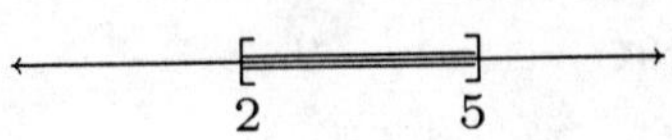

7. $3x^2 + 16x < -5$

$3x^2 + 16x + 5 < 0$

$(3x+1)(x+5) < 0$

$(3x+1)(x+5) = 0$

$3x+1=0$ or $x+5=0$

$3x=-1$ or $x=-5$

$x = -\frac{1}{3}$

Region	Interval	Test Point
A	$(-\infty, -5)$	-6
B	$\left(-5, -\frac{1}{3}\right)$	-1
C	$\left(-\frac{1}{3}, \infty\right)$	0

$x = -6$:	$[3(-6)+1](-6+5) < 0$	False
$x = -1$:	$[3(-1)+1](-1+5) < 0$	True
$x = 0$:	$[3(0)+1](0+5) < 0$	False

The solution is $\left(-5, -\frac{1}{3}\right)$.

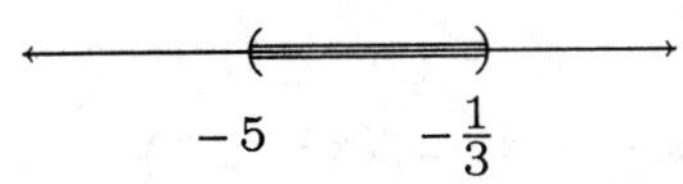

9. $(x-6)(x-4)(x-2) > 0$

$(x-6)(x-4)(x-2) = 0$

$x-6=0$ or $x-4=0$ or $x-2=0$

$x=6$ or $x=4$ or $x=2$

Region	Interval	Test Point
A	$(-\infty, 2)$	1
B	$(2, 4)$	3
C	$(4, 6)$	5
D	$(6, \infty)$	7

$x = 1$:	$(1-6)(1-4)(1-2) > 0$	False
$x = 3$:	$(3-6)(3-4)(3-2) > 0$	True
$x = 5$:	$(5-6)(5-4)(5-2) > 0$	False
$x = 7$:	$(7-6)(7-4)(7-2) > 0$	True

The solution is $(2, 4) \cup (6, \infty)$.

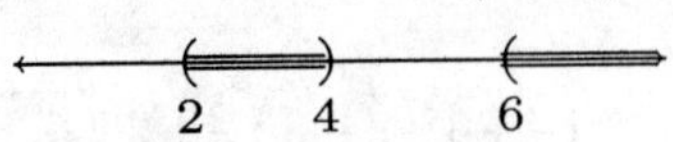

11. $x(x-1)(x+4) \le 0$

$x(x-1)(x+4) = 0$

$x = 0$ or $x-1=0$ or $x+4=0$

$x = 1$ or $x = -4$

Region	Interval	Test Point
A	$(-\infty, -4)$	-5
B	$(-4, 0)$	-1
C	$(0, 1)$	$\frac{1}{2}$
D	$(1, \infty)$	2

$x = -5$: $-5(-5-1)(-5+4) \le 0$ True

$x = -1$: $-1(-1-1)(-1+4) \le 0$ False

$x = \frac{1}{2}$: $\frac{1}{2}\left(\frac{1}{2}-1\right)\left(\frac{1}{2}+4\right) \le 0$ True

$x = 2$: $2(2-1)(2+4) \le 0$ False

The solution is $(-\infty, -4] \cup [0, 1]$.

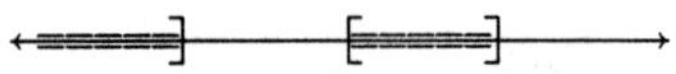

13. $(x^2-9)(x^2-4) > 0$

$(x+3)(x-3)(x+2)(x-2) > 0$

$(x+3)(x-3)(x+2)(x-2) = 0$

$x+3=0$ or $x-3=0$ or $x+2=0$ or $x-2=0$

$x=-3$ or $x=3$ or $x=-2$ or $x=2$

Region	Interval	Test Point
A	$(-\infty, -3)$	-4
B	$(-3, -2)$	$-\frac{5}{2}$
C	$(-2, 2)$	0
D	$(2, 3)$	$\frac{5}{2}$
E	$(3, \infty)$	4

$x = -4$: $(-4+3)(-4-3)(-4+2)(-4-2) > 0$ True

$x = -\frac{5}{2}$: $\left(-\frac{5}{2}+3\right)\left(-\frac{5}{2}-3\right)\left(-\frac{5}{2}+2\right)\left(-\frac{5}{2}-2\right) > 0$ False

$x = 0$: $(0+3)(0-3)(0+2)(0-2) > 0$ True

$x = \frac{5}{2}$: $\left(\frac{5}{2}+3\right)\left(\frac{5}{2}-3\right)\left(\frac{5}{2}+2\right)\left(\frac{5}{2}-2\right) > 0$ False

$x = 4$: $(4+3)(4-3)(4+2)(4-2) > 0$ True

The solution is $(-\infty, -3) \cup (-2, 2) \cup (3, \infty)$.

15. $\frac{x+7}{x-2} < 0$

$x+7=0$ and $x-2=0$

$x=-7$ and $x=2$

Region	Interval	Test Point
A	$(-\infty, -7)$	-8
B	$(-7, 2)$	0
C	$(2, \infty)$	3

$x = -8$: $\frac{-8+7}{-8-2} < 0$ False

$x = 0$: $\frac{0+7}{0-2} < 0$ True

$x = 3$: $\frac{3+7}{3-2} < 0$ False

The solution is $(-7, 2)$

17. $\frac{5}{x+1} > 0$

$x+1=0$

$x=-1$

Region	Interval	Test Point
A	$(-\infty, -1)$	-2
B	$(-1, \infty)$	0

$x = -2$: $\frac{5}{-2+1} > 0$ False

$x = 0$: $\frac{5}{0+1} > 0$ True

The solution is $(-1, \infty)$.

19. $\frac{x+1}{x-4} \geq 0$

$x+1=0$ and $x-4=0$

$x=-1$ and $x=4$

Region	Interval	Test Point
A	$(-\infty, -1)$	-2
B	$(-1, 4)$	0
C	$(4, \infty)$	5

$x=-2$: $\frac{-2+1}{-2-4} \geq 0$ True

$x=0$: $\frac{0+1}{0-4} \geq 0$ False

$x=5$: $\frac{5+1}{5-4} \geq 0$ True

The solution is $(-\infty, -1] \cup (4, \infty)$.

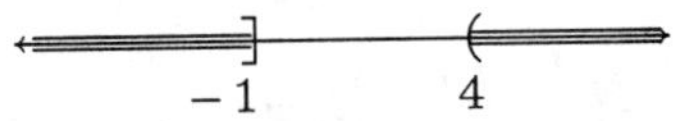

21. $\frac{3}{x-2} < 4$

$\frac{3}{x-2} - 4 < 0$

$\frac{3-4(x-2)}{x-2} < 0$

$\frac{3-4x+8}{x-2} < 0$

$\frac{11-4x}{x-2} < 0$

$11-4x=0$ and $x-2=0$

$11=4x$ and $x=2$

$x=\frac{11}{4}$

Region	Interval	Test Point
A	$(-\infty, 2)$	1
B	$\left(2, \frac{11}{4}\right)$	$\frac{5}{2}$
C	$\left(\frac{11}{4}, \infty\right)$	3

$x=1$: $\frac{11-4(1)}{1-2} < 0$ True

$x=\frac{5}{2}$: $\frac{11-4\left(\frac{5}{2}\right)}{\frac{5}{2}-2} < 0$ False

$x=3$: $\frac{11-4(3)}{4-2} < 0$ True

The solution is $(-\infty, 2) \cup \left(\frac{11}{4}, \infty\right)$.

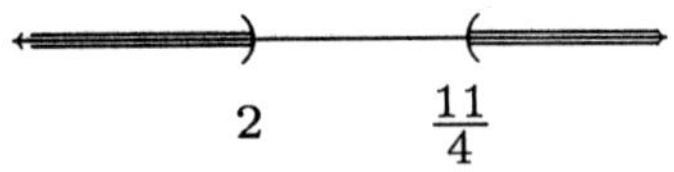

23. $\frac{x^2+6}{5x} \geq 1$

$\frac{x^2+6}{5x} - 1 \geq 0$

$\frac{x^2+6-5x}{5x} \geq 0$

$\frac{(x-2)(x-3)}{5x} \geq 0$

$x-2=0$ and $x-3=0$ and $5x=0$

$x=2$ and $x=3$ and $x=0$

Region	Interval	Test Point
A	$(-\infty, 0)$	-1
B	$(0, 2)$	1
C	$(2, 3)$	$\frac{5}{2}$
D	$(3, \infty)$	4

$x=-1$: $\frac{(-1-2)(-1-3)}{5(-1)} \geq 0$ False

$x=1$: $\frac{(1-2)(1-3)}{5(1)} \geq 0$ True

$x=\frac{5}{2}$: $\frac{\left(\frac{5}{2}-2\right)\left(\frac{5}{2}-3\right)}{5\left(\frac{5}{2}\right)} \geq 0$ False

$x=4$: $\frac{(4-2)(4-3)}{5(4)} \geq 0$ True

The solution is $(0, 2] \cup [3, \infty)$.

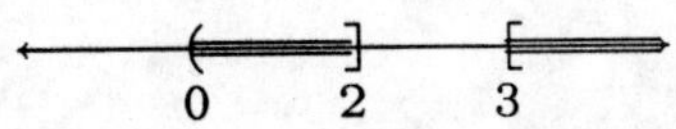

25. $(x-8)(x+7) > 0$

$(x-8)(x+7) = 0$

$x-8=0$ or $x+7=0$

$x=8$ or $x=-7$

Region	Interval	Test Point
A	$(-\infty, -7)$	-8
B	$(-7, 8)$	0
C	$(8, \infty)$	9

$x = -8$:	$(-8-8)(-8+7) > 0$	True
$x = 0$:	$(0-8)(0+7) > 0$	False
$x = 9$:	$(9-8)(9+7) > 0$	True

The solution is $(-\infty, -7) \cup (8, \infty)$.

27. $(2x-3)(4x+5) \le 0$

$(2x-3)(4x+5) = 0$

$2x-3=0$ or $4x+5=0$

$2x=3$ or $4x=-5$

$x=\frac{3}{2}$ or $x=-\frac{5}{4}$

Region	Interval	Test Point
A	$\left(-\infty, -\frac{5}{4}\right)$	-2
B	$\left(-\frac{5}{4}, \frac{3}{2}\right)$	0
C	$\left(\frac{3}{2}, \infty\right)$	2

$x = -2$:	$[2(-2)-3][4(-2)+5] \le 0$	False
$x = 0$:	$[2(0)-3][4(0)+5] \le 0$	True
$x = 2$:	$[2(2)-3][4(2)+5] \le 0$	False

The solution is $\left[-\frac{5}{4}, \frac{3}{2}\right]$.

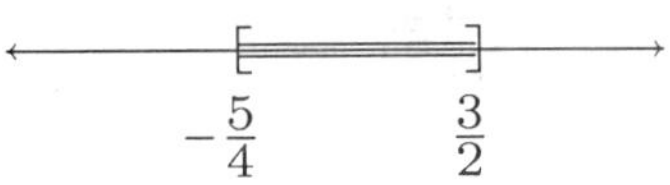

29. $x^2 > x$

$x^2 - x > 0$

$x(x-1) > 0$

$x(x-1) = 0$

$x=0$ or $x-1=0$

$x=1$

Region	Interval	Test Point
A	$(-\infty, 0)$	-1
B	$(0, 1)$	$\frac{1}{2}$
C	$(1, \infty)$	2

$x = -1$:	$-1(-1-1) > 0$	True
$x = \frac{1}{2}$:	$\frac{1}{2}\left(\frac{1}{2}-1\right) > 0$	False
$x = 2$:	$2(2-1) > 0$	True

The solution is $(-\infty, 0) \cup (1, \infty)$.

31. $(2x-8)(x+4)(x-6) \le 0$

$(2x-8)(x+4)(x-6) = 0$

$2x-8=0$ or $x+4=0$ or $x-6=0$

$2x=8$ or $x=-4$ or $x=6$

$x=4$

Regions	Interval	Test Point
A	$(-\infty, -4)$	-5
B	$(-4, 4)$	0
C	$(4, 6)$	5
D	$(6, \infty)$	7

$x = -5$:	$[2(-5)-8](-5+4)(-5-6) \le 0$	True
$x = 0$:	$[2(0)-8](0+4)(0-6) \le 0$	False
$x = 5$:	$[2(5)-8](5+4)(5-6) \le 0$	True
$x = 7$:	$[2(7)-8](7+4)(7-6) \le 0$	False

The solution is $(-\infty, -4] \cup [4, 6]$.

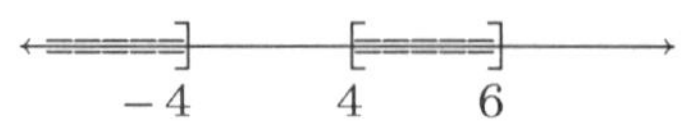

33. $6x^2 - 5x \ge 6$

$6x^2 - 5x - 6 \ge 0$

$(3x+2)(2x-3) \ge 0$

$(3x+2)(2x-3) = 0$

$3x+2=0$ or $2x-3=0$

$3x=-2$ or $2x=3$

$x=-\frac{2}{3}$ or $x=\frac{3}{2}$

Region	Interval	Test Point
A	$\left(-\infty, -\frac{2}{3}\right)$	-1
B	$\left(-\frac{2}{3}, \frac{3}{2}\right)$	0
C	$\left(\frac{3}{2}, \infty\right)$	2

$x = -1$:	$[3(-1)+2][2(-1)-3] \ge 0$	True
$x = 0$:	$[3(0)+2][2(0)-3] \ge 0$	False

$x = 2$: $[3(2)+2][2(2)-3] \geq 0$ True

The solution is $\left(-\infty, -\frac{2}{3}\right] \cup \left[\frac{3}{2}, \infty\right)$.

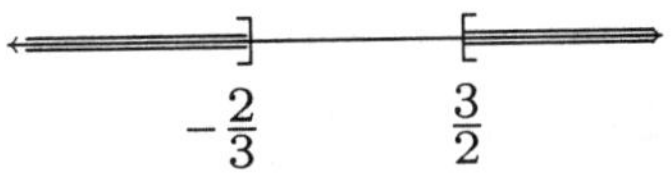

35. $x^4 - 26x^2 + 25 \geq 0$

$(x^2 - 25)(x^2 - 1) \geq 0$

$(x-5)(x+5)(x-1)(x+1) \geq 0$

$(x-5)(x+5)(x-1)(x+1) = 0$

x-5=0 or x+5=0 or x-1=0 or x+1=0

$x = 5$ or $x = -5$ or $x = 1$ or $x = -1$

Region	Interval	Test Point
A	$(-\infty, -5)$	-6
B	$(-5, -1)$	-3
C	$(-1, 1)$	0
D	$(1, 5)$	3
E	$(5, \infty)$	6

$x = -6$: $(-6-5)(-6+5)(-6-1)(-6+1) \geq 0$ True

$x = -3$: $(-3-5)(-3+5)(-3-1)(-3+1) \geq 0$ False

$x = 0$: $(0-5)(0+5)(0-1)(0+1) \geq 0$ True

$x = 3$: $(3-5)(3+5)(3-1)(3+1) \geq 0$ False

$x = 6$: $(6-5)(6+5)(6-1)(6+1) \geq 0$ True

The solution is

$(-\infty, -5] \cup [-1, 1] \cup [5, \infty)$.

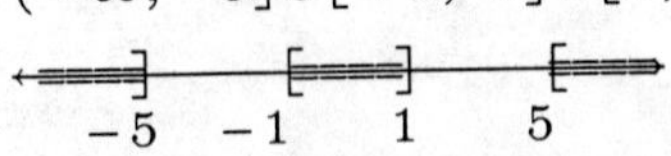

37. $(2x-7)(3x+5) > 0$

$(2x-7)(3x+5) = 0$

$2x - 7 = 0$ or $3x + 5 = 0$

$2x = 7$ or $3x = -5$

$x = \frac{7}{2}$ or $x = -\frac{5}{3}$

Region	Interval	Test Point
A	$\left(-\infty, -\frac{5}{3}\right)$	-2
B	$\left(-\frac{5}{3}, \frac{7}{2}\right)$	0
C	$\left(\frac{7}{2}, \infty\right)$	4

$[2(-2)-7][3(-2)+5) > 0$ True

$[2(0)-7][3(0)+5] > 0$ False

$[2(4)-7][2(4)+5] > 0$ True

The solution is $\left(-\infty, -\frac{5}{3}\right) \cup \left(\frac{7}{2}, \infty\right)$.

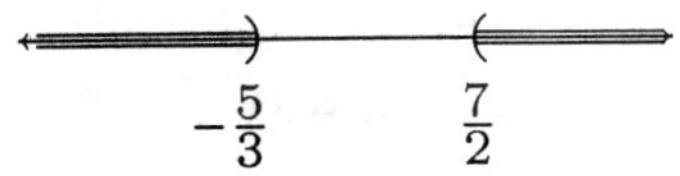

39. $\frac{x}{x-10} < 0$

$x = 0$ or $x - 10 = 0$

$x = 10$

Region	Interval	Test Point
A	$(-\infty, 0)$	-1
B	$(0, 10)$	1
C	$(10, \infty)$	11

$x = -1$: $\frac{-1}{-1-10} < 0$ False

$x = 1$: $\frac{1}{1-10} < 0$ True

$x = 11$: $\frac{11}{11-10} < 0$ False

The solution is $(0, 10)$.

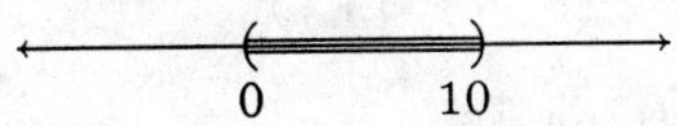

41. $\frac{x-5}{x+4} \geq 0$

$x - 5 = 0$ and $x + 4 = 0$

$x = 5$ and $x = -4$

Region	Interval	Test Point
A	$(-\infty, -4)$	-5
B	$(-4, 5)$	0
C	$(5, \infty)$	6

$x = -5$: $\frac{-5-5}{-5+4} \geq 0$ True

$x = 0$: $\frac{0-5}{0+4} \geq 0$ False

$x = 6$: $\frac{6-5}{6+4} \geq 0$ True

The solution is $(-\infty, -4) \cup [5, \infty)$.

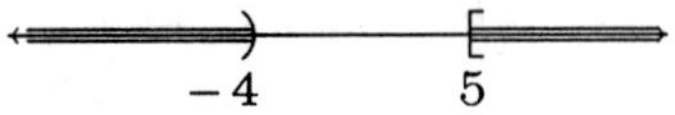

43. $\frac{x(x+6)}{(x-7)(x+1)} \geq 0$

$x = 0$ and $x+6=0$ and $x-7=0$ and $x+1=0$

$x = 0$ and $x = -6$ and $x = 7$ and $x = -1$

Region	Interval	Test Point
A	$(-\infty, -6)$	-7
B	$(-6, -1)$	-2
C	$(-1, 0)$	$-\frac{1}{2}$
D	$(0, 7)$	1
E	$(7, \infty)$	8

$x = -7$: $\frac{-7(-7+6)}{(-7-7)(-7+1)} \geq 0$ True

$x = -2$: $\frac{-2(-2+6)}{(-2-7)(-2+1)} \geq 0$ False

$x = -\frac{1}{2}$: $\frac{-\frac{1}{2}\left(-\frac{1}{2}+6\right)}{\left(-\frac{1}{2}-7\right)\left(-\frac{1}{2}+1\right)} \geq 0$ True

$x = 1$: $\frac{1(1+6)}{(1-7)(1+1)} \geq 0$ False

$x = 8$: $\frac{8(8+6)}{(8-7)(8+1)} \geq 0$ True

The solution is

$(-\infty, -6] \cup (-1, 0] \cup (7, \infty)$.

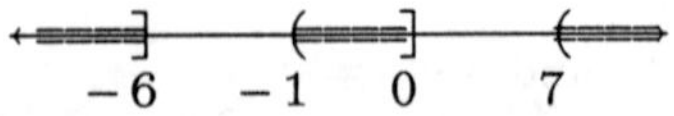

45. $\frac{-1}{x-1} > -1$

$\frac{1}{x-1} < 1$

$\frac{1}{x-1} - 1 < 0$

$\frac{1-(x-1)}{x-1} < 0$

$\frac{1-x+1}{x-1} < 0$

$\frac{2-x}{x-1} < 0$

$2 - x = 0$ or $x - 1 = 0$

$2 = x$ or $x = 1$

Region	Interval	Test Point
A	$(-\infty, 1)$	0
B	$(1, 2)$	$\frac{3}{2}$
C	$(2, \infty)$	3

$x = 0$: $\frac{2-0}{0-1} < 0$ True

$x = \frac{3}{2}$: $\frac{2-\frac{3}{2}}{\frac{3}{2}-1} < 0$ False

$x = 3$: $\frac{2-3}{3-1} < 0$ True

The solution is $(-\infty, 1) \cup (2, \infty)$.

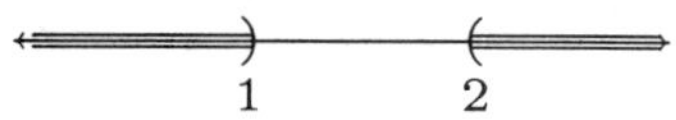

47. $\frac{x}{x+4} \leq 2$

$\frac{x}{x+4} - 2 \leq 0$

$\frac{x-2x-8}{x+4} \leq 0$

$\frac{-x-8}{x+4} \leq 0$

$-x - 8 = 0$ and $x + 4 = 0$

$-x = 8$ and $x = -4$

$x = -8$

Region	Interval	Test Point
A	$(-\infty, -8)$	-9
B	$(-8, -4)$	-5
C	$(-4, \infty)$	0

$x = -9$: $\frac{-(-9)-8}{-9+4} \leq 0$ True

$x = -5$: $\frac{-(-5)-8}{-5+4} \leq 0$ False

$x = 0$: $\frac{-0-8}{0+4} \leq 0$ True

The solution is $(-\infty, -8] \cup (-4, \infty)$.

49. $\frac{z}{z-5} \geq 2z$

$\frac{z}{z-5} - 2z \geq 0$

$\frac{z - 2z(z-5)}{z-5} \geq 0$

$\frac{z - 2z^2 + 10z}{z-5} \geq 0$

$\frac{11z - 2z^2}{z-5} \geq 0$

$\frac{z(11-2z)}{z-5} \geq 0$

$z = 0$ and $11 - 2z = 0$ and $z - 5 = 0$

$11 = 2z$ and $z = 5$

$\frac{11}{2} = z$

Region	Interval	Test Point
A	$(-\infty, 0)$	-1
B	$(0, 5)$	1
C	$\left(5, \frac{11}{2}\right)$	$\frac{21}{4}$
D	$\left(\frac{11}{2}, \infty\right)$	6

$z = -1$: $\frac{-1[11-2(-1)]}{-1-5} \geq 0$ True

$z = 1$: $\frac{1[11-2(1)]}{1-5} \geq 0$ False

$z = \frac{21}{4}$: $\frac{\frac{21}{4}\left[11 - 2\left(\frac{21}{4}\right)\right]}{\frac{21}{4} - 5} \geq 0$ True

$z = 6$: $\frac{6[11-2(6)]}{6-5} \geq 0$ False

The solution is $(-\infty, 0] \cup \left(5, \frac{11}{2}\right)$.

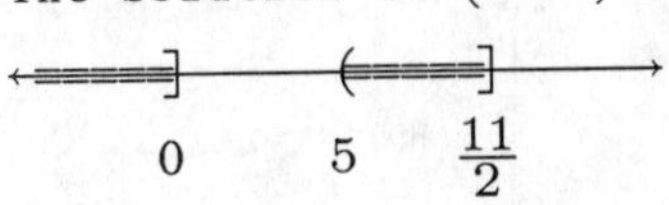

51. $\frac{(x+1)^2}{5x} > 0$

$(x+1)^2 = 0$ and $5x = 0$

$x + 1 = 0$ and $x = 0$

$x = -1$

Region	Interval	Test Point
A	$(-\infty, -1)$	-2
B	$(-1, 0)$	$-\frac{1}{2}$
C	$(-1, \infty)$	1

$x = -2$: $\frac{(-2+1)^2}{5(-2)} > 0$ False

$x = -\frac{1}{2}$: $\frac{\left(-\frac{1}{2}+1\right)^2}{5\left(-\frac{1}{2}\right)} > 0$ False

$x = 1$: $\frac{(1+1)^2}{5(1)} > 0$ True

The solution is $(0, \infty)$.

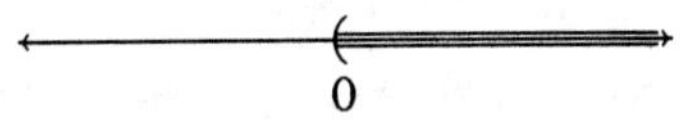

53. Let $x =$ the number.

$\frac{1}{x} =$ the reciprocal of the number.

$x - \frac{1}{x} < 0$

$\frac{x^2 - 1}{x} < 0$

$\frac{(x+1)(x-1)}{x} < 0$

$x + 1 = 0$ and $x - 1 = 0$ and $x = 0$

$x = -1$ and $x = 1$ and $x = 0$

Region	Interval	Test Point
A	$(-\infty, -1)$	-2
B	$(-1, 0)$	$-\frac{1}{2}$
C	$(0, 1)$	$\frac{1}{2}$
D	$(1, \infty)$	2

$x = -2$: $\frac{(-2+1)(-2-1)}{-2} < 0$ True

$x = -\frac{1}{2}$: $\frac{\left(-\frac{1}{2}+1\right)\left(-\frac{1}{2}-1\right)}{-\frac{1}{2}} < 0$ False

$x = \frac{1}{2}$: $\frac{\left(\frac{1}{2}+1\right)\left(\frac{1}{2}-1\right)}{\frac{1}{2}} < 0$ True

$x=2$: $\quad \frac{(2+1)(2-1)}{2}<0 \quad$ False

The solution is $(-\infty,-1)\cup(0,\ 1)$.

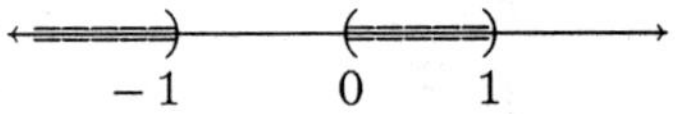

55. $P(x)=-2x^2+26x-44$

$-2x^2+26x-44>0$

$-2(x^2-13x+22)>0$

$-2(x-11)(x-2)>0$

$x-11=0$ or $x-2=0$

$x=11$ or $x=2$

Region	Interval	Test Point
A	$(-\infty,\ 2)$	0
B	$(2,\ 11)$	3
C	$(11,\ \infty)$	12

$x=0$: $\quad -2(0-11)(0-2)>0 \quad$ False

$x=3$: $\quad -2(3-11)(3-2)>0 \quad$ True

$x=12$: $\quad -2(12-11)(12-2)>0 \quad$ False

The solution is $(2,\ 11)$.

57. $f(x)=3x+1$

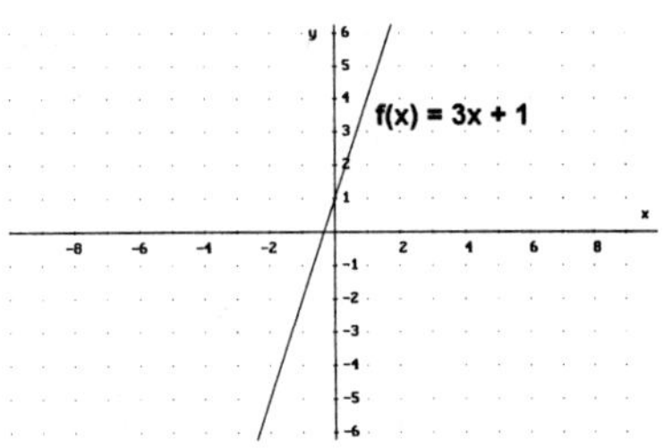

59. $f(x)=-2x+3$

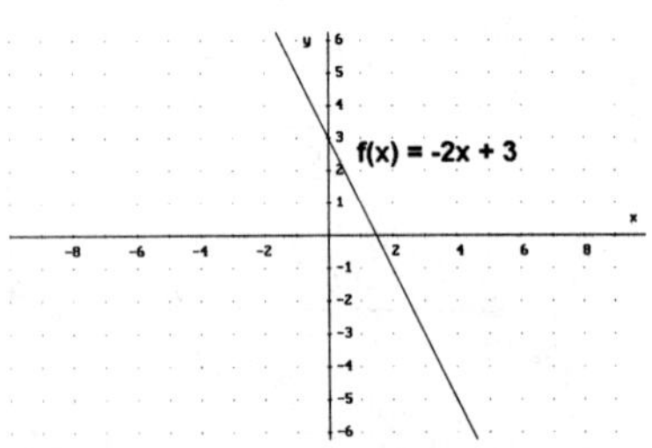

61. $g(x)=|x|+2$

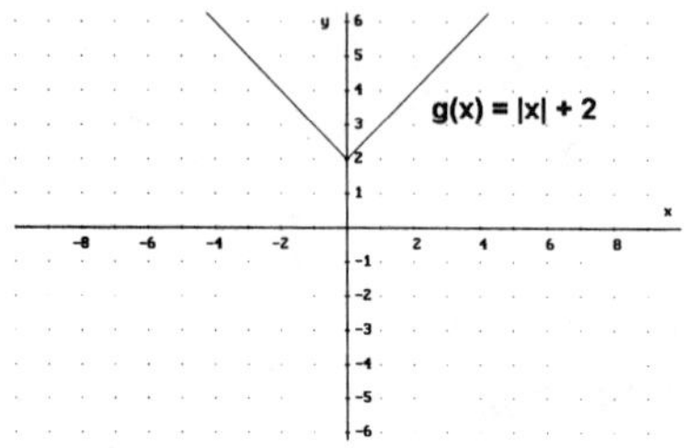

63. $F(x)=|x|-1$

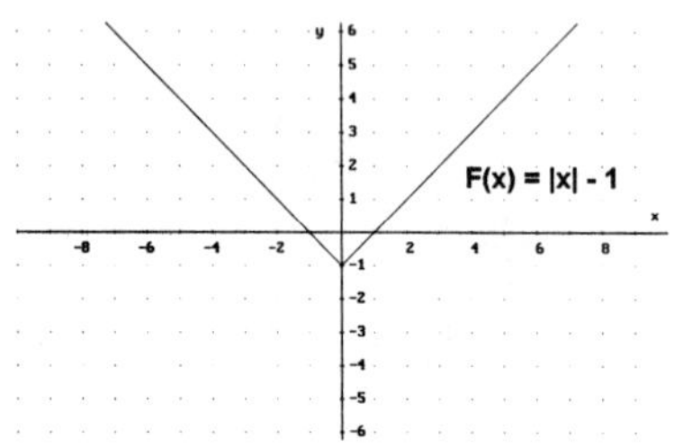

65. $F(x)=x^2-3$

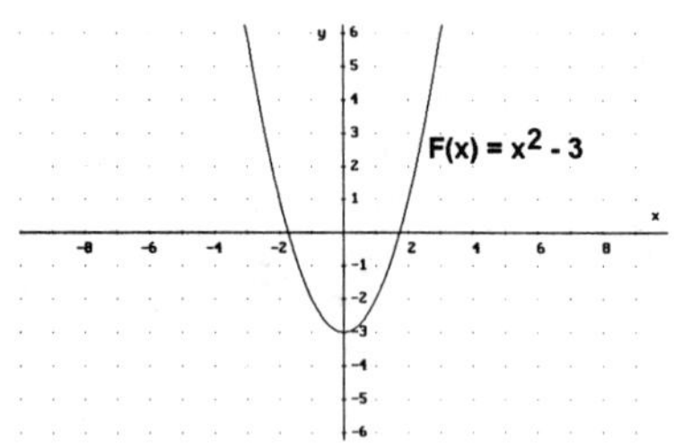

67. $H(x)=x^2+1$

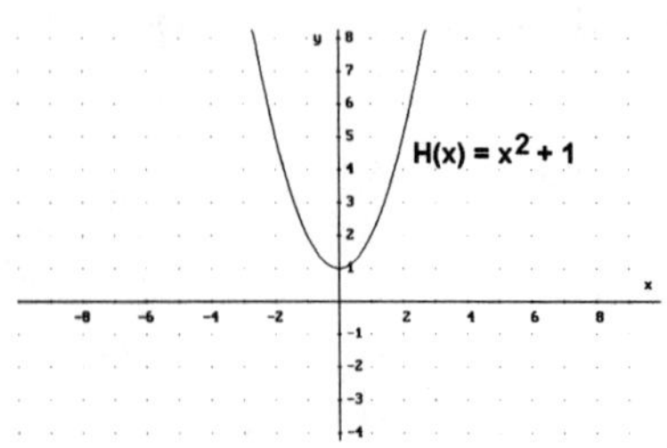

Graphing Calculator Exercise 9.5

1. $F(x)=\sqrt{x};\ G(x)=\sqrt{x}+1$

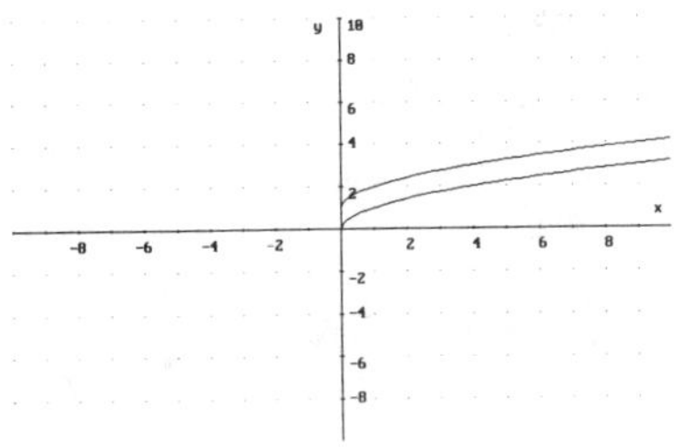

3. $H(x)=|x|;\ f(x)=|x-5|$

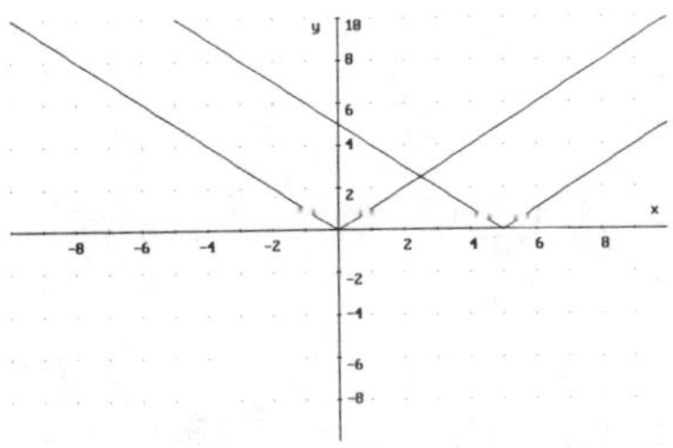

5. $f(x)=|x+4|;\ F(x)=|x+4|+3$

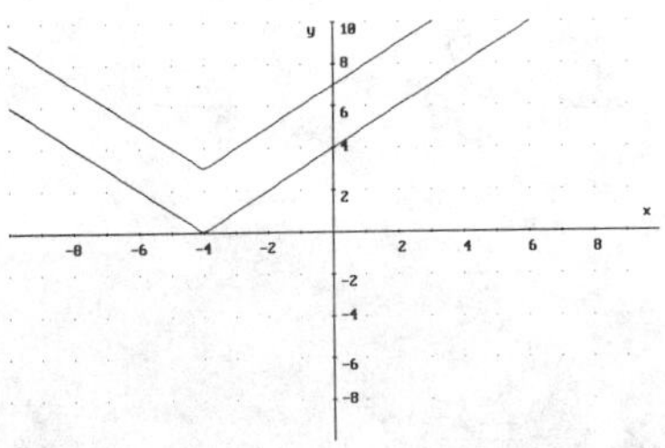

Exercise Set 9.5

1. $f(x)=x^2-1$

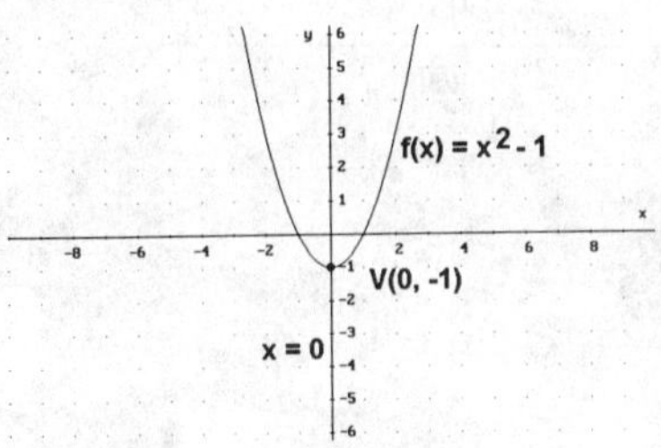

3. $h(x)=x^2+5$

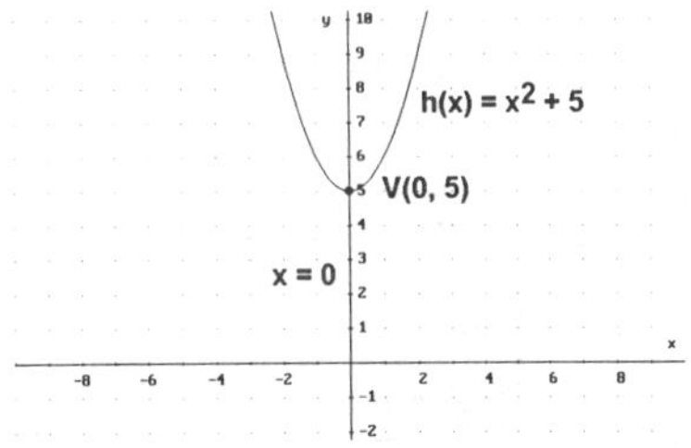

5. $g(x)=x^2+7$

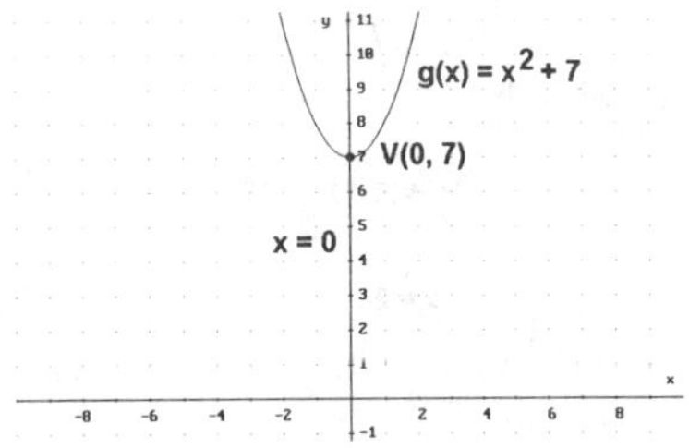

7. $f(x)=(x-5)^2$

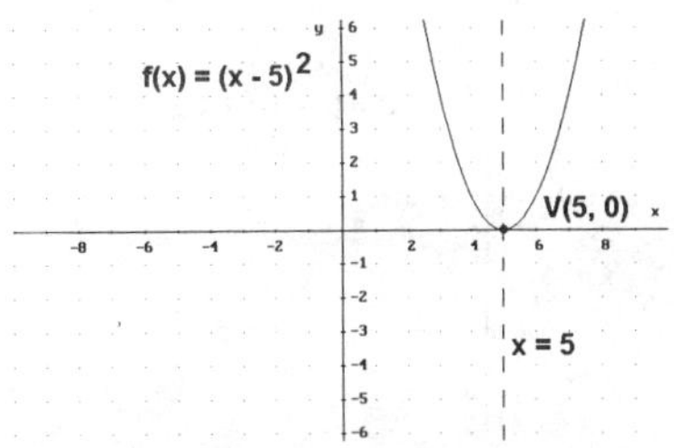

9. $h(x)=(x+2)^2$

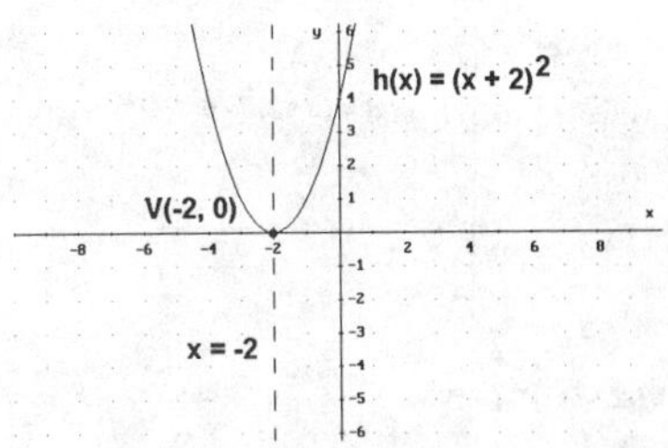

11. $G(x) = (x+3)^2$

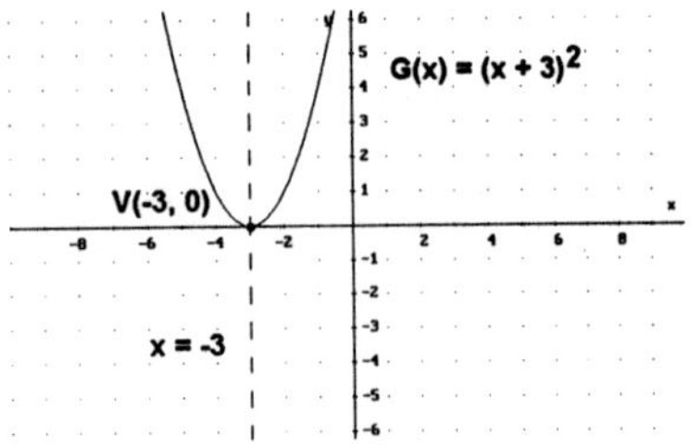

19. $g(x) = -x^2$

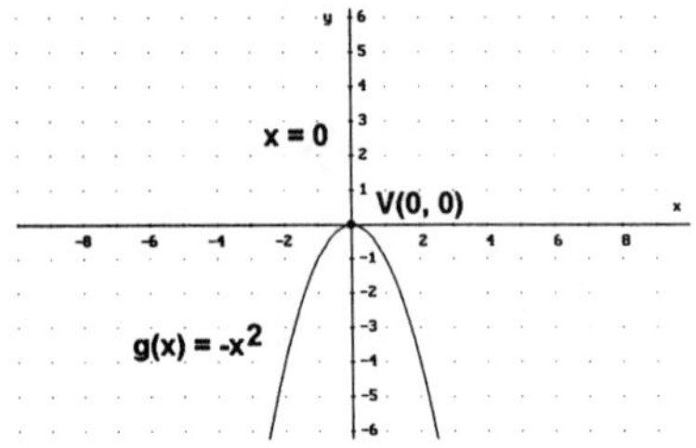

13. $f(x) = (x-2)^2 + 5$

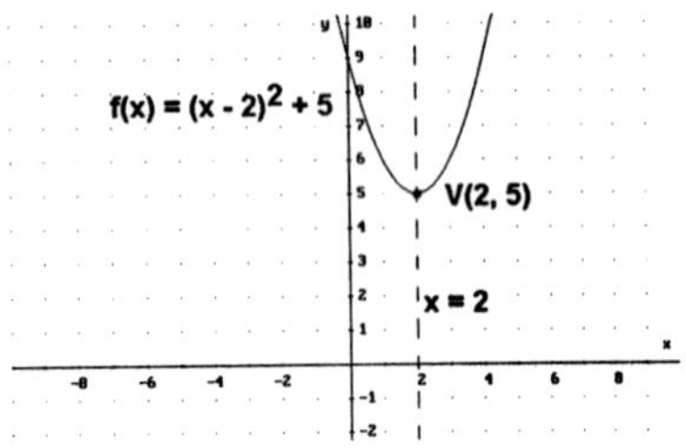

21. $h(x) = \frac{1}{3}x^2$

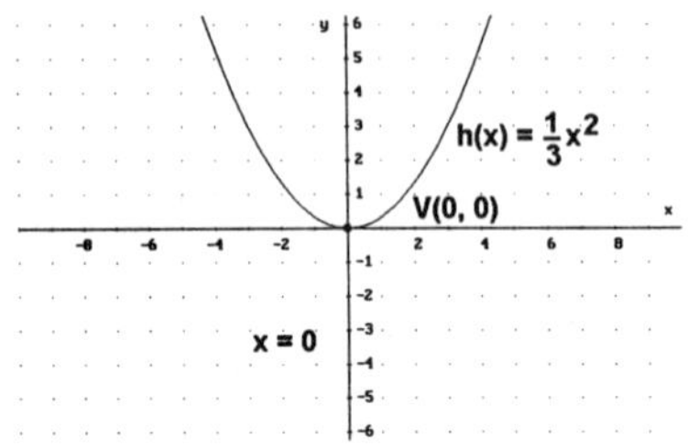

15. $h(x) = (x+1)^2 + 4$

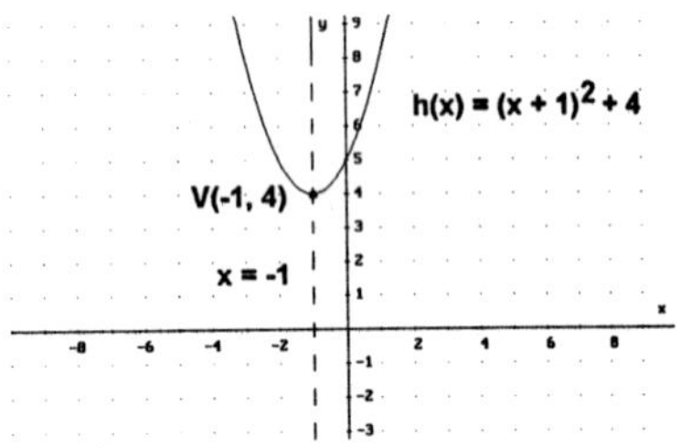

23. $H(x) = 2x^2$

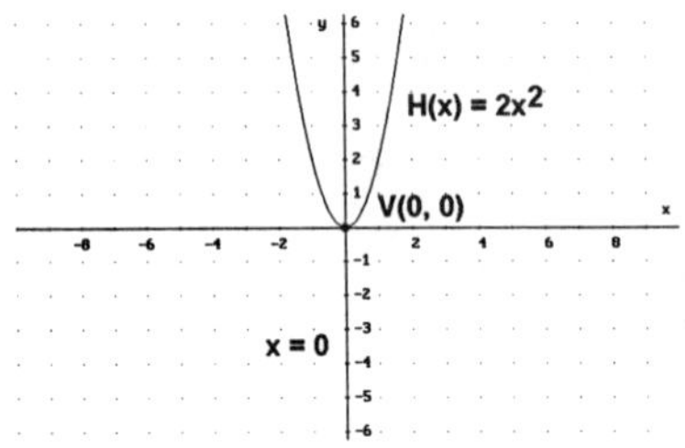

17. $g(x) = (x+2)^2 - 5$

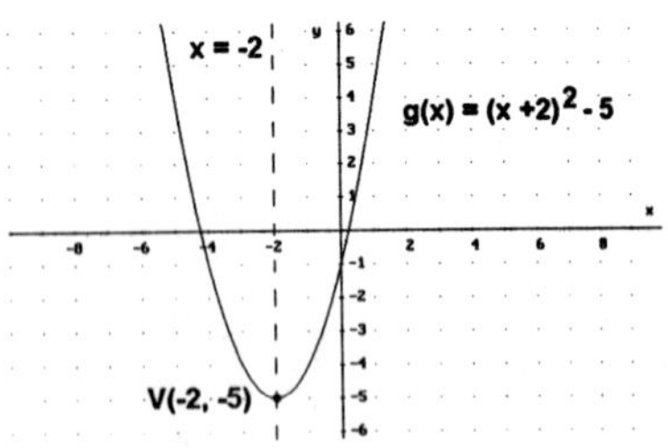

25. $f(x) = 2(x-1)^2 + 3$

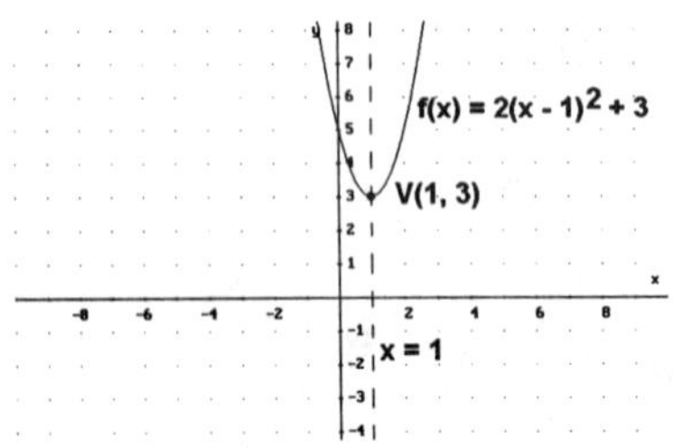

27. $h(x) = -3(x+3)^2+1$

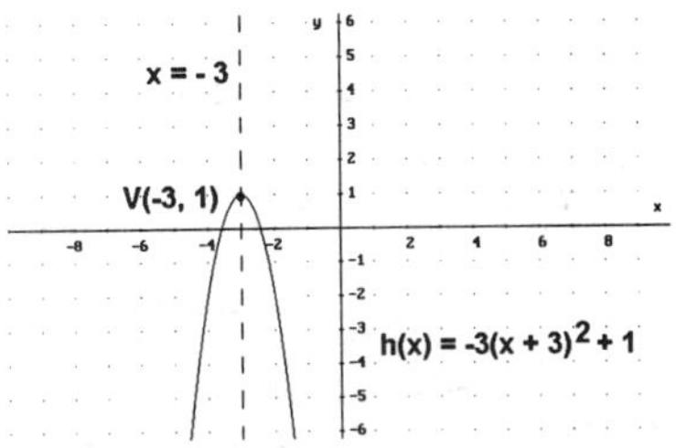

29. $H(x) = \frac{1}{2}(x-6)^2-3$

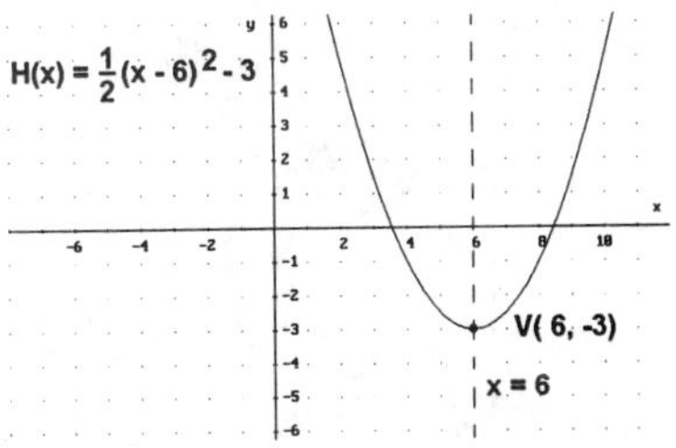

31. $f(x) = -(x-2)^2$

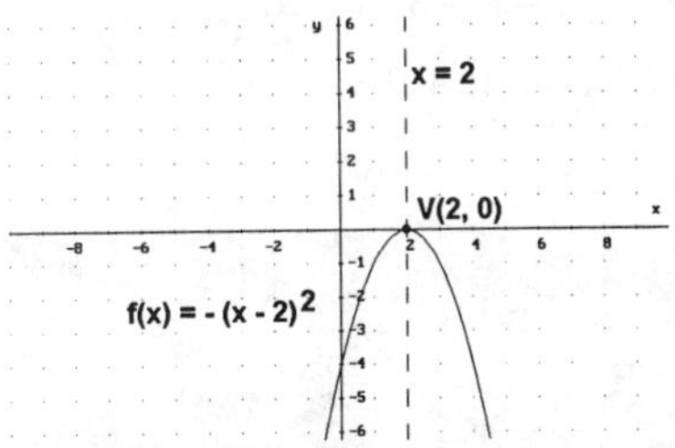

33. $F(x) = -x^2+4$

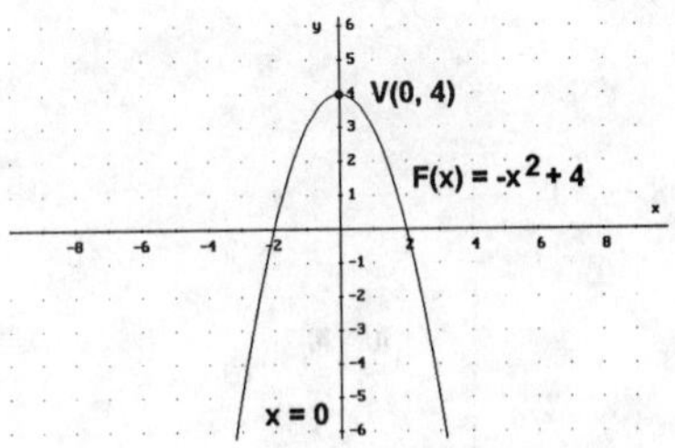

35. $F(x) = 2x^2-5$

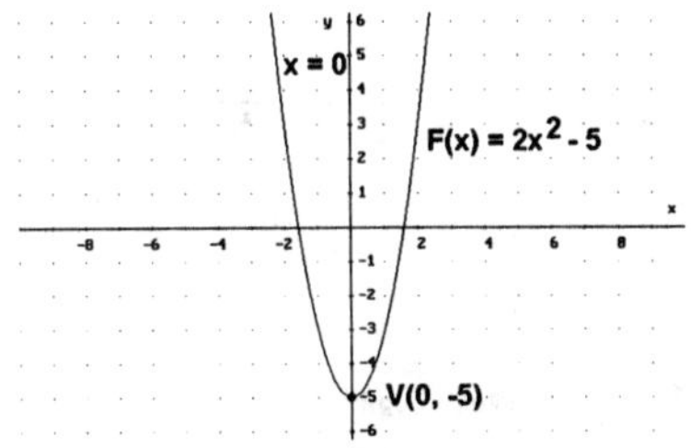

37. $h(x) = (x-6)^2+4$

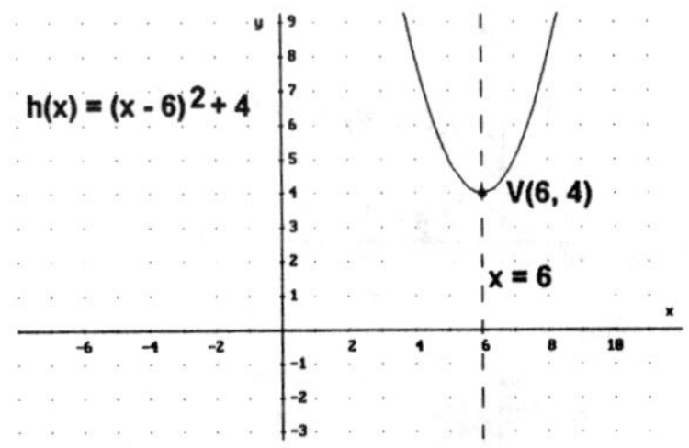

39. $F(x) = \left(x+\frac{1}{2}\right)^2-2$

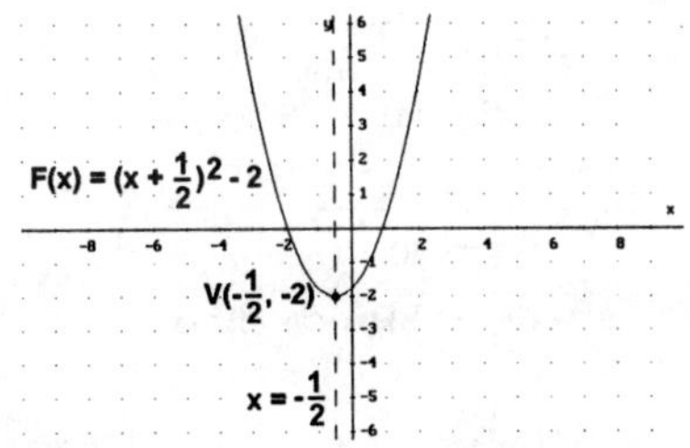

41. $F(x) = \frac{3}{2}(x+7)^2+1$

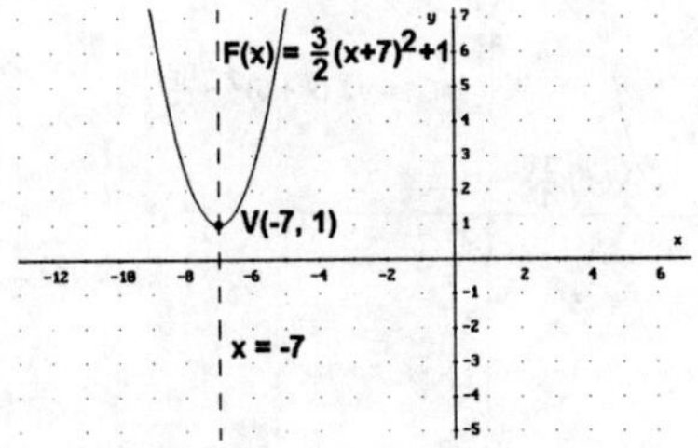

43. $f(x) = \frac{1}{4}x^2 - 9$

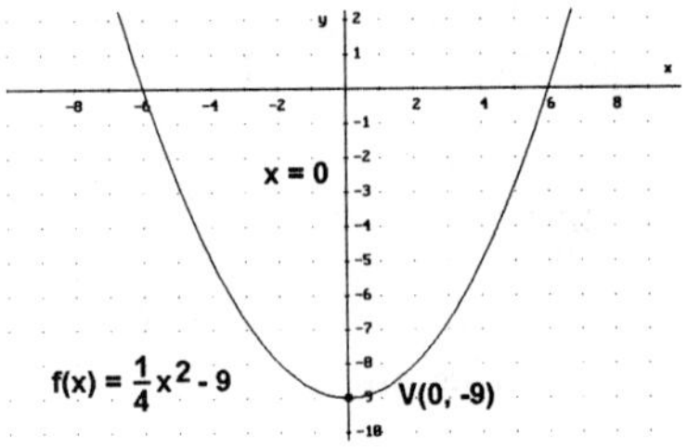

45. $G(x) = 5\left(x + \frac{1}{2}\right)^2$

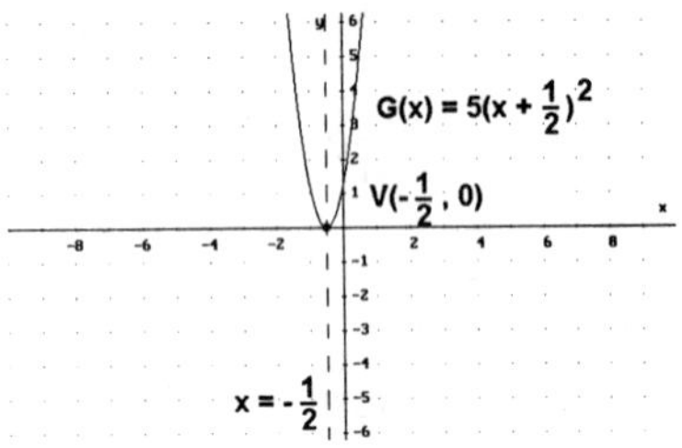

47. $f(x) = -(x-1)^2 - 1$

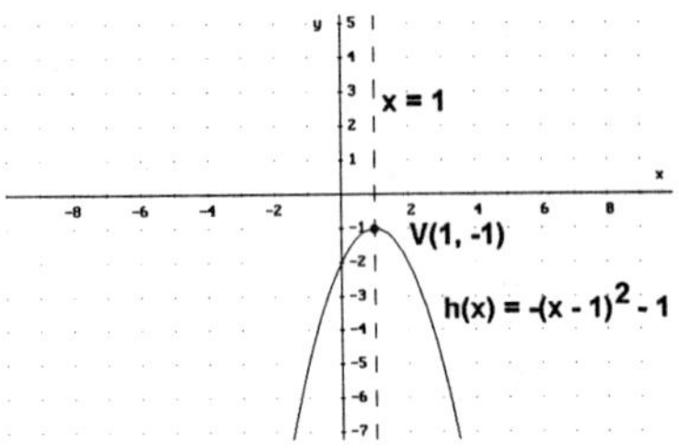

49. $g(x) = \sqrt{3}(x+5)^2 + \frac{3}{4}$

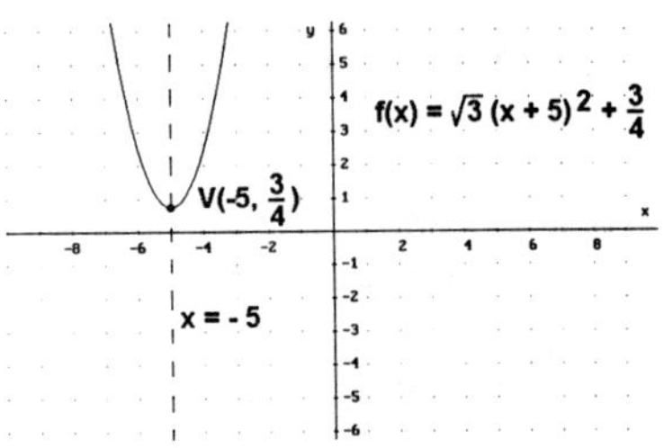

51. $h(x) = 10(x+4)^2 - 6$

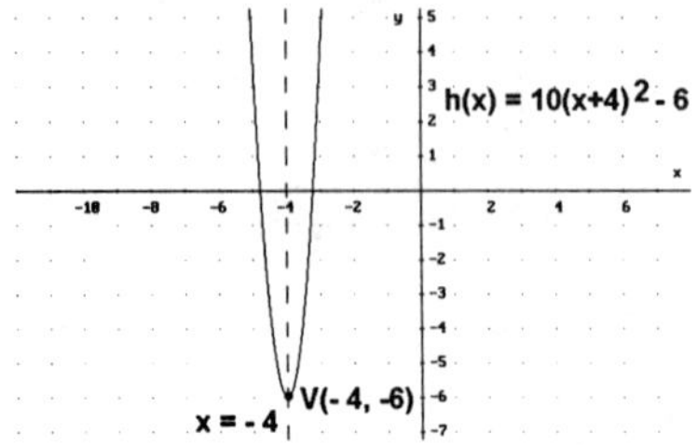

53. $f(x) = -2(x-4)^2 + 5$

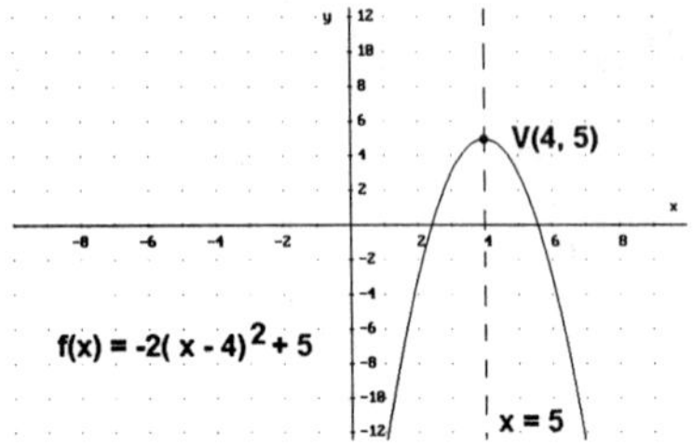

55. $f(x) = 5(x-2)^2 + 5$

57. $f(x) = 5[(x-(-3)]^2 + 6$

$f(x) = 5(x+3)^2 + 6$

59. $y = f(x) + 1$

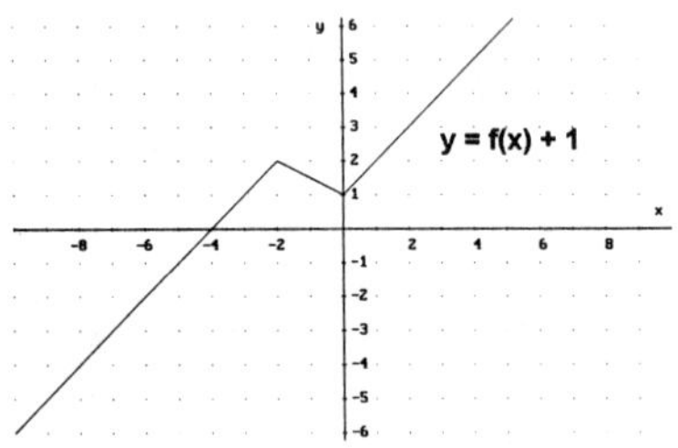

61. $y = f(x-3)$

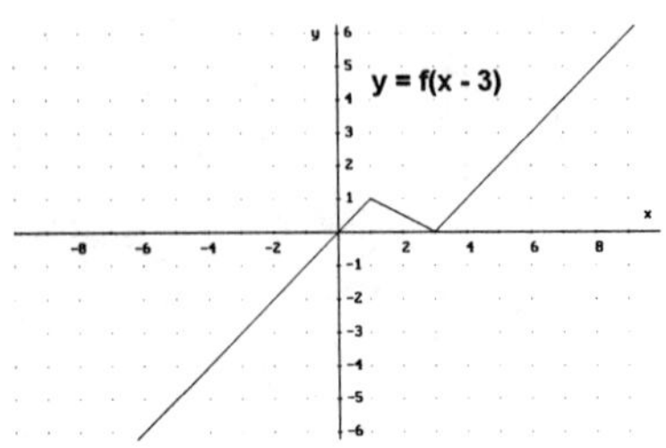

63. $y = f(x+2)+2$

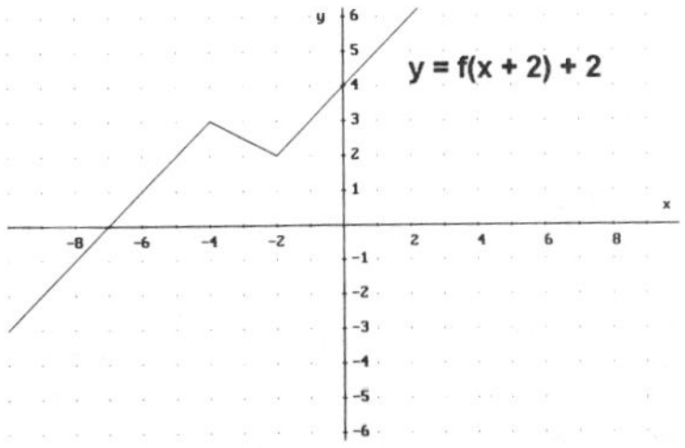

65. $x^2 + 8x$

$\left[\frac{1}{2}(8)\right]^2$

$[4]^2$

16

$x^2 + 8x + 16$

67. $z^2 - 16z$

$\left[\frac{1}{2}(-16)\right]^2$

$[-8]^2$

64

$z^2 - 16z + 64$

69. $y^2 + y$

$\left[\frac{1}{2}(1)\right]^2$

$\left[\frac{1}{2}\right]^2$

$\frac{1}{4}$

$y^2 + y + \frac{1}{4}$

71. $x^2 + 4x = 12$

$x^2 + 4x + 4 = 12 + 4$

$(x+2)^2 = 16$

$x + 2 = \pm\sqrt{16}$

$x + 2 = \pm 4$

$x = -2 \pm 4$

$x = -2 + 4$ or $x = -2 - 4$

$x = 2$ or $x = -6$

$\{-6, 2\}$

73. $z^2 + 10z - 1 = 0$

$z^2 + 10z = 1$

$z^2 + 10z + 25 = 1 + 25$

$(z+5)^2 = 26$

$z + 5 = \pm\sqrt{26}$

$z = -5 \pm \sqrt{26}$

$z = -5 + \sqrt{26}$ or $z = -5 - \sqrt{26}$

$\{-5 - \sqrt{26}, -5 + \sqrt{26}\}$

75. $z^2 - 8z = 2$

$z^2 - 8z + 16 = 2 + 16$

$(z-4)^2 = 18$

$z - 4 = \pm\sqrt{18}$

$z - 4 = \pm 3\sqrt{2}$

$z = 4 \pm 3\sqrt{2}$

$z = 4 + 3\sqrt{2}$ or $z = 4 - 3\sqrt{2}$

$\{4 - 3\sqrt{2}, 4 + 3\sqrt{2}\}$

Exercise Set 9.6

1. $f(x) = x^2 + 8x + 7$

$\frac{-b}{2a} = \frac{-8}{2(1)} = -4$ and

$f(-4) = (-4)^2 + 8(-4) + 7$

$f(-4) = 16 - 32 + 7 = -9$

Thus, $V(-4, -9)$.

3. $f(x) = -x^2 + 10x + 5$

$\frac{-b}{2a} = \frac{-10}{2(-1)} = 5$ and

$f(5) = -5^2 + 10(5) + 5$

$f(5) = -25 + 50 + 5 = 30$

Thus, $V(5, 30)$.

5. $f(x) = 5x^2 - 10x + 3$

$\frac{-b}{2a} = \frac{-(-10)}{2(5)} = 1$ and

$f(1) = 5(1)^2 - 10(1) + 3$

$f(1) = 5 - 10 + 3 = -2$

Thus, $V(1, -2)$.

7. $f(x) = -x^2 + x + 1$

$\frac{-b}{2a} = \frac{-1}{2(-1)} = \frac{1}{2}$ and

$f\left(\frac{1}{2}\right) = -\left(\frac{1}{2}\right)^2 + \frac{1}{2} + 1$

$f\left(\frac{1}{2}\right) = -\frac{1}{4} + \frac{1}{2} + 1 = \frac{5}{4}$

Thus, $V\left(\frac{1}{2}, \frac{5}{4}\right)$.

9. $f(x) = x^2 + 4x - 5$

$\frac{-b}{2a} = \frac{-4}{2(1)} = -2$ and

$f(-2) = (-2)^2 + 4(-2) - 5$

$f(-2) = 4 - 8 - 5 = -9$

Thus, $V(-2, -9)$.

The graph opens upward since $a = 1 > 0$.

$x^2 + 4x - 5 = 0$

$(x+5)(x-1) = 0$

$x + 5 = 0$ or $x - 1 = 0$

$x = -5$ or $x = 1$

The x-intercepts are -5 and 1.

$f(0) = -5$ is the y-intercept.

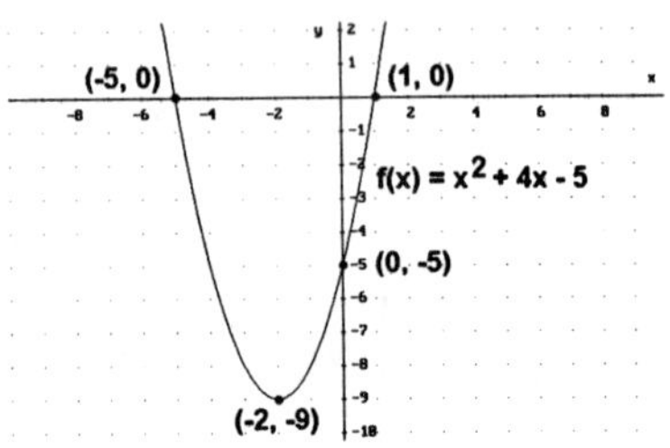

11. $f(x) = -x^2 + 2x - 1$

$\frac{-b}{2a} = \frac{-2}{2(-1)} = 1$ and

$f(1) = -1^2 + 2(1) - 1$

$f(1) = -1 + 2 - 1 = 0$

Thus, $V(1, 0)$.

The graph opens down since $a = -1 < 0$.

$-x^2 + 2x - 1 = 0$

$-(x^2 - 2x + 1) = 0$

$-(x-1)^2 = 0$

$x = 1$

The x-intercept is 1.

$f(0) = -1$ is the y-intercept.

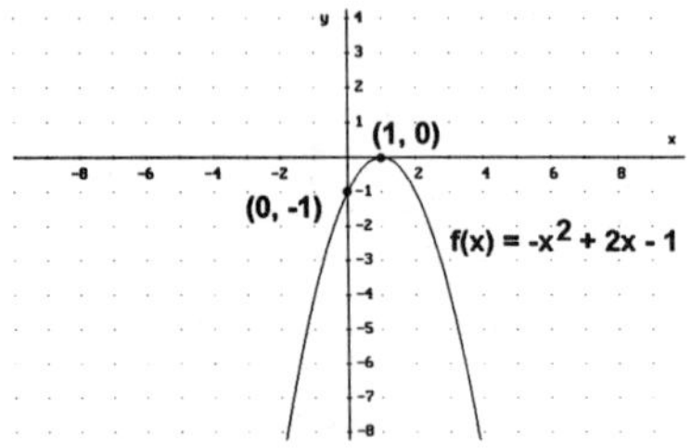

13. $f(x) = x^2 - 4$

$\frac{-b}{2a} = \frac{-0}{2(1)} = 0$ and $f(0) = -4$

Thus, $V(0, -4)$.

The graph opens upward since $a = 1 > 0$.

$x^2 - 4 = 0$

$(x+2)(x-2) = 0$

$x + 2 = 0$ or $x - 2 = 0$

$x = -2$ or $x = 2$

The x-intercepts are -2 and 2.

$f(0) = -4$ is the y-intercept.

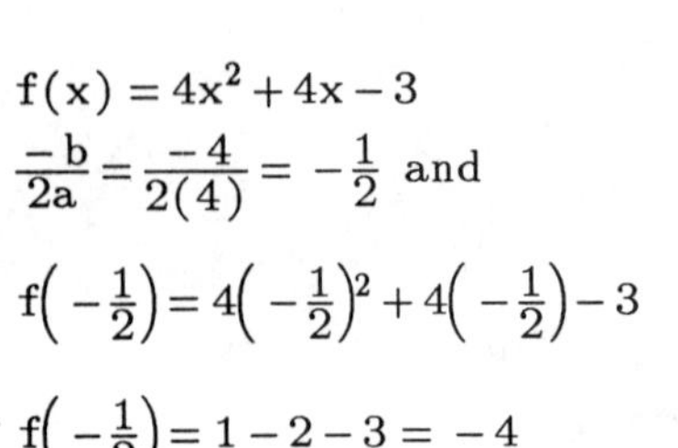

15. $f(x) = 4x^2 + 4x - 3$

$\frac{-b}{2a} = \frac{-4}{2(4)} = -\frac{1}{2}$ and

$f\left(-\frac{1}{2}\right) = 4\left(-\frac{1}{2}\right)^2 + 4\left(-\frac{1}{2}\right) - 3$

$f\left(-\frac{1}{2}\right) = 1 - 2 - 3 = -4$

Thus, $V\left(-\frac{1}{2}, -4\right)$.

The graph opens upward since $a=4>0$.

$4x^2+4x-3=0$

$(2x-1)(2x+3)=0$

$2x-1=0$ or $2x+3=0$

$2x=1$ or $2x=-3$

$x=\frac{1}{2}$ or $x=-\frac{3}{2}$

The x intercepts are $\frac{1}{2}$ and $-\frac{3}{2}$.

$f(0)=-3$ is the y-intercept.

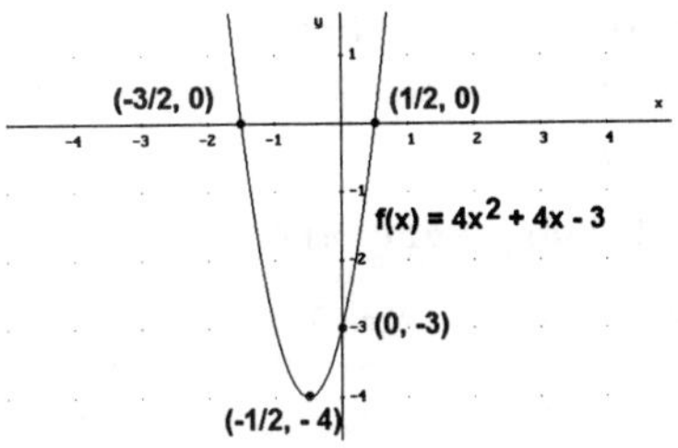

17. Let $x=$ one number.
$60-x=$ other number.

$f(x)=x(60-x)$

$f(x)=60x-x^2$

$f(x)=-x^2+60x$

$f(x)=-1(x^2-60x)$

$f(x)=-1(x^2-60x+900)+900$

$f(x)=-1(x-30)^2+900$

The maximum will occur at the vertex which is (30, 900).

The numbers are 30 and 30.

19. $f(x)=x^2+8x+15$

$f(x)=x^2+8x+\left(\frac{8}{2}\right)^2+15-16$

$f(x)=(x+4)^2-1$

Thus, $V(-4,-1)$.

The graph opens upward since $a=1>0$.

$x^2+8x+15=0$

$(x+3)(x+5)=0$

$x+3=0$ or $x+5=0$

$x=-3$ or $x=-5$

The x-intercepts are -3 and -5.

$f(0)=15$ is the y-intercept.

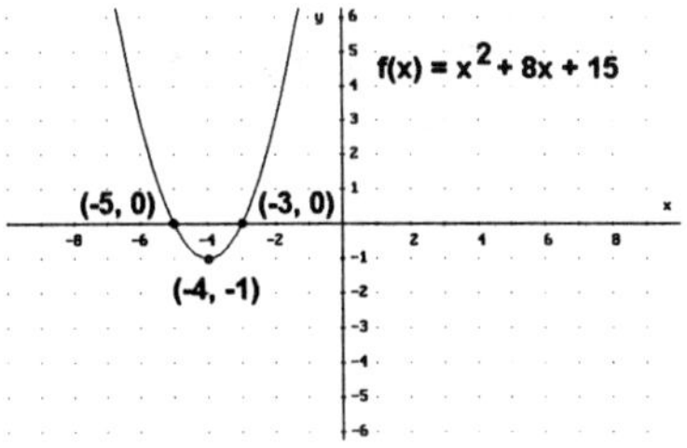

21. $f(x)=x^2-6x+5$

$f(x)=x^2-6x+\left(\frac{6}{2}\right)^2+5-9$

$f(x)=(x-3)^2-4$

Thus, $V(3,-4)$.

The graph open upward since $a=1>0$.

$x^2-6x+5=0$

$(x-1)(x-5)=0$

$x-1=0$ or $x-5=0$

$x=1$ or $x=5$

The x-intercepts are 1 and 5.

$f(0)=5$ is the y-intercept.

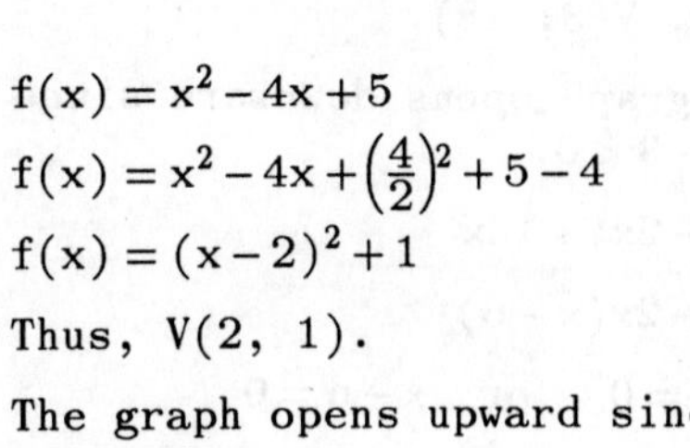

23. $f(x)=x^2-4x+5$

$f(x)=x^2-4x+\left(\frac{4}{2}\right)^2+5-4$

$f(x)=(x-2)^2+1$

Thus, $V(2,\ 1)$.

The graph opens upward since $a=1>0$.

$(x-2)^2+1=0$

$(x-2)^2=-1$

Hence, there are no x-intercepts.
$f(0)=5$ is the y-intercept.

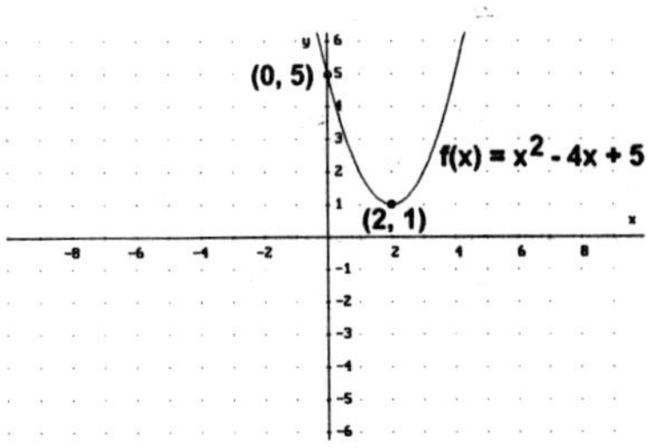

25. $f(x)=2x^2+4x+5$

$f(x)=2(x^2+2x)+5$

$f(x)=2\left[x^2+2x+\left(\frac{2}{2}\right)^2\right]+5-2$

$f(x)=2(x+1)^2+3$

Thus, $V(-1,\ 3)$.

The graph opens upward since $a=2>0$.

$f(0)=2(0+1)^2+3=5$ is the y-intercept.

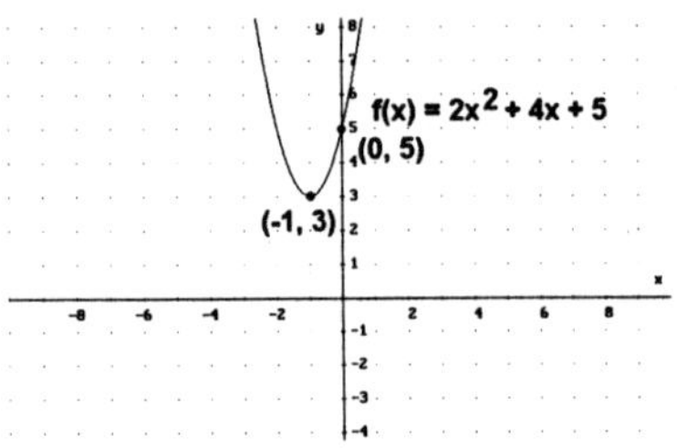

27. $f(x)=-2x^2+12x$

$f(x)=-2(x^2-6x)$

$f(x)=-2\left[x^2-6x+\left(\frac{6}{2}\right)^2\right]+18$

$f(x)=-2(x-3)^2+18$

Thus, $V(3,\ 18)$.

The graph opens downward since $a=-3<0$.

$0=-2x^2+12x$

$0=-2x(x-6)$

$-2x=0$ or $x-6=0$

$x=0$ or $x=6$

The x-intercepts are 0 and 6.

$f(0)=0$ is the y-intercept.

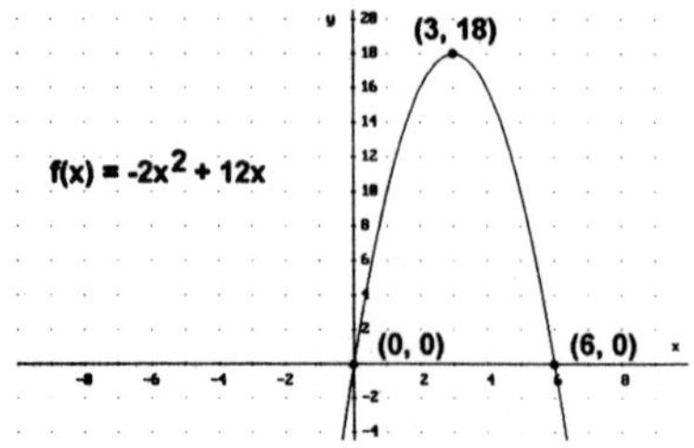

29. $f(x)=x^2+1$

$\frac{-b}{2a}=\frac{-0}{2(1)}=0$ and $f(0)=1$.

Thus $V(0,\ 1)$.

The graph opens upward since $a=1>0$.

$x^2+1=0$

$x^2=-1$, so there are no x-intercepts.

$f(0)=1$ is the y-intercept.

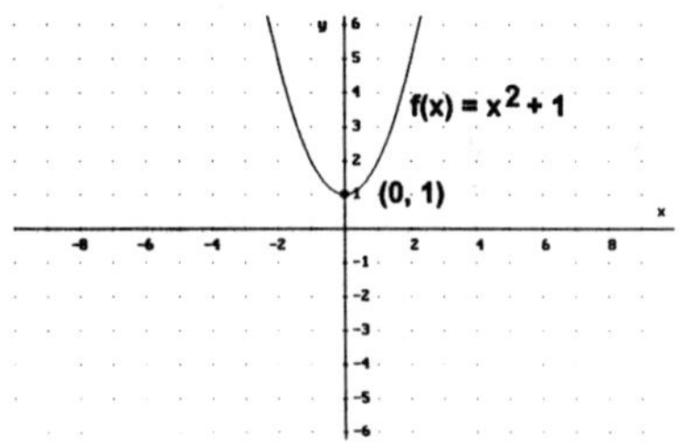

31. $f(x)=x^2-2x-15$

$\frac{-b}{2a}=\frac{-(-2)}{2(1)}=1$ and

$f(1)=1^2-2(1)-15$

$f(1)=1-2-15=-16$

Thus, $V(1,-16)$.

The graph opens upward since $a=1>0$.

$x^2-2x-15=0$

$(x-5)(x+3)=0$

$x-5=0$ or $x+3=0$

$x=5$ or $x=-3$

The x-intercepts are 5 and -3.

$f(0)=-15$ is the y-intercept.

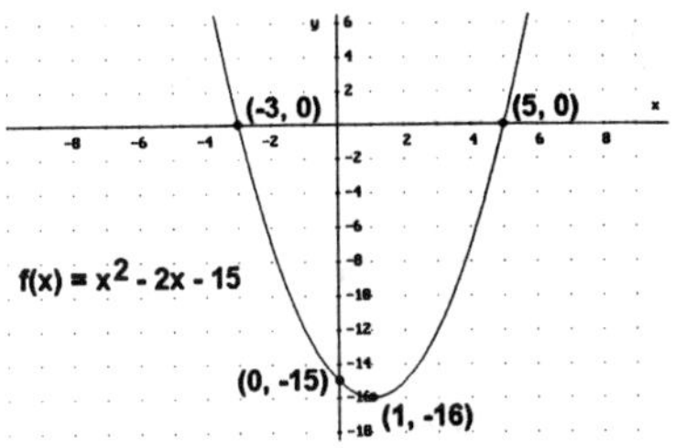

33. $f(x) = -5x^2 + 5x$

$\frac{-b}{2a} = \frac{-5}{2(-5)} = \frac{1}{2}$ and

$f\left(\frac{1}{2}\right) = -5\left(\frac{1}{2}\right)^2 + 5\left(\frac{1}{2}\right)$

$f\left(\frac{1}{2}\right) = -\frac{5}{4} + \frac{5}{2} = \frac{5}{4}$

Thus, $V\left(\frac{1}{2}, \frac{5}{4}\right)$.

The graph opens downward since $a = -5 < 0$.

$-5x^2 + 5x = 0$

$-5x(x-1) = 0$

$-5x = 0$ or $x - 1 = 0$

$x = 0$ or $x = 1$

The x-intercepts are 0 and 1.

$f(0) = 0$ is the y-intercept.

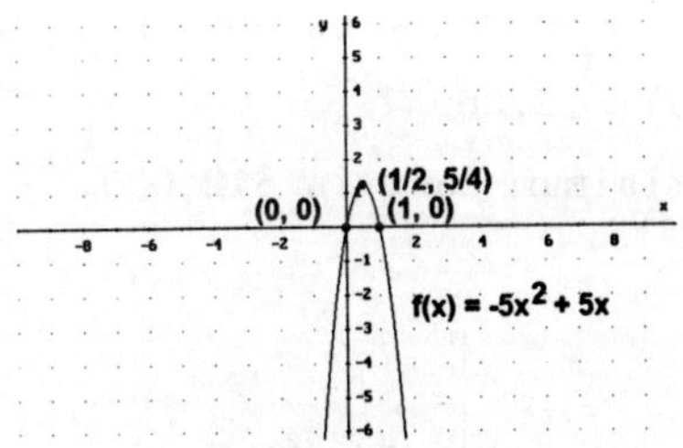

35. $f(x) = -x^2 + 2x - 12$

$\frac{-b}{2a} = \frac{-2}{2(-1)} = 1$ and

$f(1) = -1^2 + 2(1) - 12$

$f(1) = -1 + 2 - 12 = -11$

Thus, $V(1, -11)$.

The graph opens downward since $a = -1 < 0$.

$-x^2 + 2x - 12 = 0$

$x^2 - 2x = -12$

$x^2 - 2x + \left(\frac{2}{2}\right)^2 = -12 + 1$

$(x-1)^2 = -11$

so there are no x-intercepts.

$f(0) = -12$ is the y-intercept.

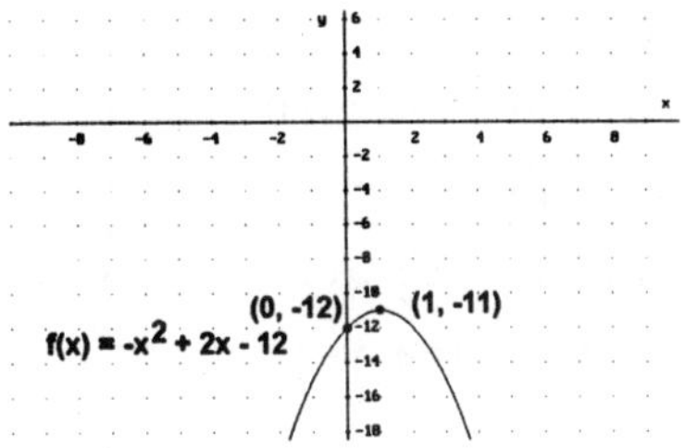

37. $f(x) = 3x^2 - 12x + 15$

$\frac{-b}{2a} = \frac{-(-12)}{2(3)} = 2$ and

$f(2) = 3(2)^2 - 12(2) + 15$

$f(2) = 12 - 24 + 15 = 3$

Thus, $V(2, 3)$.

The graph opens upward since $a = 3 > 0$.

$3x^2 - 12x + 15 = 0$

$x^2 - 4x + 5 = 0$

$x^2 - 4x + \left(\frac{4}{2}\right)^2 = -5 + 4$

$(x-2)^2 = -1$

so there are no x-intercepts.

$f(0) = 15$ is the y-intercept.

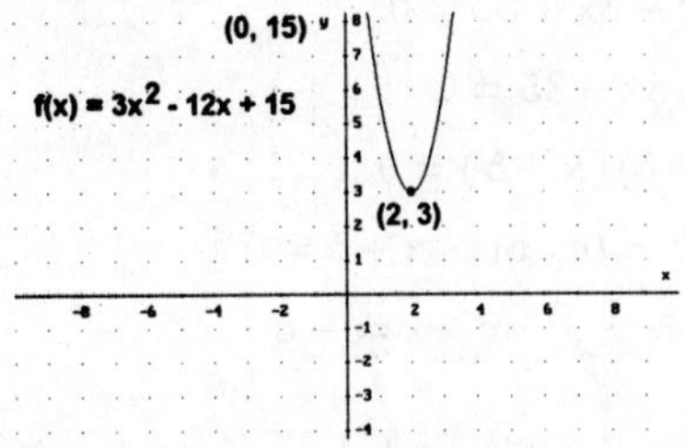

39. $f(x) = x^2 + x - 6$

$\frac{-b}{2a} = \frac{-1}{2(1)} = -\frac{1}{2}$ and

$f\left(-\frac{1}{2}\right) = \left(-\frac{1}{2}\right)^2 + \left(-\frac{1}{2}\right) - 6$

$f\left(-\frac{1}{2}\right)=\frac{1}{4}-\frac{1}{2}-6=-6\frac{1}{4}$

thus, $V\left(-\frac{1}{2},-6\frac{1}{4}\right)$.

The graph opens upward since $a=1>0$.

$x^2+x-6=0$

$(x+3)(x-2)=0$

$x+3=0$ or $x-2=0$

$x=-3$ or $x=2$

The x-intercepts are -3 and 2.

$f(0)=-6$ is the y-intercept.

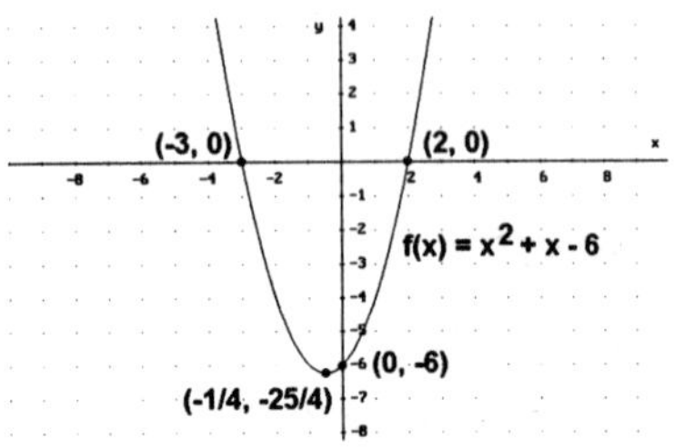

41. $f(x)=-2x^2-3x+35$

$\frac{-b}{2a}=\frac{-(-3)}{2(-2)}=-\frac{3}{4}$ and

$f\left(-\frac{3}{4}\right)=-2\left(-\frac{3}{4}\right)^2-3\left(-\frac{3}{4}\right)+35$

$f\left(-\frac{3}{4}\right)=-\frac{9}{8}+\frac{9}{4}+35=36\frac{1}{8}$

Thus, $V\left(-\frac{3}{4},\ 36\frac{1}{8}\right)$.

The graph opens downward since $a=-2<0$.

$-2x^2-3x+35=0$

$2x^2+3x-35=0$

$(2x-7)(x+5)=0$

$2x-7=0$ or $x+5=0$

$2x=7$ or $x=-5$

$x=\frac{7}{2}$

The x-intercepts are $\frac{7}{2}$ and -5.

$f(0)=35$ is the y-intercept.

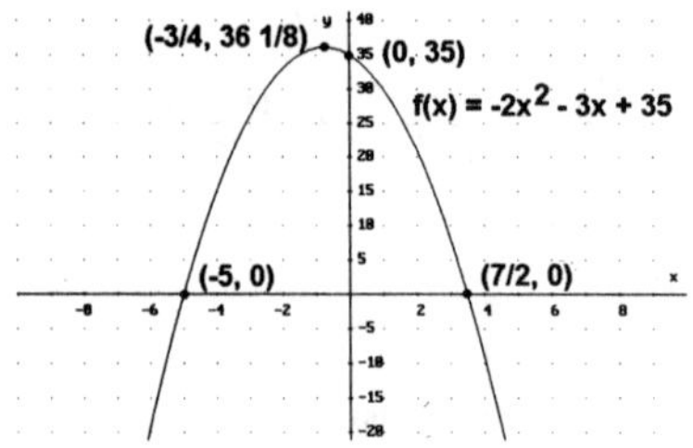

43. $h(t)=-16t^2+96t$

We seek the second coordinate of the vertex.

$\frac{-b}{2a}=\frac{-96}{2(-16)}=3$ and

$h(3)=-16(3)^2+96(3)$

$h(3)=-144+288=144$

The maximum height reached by the projectile is 144 ft.

45. $C(x)=2x^2-800x+92{,}000$

We seek the coordinates of the vertex.

a. $\frac{-b}{2a}=\frac{-(-800)}{2(2)}=200$

200 bicycles must be manufactured to minimize the cost.

b. $C(200)=2(200)^2-800(200)+92{,}000$

$C(200)=80{,}000-160{,}000+92{,}000$

$C(200)=12{,}000$

The minimum cost is $12,000.

47.

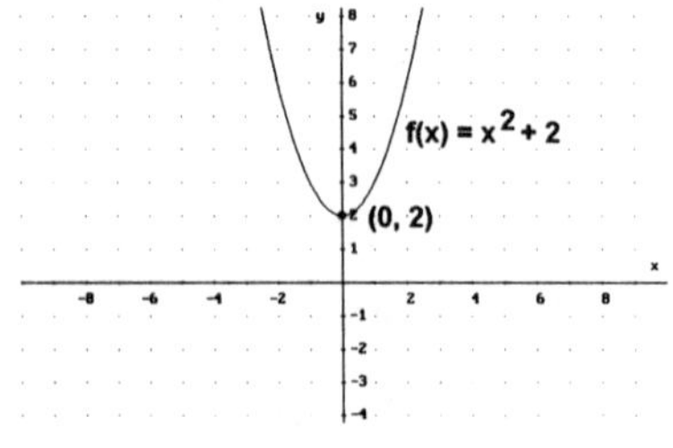

49.

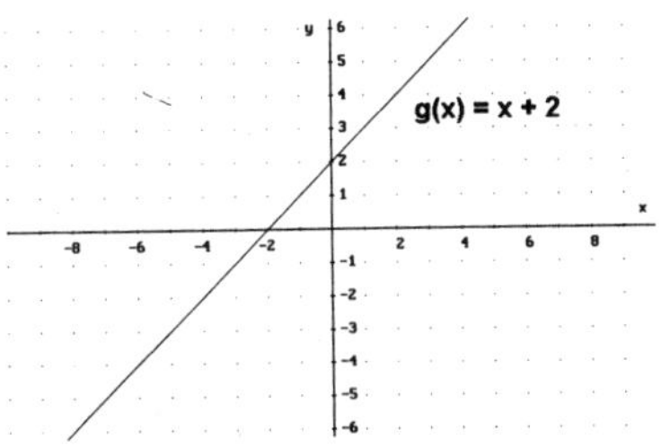

51.

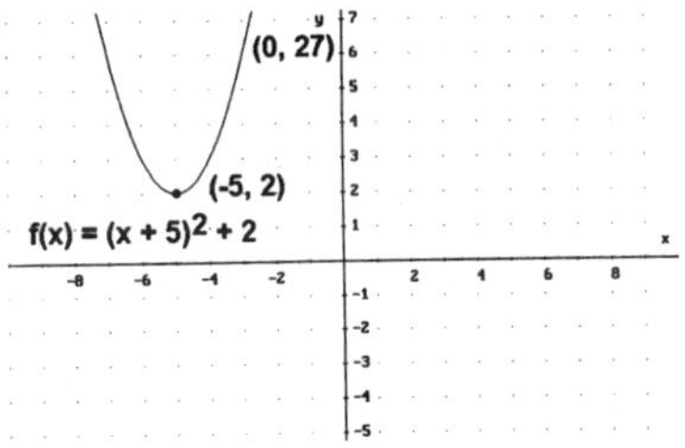

53.

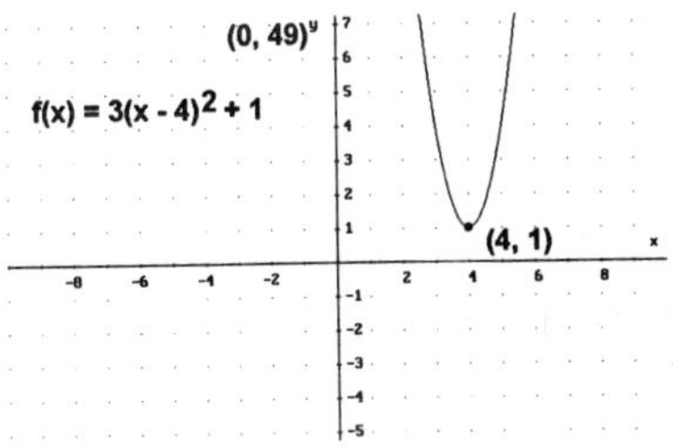

55.

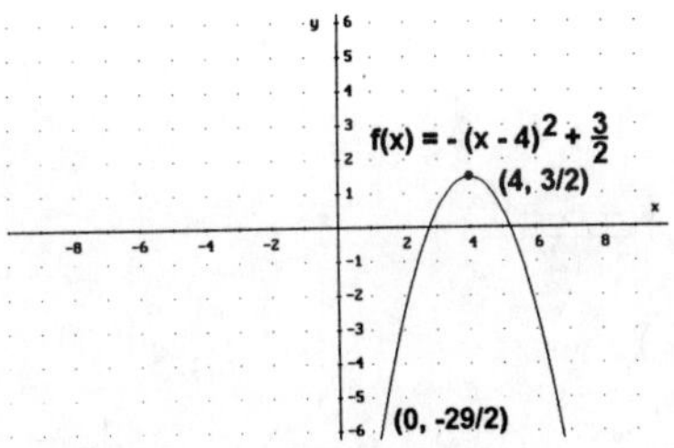

57. Not a function.

Graphing Calculator Exercise 9.7

1. $x^2 + y^2 = 55$

$y^2 = 55 - x^2$

$y = \pm\sqrt{55 - x^2}$

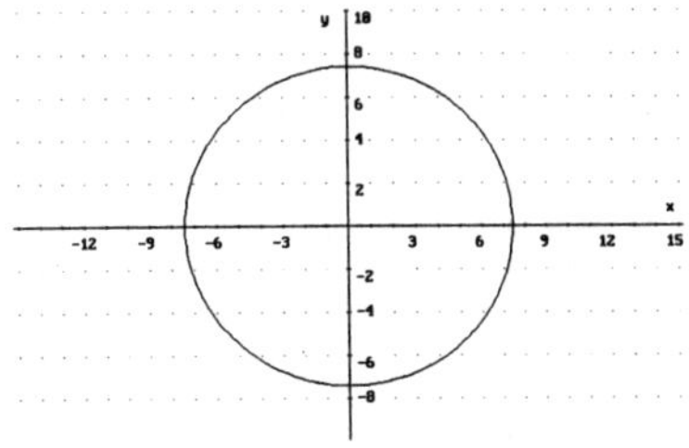

3. $7x^2 + 7y^2 - 89 = 0$

$7y^2 = 89 - 7x^2$

$y^2 = \dfrac{89 - 7x^2}{7}$

$y = \pm\sqrt{\dfrac{89 - 7x^2}{7}}$

$Y_1 = \sqrt{\dfrac{89 - 7x^2}{7}}$

$Y_2 = -\sqrt{\dfrac{89 - 7x^2}{7}}$

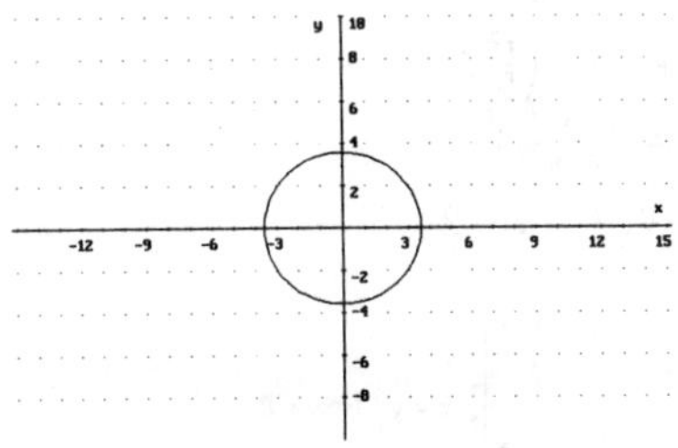

Exercise Set 9.7

1. $x = 3y^2$

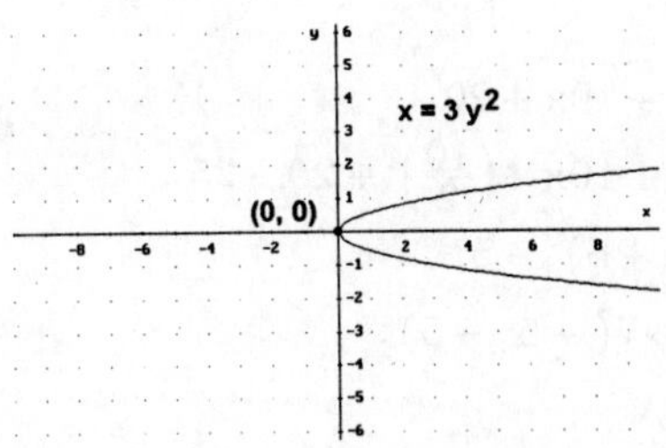

3. $x = (y-2)^2 + 3$

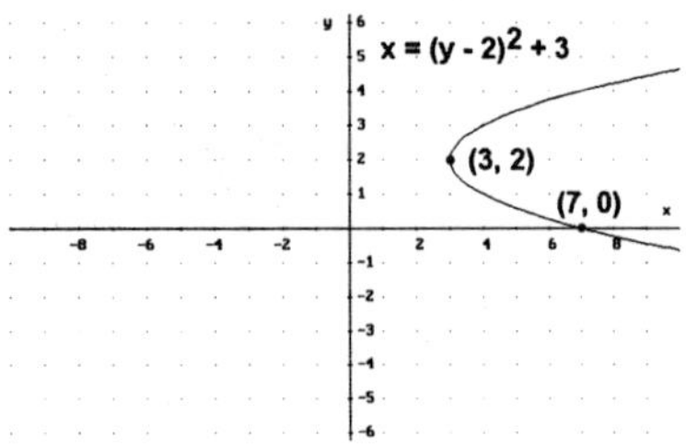

5. $y = 3(x-1)^2 + 5$

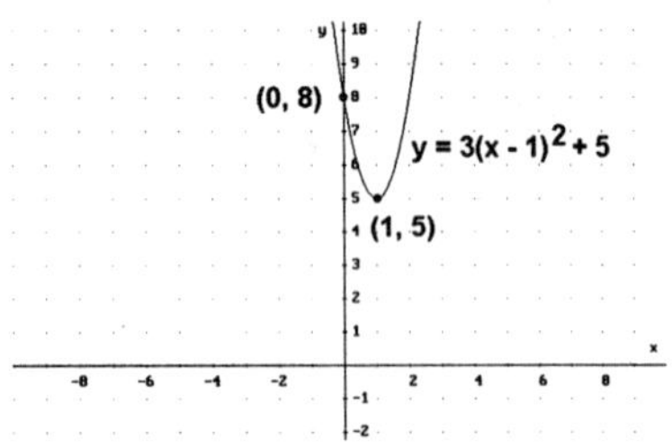

7. $x = y^2 + 6y + 8$

$x = y^2 + 6y + \left(\frac{6}{2}\right)^2 + 8 - 9$

$x = (y+3)^2 - 1$

Thus, $V(-1, -3)$.

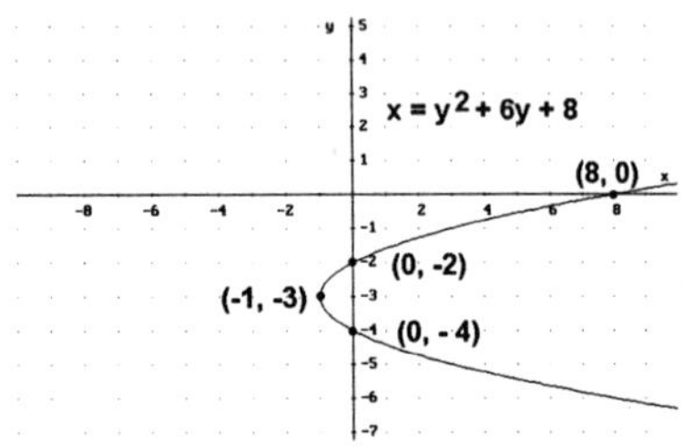

9. $y = x^2 + 10x + 20$

$y = x^2 + 10x + \left(\frac{10}{2}\right)^2 + 20 - 25$

$y = (x+5)^2 - 5$

Thus, $V(-5, -5)$.

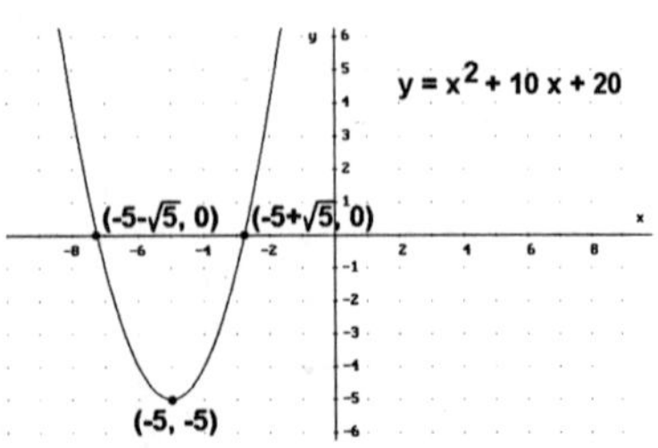

11. $x = -2y^2 + 4y + 6$

$x = -2(y^2 - 2y) + 6$

$x = -2\left[y^2 - 2y + \left(\frac{2}{2}\right)^2\right] + 6 + 2$

$x = -2(y-1)^2 + 8$

Thus, $V(8, 1)$.

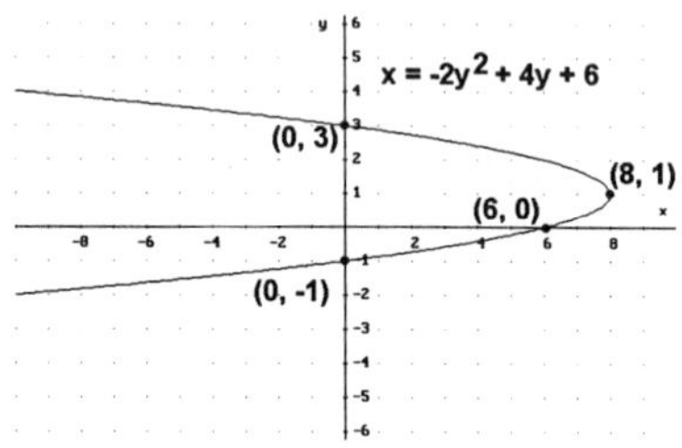

13. $(5, 1), (8, 5)$

$d = \sqrt{(8-5)^2 + (5-1)^2}$

$d = \sqrt{9+16}$

$d = \sqrt{25}$

$d = 5$

15. $(-3, 2), (1, -3)$

$d = \sqrt{[1-(-3)]^2 + (-3-2)^2}$

$d = \sqrt{16+25}$

$d = \sqrt{41}$

17. $(6, -8), (2, 4)$

$\left(\frac{6+2}{2}, \frac{-8+4}{2}\right)$

$(4, -2)$

19. $(-2, -1), (-8, 6)$

$\left(\frac{-2+(-8)}{2}, \frac{-1+6}{2}\right)$

$\left(-5, \frac{5}{2}\right)$

21. $x^2+y^2=9$

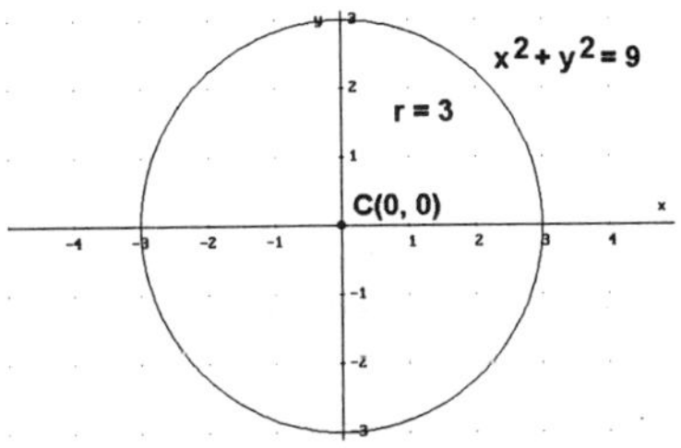

23. $x^2+(y-2)^2=1$

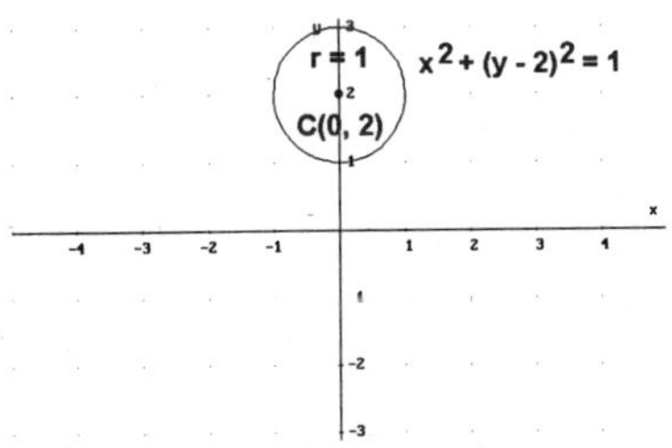

25. $(x-5)^2+(y+2)^2=1$
represents a circle of radius
$\sqrt{1}=1$ with center at $C(5,-2)$.

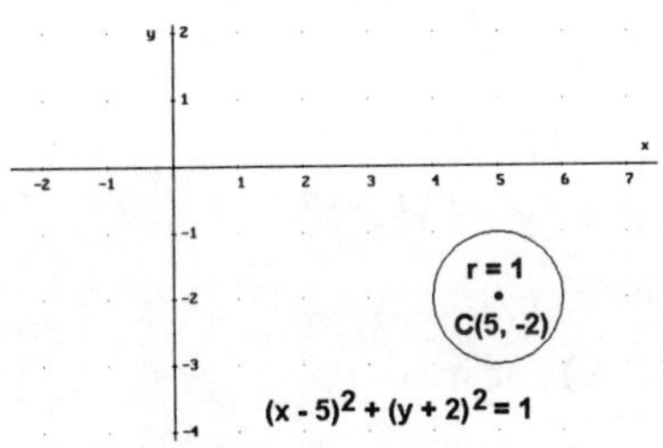

27. $C(2,\ 3);\ r=6$
$(x-2)^2+(y-3)^2=6^2$
$(x-2)^2+(y-3)^2=36$

29. $C(0,\ 0);\ r=2$
$(x-0)^2+(y-0)^2=2^2$
$x^2+y^2=4$

31. $C(-5,\ 4);\ r=\sqrt{5}$
$[x-(-5)]^2+(y-4)^2=(\sqrt{5})^2$
$(x+5)^2+(y-4)^2=5$

33. $x^2+y^2+6y=0$
$x^2+y^2+6y+\left(\frac{6}{2}\right)^2=9$
$(x-0)^2+(y+3)^2=3^2$
Thus, $C(0,-3)$ and $r=3$.

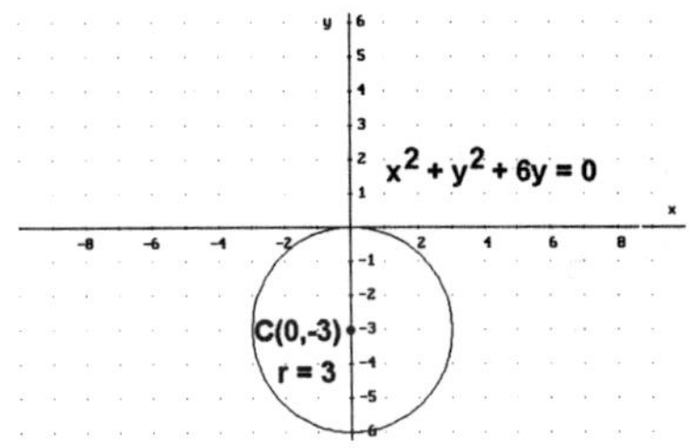

35. $x^2+y^2+2x-4y=4$
$x^2+2x+\left(\frac{2}{2}\right)^2+y^2-4y+\left(\frac{4}{2}\right)^2=4+1+4$
$(x+1)^2+(y-2)^2=9$
$(x+1)^2+(y-2)^2=3^2$
Thus, $C(-1,\ 2)$ and $r=3$.

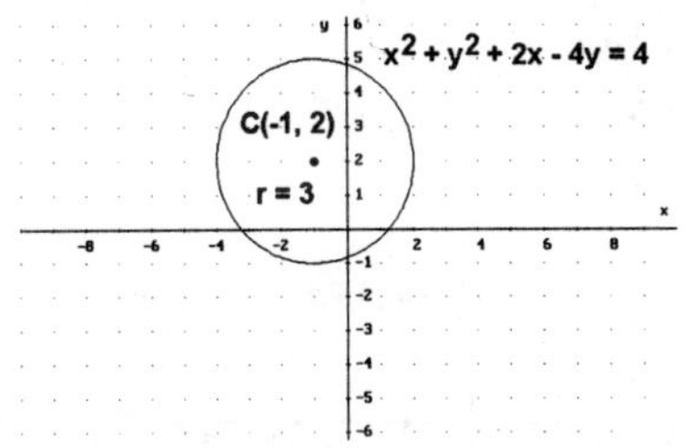

37. $(6,\ 3),\ (2,\ 4)$
$d=\sqrt{(6-2)^2+(3-4)^2}$
$d=\sqrt{16+1}$
$d=\sqrt{17}$

39. $(-2,\ 1),\ (-2,-9)$
$d=\sqrt{[-2-(-2)]^2+(-9-1)^2}$
$d=\sqrt{0+100}$
$d=\sqrt{100}$
$d=10$

41. $(4,-9),\ (1,-8)$
$d=\sqrt{(1-4)^2+[-8-(-9)]^2}$

$d = \sqrt{9+1}$

$d = \sqrt{10}$

43. $(4,\ 9),\ (6,\ 5)$

$\left(\frac{4+6}{2},\ \frac{9+5}{2}\right)$

$(5,\ 7)$

45. $(-3,\ 4),\ (-1,-2)$

$\left(\frac{-3-1}{2},\ \frac{4-2}{2}\right)$

$(-2,\ 1)$

47. $(-2,\ 5),\ (-1,\ 6)$

$\left(\frac{-2-1}{2},\ \frac{5+6}{2}\right)$

$\left(-\frac{3}{2},\ \frac{11}{2}\right)$

49. $x = y^2 + 2$

$x = (y-0)^2 + 2$

parabola

$V(2,\ 0)$

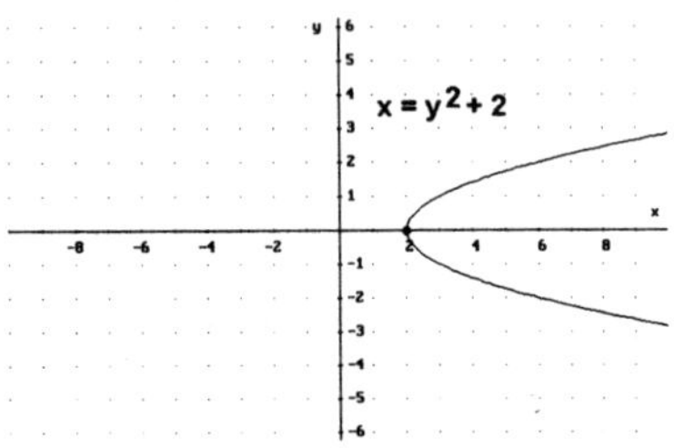

51. $y = (x+3)^2 + 3$

parabola

$V(-3,\ 3)$

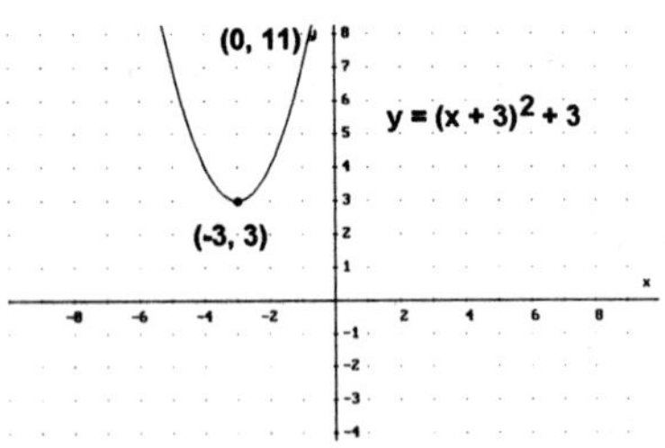

53. $x^2 + y^2 = 49$

$(x-0)^2 + (y-0)^2 = 7^2$

circle

$C(0,\ 0);\ r = 7$

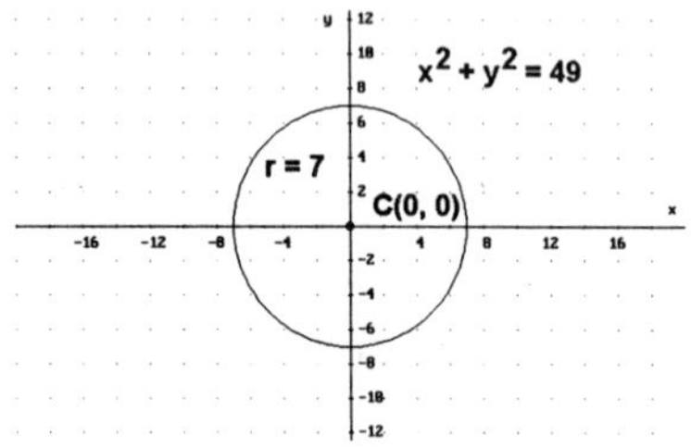

55. $x = (y-1)^2 + 4$

parabola

$V(4,\ 1)$

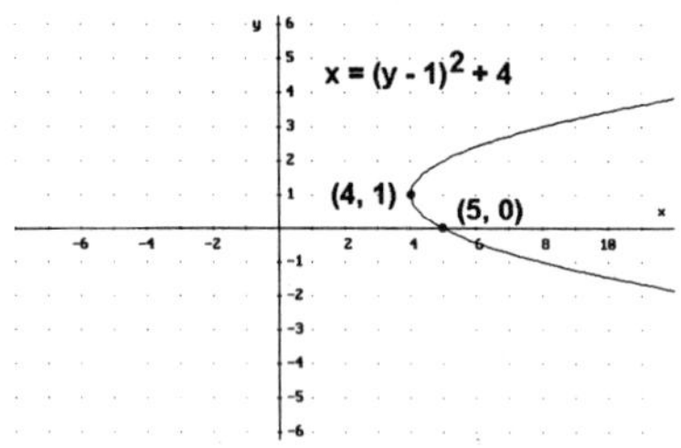

57. $(x+3)^2 + (y-1)^2 = 9$

$(x+3)^2 + (y-1)^2 = 3^2$

circle

$C(-3,\ 1);\ r = 3$

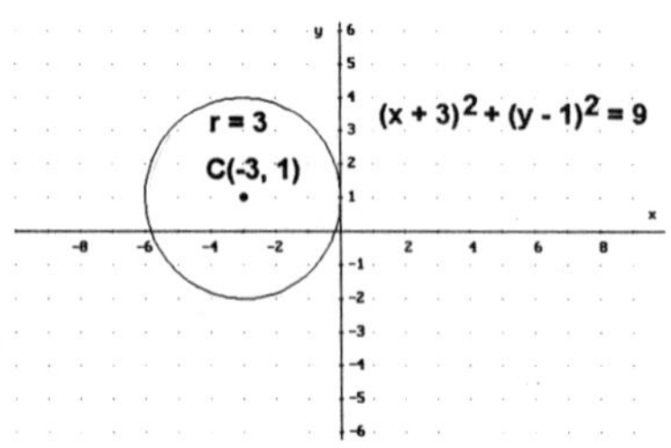

59. $x = -2(y+5)^2$

$x = -2(y+5)^2 + 0$

parabola

$V(0,-5)$

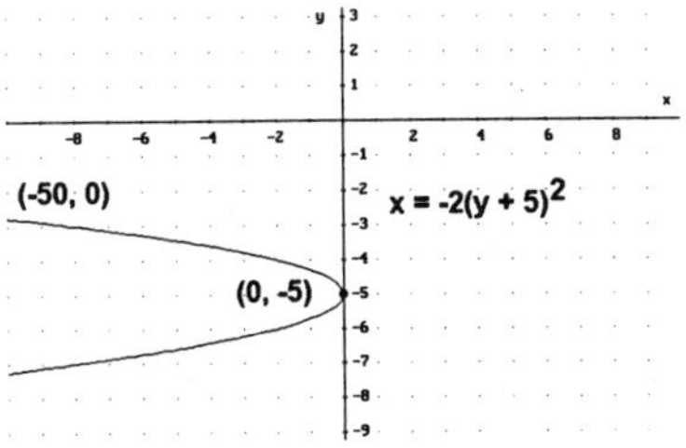

61. $x^2 + (y+5)^2 = 5$

$(x-0)^2 + (y+5)^2 = (\sqrt{5})^2$

circle

$C(0, -5);\ r = \sqrt{5}$

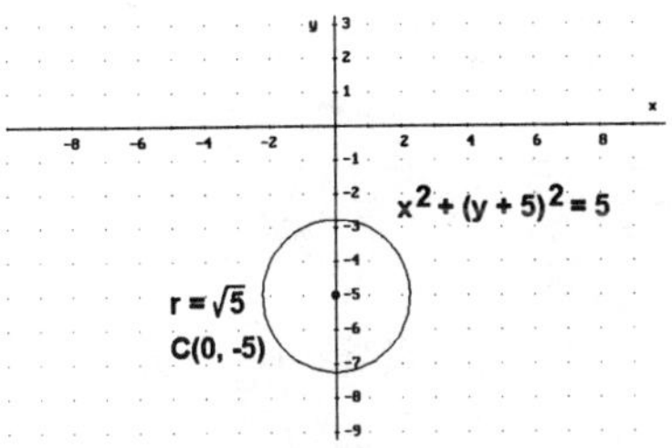

63. $y = 3(x-4)^2 + 2$

parabola

$V(4,\ 2)$

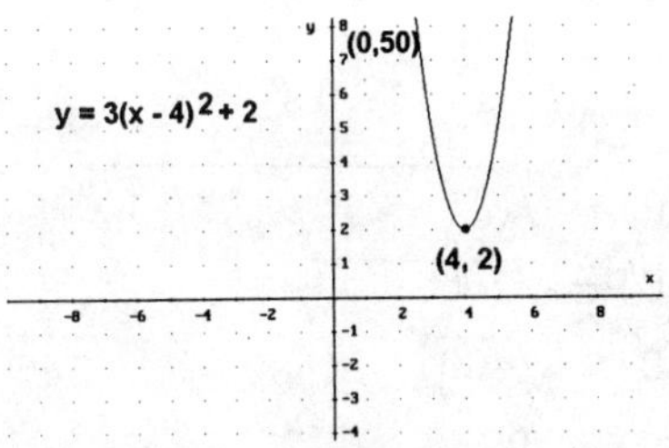

65. $2x^2 + 2y^2 = \frac{1}{2}$

$x^2 + y^2 = \frac{1}{4}$

$(x-0)^2 + (y-0)^2 = \left(\frac{1}{2}\right)^2$

circle

$C(0,\ 0);\ r = \frac{1}{2}$

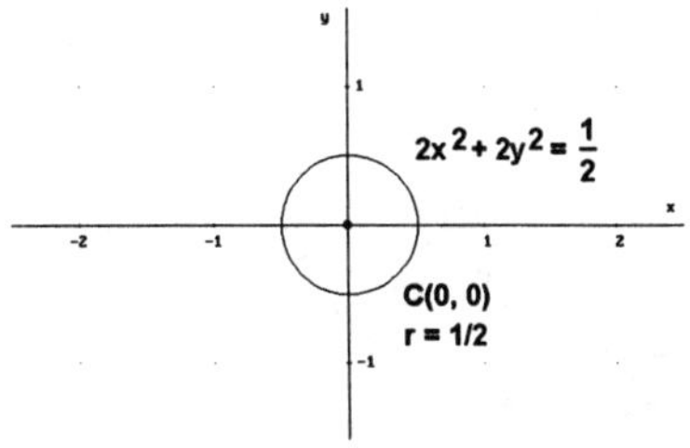

67. $y = x^2 - 2x - 15$

$y = x^2 - 2x + \left(\frac{2}{2}\right)^2 - 15 - 1$

$y = (x-1)^2 - 16$

parabola

$V(1, -16)$

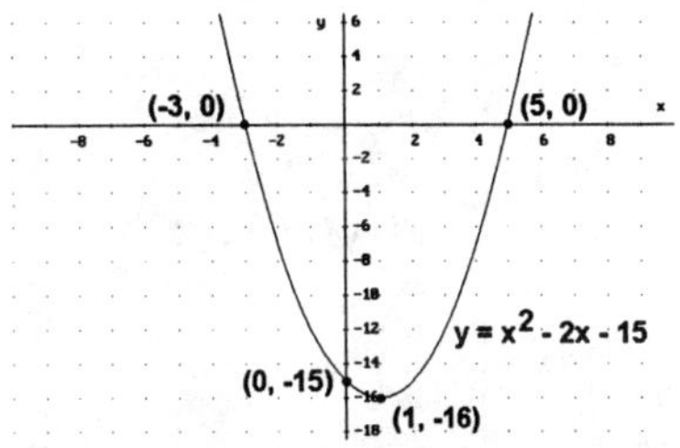

69. $x^2 + y^2 + 6x + 10y - 2 = 0$

$x^2 + 6x + \left(\frac{6}{2}\right)^2 + y^2 + 10y + \left(\frac{10}{2}\right)^2 = 2 + 9 + 25$

$(x+3)^2 + (y+5)^2 = 36$

$(x+3)^2 + (y+5)^2 = 6^2$

circle

$C(-3, -5);\ r = 6$

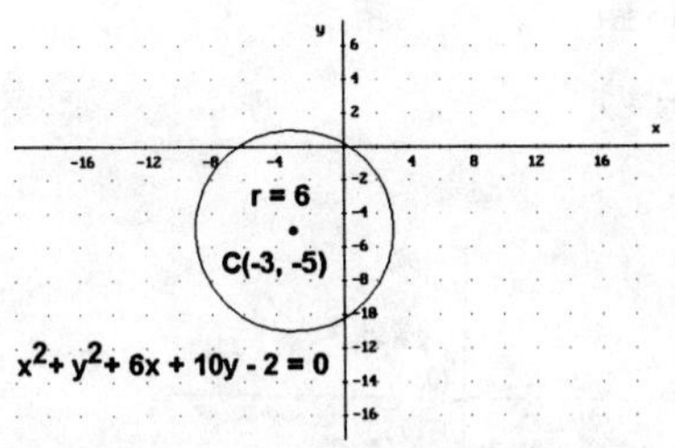

71. $x = y^2 + 6y + 2$

$x = y^2 + 6y + \left(\frac{6}{2}\right)^2 + 2 - 9$

$x = (y+3)^2 - 7$

parabola

$V(-7, -3)$

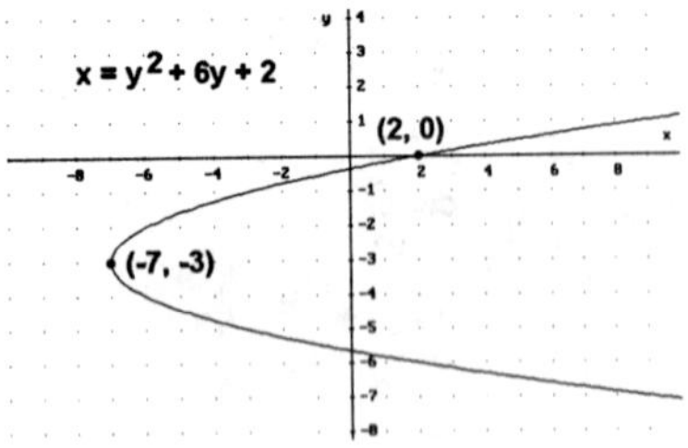

73. $x^2 + y^2 - 8y + 5 = 0$

$x^2 + y^2 - 8y + \left(\frac{8}{2}\right)^2 = -5 + 16$

$x^2 + (y-4)^2 = 11$

$(x-0)^2 + (y-4)^2 = (\sqrt{11})^2$

circle

$C(0,\ 4);\ r = \sqrt{11}$

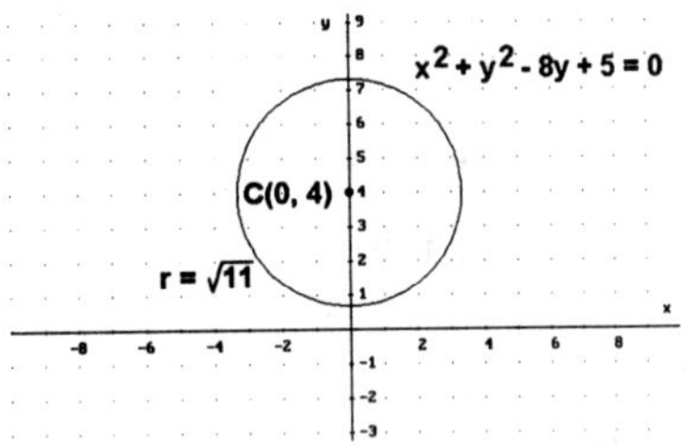

75. $x = -2y^2 - 4y$

$x = -2(y^2 + 2y)$

$x = -2\left[y^2 + 2y + \left(\frac{2}{2}\right)^2\right] + 2$

$x = -2(y+1)^2 + 2$

parabola

$V(2, -1)$

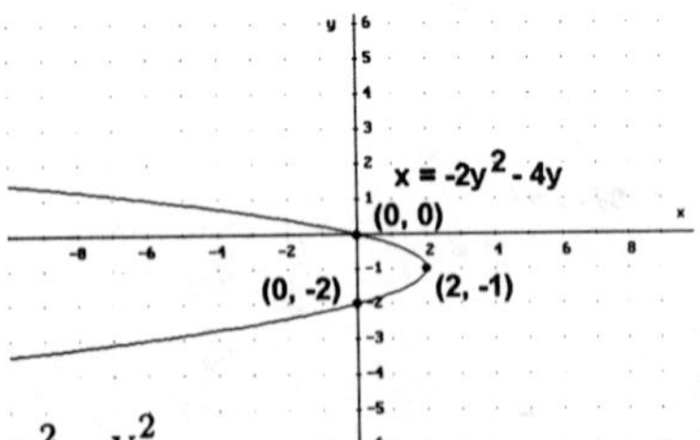

77. $\frac{x^2}{3} + \frac{y^2}{3} = 2$

$x^2 + y^2 = 6$

$(x-0)^2 + (y-0)^2 = (\sqrt{6})^2$

circle

$C(0,\ 0);\ r = \sqrt{6}$

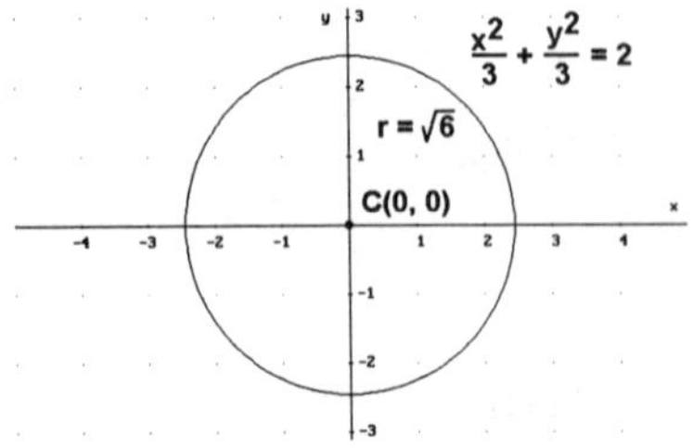

79. $y = 4x^2 - 40x + 105$

$y = 4(x^2 - 10x) + 105$

$y = 4\left[x^2 - 10x + \left(\frac{10}{2}\right)^2\right] + 105 - 100$

$y = 4(x-5)^2 + 5$

parabola

$V(5,\ 5)$

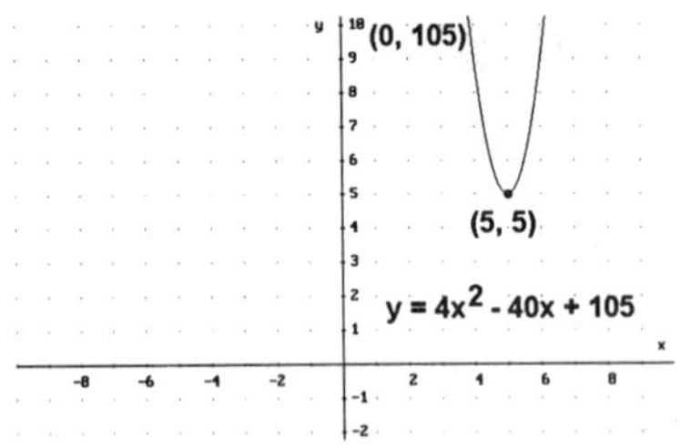

81. B(3, 1) and C(19, 13)

$d(B,\ C) = \sqrt{(19-3)^2 + (13-1)^2}$

$d(B,\ C) = \sqrt{256 + 144}$

$d(B,\ C) = \sqrt{400}$

$d(B,\ C) = 20$

Therefore the distance across the lake is 20 meters.

83a.

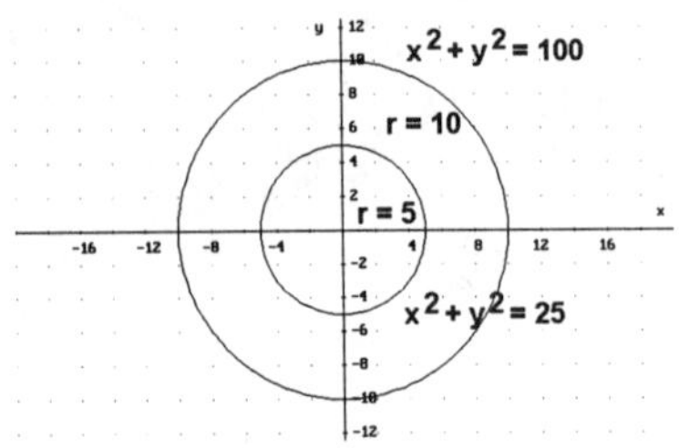

b. $(x-0)^2+(y-0)^2=\left(\frac{20}{2}\right)^2$

$x^2+y^2=100$

c. $(x-0)^2+(y-0)^2=5^2$

$x^2+y^2=25$

85. $y=2x+5$

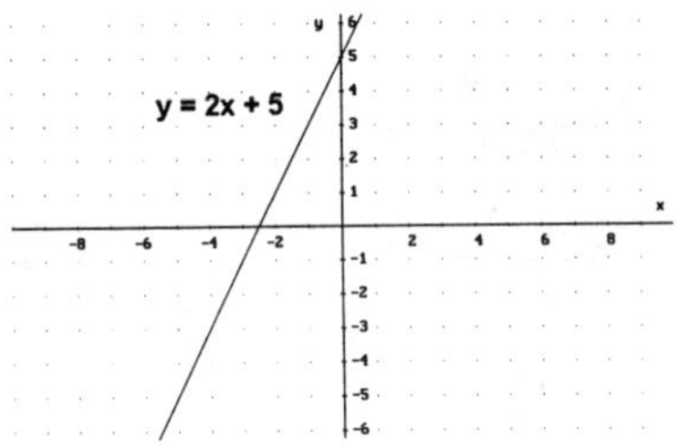

87. $y=3$

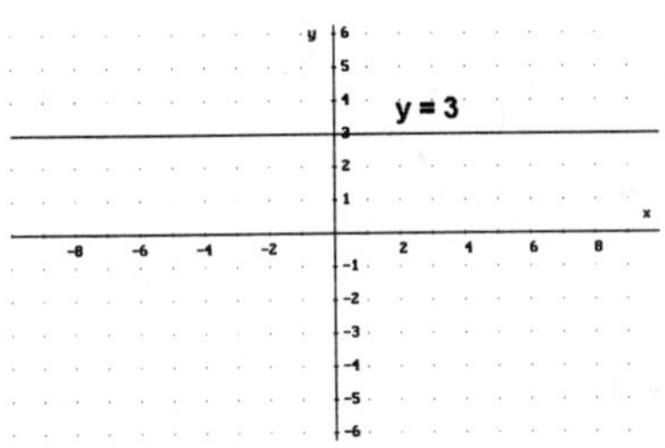

89. $\frac{1}{\sqrt{3}}=\frac{1}{\sqrt{3}}\bullet\frac{\sqrt{3}}{\sqrt{3}}=\frac{\sqrt{3}}{\sqrt{9}}=\frac{\sqrt{3}}{3}$

91. $\frac{4\sqrt{7}}{\sqrt{6}}=\frac{4\sqrt{7}}{\sqrt{6}}\bullet\frac{\sqrt{6}}{\sqrt{6}}=\frac{4\sqrt{42}}{\sqrt{36}}=\frac{4\sqrt{42}}{6}=\frac{2\sqrt{42}}{3}$

Graphing Calculator Exercise 9.8

1. $10x^2+y^2=32$

$y^2=32-10x^2$

$y=\pm\sqrt{32-10x^2}$

$Y_1=\sqrt{32-10x^2}$

$Y_2=-\sqrt{32-10x^2}$

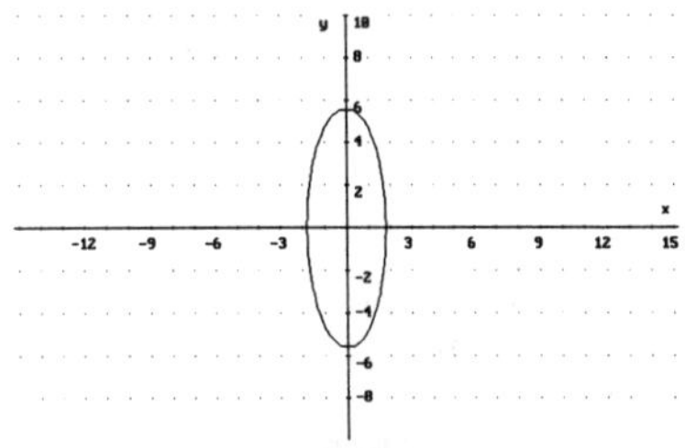

3. $7.3x^2+15.5y^2=95.2$

$15.5y^2=95.2-7.3x^2$

$y^2=\frac{95.2-7.3x^2}{15.5}$

$y=\pm\sqrt{\frac{95.2-7.3x^2}{15.5}}$

$Y_1=\sqrt{\frac{95.2-7.3x^2}{15.5}}$

$Y_2=-\sqrt{\frac{95.2-7.3x^2}{15.5}}$

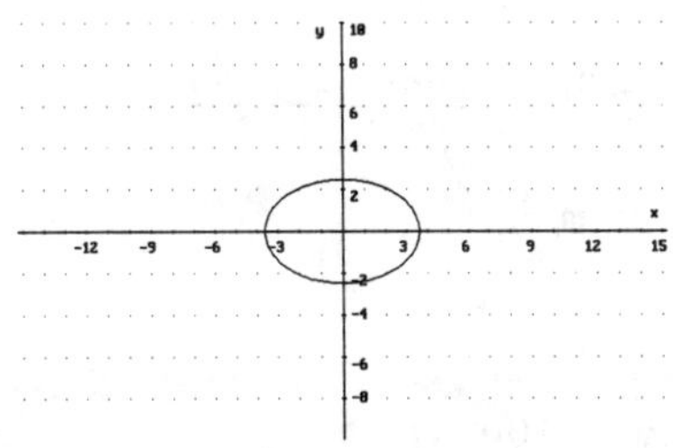

Exercise Set 9.8

1. $\frac{x^2}{4}+\frac{y^2}{25}=1$

$\frac{x^2}{2^2}+\frac{y^2}{5^2}=1$

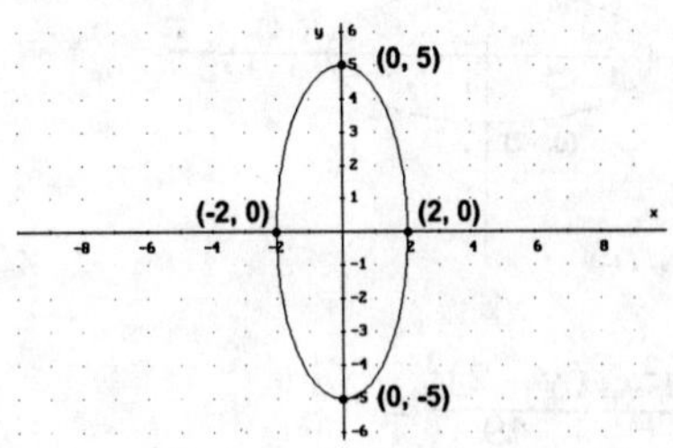

3. $\frac{x^2}{16}+\frac{y^2}{9}=1$

$\frac{x^2}{4^2}+\frac{y^2}{3^2}=1$

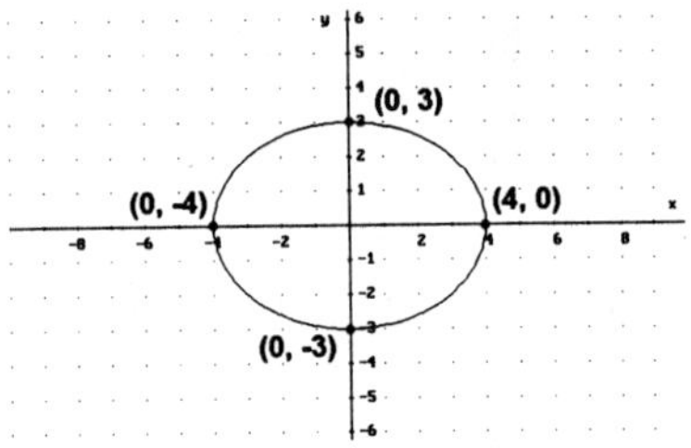

5. $9x^2+4y^2=36$

$\frac{x^2}{4}+\frac{y^2}{9}=1$

$\frac{x^2}{2^2}+\frac{y^2}{3^2}=1$

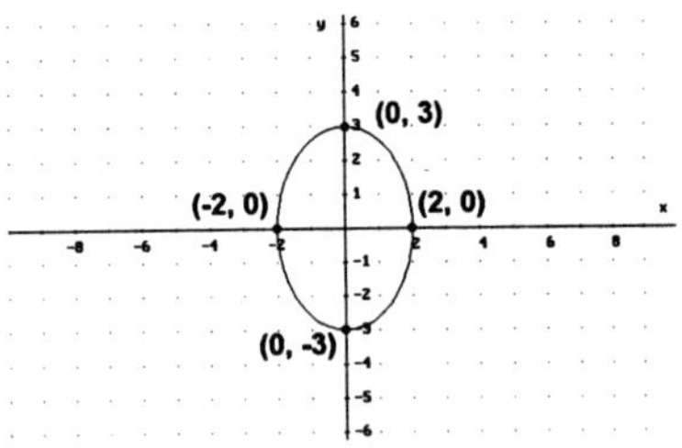

7. $4x^2+25y^2=100$

$\frac{x^2}{25}+\frac{y^2}{4}=1$

$\frac{x^2}{5^2}+\frac{y^2}{2^2}=1$

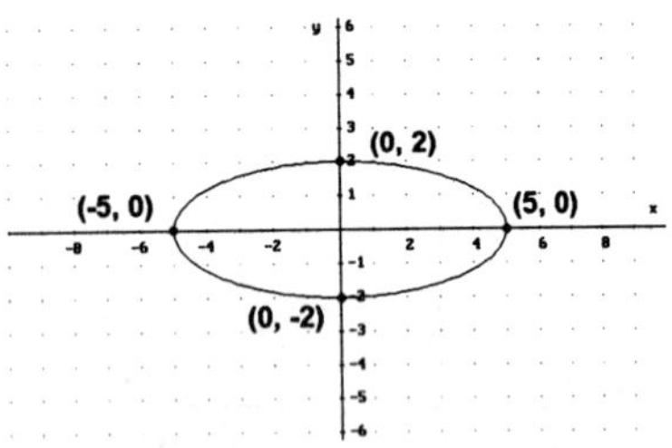

9. $\frac{(x+1)^2}{36}+\frac{(y-2)^2}{49}=1$

$\frac{(x+1)^2}{6^2}+\frac{(y-2)^2}{7^2}=1$

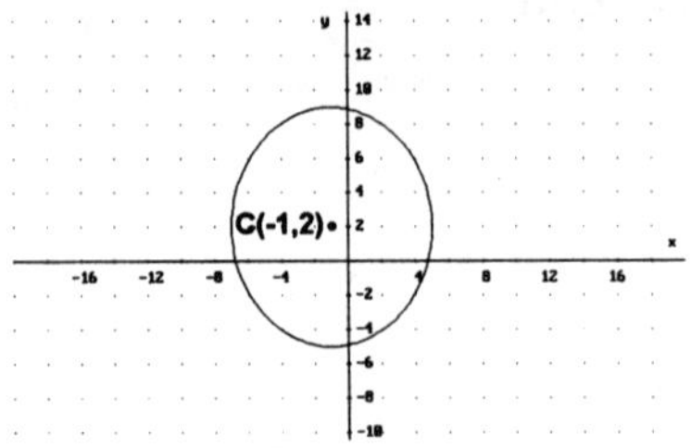

11. $\frac{(x-1)^2}{4}+\frac{(y-1)^2}{25}=1$

$\frac{(x-1)^2}{2^2}+\frac{(y-1)^2}{5^2}=1$

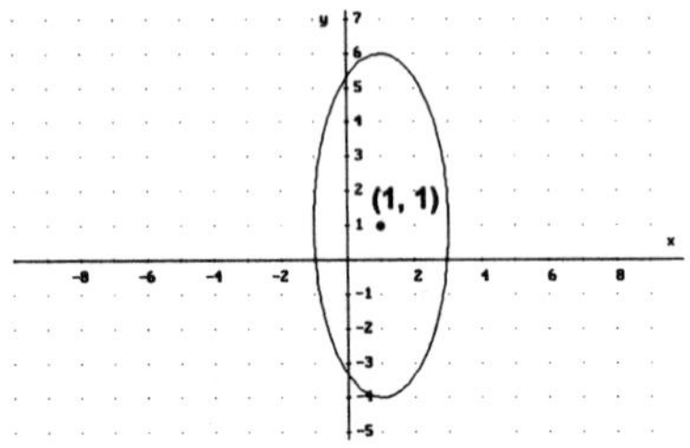

13. $\frac{x^2}{4}-\frac{y^2}{9}=1$

$\frac{x^2}{2^2}-\frac{y^2}{3^2}=1$

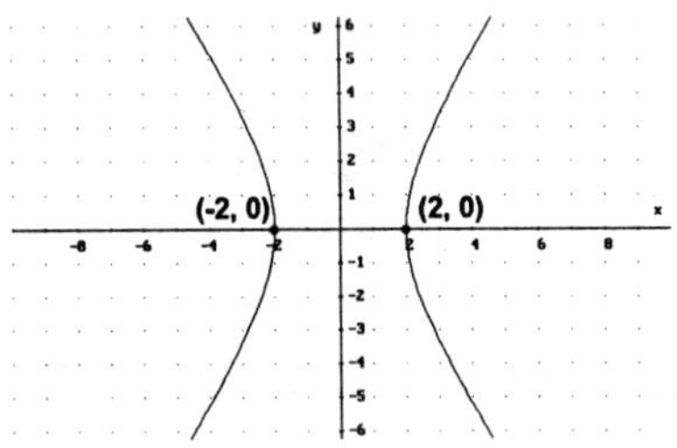

15. $\frac{y^2}{25}-\frac{x^2}{16}=1$

$\frac{y^2}{5^2}-\frac{x^2}{4^2}=1$

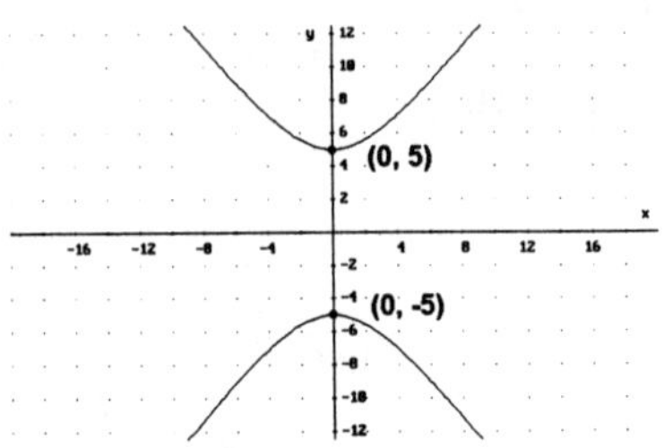

17. $x^2 - 4y^2 = 16$

$\frac{x^2}{16} - \frac{y^2}{4} = 1$

$\frac{x^2}{4^2} - \frac{y^2}{2^2} = 1$

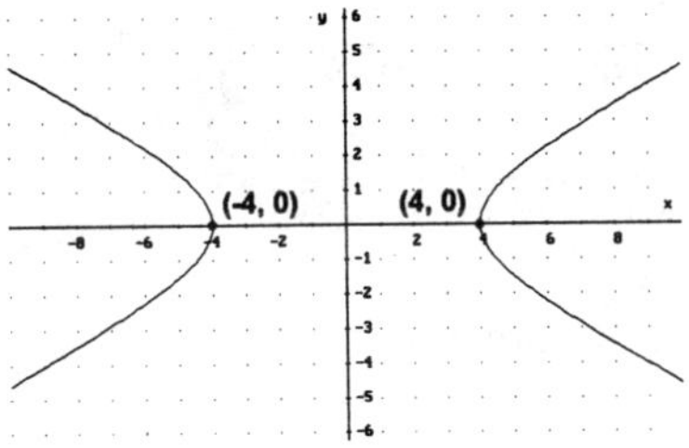

19. $16y^2 - x^2 = 16$

$\frac{y^2}{1} - \frac{x^2}{16} = 1$

$\frac{y^2}{1^2} - \frac{x^2}{4^2} = 1$

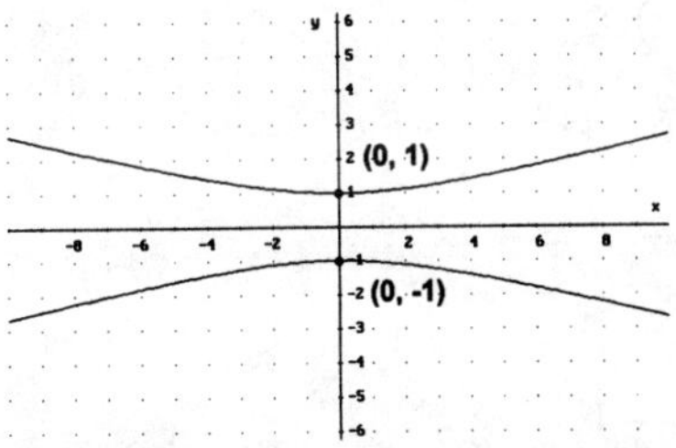

21. $(x-7)^2 + (y-2)^2 = 4$

$(x-7)^2 + (y-2)^2 = 2^2$

circle

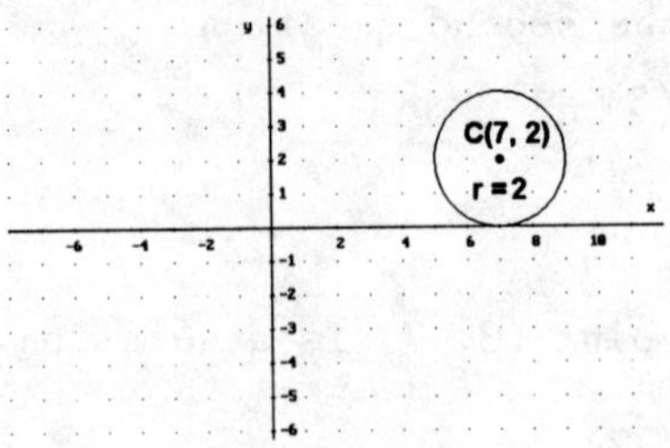

23. $y = x^2 + 12x + 36$

$y = (x+6)^2 + 0$

parabola

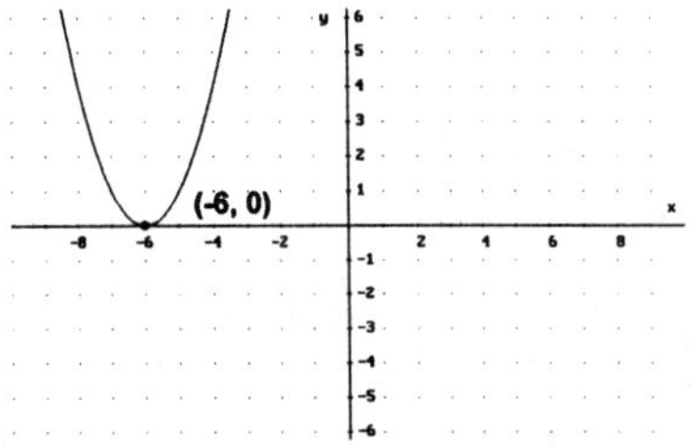

25. $\frac{y^2}{9} - \frac{x^2}{9} = 1$

$\frac{y^2}{3^2} - \frac{x^2}{3^2} = 1$

hyperbola

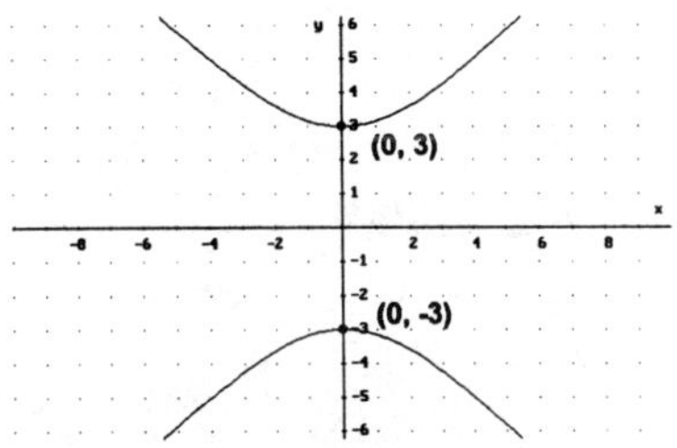

27. $\frac{x^2}{16} + \frac{y^2}{4} = 1$

$\frac{x^2}{4^2} + \frac{y^2}{2^2} = 1$

ellipse

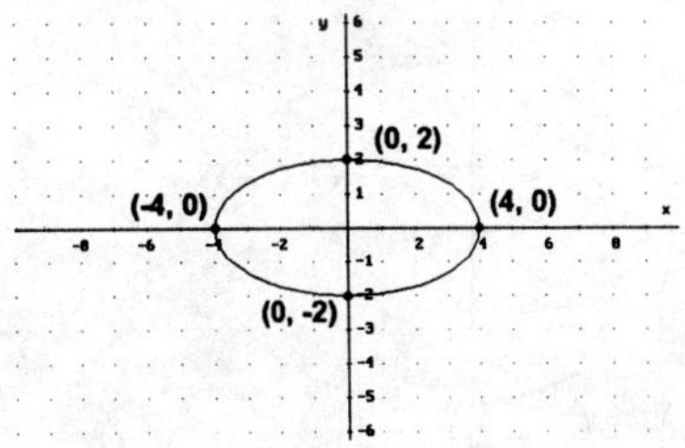

29. $x = y^2 + 4y - 1$

$x = y^2 + 4y + \left(\frac{4}{2}\right)^2 - 1 - 4$

$x = (y+2)^2 - 5$

parabola

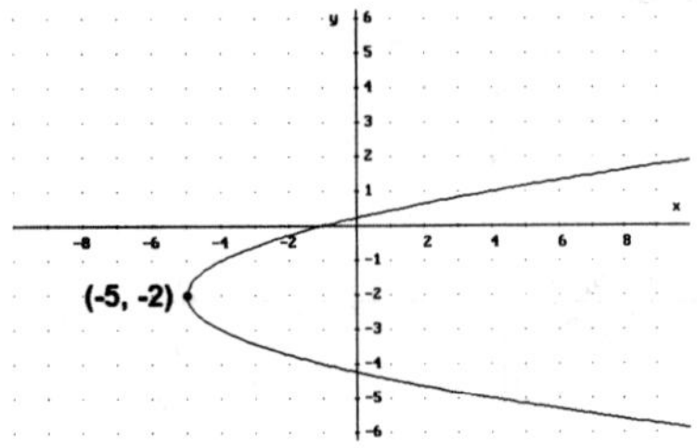

31. $9x^2-4y^2=36$

$\frac{x^2}{4}-\frac{y^2}{9}=1$

$\frac{x^2}{2^2}-\frac{y^2}{3^2}=1$

hyperbola

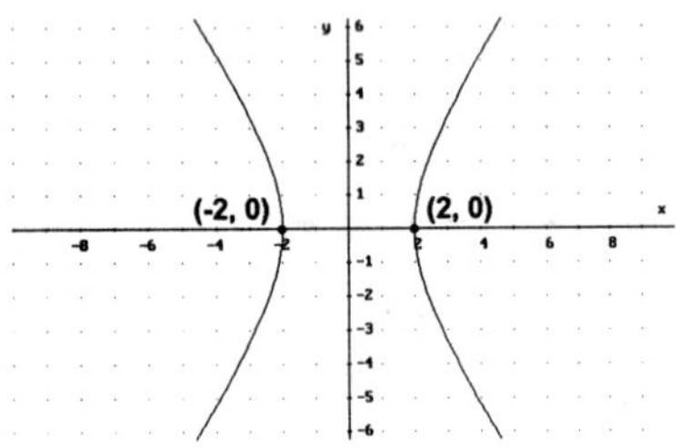

33. $\frac{(x-1)^2}{49}+\frac{(y+2)^2}{25}=1$

$\frac{(x-1)^2}{7^2}+\frac{(y+2)^2}{5^2}=1$

ellipse

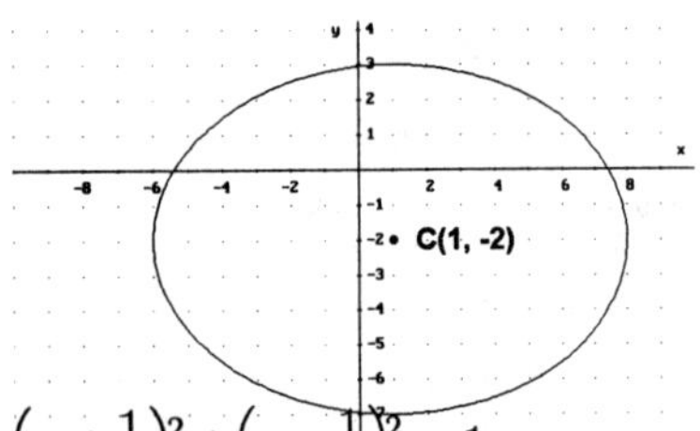

35. $\left(x+\frac{1}{2}\right)^2+\left(y-\frac{1}{2}\right)^2=1$

circle

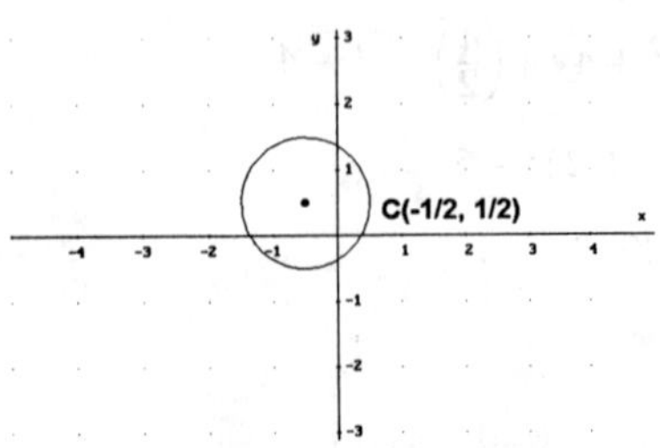

37. The equation is of the form

$\frac{x^2}{a^2}+\frac{y^2}{b^2}=1$ where

$a=130,000,000=1.30\times10^8$ and

$b=125,000,000=1.25\times10^8$.

Then

$\frac{x^2}{(1.30\times10^8)^2}+\frac{y^2}{(1.25\times10^8)^2}=1$

$\frac{x^2}{1.69\times10^{16}}+\frac{y^2}{1.5625\times10^{16}}=1$

39. $x<5$ and $x<1$

$x<1$

$(-\infty,\ 1)$

41. $2x-1\geq7$ or $-3x\leq-6$

$2x\geq8$ or $x\geq2$

$x\geq4$

$x\geq2$

$[2,\ \infty)$

43. $(2x^3)(-4x^2)=-8x^{3+2}=-8x^5$

45. $-5x^2+x^2=-4x^2$

47. $(3,\ 7)$

$\begin{cases}x=y-4\\y=2x+1\end{cases}$

For the first equation:

$3=7-4$

$3=3$

For the second equation:

$7=2(3)+1$

$7=6+1$

$7=7$

The point (3, 7) is a solution.

49. $(-1,\ 2)$

$\begin{cases}x+2y=3\\-x-y=-1\end{cases}$

In the first equation:

$-1+2(2)=3$

$-1+4=3$

$3=3$

In the second equation:

$-(-1)-2=-1$

$1-2=-1$

$-1=-1$

The point $(-1, 2)$ is a solution.

51. $\frac{(x-1)^2}{4}-\frac{(y+1)^2}{25}=1$

$\frac{(x-1)^2}{2^2}-\frac{(y+1)^2}{5^2}=1$

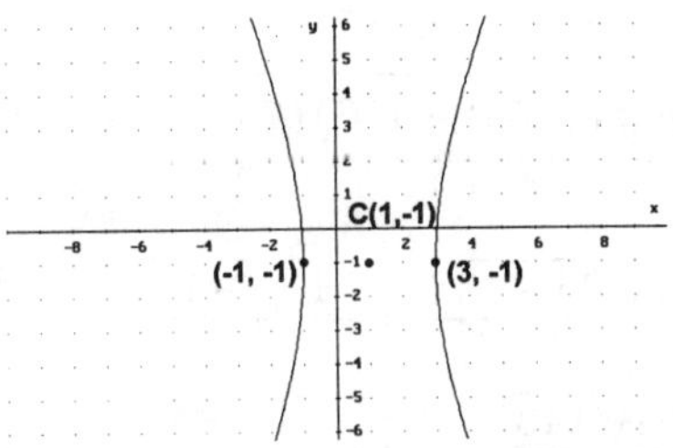

53. $\frac{y^2}{16}-\frac{(x+3)^2}{9}=1$

$\frac{y^2}{4^2}-\frac{(x+3)^2}{3^2}=1$

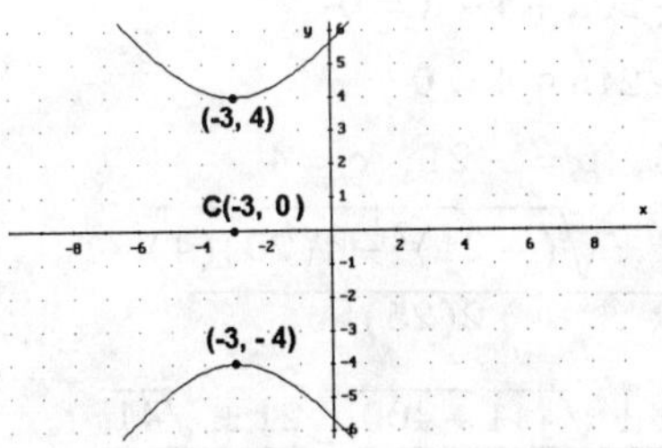

55. $\frac{(x+5)^2}{16}-\frac{(y+2)^2}{25}=1$

$\frac{(x+5)^2}{4^2}-\frac{(y+2)^2}{5^2}=1$

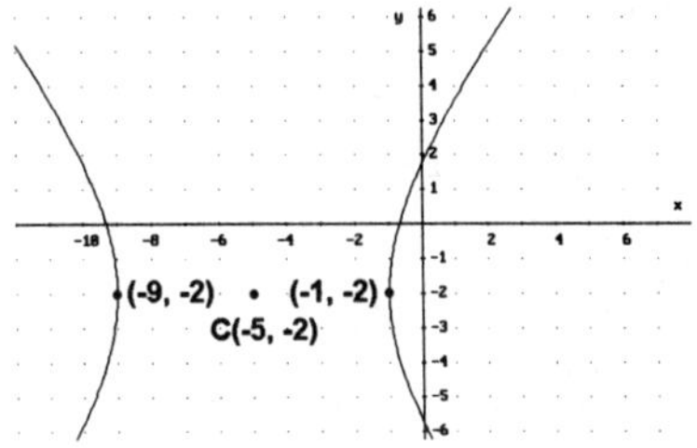

Chapter 9 Review

1. $x^2-15x+14=0$

$(x-14)(x-1)=0$

$x-14=0 \quad \text{or} \quad x-1=0$

$x=14 \quad \text{or} \quad x=1$

$\{1, 14\}$

3. $10x^2=3x+4$

$10x^2-3x-4=0$

$(5x-4)(2x+1)=0$

$5x-4=0 \quad \text{or} \quad 2x+1=0$

$5x=4 \quad \text{or} \quad 2x=-1$

$x=\frac{4}{5} \quad \text{or} \quad x=-\frac{1}{2}$

$\left\{-\frac{1}{2}, \frac{4}{5}\right\}$

5. $4m^2=196$

$m^2=49$

$m=\pm\sqrt{49}$

$m=\pm 7$

$\{-7, 7\}$

7. $(9n+1)^2=9$

$9n+1=\pm\sqrt{9}$

$9n+1=\pm 3$

$9n=-1\pm 3$

$n=\frac{-1\pm 3}{9}=\frac{2}{9}, \frac{-4}{9}$

$\left\{-\frac{4}{9}, \frac{2}{9}\right\}$

9. $z^2+3z+1=0$

$z^2+3z=-1$

$z^2+3z+\left(\frac{3}{2}\right)^2=-1+\frac{9}{4}$

$\left(z+\frac{3}{2}\right)^2=\frac{5}{4}$

$z+\frac{3}{2}=\pm\sqrt{\frac{5}{4}}$

$z+\frac{3}{2}=\pm\frac{\sqrt{5}}{\sqrt{4}}$

$z=-\frac{3}{2}\pm\frac{\sqrt{5}}{2}$

$\left\{-\frac{3}{2}-\frac{\sqrt{5}}{2},\ -\frac{3}{2}+\frac{\sqrt{5}}{2}\right\}$

11. $(2x+1)^2=x$

$4x^2+4x+1=x$

$4x^2+3x=-1$

$x^2+\frac{3}{4}x=-\frac{1}{4}$

$x^2+\frac{3}{4}x+\left(\frac{\frac{3}{4}}{2}\right)^2=-\frac{1}{4}+\frac{9}{64}$

$\left(x+\frac{3}{8}\right)^2=\frac{-7}{64}$

$x+\frac{3}{8}=\pm\sqrt{\frac{-7}{64}}$

$x+\frac{3}{8}=\pm\frac{\sqrt{7}i}{8}$

$x=-\frac{3}{8}\pm i\frac{\sqrt{7}}{8}$

$x=\frac{-3\pm i\sqrt{7}}{8}$

$\left\{\frac{-3-i\sqrt{7}}{8},\ \frac{-3+i\sqrt{7}}{8}\right\}$

13. Two complex solutions exist.

15. Since 100 is a perfect square, two distinct real solutions exist.

17. $x^2-16x+64=0$

$a=1,\ b=-16,$ and $c=64.$

$x=\frac{16\pm\sqrt{(-16)^2-4(1)(64)}}{2(1)}$

$x=\frac{16\pm\sqrt{256-256}}{2}=\frac{16\pm\sqrt{0}}{2}$

$x=8$

$\{8\}$

19. $x^2+11=0$

$a=1,\ b=0,\ c=11$

$x=\frac{-0\pm\sqrt{0^2-4(1)(11)}}{2(1)}$

$x=\frac{\pm\sqrt{-44}}{2}=\frac{\pm 2i\sqrt{11}}{2}=\pm i\sqrt{11}$

$\{-i\sqrt{11},\ i\sqrt{11}\}$

21. $6x^2+7=5x$

$6x^2-5x+7=0$

$a=6,\ b=-5,\ c=7$

$x=\frac{5\pm\sqrt{(-5)^2-4(6)(7)}}{2(6)}$

$x=\frac{5\pm\sqrt{25-168}}{12}=\frac{5\pm\sqrt{-143}}{12}$

$x=\frac{5\pm i\sqrt{143}}{12}$

$\left\{\frac{5-i\sqrt{143}}{12},\ \frac{5+i\sqrt{143}}{12}\right\}$

23. $(5a-2)^2-a=0$

$25a^2-20a+4-a=0$

$25a^2-21a+4=0$

$a=25,\ b=-21,\ c=4$

$a=\frac{21\pm\sqrt{(-21)^2-4(25)(4)}}{2(25)}$

$a=\frac{21\pm\sqrt{441-400}}{50}=\frac{21\pm\sqrt{41}}{50}$

$a=\frac{21}{50}\pm\frac{\sqrt{41}}{50}$

$\left\{\frac{21}{50}-\frac{\sqrt{41}}{50},\ \frac{21}{50}+\frac{\sqrt{41}}{50}\right\}$

25. $x^3=27$

$x^3-27=0$

$(x-3)(x^2+3x+9)=0$

$x-3=0$ or $x^2+3x+9=0$

$x=3$

$a=1,\ b=3,\ c=9$

$$x=\frac{-3\pm\sqrt{3^2-4(1)(9)}}{2(1)}$$

$$x=\frac{-3\pm\sqrt{9-36}}{2}=\frac{-3\pm\sqrt{-27}}{2}$$

$$x=\frac{-3\pm 3i\sqrt{3}}{2}$$

$$\left\{3,\frac{-3-3i\sqrt{3}}{2},\ \frac{-3+3i\sqrt{3}}{2}\right\}$$

27. $\frac{5}{x}+\frac{6}{x-2}=3$

$\frac{5(x-2)+6x}{x(x-2)}=3$

$5x-10+6x=3x(x-2)$

$11x-10=3x^2-6x$

$3x^2-17x+10=0$

$(3x-2)(x-5)=0$

$3x-2=0$ or $x-5=0$

$3x=2$ or $x=5$

$x=\frac{2}{3}$

$\left\{\frac{2}{3},\ 5\right\}$

29. $x^4-21x^2-100=0$

$(x^2-25)(x^2+4)=0$

$x^2-25=0$ or $x^2+4=0$

$x^2=25$ or $x^2=-4$

$x=\pm\sqrt{25}$ or $x=\sqrt{-4}$

$x=\pm 5$ or $x=\pm 2i$

$\{-5,\ 5,\ -2i,\ 2i\}$

31. $x^{\frac{2}{3}}-6x^{\frac{1}{3}}+5=0$

$(x^{\frac{1}{3}}-1)(x^{\frac{1}{3}}-5)=0$

$x^{\frac{1}{3}}-1=0$ or $x^{\frac{1}{3}}-5=0$

$x^{\frac{1}{3}}=1$ or $x^{\frac{1}{3}}=5$

$x=1^3$ or $x=5^3$

$x=1$ or $x=125$

$\{1,\ 125\}$

33. $a^6-a^2=a^4-1$

$a^6-a^4-a^2+1=0$

$a^2(a^4-1)-(a^4-1)=0$

$(a^2-1)(a^4-1)=0$

$(a^2-1)(a^2-1)(a^2+1)=0$

$(a^2-1)^2(a^2+1)=0$

$[(a+1)(a-1)]^2(a^2+1)=0$

$(a+1)^2(a-1)^2(a^2+1)=0$

$(a+1)^2=0$ or $(a-1)^2=0$ or $a^2+1=0$

$a+1=0$ or $a-1=0$ or $a^2=-1$

$a=-1$ or $a=1$ or $a=\sqrt{-1}$

$a=\pm i$

$\{-1,\ 1,\ -i,\ i\}$

35. Let $n=$ an even whole number.
$n+2=$ the next even whole number.

$n^2+(n+2)^2=100$

$n^2+n^2+4n+4=100$

$2n^2+4n-96=0$

$n^2+2n-48=0$

$(n+8)(n-6)=0$

$n+8=0$ or $n-6=0$

$n=-8$ or $n=6$

Discarding the negative value as extraneous, we find 6 and $6+2=8$ to be the solution.

37. $d(t)=-16t^2+30t+6$

a. $d(1)=-16(1)^2+30(1)+6$

$d(1)=-16+30+6$

$d(1)=20$ feet

b. $-16t^2+30t+6=0$

$8t^2-15t-3=0$

$a=8,\ b=-15,\ c=-3$

$$x = \frac{15 \pm \sqrt{(-15)^2 - 4(8)(-3)}}{2(8)}$$

$$x = \frac{15 \pm \sqrt{225 + 96}}{16}$$

$$x = \frac{15 \pm \sqrt{321}}{16}$$

$$x = \frac{15}{16} \pm \frac{\sqrt{321}}{16}$$

Discarding the negative value as extraneous, we find that

$$t = \frac{15}{16} + \frac{\sqrt{321}}{16} \approx 2.06 \text{ seconds.}$$

39. Let $n =$ a positive even integer.
$n + 2 =$ the second even integer.
$n + 4 =$ the third even integer.

$$n + 2 = \frac{1}{10}n(n+4) - 26$$

$$10(n+2) = n(n+4) - 260$$

$$10n + 20 = n^2 + 4n - 260$$

$$0 = n^2 - 6n - 280$$

$$0 = (n-20)(n+14)$$

$n - 20 = 0$ or $n + 14 = 0$

$n = 20$ or $n = -14$

Discarding the negative value as extraneous, we find the numbers to be 20, 22, and 24.

41. Let $x =$ the number.
$\frac{1}{x} =$ the reciprocal of the number.

$$x - \frac{1}{x} = \frac{-24}{5}$$

$$\frac{x^2 - 1}{x} = \frac{-24}{5}$$

$$5(x^2 - 1) = -24x$$

$$5x^2 - 5 = -24x$$

$$5x^2 + 24x - 5 = 0$$

$$(5x - 1)(x + 5) = 0$$

$5x - 1 = 0$ or $x + 5 = 0$

$5x = 1$ or $x = -5$

$$x = \frac{1}{5}$$

Discarding the positive value as extraneous, we find the number to be -5.

43. $2x^2 - 50 \le 0$

$$2x^2 \le 50$$

$$x^2 \le 25$$

$$-5 \le x \le 5$$

$[-5, 5]$

45. $(2x-3)(4x+5) \ge 0$

$$(2x-3)(4x+5) = 0$$

$2x - 3 = 0$ or $4x + 5 = 0$

$2x = 3$ or $4x = -5$

$x = \frac{3}{2}$ or $x = -\frac{5}{4}$

Region	Interval	Test Point
A	$\left(-\infty, -\frac{5}{4}\right)$	-2
B	$\left(-\frac{5}{4}, \frac{3}{2}\right)$	0
C	$\left(\frac{3}{2}, \infty\right)$	2

$x = -2$: $[2(-2) - 3][4(-2) + 5] \ge 0$ True

$x = 0$: $[2(0) - 3][4(0) + 5] \ge 0$ False

$x = 2$: $[2(2) - 3][4(2) + 5] \ge 0$ True

The solution is $\left(-\infty, -\frac{5}{4}\right] \cup \left[\frac{3}{2}, \infty\right)$.

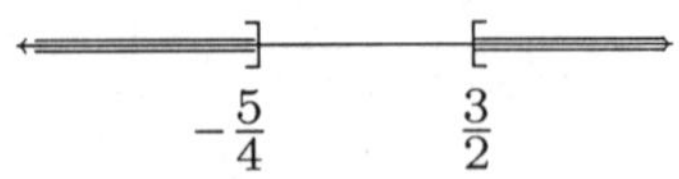

47. $\frac{x-5}{x-6} < 0$

$x - 5 = 0$ and $x - 6 = 0$

$x = 5$ and $x = 6$

Region	Interval	Test Point
A	$(-\infty, 5)$	4
B	$(5, 6)$	$\frac{11}{2}$

C	$(6, \infty)$	7

$x = 4$: $\quad \frac{4-5}{4-6} < 0$ $\quad$ False

$x = \frac{11}{2}$: $\quad \frac{\frac{11}{2}-5}{\frac{11}{2}-6} < 0$ $\quad$ True

$x = 7$: $\quad \frac{7-5}{7-6} < 0$ $\quad$ False

The solution is $(5, 6)$.

49. $\frac{(4x+3)(x-5)}{x(x+6)} > 0$

$4x+3=0$ or $x-5=0$ or $x = 0$ or $x+6=0$

$4x = -3$ or $x = 5$ or $x = 0$ or $x = -6$

$x = -\frac{3}{4}$ or $x = 5$ or $x = 0$ or $x = -6$

Region	Interval	Test Point
A	$(-\infty, -6)$	-7
B	$\left(-6, -\frac{3}{4}\right)$	-1
C	$\left(-\frac{3}{4}, 0\right)$	$-\frac{1}{2}$
D	$(0, 5)$	1
E	$(5, \infty)$	6

$x = -7$: $\quad \frac{[4(-7)+3][-7-5]}{-7(-7+6)} > 0$ True

$x = -1$: $\quad \frac{[4(-1)+3][-1-5]}{-1(-1+6)} > 0$ False

$x = -\frac{1}{2}$: $\quad \frac{\left[4\left(-\frac{1}{2}\right)+3\right]\left[-\frac{1}{2}-5\right]}{-\frac{1}{2}\left(-\frac{1}{2}+6\right)} > 0$ $\quad$ True

$x = 1$: $\quad \frac{[4(1)+3][1-5]}{1(1+6)} > 0$ $\quad$ False

$x = 6$: $\quad \frac{[4(6)+3][6-5]}{6(6+6)} > 0$ $\quad$ True

The solution is
$(-\infty, -6) \cup \left(-\frac{3}{4}, 0\right) \cup (5, \infty)$.

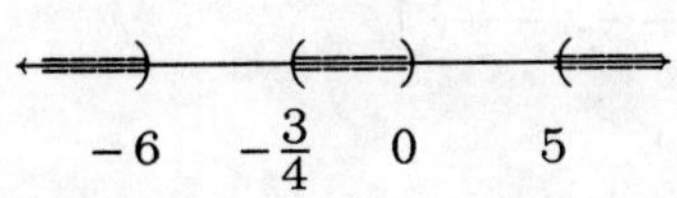

51. $\frac{x+4}{x-\frac{1}{2}} \le 0$

$x + 4 = 0$ $\quad$ and $x - \frac{1}{2} = 0$

$x = -4$ $\quad$ and $x = \frac{1}{2}$

Region	Interval	Test Point
A	$(-\infty, -4)$	-5
B	$\left(-4, \frac{1}{2}\right)$	0
C	$\left(\frac{1}{2}, \infty\right)$	1

$x = -5$: $\quad \frac{-5+4}{-5-\frac{1}{2}} \le 0$ $\quad$ False

$x = 0$: $\quad \frac{0+4}{0-\frac{1}{2}} \le 0$ $\quad$ True

$x = 1$: $\quad \frac{1+4}{1-\frac{1}{2}} \le 0$ $\quad$ False

The solution is $\left[-4, \frac{1}{2}\right)$.

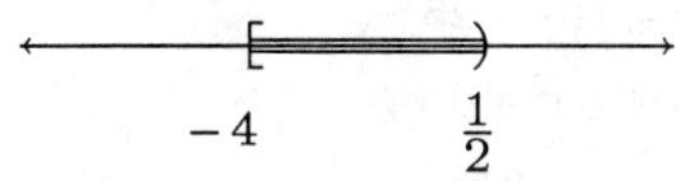

53. $\frac{x^2+10x+25}{x^2-6x+9} > 0$

$\frac{(x+5)^2}{(x-3)^2} > 0$

$\left(\frac{x+5}{x-3}\right)^2 > 0$

Since $\left(\frac{x+5}{x-3}\right)^2 > 0$ for all $x \neq 3$

we need only exclude those

x values for which

$\left(\frac{x+5}{x-3}\right)^2 = 0$

$\frac{x+5}{x-3} = 0$

$x + 5 = 0$

$x = -5$

The solution is

$(-\infty, -5) \cup (-5, 3) \cup (3, \infty)$.

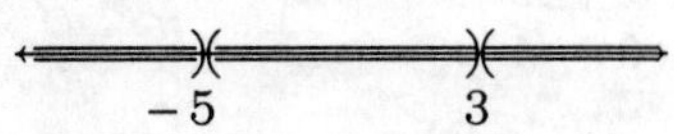

55. $g(x) = x^2 + 5$

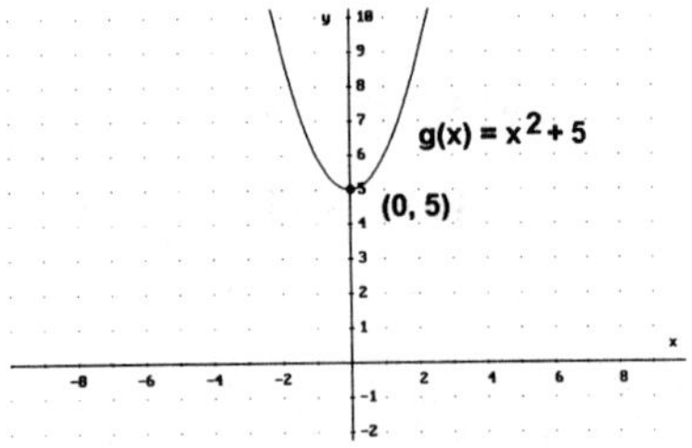

57. $f(x) = (x - 4)^2 - 2$

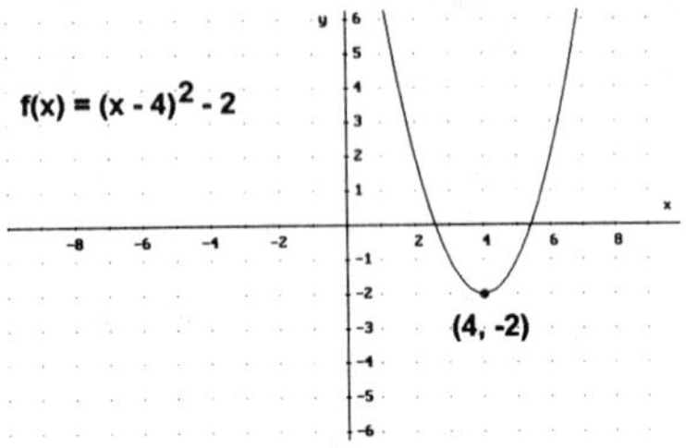

59. $f(x) = x^2 + 10x + 25$

$f(x) = (x + 5)^2 + 0$

Thus, $V(-5, 0)$.

The graph opens upward since $a = 1 > 0$.

$(x + 5)^2 = 0$

$x + 5 = 0$

$x = -5$

The x-intercept is -5.

$f(0) = 25$ is the y-intercept.

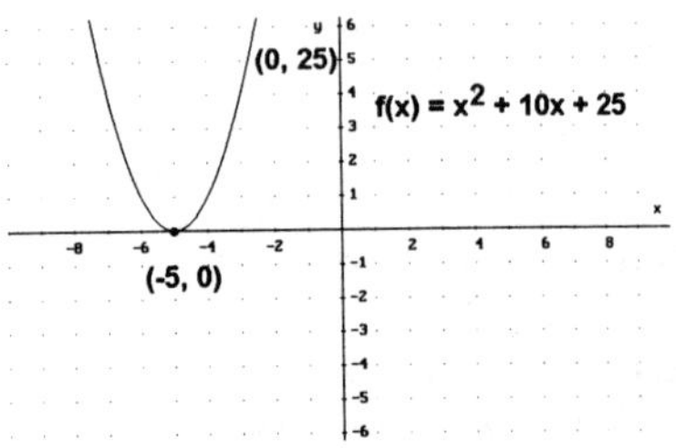

61. $f(x) = 4x^2 - 1$

$f(x) = 4(x - 0)^2 - 1$

Thus, $V(0, -1)$.

The graph opens upward since $a = 4 > 0$.

$4x^2 - 1 = 0$

$4x^2 = 1$

$x^2 = \frac{1}{4}$

$x = \pm\frac{1}{2}$

The x-intercepts are $\pm\frac{1}{2}$.

$f(0) = -1$ is the y-intercept.

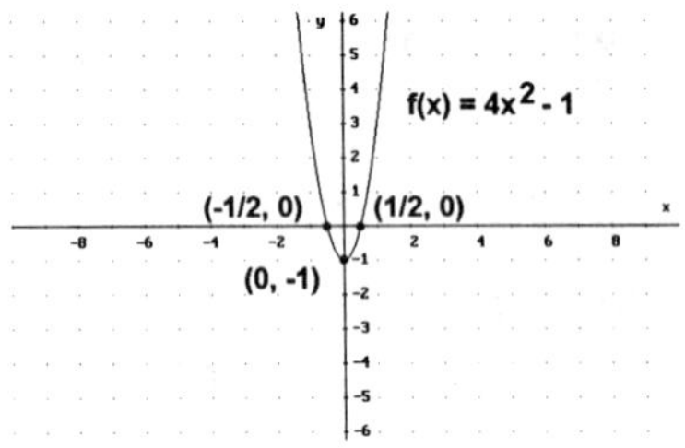

63. Let $x =$ one number.
$420 - x =$ the other number.
Let $f(x)$ represent their product.

$f(x) = x(420 - x)$

$f(x) = -x^2 + 420x$

$\frac{-b}{2a} = \frac{-420}{2(-1)} = 210$

Therefore, the numbers are both 210.

65. $(-6, 3), (8, 4)$

$d = \sqrt{[8 - (-6)]^2 + (4 - 3)^2}$

$d = \sqrt{14^2 + 1^2}$

$d = \sqrt{196 + 1}$

$d = \sqrt{197}$

67. $(-4, -6), (-1, 5)$

$d = \sqrt{[-1 - (-4)]^2 + [5 - (-6)]^2}$

$d = \sqrt{9 + 121}$

$d = \sqrt{130}$

69. $(2, 6), (-12, 4)$

$\left(\frac{2 + (-12)}{2}, \frac{6 + 4}{2}\right)$

$(-5, 5)$

71. $(-6, -5)$, $(-9, 7)$

$$\left(\frac{-6+(-9)}{2}, \frac{-5+7}{2}\right)$$

$$\left(\frac{-15}{2}, 1\right)$$

73. $C(-4, 4)$; $r = 3$

$$[x-(-4)]^2 + (y-4)^2 = 3^2$$

$$(x+4)^2 + (y-4)^2 = 9$$

75. $C(-7, -9)$; $r = \sqrt{11}$

$$[x-(-7)]^2 + [y-(-9)]^2 = (\sqrt{11})^2$$

$$(x+7)^2 + (y+9)^2 = 11$$

77. $x^2 + y^2 = 7$

$$(x-0)^2 + (y-0)^2 = (\sqrt{7})^2$$

$$C(0, 0); \; r = \sqrt{7}$$

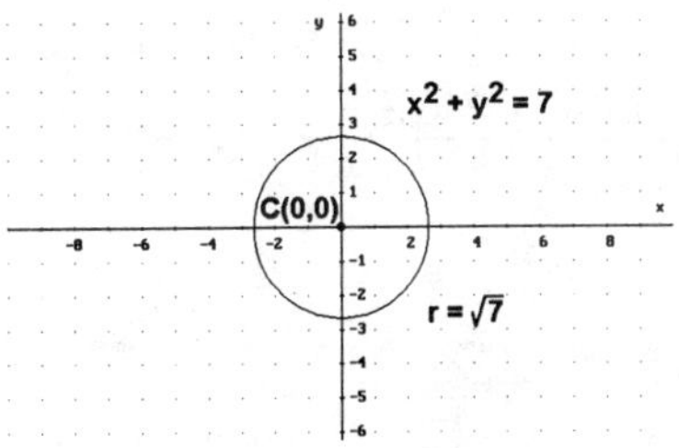

79. $x = -(y+2)^2 + 3$

$$V = (3, -2)$$

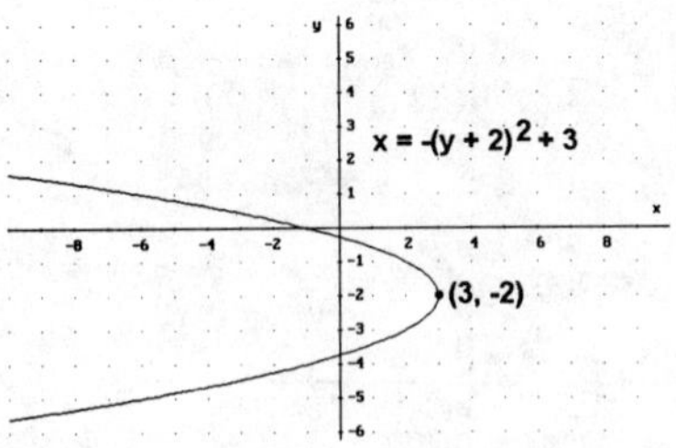

81. $y = -x^2 + 4x + 10$

$$y = -(x^2 - 4x) + 10$$

$$y = -\left[x^2 - 4x + \left(\frac{4}{2}\right)^2\right] + 10 + 4$$

$$y = -(x-2)^2 + 14$$

$$V(2, 14)$$

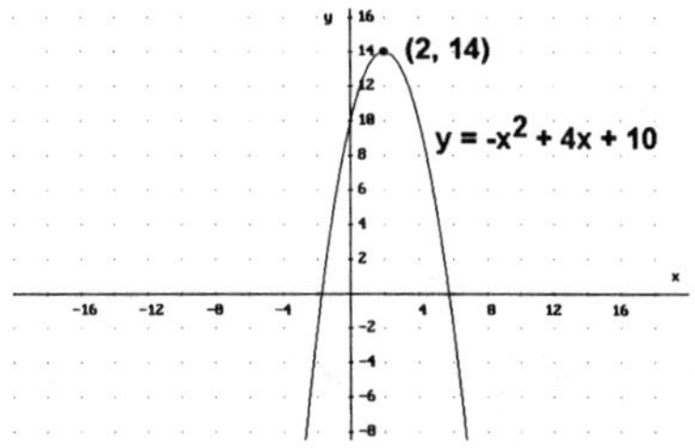

83. $x^2 + y^2 + 2x + y = \frac{3}{4}$

$$x^2 + 2x + \left(\frac{2}{2}\right)^2 + y^2 + y + \left(\frac{1}{2}\right)^2 = \frac{3}{4} + 1 + \frac{1}{4}$$

$$(x+1)^2 + \left(y + \frac{1}{2}\right)^2 = 2$$

$$(x+1)^2 + \left(y + \frac{1}{2}\right)^2 = (\sqrt{2})^2$$

$$C\left(-1, -\frac{1}{2}\right); \; r = \sqrt{2}$$

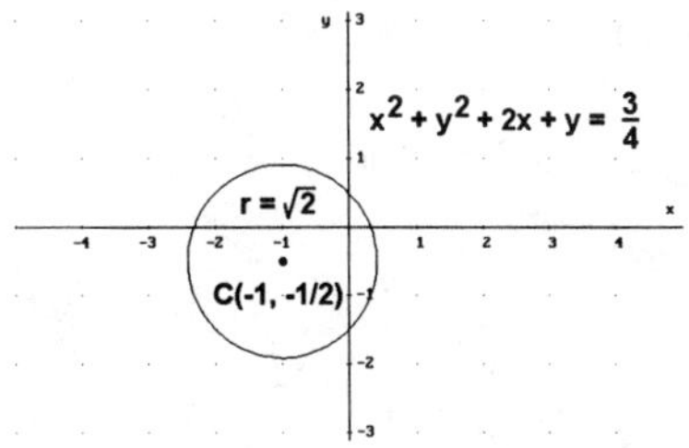

85. $4x^2 + 4y^2 + 16x + 8y = 1$

$$4x^2 + 16x + 4y^2 + 8y = 1$$

$$4(x^2 + 4x) + 4(y^2 + 2y) = 1$$

$$4\left[x^2 + 4x + \left(\frac{4}{2}\right)^2\right] + 4\left[y^2 + 2y + \left(\frac{2}{2}\right)^2\right] = 1 + 16 + 4$$

$$4(x+2)^2 + 4(y+1)^2 = 21$$

$$(x+2)^2 + (y+1)^2 = \frac{21}{4}$$

$$(x+2)^2 + (y+1)^2 = \left(\frac{\sqrt{21}}{2}\right)^2$$

$$C(-2, -1); \; r = \frac{\sqrt{21}}{2}$$

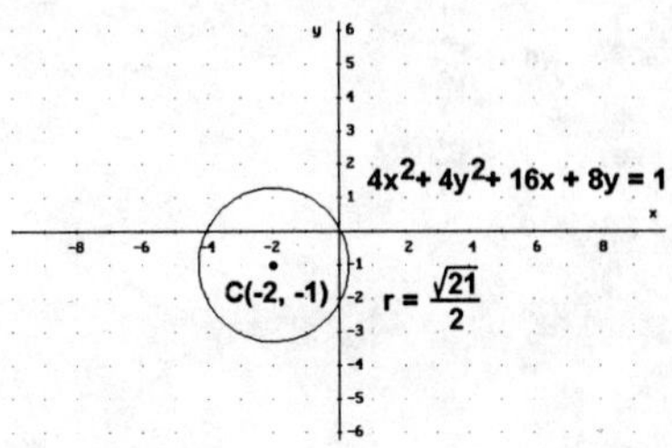

87. $y = x^2 + 6x + 9$

$y = (x+3)^2 + 0$

$V(-3,\ 0)$

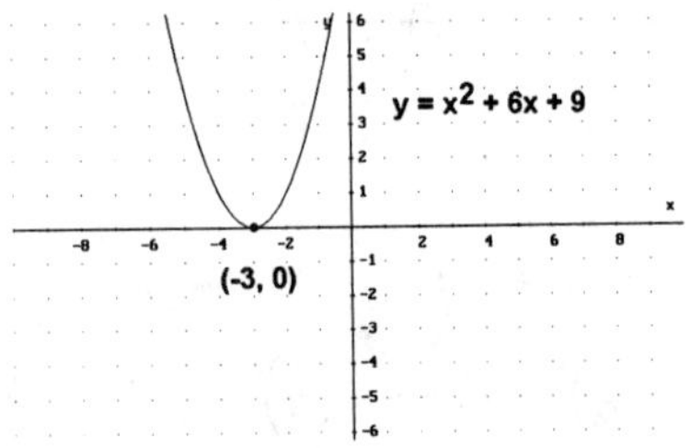

89. $C(5.6, -2.4);\ r = \frac{6.2}{2} = 3.1$

$(x-5.6)^2 + [y-(-2.4)]^2 = 3.1^2$

$(x-5.6)^2 + (y+2.4)^2 = 9.61$

91. $x^2 - \frac{y^2}{4} = 1$

$\frac{(x-0)^2}{1^2} - \frac{(y-0)^2}{2^2} = 1$

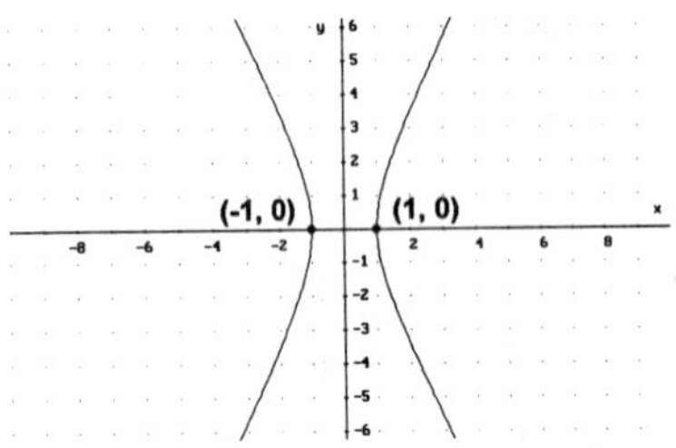

93. $\frac{y^2}{4} + \frac{x^2}{16} = 1$

$\frac{(x-0)^2}{4^2} + \frac{(y-0)^2}{2^2} = 1$

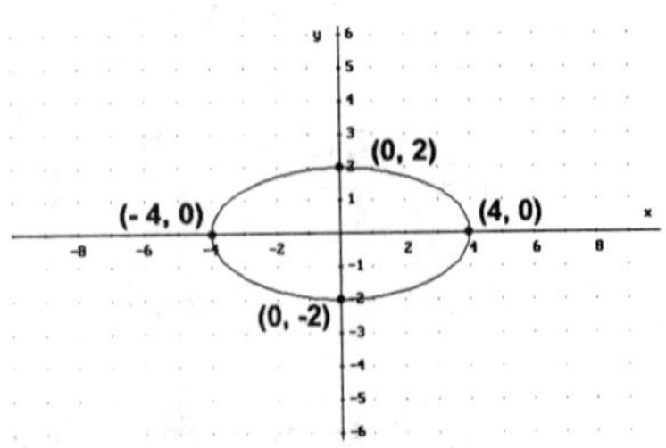

95. $\frac{x^2}{5} - \frac{y^2}{5} = 1$

$\frac{(x-0)^2}{(\sqrt{5})^2} - \frac{(y-0)^2}{(\sqrt{5})^2} = 1$

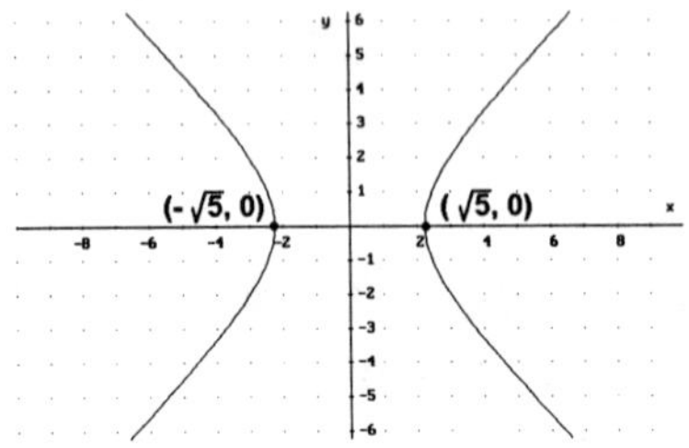

97. $4y^2 + 9x^2 = 36$

$\frac{y^2}{9} + \frac{x^2}{4} = 1$

$\frac{(x-0)^2}{2^2} + \frac{(y-0)^2}{3^2} = 1$

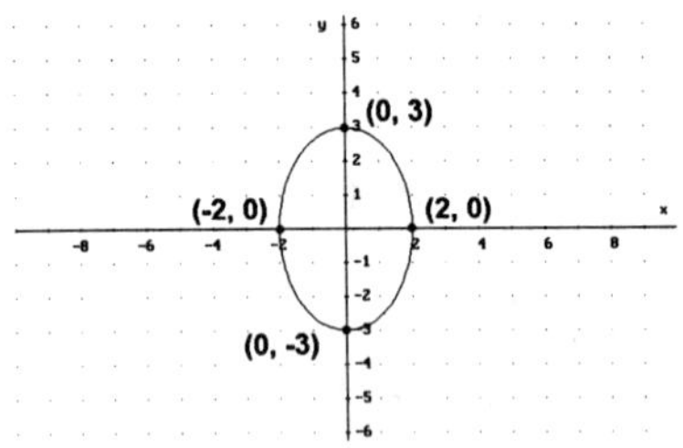

99. $\frac{(x+3)^2}{9} + \frac{(y-4)^2}{25} = 1$

$\frac{(x+3)^2}{3^2} + \frac{(y-4)^2}{5^2} = 1$

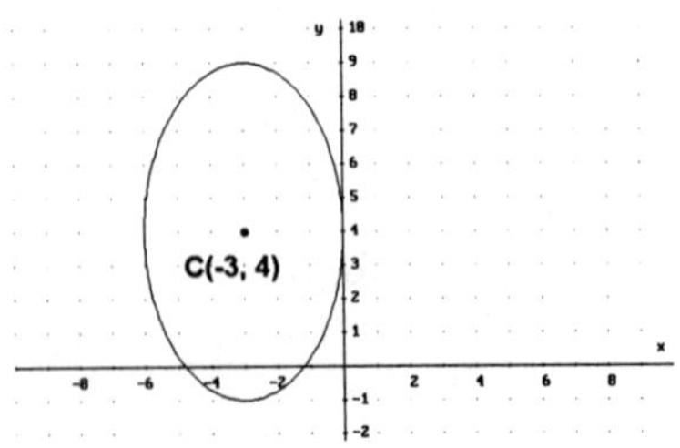

101. $36y^2 - 49x^2 = 1764$

$\frac{y^2}{49} - \frac{x^2}{36} = 1$

$\frac{(y-0)^2}{7^2} - \frac{(x-0)^2}{6^2} = 1$

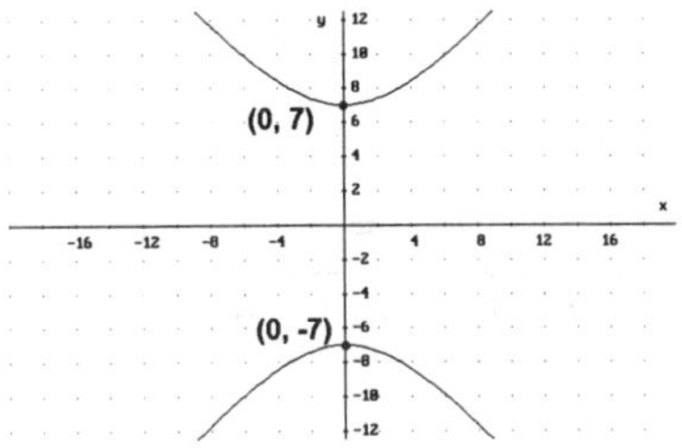

103. $x^2 = 4y^2 - 16$

$16 = 4y^2 - x^2$

$1 = \frac{y^2}{4} - \frac{x^2}{16}$

$\frac{(y-0)^2}{2^2} - \frac{(x-0)^2}{4^2} = 1$

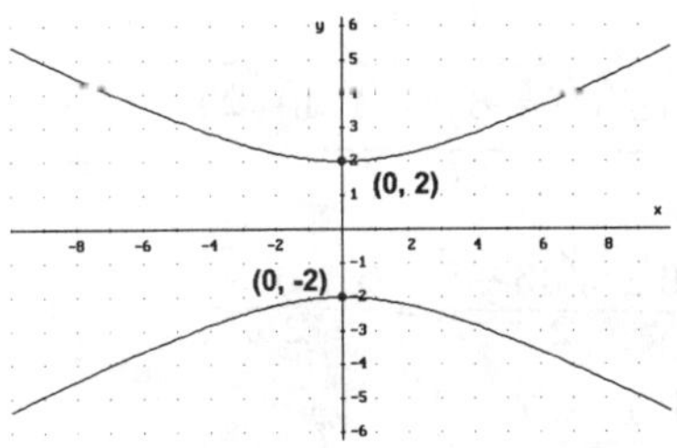

105. $y = x^2 + 4x + 6$

$y = x^2 + 4x + \left(\frac{4}{2}\right)^2 + 6 - 4$

$y = (x+2)^2 + 2$

$V(-2,\ 2)$

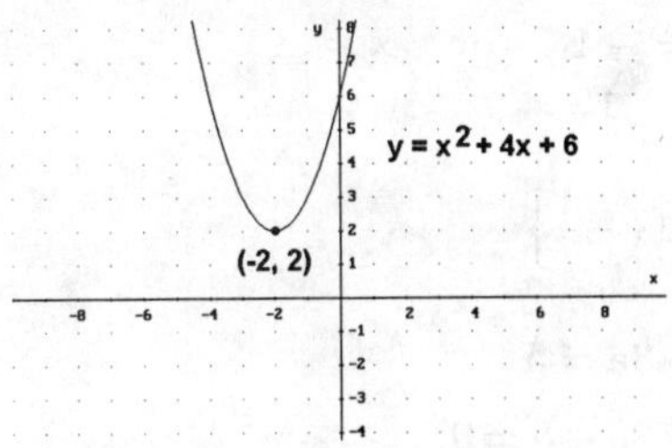

107. $y^2 + x^2 = 4x + 6$

$x^2 - 4x + y^2 = 6$

$x^2 - 4x + \left(\frac{4}{2}\right)^2 + y^2 = 6 + 4$

$(x-2)^2 + y^2 = 10$

$(x-2)^2 + (y-0)^2 = (\sqrt{10})^2$

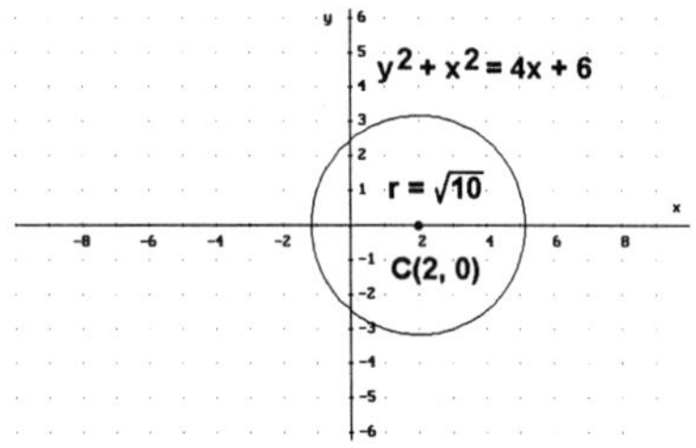

109. $x^2 + y^2 - 8y = 0$

$x^2 + y^2 - 8y + \left(\frac{8}{2}\right)^2 = 0 + 16$

$x^2 + (y-4)^2 = 16$

$(x-0)^2 + (y-4)^2 = 4^2$

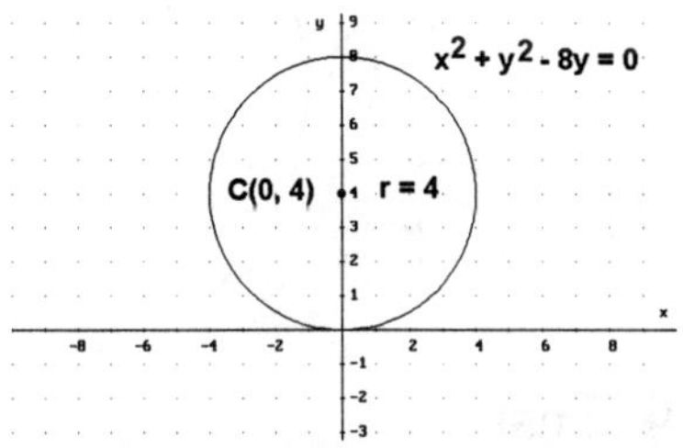

111. $x^2 - 4 = y^2$

$x^2 - y^2 = 4$

$\frac{x^2}{4} - \frac{y^2}{4} = 1$

$\frac{(x-0)^2}{2^2} - \frac{(y-0)^2}{2^2} = 1$

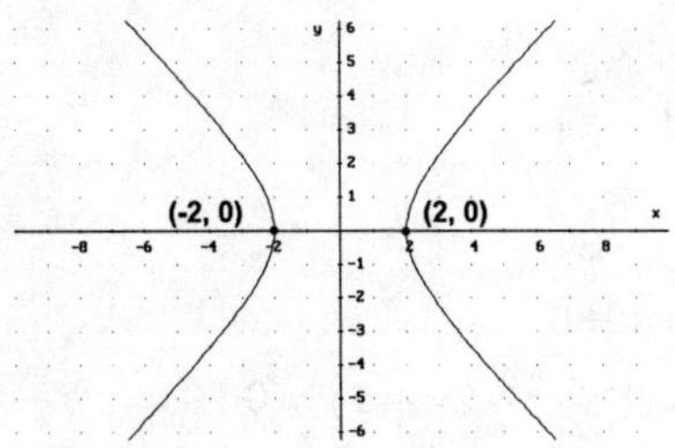

113. $6(x-2)^2 + 9(y+5)^2 = 36$

$\frac{(x-2)^2}{6} + \frac{(y+5)^2}{4} = 1$

$\frac{(x-2)^2}{(\sqrt{6})^2} + \frac{(y+5)^2}{2^2} = 1$

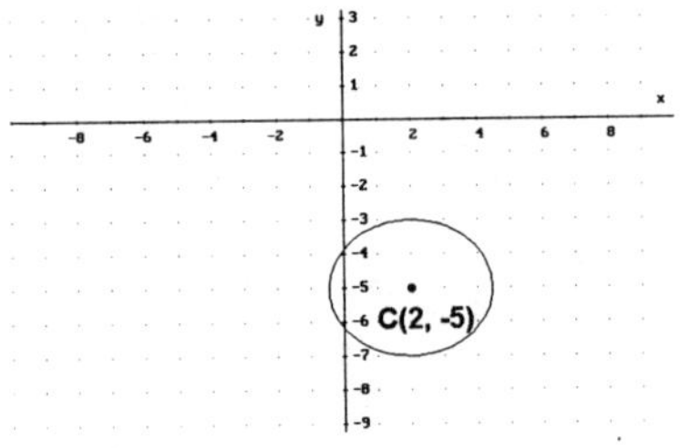

115. $\frac{x^2}{16}-\frac{y^2}{25}=2$

$\frac{(x-0)^2}{4^2}-\frac{(y-0)^2}{5^2}=1$

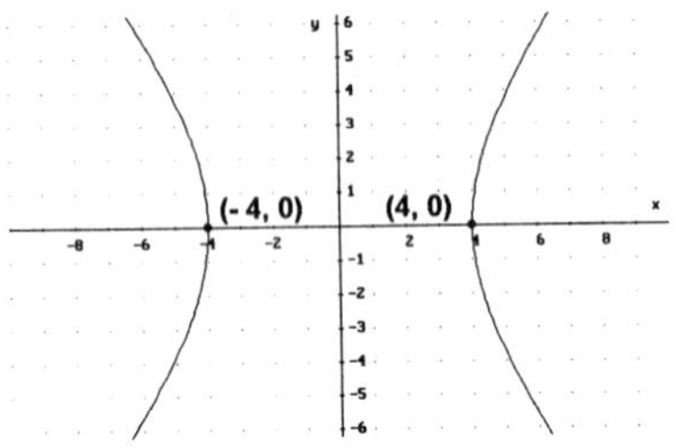

Chapter 9 Test

1. $5x^2-2x=7$

$5x^2-2x-7=0$

$(5x-7)(x+1)=0$

$5x-7=0$ or $x+1=0$

$5x=7$ or $x=-1$

$x=\frac{7}{5}$

$\left\{-1,\ \frac{7}{5}\right\}$

2. $x^3=-8$

$x^3+8=0$

$(x+2)(x^2-2x+4)=0$

$x=-2$

$a=1,\ b=-2,\ c=4$

$$x=\frac{2\pm\sqrt{(-2)^2-4(1)(4)}}{2(1)}$$

$$x=\frac{2\pm\sqrt{4-16}}{2}=\frac{2\pm\sqrt{-12}}{2}$$

$$x=\frac{2\pm 2i\sqrt{3}}{2}=1\pm i\sqrt{3}$$

$\{-2,\ 1-i\sqrt{3},\ 1+i\sqrt{3}\}$

3. $m^2-m+8=0$

$a=1,\ b=-1,\ c=8$

$$m=\frac{1\pm\sqrt{(-1)^2-4(1)(8)}}{2(1)}$$

$$m=\frac{1\pm\sqrt{1-32}}{2}=\frac{1\pm\sqrt{-31}}{2}$$

$$m=\frac{1\pm i\sqrt{31}}{2}$$

$\left\{\frac{1-i\sqrt{31}}{2},\ \frac{1+i\sqrt{31}}{2}\right\}$

4. $u^2-6u+2=0$

$a=1,\ b=-6,\ c=2$

$$u=\frac{6\pm\sqrt{(-6)^2-4(1)(2)}}{2(1)}$$

$$u=\frac{6\pm\sqrt{36-8}}{2}=\frac{6\pm\sqrt{28}}{2}$$

$$u=\frac{6\pm 2\sqrt{7}}{2}=3\pm\sqrt{7}$$

$\{3-\sqrt{7},\ 3+\sqrt{7}\}$

5. $7x^2+8x+1=0$

$(7x+1)(x+1)=0$

$7x+1=0$ or $x+1=0$

$7x=-1$ or $x=-1$

$x=-\frac{1}{7}$

$\left\{-1,-\frac{1}{7}\right\}$

6. $a^2-3a=5$

$a^2-3a-5=0$

$a=1,\ b=-3,\ c=-5$

$$a=\frac{3\pm\sqrt{(-3)^2-4(1)(-5)}}{2(1)}$$

$$a=\frac{3\pm\sqrt{9+20}}{2}=\frac{3\pm\sqrt{29}}{2}$$

$\left\{\frac{3-\sqrt{29}}{2},\ \frac{3+\sqrt{29}}{2}\right\}$

7. $\frac{4}{x+2}+\frac{2x}{x-2}=\frac{6}{x^2-4}$

$\frac{4(x-2)+2x(x+2)}{(x+2)(x-2)}=\frac{6}{(x+2)(x-2)}$

$4x-8+2x^2+4x=6$

$2x^2+8x-8=6$

$2x^2+8x-14=0$

$x^2+4x-7=0$

$a=1,\ b=4,\ c=-7$

$x=\frac{-4\pm\sqrt{4^2-4(1)(-7)}}{2(1)}$

$x=\frac{-4\pm\sqrt{16+28}}{2}=\frac{-4\pm\sqrt{44}}{2}$

$x=\frac{-4\pm 2\sqrt{11}}{2}=-2\pm\sqrt{11}$

$\{-2-\sqrt{11},\ -2+\sqrt{11}\}$

8. $x^4-8x^2-9=0$

$(x^2-9)(x^2+1)=0$

$x^2-9=0$ or $x^2+1=0$

$x^2=9$ or $x^2=-1$

$x=\pm\sqrt{9}$ or $x=\pm\sqrt{-1}$

$x=\pm 3$ or $x=\pm i$

$\{-3,\ 3,\ -i,\ i\}$

9. $x^6+1=x^4+x^2$

$x^6-x^4-x^2+1=0$

$x^4(x^2-1)-(x^2-1)=0$

$(x^4-1)(x^2-1)=0$

$(x^2+1)(x^2-1)(x^2-1)=0$

$(x^2+1)(x^2-1)^2=0$

$(x^2+1)[(x+1)(x-1)]^2=0$

$(x^2+1)(x+1)^2(x-1)^2=0$

$x^2+1=0$ or $(x+1)^2=0$ or $(x-1)^2=0$

$x^2=-1$ or $x+1=0$ or $x-1=0$

$x=\pm\sqrt{-1}$ or $x=-1$ or $x=1$

$x=\pm i$

$\{-1,\ 1,\ -i,\ i\}$

10. $(x+1)^2-15(x+1)+56=0$

Let $u=x+1$

$u^2-15u+56=0$

$(u-7)(u-8)=0$

$u-7=0$ or $u-8=0$

$u=7$ or $u=8$

Now substitute back

$x+1=7$ or $x+1=8$

$x=6$ or $x=7$

$\{6,\ 7\}$

11. $x^2-6x=-2$

$x^2-6x+\left(\frac{6}{2}\right)^2=-2+9$

$(x-3)^2=7$

$x-3=\pm\sqrt{7}$

$\{3-\sqrt{7},\ 3+\sqrt{7}\}$

12. $2a^2+5=4a$

$2a^2-4a=-5$

$a^2-2a=-\frac{5}{2}$

$a^2-2a+\left(\frac{2}{2}\right)^2=-\frac{5}{2}+1$

$(a-1)^2=-\frac{3}{2}$

$a-1=\pm\sqrt{\frac{-3}{2}}$

$a-1=\pm\frac{i\sqrt{3}}{\sqrt{2}}$

$a-1=\pm\frac{i\sqrt{6}}{2}$

$a=1\pm\frac{i\sqrt{6}}{2}$

$a=\frac{2\pm i\sqrt{6}}{2}$

$\left\{\frac{2-i\sqrt{6}}{2},\ \frac{2+i\sqrt{6}}{2}\right\}$

13. $(6x+7)(7x-12)\le 0$

$(6x+7)(7x-12)=0$

$6x+7=0$ or $7x-12=0$

$x = -\frac{7}{6}$ or $x = \frac{12}{7}$

Region	Interval	Test Point
A	$\left(-\infty, -\frac{7}{6}\right)$	-2
B	$\left(-\frac{7}{6}, \frac{12}{7}\right)$	0
C	$\left(\frac{12}{7}, \infty\right)$	2

$x = -2$	$[6(-2)+7][7(-2)-12] \le 0$	False
$x = 0$:	$[6(0)+7][7(0)-12] \le 0$	True
$x = 2$:	$[6(2)+7][7(2)-12] \le 0$	False

The solution is $\left[-\frac{7}{6}, \frac{12}{7}\right]$.

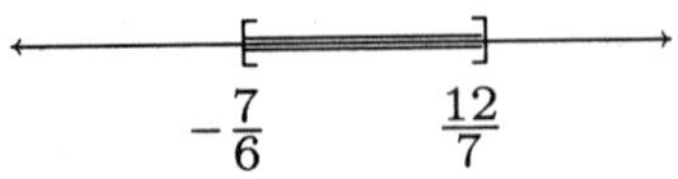

14. $(x^2-16)(x^2-25) > 0$

Let $u = x^2$

$(u-16)(u-25) > 0$

$(u-16)(u-25) = 0$

$u - 16 = 0$ or $u - 25 = 0$

$u = 16$ or $u = 25$

Region	Interval	Test Point
A	$(-\infty, 16)$	15
B	$(16, 25)$	20
C	$(25, \infty)$	30

$u = 15$:	$(15-16)(15-25) > 0$	True
$u = 20$:	$(20-16)(20-25) > 0$	False
$u = 30$:	$(30-16)(30-25) > 0$	True

$u < 16$ or $u > 25$

Now substituting back,

$x^2 < 16$ or $x^2 > 25$

$-4 < x < 4$ or $x < -5$ or $x > 5$

$(-\infty, -5) \cup (-4, 4) \cup (5, \infty)$

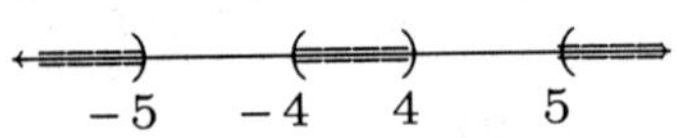

15. $\frac{2x-11}{3x+12} \ge 0$

$2x - 11 = 0$ and $3x + 12 = 0$

$2x = 11$ and $3x = -12$

$x = \frac{11}{2}$ and $x = -4$

Region	Interval	Test Point
A	$(-\infty, -4)$	-5
B	$\left(-4, \frac{11}{2}\right)$	0
C	$\left(\frac{11}{2}, \infty\right)$	6

$x = -5$:	$\frac{2(-5)-11}{3(-5)+12} \ge 0$	True
$x = 0$:	$\frac{2(0)-11}{3(0)+12} \ge 0$	False
$x = 6$:	$\frac{2(6)-11}{3(6)+12} \ge 0$	True

The solution is $(-\infty, -4) \cup \left[\frac{11}{2}, \infty\right)$.

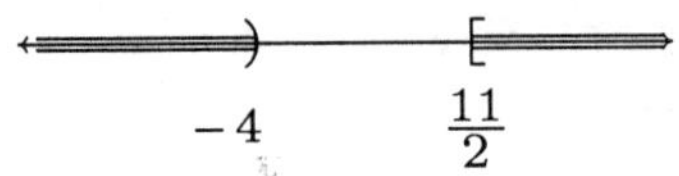

16. $\frac{7x-14}{x^2-9} \le 0$

$7x - 14 = 0$ and $x^2 - 9 = 0$

$7x = 14$ and $x^2 = 9$

$x = 2$ and $x = \pm\sqrt{9}$

$x = \pm 3$

Region	Interval	Test Point
A	$(-\infty, -3)$	-4
B	$(-3, 2)$	0
C	$(2, 3)$	$\frac{5}{2}$
D	$(3, \infty)$	4

$x = -4$:	$\frac{7(-4)-14}{(-4)^2-9} \le 0$	True
$x = 0$:	$\frac{7(0)-14}{0^2-9} \le 0$	False
$x = \frac{5}{2}$:	$\frac{7\left(\frac{5}{2}\right)-14}{\left(\frac{5}{2}\right)^2-9} \le 0$	True
$x = 4$:	$\frac{7(4)-14}{4^2-9} \le 0$	False

The solution is $(-\infty, -3) \cup [2, 3)$.

17. $(-6, 3), (-8, -7)$

$d = \sqrt{[-8-(-6)]^2 + (-7-3)^2}$

$d = \sqrt{2^2 + 10^2} = \sqrt{104} = 2\sqrt{26}$

18. $(-2, -5), (-6, 12)$

$\left(\frac{-2+(-6)}{2}, \frac{-5+12}{2}\right)$

$\left(-4, \frac{7}{2}\right)$

19. $y = 2(x+3)^2 + 1$

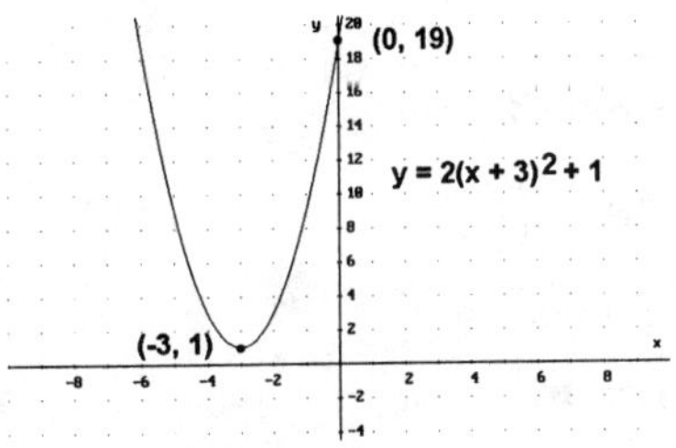

20. $x^2 + y^2 = 36$

$(x-0)^2 + (y-0)^2 = 6^2$

$C(0, 0);\ r = 6$

$y = 0$

$x^2 + 0^2 = 36$

$x^2 = 36$

$x = \pm 6$

are the x-intercepts.

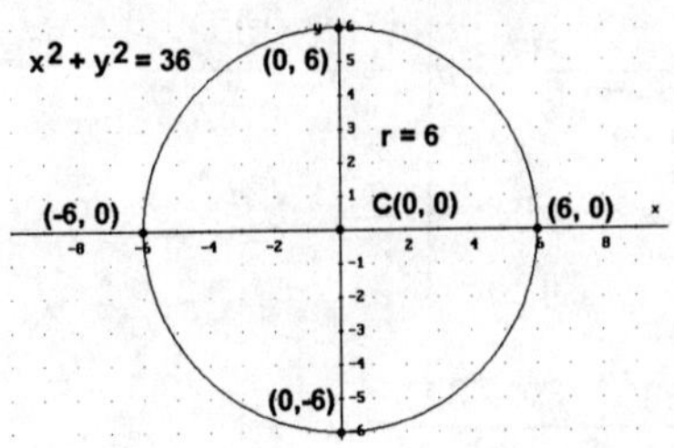

21. $x^2 - y^2 = 36$

$\frac{x^2}{36} - \frac{y^2}{36} = 1$

$\frac{(x-0)^2}{6^2} - \frac{(y-0)^2}{6^2} = 1$

$C(0, 0),\ V_1(-6, 0),\ V_2(6, 0)$

$x = 0$

$0^2 - y^2 = 36$

$-y^2 = 36$

$y^2 = -36$

So there are no y-intercepts.

$y = 0$

$x^2 - 0^2 = 36$

$x^2 = 36$

$x = \pm 6$

are the x-intercepts. The asymptotes are given by $y - 0 = \pm\frac{6}{6}(x-0)$ or $y = \pm x$.

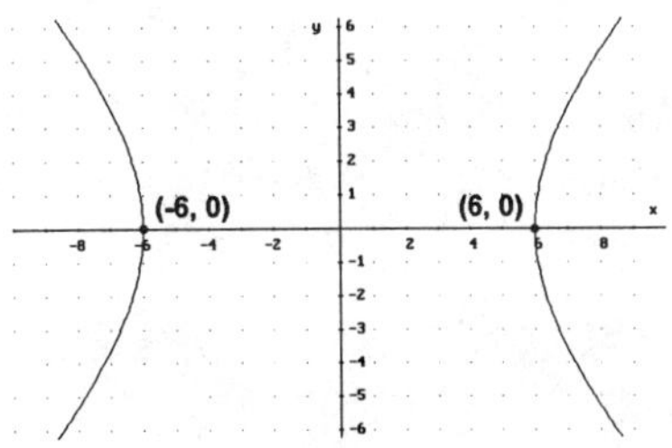

22. $16x^2 + 9y^2 = 144$

$\frac{x^2}{9} + \frac{y^2}{16} = 1$

$\frac{(x-0)^2}{3^2} + \frac{(y-0)^2}{4^2} = 1$

$C(0, 0),\ V_1(0, -4),\ V_2(0, 4)$

$x = 0$

$16(0)^2 + 9y^2 = 144$

$9y^2 = 144$

$y^2 = 16$

$y = \pm 4$ are the y-intercepts.

$y = 0$

$16x^2 + 9(0)^2 = 144$

$16x^2 = 144$

$x^2 = 9$

$x = \pm 3$ are the x-intercepts.

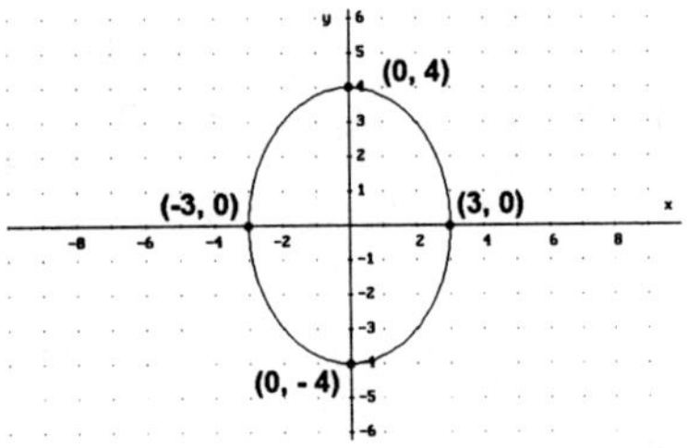

23. $y = x^2 - 8x + 16$

$y = (x-4)^2 + 0$

V(4, 0)

The graph opens upward since $a = 1 > 0$.

$y = 0$

$(x-4)^2 = 0$

$x - 4 = 0$

$x = 4$

The x-intercept is 4.

$x = 0$

$y = 0^2 - 8(0) + 16$

$y = 16$

The y-intercept is 16.

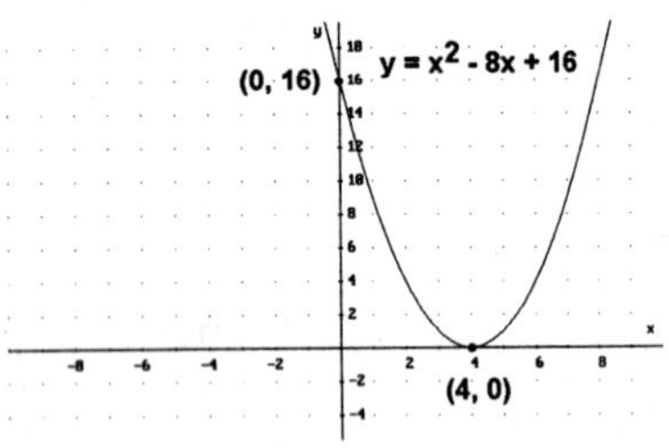

24. $x^2 + y^2 + 6x = 16$

$x^2 + 6x + \left(\frac{6}{2}\right)^2 + y^2 = 16 + 9$

$(x+3)^2 + y^2 = 25$

$(x+3)^2 + (y-0)^2 = 5^2$

$C(-3,\ 0);\ r = 5$

$x = 0$

$y^2 = 16$

$y = \pm 4$ are the y-intercepts.

$y = 0$

$(x+3)^2 = 25$

$x + 3 = \pm 5$

$x = -3 \pm 5$

$x = 2$ and -8 are the x-intercepts.

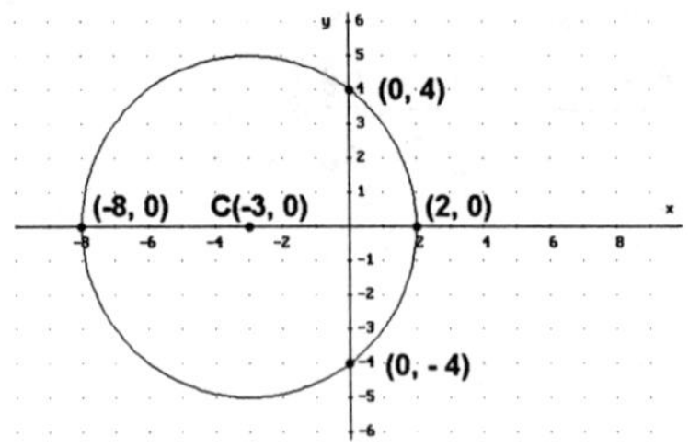

25. $x = y^2 + 8y - 3$

$x = y^2 + 8y + \left(\frac{8}{2}\right)^2 - 3 - 16$

$x = (y+4)^2 - 19$

$V(-19, -4)$

$x = 0$

$0 = (y+4)^2 - 19$

$19 = (y+4)^2$

$y = -4 \pm \sqrt{19}$ are the y-intercepts.

$y = 0$

$x = 0^2 + 8(0) - 3$

$x = -3$ is the x-intercept.

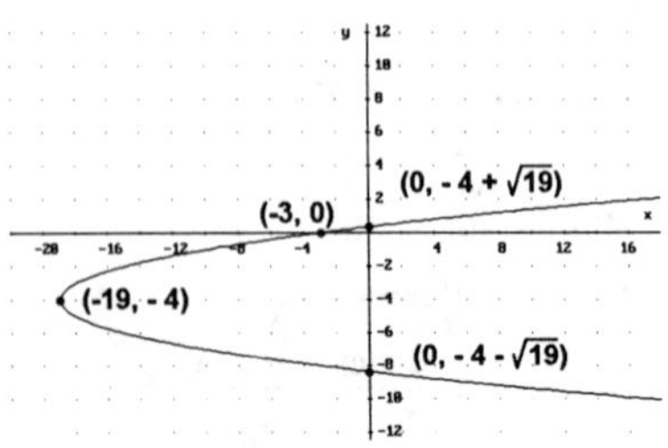

26. $\frac{(x-4)^2}{16} + \frac{(y-3)^2}{9} = 1$

$\frac{(x-4)^2}{4^2} + \frac{(y-3)^2}{3^2} = 1$

$C(4, 3)$, $V_1(0, 3)$, $V_2(8, 3)$

$x = 0$

$\frac{(0-4)^2}{16} + \frac{(y-3)^2}{9} = 1$

$1 + \frac{(y-3)^2}{9} = 1$

$\frac{(y-3)^2}{9} = 0$

$(y-3)^2 = 0$

$y - 3 = 0$

$y = 3$ is the y-intercept.

$y = 0$

$\frac{(x-4)^2}{16} + \frac{(0-3)^2}{9} = 1$

$\frac{(x-4)^2}{16} + 1 = 1$

$\frac{(x-4)^2}{16} = 0$

$(x-4)^2 = 0$

$x - 4 = 0$

$x = 4$ is the x-intercept.

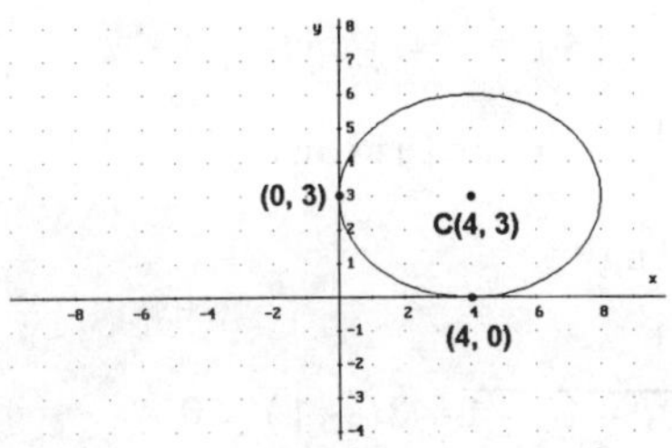

27. $s(t) = -16t^2 - 256$

a. Compute s(0).

$s(0) = -16(0)^2 + 256$

$s(0) = 256$ ft.

b. Solve $s(t) = 0$.

$-16t^2 + 256 = 0$

$t^2 - 16 = 0$

$t^2 = 16$

$t = \pm\sqrt{16} = \pm 4$

Discarding the negative value, we find that it takes 4 seconds for the stone to hit the water.

28. Let n = the first odd whole number.
$n + 2$ = the second whole number.
$n + 4$ = the third whole number.

$n(n+4) = 42(n+2) + 39$

$n^2 + 4n = 42n + 84 + 39$

$n^2 + 4n = 42n + 123$

$n^2 - 38n - 123 = 0$

$(n-41)(n+3) = 0$

$n - 41 = 0$ or $n + 3 = 0$

$n = 41$ or $n = -3$

Discarding the negative value, we find that 41, 43, and 45 is the solution.

Chapter 9 Cumulative Review

1. $y = mx + b$

$y - b = mx$

$\frac{y-b}{m} = x$

3. 72% of 200

$0.72(200)$

144

5. $\left|2x - \frac{1}{10}\right| < -13$

No solution.

Absolute value can not be less than a negative.

{ }

7a. function

b. function

c. not a function

d. function

e. not a function

f. not a function

9a. $(st)^4 = s^4t^4$

b. $(\frac{m}{n})^7 = \frac{m^7}{n^7}$

c. $(2a)^3 = 2^3a^3 = 8a^3$

d. $(-5x^2y^3z)^2 = (-5)^2x^4y^6z^2 = 25x^4y^6z^2$

e. $\left(\frac{2x^4}{3y^5}\right)^4 = \frac{2^4x^{16}}{3^4y^{20}} = \frac{16x^{16}}{81y^{20}}$

11a. $(x-3)(x+3)$

$x^2+3x-3x-9$

x^2-9

b. $(4y+1)(4y-1)$

$16y^2-4y+4y-1$

$16y^2-1$

c. $(x^2+2y)(x^2-2y)$

$x^4-2x^2y+2x^2y-4y^2$

x^4-4y^2

13. y^3-27

$(y-3)(y^2+3y+9)$

15a. $f(x) = \frac{8x^3+7x^2+20}{2}$

Domain: $\{x|x$ is a real number$\}$.

b. $g(x) = \frac{5x^2-3}{x-1}$

The function is undefined when

$x-1=0$

$x=1$

Domain: $\{x|x$ is a real number, $x \neq 1\}$.

c. $f(x) = \frac{7x-2}{2x^2+7x+6}$

The function is undefined when

$2x^2+7x+6=0$

$(2x+3)(x+2)=0$

$2x+3=0$ or $x+2=0$

$2x=-3$ or $x=-2$

$x=-\frac{3}{2}$

Domain: $\{x|x$ is a real number, $x \neq -\frac{3}{2}$, $x \neq -2\}$

17. $\sqrt{-10x-1}+3x=0$

$\sqrt{-10x-1} = -3x$

$(\sqrt{-10x-1})^2 = (-3x)^2$

$-10x-1 = 9x^2$

$0 = 9x^2+10x+1$

$0 = (9x+1)(x+1)$

$9x+1=0$ or $x+1=0$

$9x=-1$ or $x=-1$

$x=-\frac{1}{9}$

Checking $x=-\frac{1}{9}$

$\sqrt{-10\left(-\frac{1}{9}\right)-1}+3\left(-\frac{1}{9}\right)=0$

$\sqrt{\frac{10}{9}-1}-\frac{1}{3}=0$

$\sqrt{\frac{10}{9}-\frac{9}{9}}-\frac{1}{3}=0$

$\sqrt{\frac{1}{9}}-\frac{1}{3}=0$

$\frac{1}{3}-\frac{1}{3}=0$

$0=0$

$x=-\frac{1}{9}$ is a solution.

Checking

$x=-1$

$\sqrt{-10(-1)-1}+3(-1)=0$

$\sqrt{10-1}-3=0$

$\sqrt{9}-3=0$

$3-3=0$

$0=0$

$x=-1$ is a solution.

The solution set is $\left\{-\frac{1}{9}, -1\right\}$.

19. $(x+1)^2=12$

$x+1 = \pm\sqrt{12}$

$x+1 = \pm\sqrt{4}\sqrt{3}$

$x+1 = \pm 2\sqrt{3}$

$x = -1 \pm 2\sqrt{3}$

$\{-1 - 2\sqrt{3}, -1 + 2\sqrt{3}\}$

21. $(x + 2)(x - 1)(x - 5) \leq 0$

$x + 2 = 0$ or $x - 1 = 0$ or $x - 5 = 0$

$x = -2$ or $x = 1$ or $x = 5$

Region	Interval	Test Point
A	$(-\infty, -2)$	-3
B	$(-1, 1)$	0
C	$(1, 5)$	2
D	$(5, \infty)$	6

$x = -3$:	$(-3+2)(-3-1)(-3-5) \leq 0$	True
$x = 0$:	$(0 + 2)(0 - 1)(0 - 5) \leq 0$	False
$x = 2$:	$(2 + 2)(2 - 1)(2 - 5) \leq 0$	True
$x = 6$:	$(6 + 2)(6 - 1)(6 - 5) \leq 0$	False

The solution is $(-\infty, -2] \cup [1, 5]$.

23. $f(x) = x^2 - 4x - 12$

$f(x) = x^2 - 4x + 4 - 4 - 12$

$f(x) = (x - 2)^2 - 16$

$V(2, -16)$

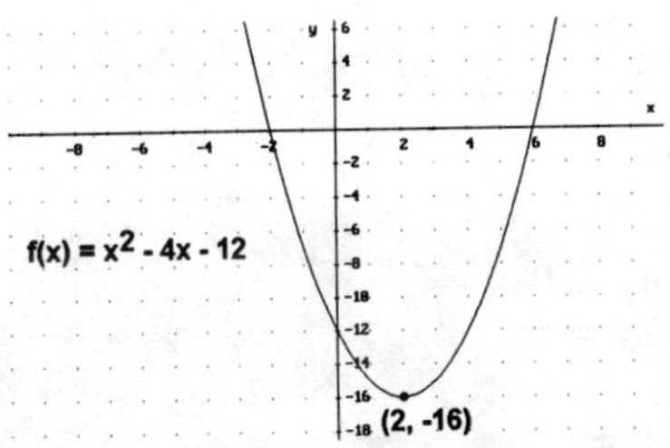

25. $x^2 + y^2 + 4x - 8y = 16$

$x^2 + 4x + 4 + y^2 - 8y + 16 = 16 + 4 + 16$

$(x + 2)^2 + (y - 4)^2 = 36$

circle

$C(-2, 4)$; $r = 6$

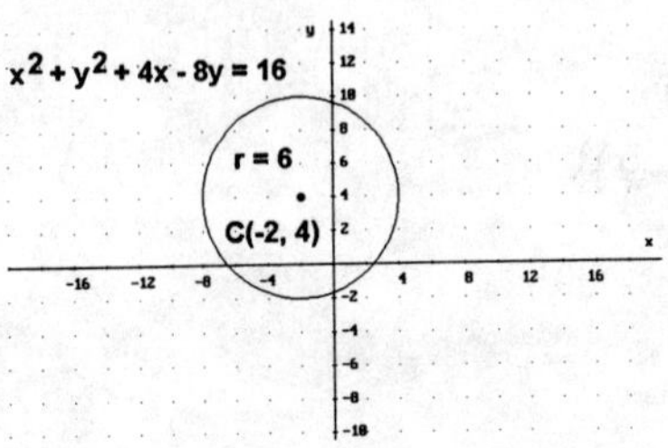

Graphing Calculator Exercise 10.1

1. $\begin{cases} y = -2.68x + 1.21 \\ y = 5.22x - 1.68 \end{cases}$

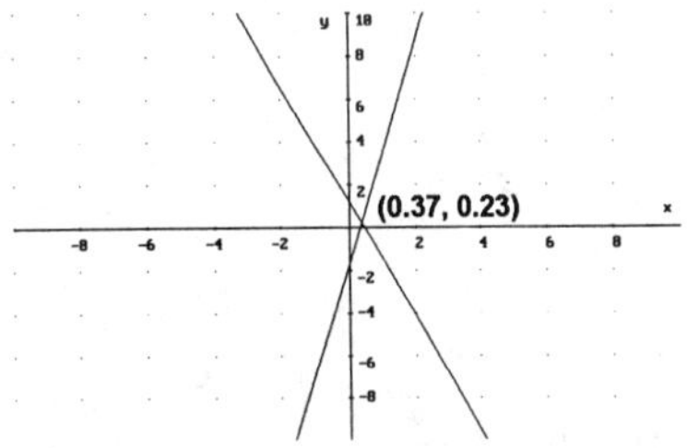

$x = 0.37,\ y = 0.23$

$\{(0.37,\ 0.23)\}$

3. $\begin{cases} 4.3x - 2.9y = 5.6 \\ 8.1x + 7.6y = -14.1 \end{cases}$

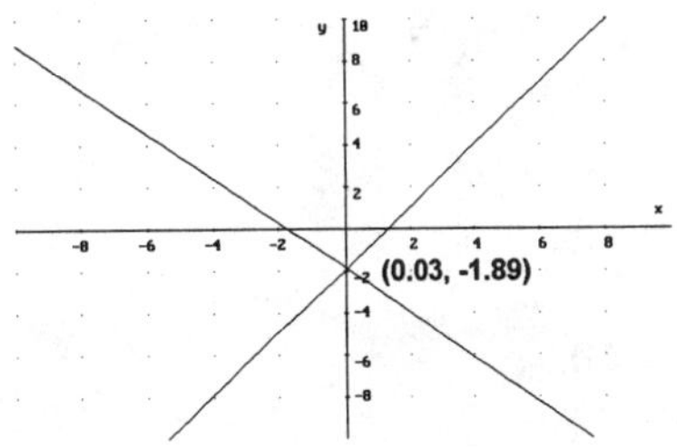

$x = 0.03,\ y = -1.89$

$\{(0.03, -1.89)\}$

Exercise Set 10.1

1. $\begin{cases} x + y = 1 \\ x - 2y = 4 \end{cases}$

$\{(2, -1)\}$

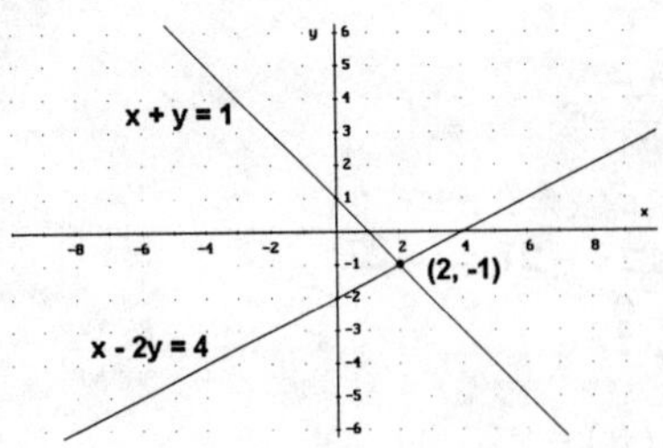

3. $\begin{cases} 2y - 4 = 0 \\ x + 2y = 5 \end{cases}$

$\{(1,\ 2)\}$

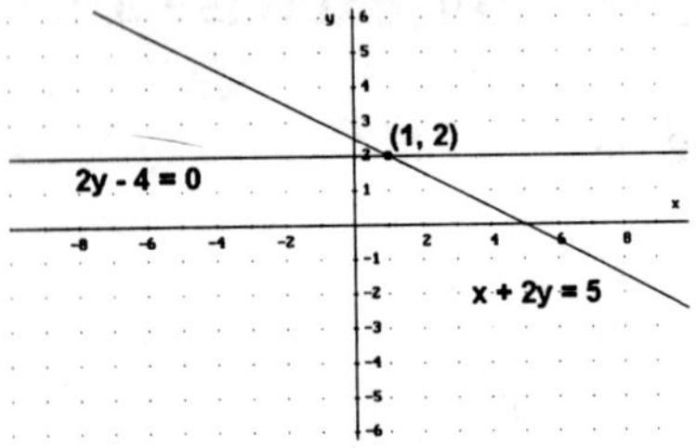

5. $\begin{cases} 3x - y = 4 \\ 6x - 2y = 4 \end{cases}$

No solution.

{ }

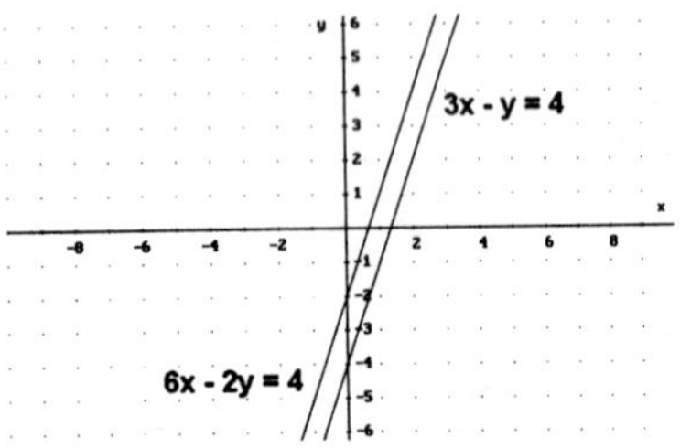

7. $\begin{cases} x + y = 10 \\ y = 4x \end{cases}$

$x + 4x = 10$
$5x = 10$
$x = 2$

$y = 4(2)$
$y = 8$

$\{(2,\ 8)\}$

9. $\begin{cases} 4x - y = 9 \\ 2x + 3y = -27 \end{cases}$

$4x - 9 = y$
$y = 4x - 9$

$2x + 3(4x - 9) = -27$
$2x + 12x - 27 = -27$
$14x = 0$
$x = 0$

$y = 4(0) - 9$
$y = -9$

$\{(0, -9)\}$

11. $\begin{cases} \frac{1}{2}x + \frac{3}{4}y = -\frac{1}{4} \\ \frac{3}{4}x - \frac{1}{4}y = 1 \end{cases}$

$\begin{cases} 2x + 3y = -1 \\ 3x - y = 4 \end{cases}$

$3x - 4 = y$
$y = 3x - 4$

$2x + 3(3x - 4) = -1$
$2x + 9x - 12 = -1$
$11x = 11$
$x = 1$

$y = 3(1) - 4$
$y = -1$

$\{(1, -1)\}$

13. $\begin{cases} \frac{x}{3} + y = \frac{4}{3} \\ -x + 2y = 11 \end{cases}$

$\begin{cases} x + 3y = 4 \\ -x + 2y = 11 \end{cases}$

$2y - 11 = x$
$x = 2y - 11$

$2y - 11 + 3y = 4$
$5y = 15$
$y = 3$

$x = 2(3) - 11$
$x = -5$

$\{(-5,\ 3)\}$

15. $\begin{cases} 2x - 4y = 0 \\ x + 2y = 5 \end{cases}$

$\begin{cases} x - 2y = 0 \\ x + 2y = 5 \end{cases}$

$2x = 5$

$x = \frac{5}{2}$

$\frac{5}{2} - 2y = 0$

$\frac{5}{2} = 2y$

$y = \frac{5}{4}$

$\left\{\left(\frac{5}{2},\ \frac{5}{4}\right)\right\}$

17. $\begin{cases} 5x+2y=1 \\ x-3y=7 \end{cases}$

$\begin{cases} 5x+2y=1 \\ -5x+15y=-35 \end{cases}$

$17y=-34$
$y=-2$

$x-3(-2)=7$
$x+6=7$
$x=1$

$\{(1,-2)\}$

19. $\begin{cases} 5x-2y=27 \\ -3x+5y=18 \end{cases}$

$\begin{cases} 15x-6y=81 \\ -15x+25y=90 \end{cases}$

$19y=171$
$y=9$

$5x-2(9)=27$
$5x-18=27$
$5x=45$
$x=9$

$\{(9,\ 9)\}$

21. $\begin{cases} 3x-5y=11 \\ 2x-6y=2 \end{cases}$

$\begin{cases} 3x-5y=11 \\ x-3y=1 \end{cases}$

$\begin{cases} 3x-5y=11 \\ -3x+9y=-3 \end{cases}$

$4y=8$
$y=2$

$x-3(2)=1$
$x-6=1$
$x=7$

$\{(7,\ 2)\}$

23. $\begin{cases} x-2y=4 \\ 2x-4y=4 \end{cases}$

$\begin{cases} 2x-4y=8 \\ 2x-4y=4 \end{cases}$

Inconsistent system.
No solution.

$\{\ \}$

25. $\begin{cases} 3x+y=1 \\ 2y=2-6x \end{cases}$

$\begin{cases} 3x+y=1 \\ 6x+2y=2 \end{cases}$

$\begin{cases} 6x+2y=2 \\ 6x+2y=2 \end{cases}$

Dependent system.
$\{(x,\ y) \mid 3x+y=1\}$

27. $\begin{cases} 2x+5y=8 \\ 6x+y=10 \end{cases}$

$\begin{cases} -6x-15y=-24 \\ 6x+y=10 \end{cases}$

$-14y=-14$
$y=1$

$6x+1=10$
$6x=9$

$x=\frac{9}{6}=\frac{3}{2}$

$\left\{\left(\frac{3}{2},\ 1\right)\right\}$

29. $\begin{cases} x+y=1 \\ x-2y=4 \end{cases}$

$\begin{cases} x+y=1 \\ -x+2y=-4 \end{cases}$

$3y=-3$
$y=-1$

$x+(-1)=1$
$x=2$

$\{(2,-1)\}$

31. $\begin{cases} \frac{1}{3}x+y=\frac{4}{3} \\ -\frac{1}{4}x-\frac{1}{2}y=-\frac{1}{4} \end{cases}$

$\begin{cases} x+3y=4 \\ -x-2y=-1 \end{cases}$

$y=3$

$x+3(3)=4$
$x+9=4$
$x=-5$

$\{(-5,\ 3)\}$

33. $\begin{cases} 2x+6y=8 \\ 3x+9y=12 \end{cases}$

$\begin{cases} x+3y=4 \\ x+3y=4 \end{cases}$

Dependent system.
$\{(x,\ y) \mid x+3y=4\}$

35. $\begin{cases} 4x+2y=5 \\ 2x+y=-1 \end{cases}$

$\begin{cases} 4x+2y=5 \\ 4x+2y=-2 \end{cases}$

Inconsistent system.
No solution.

$\{\ \}$

37. $\begin{cases} 10y-2x=1 \\ 5y=4-6x \end{cases}$

$\begin{cases} 10y=2x+1 \\ 10y=-12x+8 \end{cases}$

$2x+1=-12x+8$
$14x=7$
$x=\frac{7}{14}=\frac{1}{2}$

$10y-2\left(\frac{1}{2}\right)=1$
$10y-1=1$
$10y=2$
$y=\frac{2}{10}=\frac{1}{5}$

$\left\{\left(\frac{1}{2},\ \frac{1}{5}\right)\right\}$

39. $\begin{cases} \frac{3}{4}x+\frac{5}{2}y=11 \\ \frac{1}{16}x-\frac{3}{4}y=-1 \end{cases}$

$\begin{cases} 3x+10y=44 \\ x-12y=-16 \end{cases}$

$\begin{cases} 3x+10y=44 \\ -3x+36y=48 \end{cases}$

$46y=92$
$y=2$

$x-12(2)=-16$
$x-24=-16$
$x=8$

$\{(8,\ 2)\}$

41. $\begin{cases} x=3y+2 \\ 5x-15y=10 \end{cases}$

$5(3y+2)-15y=10$
$3y+2-3y=2$
$2=2$

Dependent system.
$\{(x,\ y) \mid x=3y+2\}$

43. $\begin{cases} 2x-y=-1 \\ y=-2x \end{cases}$

$2x-(-2x)=-1$
$4x=-1$
$x=-\frac{1}{4}$
$y=-2\left(-\frac{1}{4}\right)=\frac{1}{2}$

$\left\{\left(-\frac{1}{4},\ \frac{1}{2}\right)\right\}$

45. $\begin{cases} 2x=6 \\ y=5-x \end{cases}$

$x=3$

$y=5-3=2$

$\{(3,\ 2)\}$

47. $\begin{cases} \frac{x+5}{2}=\frac{6-4y}{3} \\ \frac{3x}{5}=\frac{21-7y}{10} \end{cases}$

$\begin{cases} 3x+15=12-8y \\ 30x=105-35y \end{cases}$

$\begin{cases} 3x+8y=-3 \\ 6x=21-7y \end{cases}$

$\begin{cases} 6x+16y=-6 \\ 6x+7y=21 \end{cases}$

$9y=-27$
$y=-3$

$3x+8(-3)=-3$
$3x-24=-3$
$3x=21$

$x=7$

$\{(7,-3)\}$

49. $\begin{cases}4x-7y=7\\12x-21y=24\end{cases}$

$\begin{cases}4x-7y=7\\4x-7y=8\end{cases}$

Inconsistent system.
No solution.

$\{\ \}$

51. $\begin{cases}\frac{2}{3}x-\frac{3}{4}y=-1\\-\frac{1}{6}x+\frac{3}{8}y=1\end{cases}$

$\begin{cases}8x-9y=-12\\-4x+9y=24\end{cases}$

$4x=12$
$x=3$

$-4(3)+9y=24$
$-12+9y=24$
$9y=36$
$y=4$

$\{(3,\ 4)\}$

53. $\begin{cases}0.7x-0.2y=-1.6\\0.2x-y=-1.4\end{cases}$

$\begin{cases}7x-2y=-16\\x-\ 5y=-7\end{cases}$

$\begin{cases}7x-2y=-16\\-7x+35y=49\end{cases}$

$33y=33$
$y=1$

$x-5(1)=-7$
$x-5=-7$
$x=-2$

$\{(-2,\ 1)\}$

55. Let $x=$ one number.
Then $y=$ the other number.

$\begin{cases}x+y=45\\x=2y\end{cases}$

$2y+y=45$
$3y=45$

$y=15$

$x=2(15)$
$x=30$

15 and 30

57. 1984 and 1988.

59. $x^2+y^2=9$

$(x-0)^2+(y-0)^2=3^2$

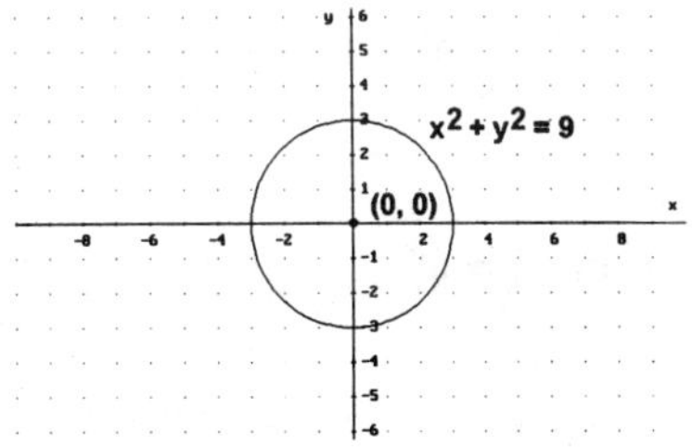

61. $\frac{x^2}{25}+\frac{y^2}{4}=1$

$\frac{(x-0)^2}{5^2}+\frac{(y-0)^2}{2^2}=1$

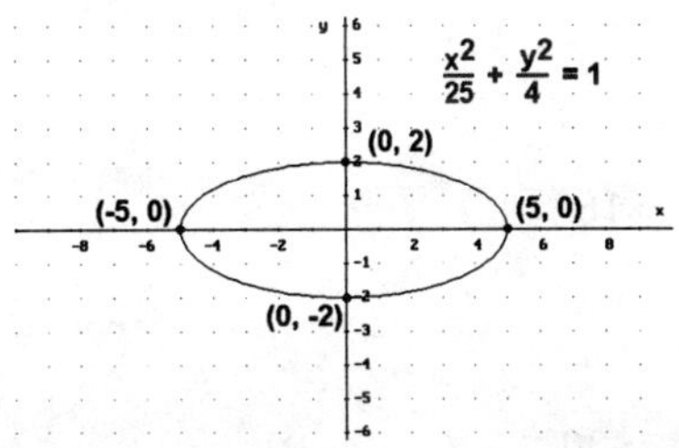

63. $\sqrt{-4}=2i$

65. $\sqrt{-20}=\sqrt{4}\sqrt{5}\sqrt{-1}=2i\sqrt{5}$

67. $\begin{array}{l}2x-y+3z=\ 7\\ \underline{5x+y-\ \ z=10}\\ 7x\qquad +2z=17\end{array}$

69. $\begin{array}{l}x+y-z=2\\ \underline{x+y+z=2}\\ 2x+2y\ \ =4\end{array}$

71. $\begin{cases}\frac{1}{x}+y=12\\\frac{3}{x}-y=4\end{cases}$

$\frac{4}{x}=16$

$4 = 16x$

$x = \frac{4}{16} = \frac{1}{4}$ so $\frac{1}{x} = 4$

$4 + y = 12$
$y = 8$

$\left\{\left(\frac{1}{4}, 8\right)\right\}$

73. $\begin{cases} \frac{1}{x} + \frac{1}{y} = 5 \\ \frac{1}{x} - \frac{1}{y} = 1 \end{cases}$

$\frac{2}{x} = 6$

$2 = 6x$

$x = \frac{2}{6} = \frac{1}{3}$ so $\frac{1}{x} = 3$

$3 - \frac{1}{y} = 1$

$2 = \frac{1}{y}$

$y = \frac{1}{2}$

$\left\{\left(\frac{1}{3}, \frac{1}{2}\right)\right\}$

75. $\begin{cases} \frac{2}{x} + \frac{3}{y} = -1 \\ \frac{3}{x} - \frac{2}{y} = 18 \end{cases}$

$\begin{cases} \frac{6}{x} + \frac{9}{y} = -3 \\ \frac{6}{x} - \frac{4}{y} = 36 \end{cases}$

$\frac{13}{y} = -39$

$13 = -39y$

$y = -\frac{13}{39} = -\frac{1}{3}$ so $\frac{1}{y} = -3$

$\frac{2}{x} + 3(-3) = -1$

$\frac{2}{x} - 9 = -1$

$\frac{2}{x} = 8$

$2 = 8x$

$x = \frac{2}{8} = \frac{1}{4}$

$\left\{\left(\frac{1}{4}, -\frac{1}{3}\right)\right\}$

77. $\begin{cases} \frac{2}{x} - \frac{4}{y} = 5 \\ \frac{1}{x} - \frac{2}{y} = \frac{3}{2} \end{cases}$

$\begin{cases} \frac{2}{x} - \frac{4}{y} = 5 \\ \frac{2}{x} - \frac{4}{y} = 3 \end{cases}$

Inconsistent system.
No solution.

{ }

Exercise Set 10.2

1. $\begin{cases} x + y = 3 \\ 2y = 10 \\ 3x + 2y - 3z = 1 \end{cases}$

The second equation yields $y = 5$.

$x + 5 = 3$
$x = -2$

$3(-2) + 2(5) - 3z = 1$
$-6 + 10 - 3z = 1$
$4 - 3z = 1$
$3 = 3z$
$z = 1$

$\{(-2, 5, 1)\}$

3. $\begin{cases} 2x + 2y + z = 1 \\ -x + y + 2z = 3 \\ x + 2y + 4z = 0 \end{cases}$

Add equations 2 and 3.
$3y + 6z = 3$
$y + 2z = 1$

Add twice equation 2 to equation 1.
$4y + 5z = 7$

$\begin{cases} y + 2z = 1 \\ 4y + 5z = 7 \end{cases}$

$\begin{cases} 4y + 8z = 4 \\ 4y + 5z = 7 \end{cases}$

Subtract.

$3z = -3$
$z = -1$

$y + 2(-1) = 1$
$y - 2 = 1$
$y = 3$

$x + 2(3) + 4(-1) = 0$
$x + 6 - 4 = 0$
$x + 2 = 0$
$x = -2$

$\{(-2, 3, -1)\}$

5. $\begin{cases} x - 2y + z = -5 \\ -3x + 6y - 3z = 15 \\ 2x - 4y + 2z = -10 \end{cases}$

$\begin{cases} x - 2y + z = -5 \\ x - 2y + z = -5 \\ x - 2y + z = -5 \end{cases}$

Dependent system.
$\{(x, y, z) \mid x - 2y + z = -5\}$

7. $\begin{cases} 4x - y + 2z = 5 \\ 2y + z = 4 \\ 4x + y + 3z = 10 \end{cases}$

Subtract equation 1 from equation 3.

$\begin{cases} 2y + z = 5 \\ 2y + z = 4 \end{cases}$

Inconsistent system.
No solution.

$\{\ \}$

9. $\begin{cases} x + 5z = 0 \\ 5x + y = 0 \\ y - 3z = 0 \end{cases}$

Subtract equation 3 from equation 2.

$\begin{cases} 5x + 3z = 0 \\ x + 5z = 0 \end{cases}$

$\begin{cases} 5x + 3z = 0 \\ 5x + 25z = 0 \end{cases}$

Subtract.
$-22z = 0$
$z = 0$

$5x + 3(0) = 0$
$5x = 0$
$x = 0$

$5(0) + y = 0$
$y = 0$

$\{(0, 0, 0)\}$

11. $\begin{cases} 6x - 5z = 17 \\ 5x - y + 3z = -1 \\ 2x + y = -41 \end{cases}$

Add equations 2 and 3.
$\begin{cases} 7x + 3z = -42 \\ 6x - 5z = 17 \end{cases}$

$\begin{cases} 35x + 15z = -210 \\ 18x - 15z = 51 \end{cases}$

Add.

$53x = -159$
$x = -3$

$6(-3) - 5z = 17$
$-18 - 5z = 17$
$-5z = 35$
$z = -7$

$2(-3) + y = -41$
$-6 + y = -41$
$y = -35$

$\{(-3, -35, -7)\}$

13. $\begin{cases} x + y + z = 8 \\ 2x - y - z = 10 \\ x - 2y - 3z = 22 \end{cases}$

Add equations 1 and 2.

$3x = 18$
$x = 6$

Add twice equation 1 to equation 3.

$3x - z = 38$
$3(6) - z = 38$
$18 - z = 38$
$-z = 20$
$z = -20$

$6 + y + (-20) = 8$
$y - 14 = 8$
$y = 22$

$\{(6, 22, -20)\}$

15. $\begin{cases} x+2y-z=5 \\ 6x+y+z=7 \\ 2x+4y-2z=5 \end{cases}$

Add equation 1 and 2.
$7x+3y=12$

Add twice equation 2 to equation 3.

$\begin{cases} 14x+6y=19 \\ 7x+3y=12 \end{cases}$

$\begin{cases} 14x+6y=19 \\ 14x+6y=24 \end{cases}$

Inconsistent system.
No solution.

{ }

17. $\begin{cases} 2x-3y+z=2 \\ x-5y+5z=3 \\ 3x-y-3z=1 \end{cases}$

Add −2 times equation 2 to equation 1.

$7y-9z=-4$

Add −3 times equation 2 to equation 3.

$14y-18z=-8$

$\begin{cases} 7y-9z=-4 \\ 14y-18z=-8 \end{cases}$

Since equation 2 is twice equation 1, the system is dependent. Solve the first equation for y:

$7y=9z-4$

$y=\frac{9}{7}z-\frac{4}{7}$

Now substitute this into the second of the original equations:

$x-5\left(\frac{9}{7}z-\frac{4}{7}\right)+5z=3$

$x-\frac{45}{7}z+\frac{20}{7}+5z=3$

$x-\frac{10}{7}z=\frac{1}{7}$

$x=\frac{10}{7}z+\frac{1}{7}$

$\left\{\left(\frac{10}{7}z+\frac{1}{7}, \frac{9}{7}z-\frac{4}{7}, z\right) \mid z \text{ is any real number}\right\}$

19. $\begin{cases} -2x-4y+6z=-8 \\ x+2y-3z=4 \\ 4x+8y-12z=16 \end{cases}$

Add 2 times equation 2 to equation 1.
$0=0$

Add −4 times equation 2 to equation 3.
$0=0$

The system is dependent.
$\{(x, y, z) \mid x+2y-3z=4\}$

21. $\begin{cases} 2x+2y-3z=1 \\ y+2z=-14 \\ 3x-2y=-1 \end{cases}$

Add equations 1 and 3.
$5x-3z=0$

Add twice equation 2 to equation 3.
$3x+4z=-29$

$\begin{cases} 5x-3z=0 \\ 3x+4z=-29 \end{cases}$

$\begin{cases} 20x-12z=0 \\ 9x+12z=-87 \end{cases}$

Add.

$29x=-87$
$x=-3$

$5(-3)-3z=0$
$3z=-15$
$z=-5$

$y+2(-5)=-14$
$y-10=-14$
$y=-4$

$\{(-3, -4, -5)\}$

23. $\begin{cases} \frac{3}{4}x-\frac{1}{3}y+\frac{1}{2}z=9 \\ \frac{1}{6}x+\frac{1}{3}y-\frac{1}{2}z=2 \\ \frac{1}{2}x-y+\frac{1}{2}z=2 \end{cases}$

$\begin{cases} 9x-4y+6z=108 \\ x+2y-3z=12 \\ x-2y+z=4 \end{cases}$

Add twice equation 2 to equation 1.

$11x = 132$
$x = 12$

Add equations 2 and 3.

$2x - 2z = 16$
$x - z = 8$

$12 - z = 8$
$4 = z$
$z = 4$

$12 - 2y + 4 = 4$
$12 - 2y = 0$
$12 = 2y$
$y = 6$

$\{(12, 6, 4)\}$

25. $x^2 + 4x + 1 = 0$

$a = 1, \ b = 4, \ c = 1$

$$x = \frac{-4 \pm \sqrt{4^2 - 4(1)(1)}}{2(1)}$$

$$x = \frac{-4 \pm \sqrt{16 - 4}}{2} = \frac{-4 \pm \sqrt{12}}{2}$$

$$x = \frac{-4 \pm 2\sqrt{3}}{2} = -2 \pm \sqrt{3}$$

$\{-2 + \sqrt{3}, -2 - \sqrt{3}\}$

27. $3x^2 - x + 2 = 0$

$a = 3, \ b = -1, \ c = 2$

$$x = \frac{1 \pm \sqrt{(-1)^2 - 4(3)(2)}}{2(3)}$$

$$x = \frac{1 \pm \sqrt{1 - 24}}{6} = \frac{1 \pm \sqrt{-23}}{6}$$

$$x = \frac{1 \pm i\sqrt{23}}{6}$$

$\left\{\frac{1 - i\sqrt{23}}{6}, \ \frac{1 + i\sqrt{23}}{6}\right\}$

29. $\dfrac{\frac{1}{x}}{\frac{5}{x^2} - \frac{3}{x}} = \dfrac{x}{5 - 3x}$

31. $\sqrt{20} = \sqrt{4}\sqrt{5} = 2\sqrt{5}$

33. $\sqrt[3]{54} = \sqrt[3]{27}\sqrt[3]{2} = 3\sqrt[3]{2}$

35. $\sqrt[4]{32} = \sqrt[4]{16}\sqrt[4]{2} = 2\sqrt[4]{2}$

37. $\begin{cases} x + y - w = 0 \\ y + 2z + w = 3 \\ x + z = 1 \\ 2x - y - w = -1 \end{cases}$

Add equation 2 to equations 1 and 4.

$\begin{cases} x + 2y + 2z = 3 \\ x + z = 1 \\ 2x + 2z = 2 \end{cases}$

which is equivalent to the system:

$\begin{cases} x + 2y + 2z = 3 \\ x + z = 1 \end{cases}$

since the third equation is twice the second equation.

Now subtract the second equation above from the first.

$2y + z = 2$
$2y = -z + 2$

$y = -\frac{1}{2}z + 1$

The system is dependent.

Now substitute this last equation into the original equation 2.

$-\frac{1}{2}z + 1 + 2z + w = 3$

$\frac{3}{2}z + w = 2$

$w = -\frac{3}{2}z + 2$

Now substitute for both y and w in the original equation 1.

$x + \left(-\frac{1}{2}z + 1\right) - \left(-\frac{3}{2}z + 2\right) = 0$

$x + z - 1 = 0$
$x = -z + 1$

$\left\{\left(-z + 1, -\frac{1}{2}z + 1, \ z, -\frac{3}{2}z + 2\right) | z \text{ is any real number}\right\}$

39. $\begin{cases} x + y + z + w = 5 \\ 2x + y + z + w = 6 \\ x + y + z = 2 \\ x + y = 0 \end{cases}$

Subtract equation 1 from equation 2.
$x = 1$

Substitute in equation 4.
$1 + y = 0$
$y = -1$

Substitute both in equation 3.
$1 + (-1) + z = 2$
$z = 2$

Substituting back.
$1 + (-1) + 2 + w = 5$
$2 + w = 5$
$w = 3$

$\{(1, -1, 2, 3)\}$

Exercise Set 10.3

1. Let $m =$ the first number and $n =$ the second number.

$$\begin{cases} m = n + 2 \\ 2m = 3n - 4 \end{cases}$$

Substitute.
$2(n + 2) = 3n - 4$
$2n + 4 = 3n - 4$
$8 = n$
$n = 8$

$m = 8 + 2 = 10$

The numbers are 10 and 8.

3. Let $p =$ the speed of the plane in still air and $w =$ the speed of the wind.

$$\begin{cases} p + w = 560 \\ p - w = 480 \end{cases}$$

Add.
$2p = 1040$
$p = 520$

$520 + w = 560$
$w = 40$

The speed of the plane in still air is 520 mph and the speed of the wind is 40 mph.

5. Let $x =$ the number of quarts of 4% butterfat milk and $y =$ the number of quarts of 1% butterfat milk.

$$\begin{cases} x + y = 60 \\ 0.04x + 0.01y = 0.02(60) \end{cases}$$

$$\begin{cases} x + y = 60 \\ 4x + y = 120 \end{cases}$$

Subtract.
$-3x = -60$
$x = 20$

$20 + y = 60$
$y = 40$

20 quarts of 4% butterfat milk and 40 quarts of 1% butterfat milk should be used.

7. Let $l =$ length of the pen and $w =$ the width of the pen.

$$\begin{cases} 2l + 2w = 156 \\ l = 2w \end{cases}$$

Substitute.
$2(2w) + 2w = 156$
$4w + 2w = 156$
$6w = 156$
$w = 26$

$l = 2(26) = 52$

The length of the pen is 52 feet and its width is 26 feet.

9. Let $l =$ the number of large frames purchased and $s =$ the number of small frames purchased.

$$\begin{cases} l + s = 22 \\ 15l + 8s = 239 \end{cases}$$

$$\begin{cases} 8l + 8s = 176 \\ 15l + 8s = 239 \end{cases}$$

Subtract.
$-7l = -63$
$l = 9$

$9 + s = 22$
$s = 13$

She bought 9 large frames and 13 small frames.

11. Let $m =$ the first number and $n =$ the second number.

$$\begin{cases} m = n - 2 \\ 2m = 3n + 4 \end{cases}$$

Substitute.

$2(n-2) = 3n + 4$
$2n - 4 = 3n + 4$
$-8 = n$
$n = -8$

$m = -8 - 2$
$m = -10$

The numbers are -10 and -8.

13. Let $x =$ the price of each tablet and $y =$ the price of each pen.

$$\begin{cases} 7x + 4y = 6.40 \\ 2x + 19y = 5.40 \end{cases}$$

$$\begin{cases} 14x + 8y = 12.80 \\ 14x + 133y = 37.80 \end{cases}$$

Subtract the first equation from the second.

$125y = 25$

$y = \frac{25}{125} = 0.20$

$7x + 4(0.20) = 6.40$
$7x + 0.80 = 6.40$
$7x = 5.60$
$x = 0.80$

Tablets cost \$0.80 each and pens cost \$0.20 each.

15. Let $p =$ the speed of the plane in still air and $w =$ the speed of the wind.

First note:

$\frac{2160 \text{ mi}}{3 \text{ hr}} = 720\frac{\text{mi}}{\text{hr}}$ and

$\frac{2160 \text{ mi}}{4 \text{ hr}} = 540\frac{\text{mi}}{\text{hr}}$

$$\begin{cases} p + w = 720 \\ p - w = 540 \end{cases}$$

Add.

$2p = 1260$
$p = 630$

$630 + w = 720$

$w = 90$

The speed of the plane in still air is 630 mi/hr and the speed of the wind is 90 mi/hr.

17. Let $s =$ the length of the shortest side, $l =$ the length of the longest side, and $w =$ the length of the two middle sides.

$$\begin{cases} s + 2m + l = 29 \\ l = 2s \\ m = s + 2 \end{cases}$$

Substituting:

$s + 2(s+2) + 2s = 29$
$s + 2s + 4 + 2s = 29$
$5s + 4 = 29$
$5s = 25$
$s = 5$

$l = 2(5)$
$l = 10$

$m = 5 + 2$
$m = 7$

The shortest side is 5 inches, the two middle sides are 7 inches, and the longest side is 10 inches.

19. Let $n =$ the number of nickels and $d =$ the number of dimes.

$$\begin{cases} 0.05n + 0.10d = 2.70 \\ n + d = 39 \end{cases}$$

$$\begin{cases} 5n + 10d = 270 \\ 5n + 5d = 195 \end{cases}$$

Subtract.

$5d = 75$
$d = 15$

$n + 15 = 39$
$n = 24$

She has 24 nickels and 15 dimes.

21. Let $x =$ the first number, $y =$ the second number, and $z =$ the third number.

$$\begin{cases} x + y + z = 40 \\ x = y + 5 \\ x = 2z \end{cases}$$

$$\begin{cases} x+y+z=40 \\ y=x-5 \\ z=\frac{1}{2}x \end{cases}$$

Substitute.

$x+x-5+\frac{1}{2}x=40$

$\frac{5}{2}x-5=40$

$\frac{5}{2}x=45$

$x=\frac{2}{5}(45)=18$

$y=18-5=13$

$z=\frac{1}{2}(18)=9$

The three numbers are 18, 13, and 9.

23. Let $x=$ total weekly sales and $y=$ total weekly salary.

$$\begin{cases} y=200+0.05x \\ y=0.15x \end{cases}$$

Substitute.
$200+0.05x=.15x$
$200=0.10x$
$x=2000$

Jack's salary would be the same, regardless of pay arrangement, at $2,000 worth of sales.

25. Let $m=$ the number of 10 dollar bills and $n=$ the number of 20 dollar bills.

$$\begin{cases} m+n=85 \\ 10m+20n=1480 \end{cases}$$

$$\begin{cases} m+n=85 \\ m+2n=148 \end{cases}$$

Subtract.

$-n=-63$
$n=63$

$m+63=85$
$m=22$

He had 22 10-dollar bills and 63 20-dollar bills.

27. Let $p=$ the number of pennies, $n=$ the number of nickels, and $d=$ the number of dimes.

$$\begin{cases} 0.01p+0.05n+0.10d=3.42 \\ d=2n \\ p=n+4 \end{cases}$$

Substitute.
$0.01(n+4)+0.05n+0.10(2n)=3.42$
$0.01n+0.04+0.05n+0.2n=3.42$
$0.26n+0.04=3.42$
$0.26n=3.38$
$n=13$

$d=2(13)=26$

$p=13+4=17$

She has 13 nickels, 26 dimes, and 17 pennies.

29. Let $a=$ the number of units of mix A, $b=$ the number of units of mix B, and $c=$ the number of units of mix C.

$$\begin{cases} 4a+6b+4c=30 \\ 6a+b+c=16 \\ 3a+2b+12c=24 \end{cases}$$

Multiply equation 2 by -6 and add to equation 1.

$-32a-2c=-66$
$16a+c=33$

Multiply equation 2 by -2 and add to equation 3.

$-9a+10c=-8$

$$\begin{cases} 16a+c=33 \\ -9a+10c=-8 \end{cases}$$

Multiply the first equation above by -10 and add to the second equation above.

$-169a=-338$
$a=2$

$16(2)+c=33$
$32+c=33$
$c=1$

$6(2)+b+1=16$
$12+b+1=16$
$b+13=16$
$b=3$

Two units of Mix A, 3 units of Mix B, and 1 unit of Mix C are needed daily.

31. $x^2 + xy + 3x + 3y$

$(x+3)(x+y)$

33. $(x+5)^2 = x^2 + 10x + 25$

35. $(2x-y)^2 = 4x^2 - 4xy + y^2$

37. $(-1)(-5) - (6)(3)$

$5 - 18$

-13

39. $4(-10) - (2)(-2)$

$-40 - (-4)$

$-40 + 4$

-36

41. $(-3)(-3) - (-1)(-9)$

$9 - (+9)$

$9 - 9$

0

Exercise Set 10.4

1. $\begin{vmatrix} 3 & 5 \\ -1 & 7 \end{vmatrix}$

$3(7) - 5(-1)$

$21 + 5 = 26$

3. $\begin{vmatrix} 9 & -2 \\ 4 & -3 \end{vmatrix}$

$9(-3) - 4(-2)$

$-27 + 8 = -19$

5. $\begin{vmatrix} -2 & 9 \\ 4 & -18 \end{vmatrix}$

$-2(-18) - 9(4)$

$36 - 36 = 0$

7. $\begin{cases} 2y - 4 = 0 \\ x + 2y = 5 \end{cases}$

$\begin{cases} 2y = 4 \\ x + 2y = 5 \end{cases}$

$D = \begin{vmatrix} 0 & 2 \\ 1 & 2 \end{vmatrix} = 0(2) - 2(1) = 0 - 2 = -2$

$D_x = \begin{vmatrix} 4 & 2 \\ 5 & 2 \end{vmatrix} = 4(2) - 2(5) = 8 - 10 = -2$

$D_y = \begin{vmatrix} 0 & 4 \\ 1 & 5 \end{vmatrix} = 0(5) - 4(1) = 0 - 4 = -4$

$x = \frac{-2}{-2} = 1$ and $y = \frac{-4}{-2} = 2$

$\{(1, 2)\}$

9. $\begin{cases} 3x + y = 1 \\ 2y = 2 - 6x \end{cases}$

$\begin{cases} 3x + y = 1 \\ 6x + 2y = 2 \end{cases}$

$D = \begin{vmatrix} 3 & 1 \\ 6 & 2 \end{vmatrix} = 3(2) - 6(1) = 6 - 6 = 0$

Thus, this system cannot be solved using Cramer's rule. Since equation 2 is 2 times equation 1, the system is dependent.

$\{(x, y) \mid 3x + y = 1\}$

11. $\begin{cases} 5x - 2y = 27 \\ -3x + 5y = 18 \end{cases}$

$D = \begin{vmatrix} 5 & -2 \\ -3 & 5 \end{vmatrix} = 5(5) - (-2)(-3) = 19$

$D_x = \begin{vmatrix} 27 & -2 \\ 18 & 5 \end{vmatrix} = 27(5) - (-2)18 = 171$

$D_y = \begin{vmatrix} 5 & 27 \\ -3 & 18 \end{vmatrix} = 5(18) - 27(-3) = 171$

$x=\frac{171}{19}=9$ and $y=\frac{171}{19}=9$

$\{(9,\ 9)\}$

13. $\begin{vmatrix} 2 & 1 & 0 \\ 0 & 5 & -3 \\ 4 & 0 & 2 \end{vmatrix}$

$2\begin{vmatrix} 5 & -3 \\ 0 & 2 \end{vmatrix} - 1\begin{vmatrix} 0 & -3 \\ 4 & 2 \end{vmatrix} + 0\begin{vmatrix} 0 & 5 \\ 4 & 0 \end{vmatrix}$

$2[5(2)-(-3)(0)]-[0(2)-4(-3)]+0$

$2(10)-12=8$

15. $\begin{vmatrix} 4 & -6 & 0 \\ -2 & 3 & 0 \\ 4 & -6 & 1 \end{vmatrix}$

$0\begin{vmatrix} -2 & 3 \\ 4 & -6 \end{vmatrix} - 0\begin{vmatrix} 4 & -6 \\ 4 & -6 \end{vmatrix} + 1\begin{vmatrix} 4 & -6 \\ -2 & 3 \end{vmatrix}$

$0-0+[4(3)-(-6)(-2)]=0$

17. $\begin{vmatrix} 3 & 6 & -3 \\ -1 & -2 & 3 \\ 4 & -1 & 6 \end{vmatrix}$

$3\begin{vmatrix} -2 & 3 \\ -1 & 6 \end{vmatrix} - 6\begin{vmatrix} -1 & 3 \\ 4 & 6 \end{vmatrix} + (-3)\begin{vmatrix} -1 & -2 \\ 4 & -1 \end{vmatrix}$

$3[-2(6)-3(-1)]-6[-1(6)-3(4)]-3[(-1)(-1)-(-2)4]$

$3(-9)-6(-18)-3(9)$

$-27+108-27=54$

19. $\begin{cases} 3x+z=-1 \\ -x-3y+z=7 \\ 3y+z=5 \end{cases}$

$D=\begin{vmatrix} 3 & 0 & 1 \\ -1 & -3 & 1 \\ 0 & 3 & 1 \end{vmatrix}$

$D=3\begin{vmatrix} -3 & 1 \\ 3 & 1 \end{vmatrix} - 0\begin{vmatrix} -1 & 1 \\ 0 & 1 \end{vmatrix} + 1\begin{vmatrix} -1 & -3 \\ 0 & 3 \end{vmatrix}$

$D=3[-3(1)-1(3)]-0+[-1(3)-(-3)0]$

$D=3(-6)-3=-21$

$D_x=\begin{vmatrix} -1 & 0 & 1 \\ 7 & -3 & 1 \\ 5 & 3 & 1 \end{vmatrix}$

$D_x=-1\begin{vmatrix} -3 & 1 \\ 3 & 1 \end{vmatrix} - 0\begin{vmatrix} 7 & 1 \\ 5 & 1 \end{vmatrix} + 1\begin{vmatrix} 7 & -3 \\ 5 & 3 \end{vmatrix}$

$D_x=-[-3(1)-1(3)]-0+[7(3)-(-3)5]$

$D_x=6+36=42$

$D_y=\begin{vmatrix} 3 & -1 & 1 \\ -1 & 7 & 1 \\ 0 & 5 & 1 \end{vmatrix}$

$D_y=3\begin{vmatrix} 7 & 1 \\ 5 & 1 \end{vmatrix} -(-1)\begin{vmatrix} -1 & 1 \\ 0 & 1 \end{vmatrix} + 1\begin{vmatrix} -1 & 7 \\ 0 & 5 \end{vmatrix}$

$D_y=3[7(1)-1(5)]+1[(-1)-1(0)]+[-1(5)-7(0)]$

$D_y=3(2)+(-1)+(-5)=0$

$D_z=\begin{vmatrix} 3 & 0 & -1 \\ -1 & -3 & 7 \\ 0 & 3 & 5 \end{vmatrix}$

$D_z=3\begin{vmatrix} -3 & 7 \\ 3 & 5 \end{vmatrix} - 0\begin{vmatrix} -1 & 7 \\ 0 & 5 \end{vmatrix} - 1\begin{vmatrix} -1 & -3 \\ 0 & 3 \end{vmatrix}$

$D_z=3[-3(5)-7(3)]-0-[-1(3)-(-3)0]$

$D_z=3(-36)-(-3)=-105$

$x=\frac{42}{-21}=-2$

$y=\frac{0}{-21}=0$

$z=\frac{-105}{-21}=5$

$\{(-2,\ 0\ 5)\}$

21. $\begin{cases} x+y+z=8 \\ 2x-y-z=10 \\ x-2y+3z=22 \end{cases}$

$D=\begin{vmatrix} 1 & 1 & 1 \\ 2 & -1 & -1 \\ 1 & -2 & 3 \end{vmatrix}$

$D=1\begin{vmatrix} -1 & -1 \\ -2 & 3 \end{vmatrix}-1\begin{vmatrix} 2 & -1 \\ 1 & 3 \end{vmatrix}+1\begin{vmatrix} 2 & -1 \\ 1 & -2 \end{vmatrix}$

$D=(-3-2)-[6-(-1)]+[-4-(-1)]$

$D=-5-7-3=-15$

$D_x=\begin{vmatrix} 8 & 1 & 1 \\ 10 & -1 & -1 \\ 22 & -2 & 3 \end{vmatrix}$

$D_x=8\begin{vmatrix} -1 & -1 \\ -2 & 3 \end{vmatrix}-1\begin{vmatrix} 10 & -1 \\ 22 & 3 \end{vmatrix}+1\begin{vmatrix} 10 & -1 \\ 22 & -2 \end{vmatrix}$

$D_x=8(-3-2)-[30-(-22)]+[-20-(-22)]$

$D_x=8(-5)-52+2=-90$

$D_y=\begin{vmatrix} 1 & 8 & 1 \\ 2 & 10 & -1 \\ 1 & 22 & 3 \end{vmatrix}$

$D_y=1\begin{vmatrix} 10 & -1 \\ 22 & 3 \end{vmatrix}-8\begin{vmatrix} 2 & -1 \\ 1 & 3 \end{vmatrix}+1\begin{vmatrix} 2 & 10 \\ 1 & 22 \end{vmatrix}$

$D_y=[30-(-22)]-8[6-(-1)]+[44-10]$

$D_y=52-8(7)+34$

$D_y=52-56+34=30$

$D_z=\begin{vmatrix} 1 & 1 & 8 \\ 2 & -1 & 10 \\ 1 & -2 & 22 \end{vmatrix}$

$D_z=1\begin{vmatrix} -1 & 10 \\ -2 & 22 \end{vmatrix}-1\begin{vmatrix} 2 & 10 \\ 1 & 22 \end{vmatrix}+8\begin{vmatrix} 2 & -1 \\ 1 & -2 \end{vmatrix}$

$D_z=[-22-(-20)]-[44-10]+8[-4-(-1)]$

$D_z=-2-34+8(-3)=-36-24=-60$

$x=\frac{-90}{-15}=6$

$y=\frac{30}{-15}=-2$

$z=\frac{-60}{-15}=4$

$\{(6,-2,\ 4)\}$

23. $\begin{vmatrix} 10 & -1 \\ -4 & 2 \end{vmatrix}=10(2)-(-1)(-4)$

$20-4=16$

25. $\begin{vmatrix} 1 & 0 & 4 \\ 1 & -1 & 2 \\ 3 & 2 & 1 \end{vmatrix}$

$1\begin{vmatrix} -1 & 2 \\ 2 & 1 \end{vmatrix}-0\begin{vmatrix} 1 & 2 \\ 3 & 1 \end{vmatrix}+4\begin{vmatrix} 1 & -1 \\ 3 & 2 \end{vmatrix}$

$1[-1-4]-0+4[2-(-3)]$

$-5+4(5)=-5+20=15$

27. $\begin{vmatrix} \frac{3}{4} & \frac{5}{2} \\ -\frac{1}{6} & \frac{7}{3} \end{vmatrix}=\frac{3}{4}\bullet\frac{7}{3}-\frac{5}{2}\left(-\frac{1}{6}\right)$

$\frac{21}{12}+\frac{5}{12}=\frac{26}{12}=\frac{13}{6}$

29. $\begin{vmatrix} 4 & -2 & 2 \\ 6 & -1 & 3 \\ 2 & 1 & 1 \end{vmatrix}$

$4\begin{vmatrix} -1 & 3 \\ 1 & 1 \end{vmatrix}-(-2)\begin{vmatrix} 6 & 3 \\ 2 & 1 \end{vmatrix}+2\begin{vmatrix} 6 & -1 \\ 2 & 1 \end{vmatrix}$

$4[-1-3]+2[6-6]+2[6-(-2)]$

$4(-4)+2(0)+2(8)=-16+0+16=0$

31. $\begin{vmatrix} -2 & 5 & 4 \\ 5 & -1 & 3 \\ 4 & 1 & 2 \end{vmatrix}$

$-2\begin{vmatrix} -1 & 3 \\ 1 & 2 \end{vmatrix}-5\begin{vmatrix} 5 & 3 \\ 4 & 2 \end{vmatrix}+4\begin{vmatrix} 5 & -1 \\ 4 & 1 \end{vmatrix}$

$-2[-2-3]-5[10-12]+4[5-(-4)]$

$-2(-5)-5(-2)+4(9)=10+10+36=56$

33. $\begin{cases} 2x-5y=4 \\ x+2y=-7 \end{cases}$

$D=\begin{vmatrix} 2 & -5 \\ 1 & 2 \end{vmatrix}=2(2)-(-5)(1)$

$D=4+5=9$

$D_x=\begin{vmatrix} 4 & -5 \\ -7 & 2 \end{vmatrix}=4(2)-(-5)(-7)$

$D_x=8-35=-27$

$D_y=\begin{vmatrix} 2 & 4 \\ 1 & -7 \end{vmatrix}=2(-7)-4(1)$

$D_y=-14-4=-18$

$x=\frac{-27}{9}=-3$ and $y=\frac{-18}{9}=-2$

$\{(-3,-2)\}$

35. $\begin{cases} 4x+2y=5 \\ 2x+y=-1 \end{cases}$

$D=\begin{vmatrix} 4 & 2 \\ 2 & 1 \end{vmatrix}=4(1)-2(2)=4-4=0$

Thus Cramer's Rule cannot be used to solve the system. Multiply equation 2 by 2 yielding the new system:

$\begin{cases} 4x+2y=5 \\ 4x+2y=-2 \end{cases}$

Therefore the system is inconsistent. No solution.

{ }

37. $\begin{cases} 2x+2y+z=1 \\ -x+y+2z=3 \\ x+2y+4z=0 \end{cases}$

$D=\begin{vmatrix} 2 & 2 & 1 \\ -1 & 1 & 2 \\ 1 & 2 & 4 \end{vmatrix}$

$D=2\begin{vmatrix} 1 & 2 \\ 2 & 4 \end{vmatrix}-2\begin{vmatrix} -1 & 2 \\ 1 & 4 \end{vmatrix}+1\begin{vmatrix} -1 & 1 \\ 1 & 2 \end{vmatrix}$

$D=2(4-4)-2(-4-2)+(-2-1)$

$D=2(0)-2(-6)+(-3)$

$D=0+12-3=9$

$D_x=\begin{vmatrix} 1 & 2 & 1 \\ 3 & 1 & 2 \\ 0 & 2 & 4 \end{vmatrix}$

$D_x=1\begin{vmatrix} 1 & 2 \\ 2 & 4 \end{vmatrix}-3\begin{vmatrix} 2 & 1 \\ 2 & 4 \end{vmatrix}+0\begin{vmatrix} 2 & 1 \\ 1 & 2 \end{vmatrix}$

$D_x=(4-4)-3(8-2)+0$

$D_x=0-3(6)=-18$

$D_y=\begin{vmatrix} 2 & 1 & 1 \\ -1 & 3 & 2 \\ 1 & 0 & 4 \end{vmatrix}$

$D_y=1\begin{vmatrix} 1 & 1 \\ 3 & 2 \end{vmatrix}-0\begin{vmatrix} 2 & 1 \\ -1 & 2 \end{vmatrix}+4\begin{vmatrix} 2 & 1 \\ -1 & 3 \end{vmatrix}$

$D_y=(2-3)-0+4[6-(-1)]$

$D_y=-1+4(7)=-1+28=27$

$D_z=\begin{vmatrix} 2 & 2 & 1 \\ -1 & 1 & 3 \\ 1 & 2 & 0 \end{vmatrix}$

$$D_z = 1\begin{vmatrix} 2 & 1 \\ 1 & 3 \end{vmatrix} - 2\begin{vmatrix} 2 & 1 \\ -1 & 3 \end{vmatrix} + 0\begin{vmatrix} 2 & 2 \\ -1 & 1 \end{vmatrix}$$

$D_z = (6-1) - 2[6-(-1)] + 0$

$D_z = 5 - 2(7) = 5 - 14 = -9$

$x = \frac{-18}{9} = -2$

$y = \frac{27}{9} = 3$

$z = \frac{-9}{9} = -1$

$\{(-2, 3, -1)\}$

39. $\begin{cases} \frac{2}{3}x - \frac{3}{4}y = -1 \\ -\frac{1}{6}x + \frac{3}{4}y = \frac{5}{2} \end{cases}$

$$D = \begin{vmatrix} \frac{2}{3} & -\frac{3}{4} \\ -\frac{1}{6} & \frac{3}{4} \end{vmatrix} = \frac{2}{3} \bullet \frac{3}{4} - \left(-\frac{3}{4}\right)\left(-\frac{1}{6}\right)$$

$D = \frac{1}{2} - \frac{1}{8} = \frac{3}{8}$

$$D_x = \begin{vmatrix} -1 & -\frac{3}{4} \\ \frac{5}{2} & \frac{3}{4} \end{vmatrix} = (-1)\frac{3}{4} - \left(-\frac{3}{4}\right)\frac{5}{2}$$

$D_x = -\frac{3}{4} + \frac{15}{8} = \frac{9}{8}$

$$D_y = \begin{vmatrix} \frac{2}{3} & -1 \\ -\frac{1}{6} & \frac{5}{2} \end{vmatrix} = \frac{2}{3} \bullet \frac{5}{2} - (-1)\left(-\frac{1}{6}\right)$$

$D_y = \frac{5}{3} - \frac{1}{6} = \frac{3}{2}$

$x = \frac{\frac{9}{8}}{\frac{3}{8}} = 3$ and $y = \frac{\frac{3}{2}}{\frac{3}{8}} = 4$

$\{(3, 4)\}$

41. $\begin{cases} 0.7x - 0.2y = -1.6 \\ 0.2x - y = -1.4 \end{cases}$

$$D = \begin{vmatrix} 0.7 & -0.2 \\ 0.2 & -1 \end{vmatrix}$$

$D = 0.7(-1) - (-0.2)(0.2)$

$D = -0.7 + 0.04 = -0.66$

$$D_x = \begin{vmatrix} -1.6 & -0.2 \\ -1.4 & -1 \end{vmatrix}$$

$D_x = (-1.6)(-1) - (-0.2)(-1.4)$

$D_x = 1.6 - 0.28 = 1.32$

$$D_y = \begin{vmatrix} 0.7 & -1.6 \\ 0.2 & -1.4 \end{vmatrix}$$

$D_y = (0.7)(-1.4) - (-1.6)(0.2)$

$D_y = -0.98 + 0.32 = -0.66$

$x = \frac{1.32}{-0.66} = -2$ and $y = \frac{-0.66}{-0.66} = 1$

$\{(-2, 1)\}$

43. $\begin{cases} -2x + 4y - 2z = 6 \\ x - 2y + z = -3 \\ 3x - 6y + 3y = -9 \end{cases}$

$$D = \begin{vmatrix} -2 & 4 & -2 \\ 1 & -2 & 1 \\ 3 & -6 & 3 \end{vmatrix}$$

$$D = -2\begin{vmatrix} -2 & 1 \\ -6 & 3 \end{vmatrix} - 4\begin{vmatrix} 1 & 1 \\ 3 & 3 \end{vmatrix} - 2\begin{vmatrix} 1 & -2 \\ 3 & -6 \end{vmatrix}$$

$D = -2[-6-(-6)] - 4[3-3] - 2[-6-(-6)]$

$D = -2(0) - 4(0) - 2(0) = 0$

Therefore, Cramer's rule will not provide the solution. Note that equation 1 is -2 times equation 2 and that equation 3 is 3 times equation 2. Thus, the system is dependent.
$\{(x, y, z) \mid x - 2y + z = -3\}$

45. $\begin{cases} x - 2y + z = -5 \\ 3y + 2z = 4 \\ 3x - y = -2 \end{cases}$

$$D = \begin{vmatrix} 1 & -2 & 1 \\ 0 & 3 & 2 \\ 3 & -1 & 0 \end{vmatrix}$$

$$D = 1\begin{vmatrix} 3 & 2 \\ -1 & 0 \end{vmatrix} - 0\begin{vmatrix} -2 & 1 \\ -1 & 0 \end{vmatrix} + 3\begin{vmatrix} -2 & 1 \\ 3 & 2 \end{vmatrix}$$

$D = [0-(-2)] - 0 + 3[-4-3]$

$D = 2 + 3(-7) = -19$

$$D_x = \begin{vmatrix} -5 & -2 & 1 \\ 4 & 3 & 2 \\ -2 & -1 & 0 \end{vmatrix}$$

$$D_x = 1\begin{vmatrix} 4 & 3 \\ -2 & -1 \end{vmatrix} - 2\begin{vmatrix} -5 & -2 \\ -2 & -1 \end{vmatrix} + 0\begin{vmatrix} -5 & -2 \\ 4 & 3 \end{vmatrix}$$

$D_x = [-4-(-6)] - 2[5-4] + 0$

$D_x = 2 - 2(1) = 0$

$$D_y = \begin{vmatrix} 1 & -5 & 1 \\ 0 & 4 & 2 \\ 3 & -2 & 0 \end{vmatrix}$$

$$D_y = 1\begin{vmatrix} 4 & 2 \\ -2 & 0 \end{vmatrix} - 0\begin{vmatrix} -5 & 1 \\ -2 & 0 \end{vmatrix} + 3\begin{vmatrix} -5 & 1 \\ 4 & 2 \end{vmatrix}$$

$D_y = [0-(-4)] - 0 + 3(-10-4)$

$D_y = 4 + 3(-14) = 4 - 42 = -38$

$$D_z = \begin{vmatrix} 1 & -2 & -5 \\ 0 & 3 & 4 \\ 3 & -1 & -2 \end{vmatrix}$$

$$D_z = 1\begin{vmatrix} 3 & 4 \\ -1 & -2 \end{vmatrix} - 0\begin{vmatrix} -2 & -5 \\ -1 & -2 \end{vmatrix} + 3\begin{vmatrix} -2 & -5 \\ 3 & 4 \end{vmatrix}$$

$D_z = [-6-(-4)] - 0 + 3[-8-(-15)]$

$D_z = -2 + 3(7) = 19$

$x = \dfrac{0}{-19} = 0$

$y = \dfrac{-38}{-19} = 2$

$z = \dfrac{19}{-19} = -1$

$\{(0, 2, -1)\}$

47. $\begin{cases} 3x - y + z = 2 \\ -x + 2y + 3z = 6 \end{cases}$

Multiply equation 1 by 2 and add to equation 2.

$5x + 5z = 10$

49. $-3(x + 2y - z) = -3(0)$

$-3x - 6y + 3z = 0$

$$\begin{array}{r} -3x - 6y + 3z = 0 \\ +\quad 3x + \ y - \ z = 2 \\ \hline -5y + 2z = 2 \end{array}$$

51. $(5 + i)(2 - 3i)$

$10 - 15i + 2i - 3i^2$

$10 - 13i - 3(-1)$

$13 - 13i$

53. $(3 - 4i)(3 + 4i)$

$9 + 12i - 12i - 16i^2$

$9 - 16(-1) = 25$

55. $$\begin{vmatrix} 5 & 0 & 0 & 0 \\ 0 & 4 & 2 & -1 \\ 1 & 3 & -2 & 0 \\ 0 & -3 & 1 & 2 \end{vmatrix}$$

$$5\begin{vmatrix} 4 & 2 & -1 \\ 3 & -2 & 0 \\ -3 & 1 & 2 \end{vmatrix} - 0\begin{vmatrix} 0 & 2 & -1 \\ 1 & -2 & 0 \\ 0 & 1 & 2 \end{vmatrix} + 0\begin{vmatrix} 0 & 4 & -1 \\ 1 & 3 & 0 \\ 0 & -3 & 2 \end{vmatrix} - 0\begin{vmatrix} 0 & 4 & 2 \\ 1 & 3 & -2 \\ 0 & -3 & 1 \end{vmatrix}$$

$$5\left[-1\begin{vmatrix} 3 & -2 \\ -3 & 1 \end{vmatrix} - 0\begin{vmatrix} 4 & 2 \\ -3 & 1 \end{vmatrix} + 2\begin{vmatrix} 4 & 2 \\ 3 & -2 \end{vmatrix}\right]$$

$5[-(3-6) - 0 + 2(-8-6)]$

$5[3 + 2(-14)] = 5[3 - 28]$

$5[-25] = -125$

57. $\begin{vmatrix} 4 & 0 & 2 & 5 \\ 0 & 3 & -1 & 1 \\ 0 & 0 & 2 & 0 \\ 0 & 0 & 0 & 1 \end{vmatrix}$

$$4\begin{vmatrix} 3 & -1 & 1 \\ 0 & 2 & 0 \\ 0 & 0 & 1 \end{vmatrix} - 0\begin{vmatrix} 0 & 2 & 5 \\ 0 & 2 & 0 \\ 0 & 0 & 1 \end{vmatrix} + 0\begin{vmatrix} 0 & 2 & 5 \\ 3 & -1 & 1 \\ 0 & 0 & 1 \end{vmatrix} - 0\begin{vmatrix} 0 & 2 & 5 \\ 3 & -1 & 1 \\ 0 & 2 & 0 \end{vmatrix}$$

$$4\left[3\begin{vmatrix} 2 & 0 \\ 0 & 1 \end{vmatrix} - 0\begin{vmatrix} -1 & 1 \\ 0 & 1 \end{vmatrix} + 0\begin{vmatrix} -1 & 1 \\ 2 & 0 \end{vmatrix}\right]$$

$4[3(2-0)-0+0] = 12(2) = 24$

Exercise Set 10.5

1. $\begin{cases} x+y=1 \\ x-2y=4 \end{cases}$

$$\left[\begin{array}{cc|c} 1 & 1 & 1 \\ 1 & -2 & 4 \end{array}\right]$$

$$\left[\begin{array}{cc|c} 1 & 1 & 1 \\ 0 & -3 & 3 \end{array}\right]$$

$$\left[\begin{array}{cc|c} 1 & 1 & 1 \\ 0 & 1 & -1 \end{array}\right]$$

$$\left[\begin{array}{cc|c} 1 & 0 & 2 \\ 0 & 1 & -1 \end{array}\right]$$

$\{(2, -1)\}$

3. $\begin{cases} 2y-4=0 \\ x+2y=0 \end{cases}$

$\begin{cases} 2y=4 \\ x+2y=0 \end{cases}$

$$\left[\begin{array}{cc|c} 0 & 2 & 4 \\ 1 & 2 & 0 \end{array}\right]$$

$$\left[\begin{array}{cc|c} 1 & 2 & 0 \\ 0 & 2 & 4 \end{array}\right]$$

$$\left[\begin{array}{cc|c} 1 & 2 & 0 \\ 0 & 1 & 2 \end{array}\right]$$

$$\left[\begin{array}{cc|c} 1 & 0 & -4 \\ 0 & 1 & 2 \end{array}\right]$$

$\{(-4, 2)\}$

5. $\begin{cases} x+y=3 \\ 2y=10 \\ 3x+2y-4z=12 \end{cases}$

$$\left[\begin{array}{ccc|c} 1 & 1 & 0 & 3 \\ 0 & 2 & 0 & 10 \\ 3 & 2 & -4 & 12 \end{array}\right]$$

$$\left[\begin{array}{ccc|c} 1 & 1 & 0 & 3 \\ 0 & 2 & 0 & 10 \\ 0 & -1 & -4 & 3 \end{array}\right]$$

$$\left[\begin{array}{ccc|c} 1 & 1 & 0 & 3 \\ 0 & 1 & 0 & 5 \\ 0 & -1 & -4 & 3 \end{array}\right]$$

$$\left[\begin{array}{ccc|c} 1 & 0 & 0 & -2 \\ 0 & 1 & 0 & 5 \\ 0 & -1 & -4 & 3 \end{array}\right]$$

$$\left[\begin{array}{ccc|c} 1 & 0 & 0 & -2 \\ 0 & 1 & 0 & 5 \\ 0 & 0 & -4 & 8 \end{array}\right]$$

$$\left[\begin{array}{ccc|c} 1 & 0 & 0 & -2 \\ 0 & 1 & 0 & 5 \\ 0 & 0 & 1 & -2 \end{array}\right]$$

$\{(-2, 5, -2)\}$

7. $\begin{cases} 2y - z = -7 \\ x + 4y + z = -4 \\ 5x - y + 2z = 13 \end{cases}$

$$\left[\begin{array}{ccc|c} 0 & 2 & -1 & -7 \\ 1 & 4 & 1 & -4 \\ 5 & -1 & 2 & 13 \end{array}\right]$$

$$\left[\begin{array}{ccc|c} 1 & 4 & 1 & -4 \\ 0 & 2 & -1 & -7 \\ 5 & -1 & 2 & 13 \end{array}\right]$$

$$\left[\begin{array}{ccc|c} 1 & 4 & 1 & -4 \\ 0 & 2 & -1 & -7 \\ 0 & -21 & -3 & 33 \end{array}\right]$$

$$\left[\begin{array}{ccc|c} 1 & 4 & 1 & -4 \\ 0 & 1 & -\frac{1}{2} & -\frac{7}{2} \\ 0 & -21 & -3 & 33 \end{array}\right]$$

$$\left[\begin{array}{ccc|c} 1 & 0 & 3 & 10 \\ 0 & 1 & -\frac{1}{2} & -\frac{7}{2} \\ 0 & -21 & -3 & 33 \end{array}\right]$$

$$\left[\begin{array}{ccc|c} 1 & 0 & 3 & 10 \\ 0 & 1 & -\frac{1}{2} & -\frac{7}{2} \\ 0 & 0 & -\frac{27}{2} & -\frac{81}{2} \end{array}\right]$$

$$\left[\begin{array}{ccc|c} 1 & 0 & 3 & 10 \\ 0 & 1 & -\frac{1}{2} & -\frac{7}{2} \\ 0 & 0 & 1 & 3 \end{array}\right]$$

$$\left[\begin{array}{ccc|c} 1 & 0 & 0 & 1 \\ 0 & 1 & -\frac{1}{2} & -\frac{7}{2} \\ 0 & 0 & 1 & 3 \end{array}\right]$$

$$\left[\begin{array}{ccc|c} 1 & 0 & 0 & 1 \\ 0 & 1 & 0 & -2 \\ 0 & 0 & 1 & 3 \end{array}\right]$$

$\{(1, -2, 3)\}$

9. $\begin{cases} x - 2y = 4 \\ 2x - 4y = 4 \end{cases}$

$$\left[\begin{array}{cc|c} 1 & -2 & 4 \\ 2 & -4 & 4 \end{array}\right]$$

$$\left[\begin{array}{cc|c} 1 & -2 & 4 \\ 0 & 0 & -4 \end{array}\right]$$

Inconsistent system.
No solution.

$\{\ \}$

11. $\begin{cases} 3x - 3y = 9 \\ 2x - 2y = 6 \end{cases}$

$$\left[\begin{array}{cc|c} 3 & -3 & 9 \\ 2 & -2 & 6 \end{array}\right]$$

$$\left[\begin{array}{cc|c} 1 & -1 & 3 \\ 2 & -2 & 6 \end{array}\right]$$

$$\left[\begin{array}{cc|c} 1 & -1 & 3 \\ 0 & 0 & 0 \end{array}\right]$$

Dependent system.

$\{(x, y) \mid x - y = 3\}$

13. $\begin{cases} x - 4 = 0 \\ x + y = 1 \end{cases}$

$\begin{cases} x = 4 \\ x + y = 1 \end{cases}$

$$\left[\begin{array}{cc|c} 1 & 0 & 4 \\ 1 & 1 & 1 \end{array}\right]$$

$$\left[\begin{array}{cc|c} 1 & 0 & 4 \\ 0 & 1 & -3 \end{array}\right]$$

$\{(4, -3)\}$

15. $\begin{cases} x+y+z=2 \\ 2x-z=5 \\ 3y+z=2 \end{cases}$

$$\left[\begin{array}{ccc|c} 1 & 1 & 1 & 2 \\ 2 & 0 & -1 & 5 \\ 0 & 3 & 1 & 2 \end{array}\right]$$

$$\left[\begin{array}{ccc|c} 1 & 1 & 1 & 2 \\ 0 & -2 & -3 & 1 \\ 0 & 3 & 1 & 2 \end{array}\right]$$

$$\left[\begin{array}{ccc|c} 1 & 1 & 1 & 2 \\ 0 & 1 & \frac{3}{2} & -\frac{1}{2} \\ 0 & 3 & 1 & 2 \end{array}\right]$$

$$\left[\begin{array}{ccc|c} 1 & 0 & -\frac{1}{2} & \frac{5}{2} \\ 0 & 1 & \frac{3}{2} & -\frac{1}{2} \\ 0 & 3 & 1 & 2 \end{array}\right]$$

$$\left[\begin{array}{ccc|c} 1 & 0 & -\frac{1}{2} & \frac{5}{2} \\ 0 & 1 & \frac{3}{2} & -\frac{1}{2} \\ 0 & 0 & -\frac{7}{2} & \frac{7}{2} \end{array}\right]$$

$$\left[\begin{array}{ccc|c} 1 & 0 & -\frac{1}{2} & \frac{5}{2} \\ 0 & 1 & \frac{3}{2} & -\frac{1}{2} \\ 0 & 0 & 1 & -1 \end{array}\right]$$

$$\left[\begin{array}{ccc|c} 1 & 0 & 0 & 2 \\ 0 & 1 & \frac{3}{2} & -\frac{1}{2} \\ 0 & 0 & 1 & -1 \end{array}\right]$$

$$\left[\begin{array}{ccc|c} 1 & 0 & 0 & 2 \\ 0 & 1 & 0 & 1 \\ 0 & 0 & 1 & -1 \end{array}\right]$$

$\{(2, 1, -1)\}$

17. $\begin{cases} 5x-2y=27 \\ -3x+5y=18 \end{cases}$

$$\left[\begin{array}{cc|c} 5 & -2 & 27 \\ -3 & 5 & 18 \end{array}\right]$$

$$\left[\begin{array}{cc|c} 1 & -\frac{2}{5} & \frac{27}{5} \\ -3 & 5 & 18 \end{array}\right]$$

$$\left[\begin{array}{cc|c} 1 & -\frac{2}{5} & \frac{27}{5} \\ 0 & \frac{19}{5} & \frac{171}{5} \end{array}\right]$$

$$\left[\begin{array}{cc|c} 1 & -\frac{2}{5} & \frac{27}{5} \\ 0 & 1 & 9 \end{array}\right]$$

$$\left[\begin{array}{cc|c} 1 & 0 & 9 \\ 0 & 1 & 9 \end{array}\right]$$

$\{(9, 9)\}$

19. $\begin{cases} 4x-7y=7 \\ 12x-21y=24 \end{cases}$

$$\left[\begin{array}{cc|c} 4 & -7 & 7 \\ 12 & -21 & 24 \end{array}\right]$$

$$\left[\begin{array}{cc|c} 1 & -\frac{7}{4} & \frac{7}{4} \\ 12 & -21 & 24 \end{array}\right]$$

$$\left[\begin{array}{cc|c} 1 & -\frac{7}{4} & \frac{7}{4} \\ 0 & 0 & 3 \end{array}\right]$$

Inconsistent system.
No solution.

{ }

21. $\begin{cases} 4x - y + 2z = 5 \\ 2y + z = 4 \\ 4x + y + 3z = 10 \end{cases}$

$$\left[\begin{array}{ccc|c} 4 & -1 & 2 & 5 \\ 0 & 2 & 1 & 4 \\ 4 & 1 & 3 & 10 \end{array}\right]$$

$$\left[\begin{array}{ccc|c} 1 & -\frac{1}{4} & \frac{1}{2} & \frac{5}{4} \\ 0 & 2 & 1 & 4 \\ 4 & 1 & 3 & 10 \end{array}\right]$$

$$\left[\begin{array}{ccc|c} 1 & -\frac{1}{4} & \frac{1}{2} & \frac{5}{4} \\ 0 & 2 & 1 & 4 \\ 0 & 2 & 1 & 5 \end{array}\right]$$

$$\left[\begin{array}{ccc|c} 1 & -\frac{1}{4} & \frac{1}{2} & \frac{5}{4} \\ 0 & 1 & \frac{1}{2} & 2 \\ 0 & 2 & 1 & 5 \end{array}\right]$$

$$\left[\begin{array}{ccc|c} 1 & 0 & \frac{5}{8} & \frac{7}{4} \\ 0 & 1 & \frac{1}{2} & 2 \\ 0 & 2 & 1 & 5 \end{array}\right]$$

$$\left[\begin{array}{ccc|c} 1 & 0 & \frac{5}{8} & \frac{7}{4} \\ 0 & 1 & \frac{1}{2} & 2 \\ 0 & 0 & 0 & 1 \end{array}\right]$$

Inconsistent system.
No solution.

{ }

23. $\begin{cases} 4x + y + z = 3 \\ -x + y - 2z = -11 \\ x + 2y + 2z = -1 \end{cases}$

$$\left[\begin{array}{ccc|c} 4 & 1 & 1 & 3 \\ -1 & 1 & -2 & -11 \\ 1 & 2 & 2 & -1 \end{array}\right]$$

$$\left[\begin{array}{ccc|c} 1 & \frac{1}{4} & \frac{1}{4} & \frac{3}{4} \\ -1 & 1 & -2 & -11 \\ 1 & 2 & 2 & -1 \end{array}\right]$$

$$\left[\begin{array}{ccc|c} 1 & \frac{1}{4} & \frac{1}{4} & \frac{3}{4} \\ 0 & \frac{5}{4} & -\frac{7}{4} & -\frac{41}{4} \\ 1 & 2 & 2 & -1 \end{array}\right]$$

$$\left[\begin{array}{ccc|c} 1 & \frac{1}{4} & \frac{1}{4} & \frac{3}{4} \\ 0 & \frac{5}{4} & -\frac{7}{4} & -\frac{41}{4} \\ 0 & \frac{7}{4} & \frac{7}{4} & -\frac{7}{4} \end{array}\right]$$

$$\left[\begin{array}{ccc|c} 1 & \frac{1}{4} & \frac{1}{4} & \frac{3}{4} \\ 0 & 1 & -\frac{7}{5} & -\frac{41}{5} \\ 0 & \frac{7}{4} & \frac{7}{4} & -\frac{7}{4} \end{array}\right]$$

$$\left[\begin{array}{ccc|c} 1 & 0 & \frac{3}{5} & \frac{14}{5} \\ 0 & 1 & -\frac{7}{5} & -\frac{41}{5} \\ 0 & \frac{7}{4} & \frac{7}{4} & -\frac{7}{4} \end{array}\right]$$

$$\left[\begin{array}{ccc|c} 1 & 0 & \frac{3}{5} & \frac{14}{5} \\ 0 & 1 & -\frac{7}{5} & -\frac{41}{5} \\ 0 & 0 & \frac{21}{5} & \frac{63}{5} \end{array}\right]$$

$$\left[\begin{array}{ccc|c} 1 & 0 & \frac{3}{5} & \frac{14}{5} \\ 0 & 1 & -\frac{7}{5} & -\frac{41}{5} \\ 0 & 0 & 1 & 3 \end{array}\right]$$

$$\left[\begin{array}{ccc|c} 1 & 0 & 0 & 1 \\ 0 & 1 & -\frac{7}{5} & -\frac{41}{5} \\ 0 & 0 & 1 & 3 \end{array}\right]$$

$$\left[\begin{array}{ccc|c} 1 & 0 & 0 & 1 \\ 0 & 1 & 0 & -4 \\ 0 & 0 & 1 & 3 \end{array}\right]$$

$\{(1, -4, 3)\}$

25. Let $n =$ the number.

$25 - 2n = 13$

$12 = 2n$

$n = 6$

The number is 6.

27. Let $n =$ the number.

$4n - 5 = 2n + 3$

$2n = 8$

$n = 4$

The number is 4.

29. Let $w =$ the width of the rectangle so $w + 4 =$ the length of the rectangle.

$2w + 2(w + 4) = 28$

$w + w + 4 = 14$

$2w + 4 = 14$

$2w = 10$

$w = 5$

so $w + 4 = 9$

The dimensions of the rectangle are 5 km by 9 km.

31. $(x-5)^2 + (y+1)^2 = 9$

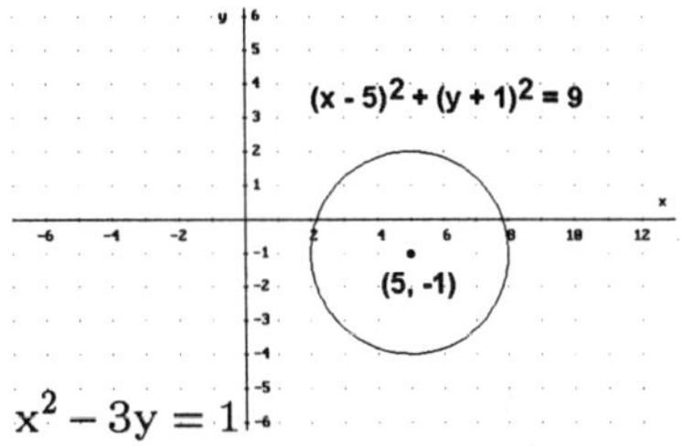

33. $x^2 - 3y = 1$

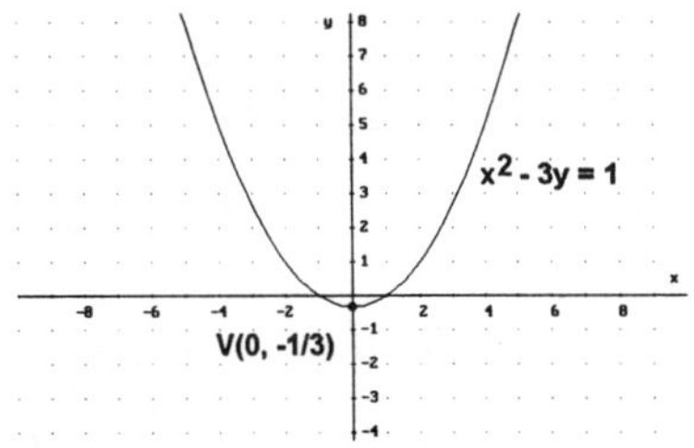

Exercise Set 10.6

1. $\begin{cases} x^2 + y^2 = 25 \\ 4x + 3y = 0 \end{cases}$

Solve equation 2 for y.

$3y = -4x$

$y = \frac{-4x}{3}$

Substitute.

$x^2 + \left(-\frac{4x}{3}\right)^2 = 25$

$x^2 + \frac{16x^2}{9} = 25$

$\frac{25}{9}x^2 = 25$

$\frac{x^2}{9} = 1$

$x^2 = 9$

$x = \pm\sqrt{9} = \pm 3$

$x = 3$: $\quad y = -\frac{4}{3}(3) = -4$

$x = -3$: $\quad y = -\frac{4}{3}(-3) = 4$

$\{(3, -4), (-3, 4)\}$

3. $\begin{cases} x^2+4y^2=10 \\ y=x \end{cases}$

Substitute.

$x^2+4x^2=10$

$5x^2=10$

$x^2=2$

$x=\pm\sqrt{2}$

$x=\sqrt{2}$: $y=\sqrt{2}$

$x=-\sqrt{2}$: $y=-\sqrt{2}$

$\{(\sqrt{2}, \sqrt{2}), (-\sqrt{2}, -\sqrt{2})\}$

5. $\begin{cases} y^2=4-x \\ x-2y=4 \end{cases}$

$-2y=4-x$

Substitute.

$y^2=-2y$

$y^2+2y=0$

$y(y+2)=0$

$y=0$ or $y+2=0$

$y=-2$

$y=0$: $x-2(0)=4$

$x=4$

$y=-2$: $x-2(-2)=4$

$x+4=4$

$x=0$

$\{(4, 0), (0, -2)\}$

7. $\begin{cases} x^2+y^2=9 \\ 16x^2-4y^2=64 \end{cases}$

$\begin{cases} x^2+y^2=9 \\ 4x^2-y^2=16 \end{cases}$

Add.

$5x^2=25$

$x^2=5$

$x=\pm\sqrt{5}$

Substitute back.

$5+y^2=9$

$y^2=4$

$y=\pm 2$

$\{(\sqrt{5}, 2), (\sqrt{5}, -2), (-\sqrt{5}, 2), (-\sqrt{5}, -2)\}$

9. $\begin{cases} x^2+2y^2=2 \\ x-y=2 \end{cases}$

$x=y+2$

Substitute.

$(y+2)^2+2y^2=2$

$y^2+4y+4+2y^2=2$

$3y^2+4y+4=2$

$3y^2+4y+2=0$

$b^2-4ac=4^2-4(3)(2)$

$b^2-4ac=16-24=-8<0$

Therefore, no real solutions exist.

$\{\ \}$

11. $\begin{cases} y=x^2-3 \\ 4x-y=6 \end{cases}$

Substitute.

$4x-(x^2-3)=6$

$4x-x^2+3=6$

$0=x^2-4x+3$

$0=(x-3)(x-1)$

$x-3=0$ or $x-1=0$

$x=3$ or $x=1$

$x=3$: $y=3^2-3=9-3=6$

$x=1$: $y=1^2-3=1-3=-2$

$\{(3, 6), (1, -2)\}$

13. $\begin{cases} y=x^2 \\ 3x+y=10 \end{cases}$

Substitute.

$3x+x^2=10$

$x^2+3x-10=0$

$(x+5)(x-2)=0$

$x+5=0$ or $x-2=0$

$x=-5$ or $x=2$

$x = -5$: $y = (-5)^2 = 25$

$x = 2$: $y = 2^2 = 4$

$\{(-5, 25), (2, 4)\}$

15. $\begin{cases} y = 2x^2 + 1 \\ x + y = -1 \end{cases}$

Substitute.

$x + 2x^2 + 1 = -1$

$2x^2 + x + 1 = -1$

$2x^2 + x + 2 = 0$

$b^2 - 4ac = 1^2 - 4(2)(2)$

$b^2 - 4ac = 1 - 16 = -15 < 0$

Therefore, no real solutions exist.

$\{\ \}$

17. $\begin{cases} y = x^2 - 4 \\ y = x^2 - 4x \end{cases}$

Substitute.

$x^2 - 4 = x^2 - 4x$

$-4 = -4x$

$x = 1$

$y = 1^2 - 4 = -3$

$\{(1, -3)\}$

19. $\begin{cases} 2x^2 + 3y^2 = 14 \\ -x^2 + y^2 = 3 \end{cases}$

$y^2 = x^2 + 3$

Substitute.

$2x^2 + 3(x^2 + 3) = 14$

$2x^2 + 3x^2 + 9 = 14$

$5x^2 + 9 = 14$

$5x^2 = 5$

$x^2 = 1$

$x = \pm 1$

Substitute back.

$y^2 = 1 + 3$

$y^2 = 4$

$y = \pm 2$

$\{(1, -2), (1, 2), (-1, -2), (-1, 2)\}$

21. $\begin{cases} x^2 + y^2 = 1 \\ x^2 + (y+3)^2 = 4 \end{cases}$

Subtract equation 1 from equation 2.

$(y+3)^2 - y^2 = 3$

$y^2 + 6y + 9 - y^2 = 3$

$6y + 9 = 3$

$6y = -6$

$y = -1$

Substitute back.

$x^2 + (-1)^2 = 1$

$x^2 + 1 = 1$

$x^2 = 0$

$x = 0$

$\{(0, -1)\}$

23. $\begin{cases} y = x^2 + 2 \\ y = -x^2 + 4 \end{cases}$

Substitute.

$x^2 + 2 = -x^2 + 4$

$2x^2 = 2$

$x^2 = 1$

$x = \pm 1$

Substitute back.

$y = 1 + 2 = 3$

$\{(1, 3), (-1, 3)\}$

25. $\begin{cases} 3x^2 + y^2 = 9 \\ 3x^2 - y^2 = 9 \end{cases}$

Subtract.

$2y^2 = 0$

$y^2 = 0$

$y = 0$

Substitute back.

$3x^2 + 0 = 9$
$3x^2 = 9$

$x^2 = 3$

$x = \pm\sqrt{3}$

$\{(\sqrt{3},\ 0),\ (-\sqrt{3},\ 0)\}$

27. $\begin{cases} x^2 + 3y^2 = 6 \\ x^2 - 3y^2 = 10 \end{cases}$

Add.

$2x^2 = 16$

$x^2 = 8$

$x = \pm\sqrt{8}$

$x = \pm 2\sqrt{2}$

Substitute back.

$8 + 3y^2 = 6$

$3y^2 = -2$

$y^2 = -\frac{2}{3}$

Therefore, no real solutions exist.

$\{\ \}$

29. $\begin{cases} x^2 + y^2 = 36 \\ y = \frac{1}{6}x^2 - 6 \end{cases}$

$y + 6 = \frac{1}{6}x^2$

$x^2 = 6(y + 6)$

Substitute.

$6(y + 6) + y^2 = 36$

$6y + 36 + y^2 = 36$

$6y + y^2 = 0$

$y(6 + y) = 0$

$y = 0$ or $6 + y = 0$

$y = -6$

$y = 0$: $x^2 + 0^2 = 36$

$x^2 = 36$

$x = \pm 6$

$y = -6$: $x^2 + (-6)^2 = 36$

$x^2 + 36 = 36$

$x^2 = 0$

$x = 0$

$\{(6,\ 0),\ (-6,\ 0),\ (0, -6)\}$

31. $x > -3$

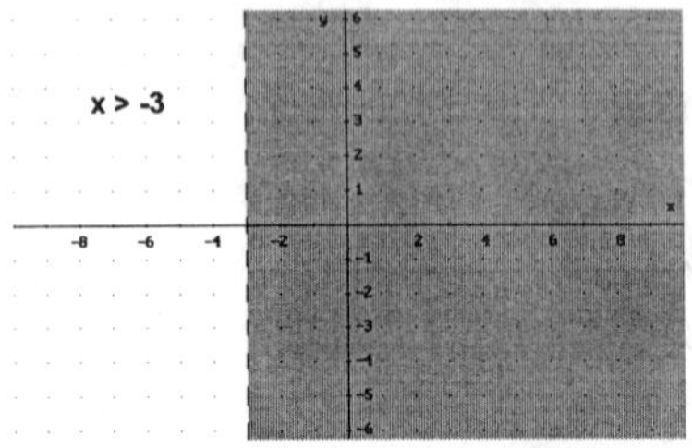

33. $y < 2x - 1$

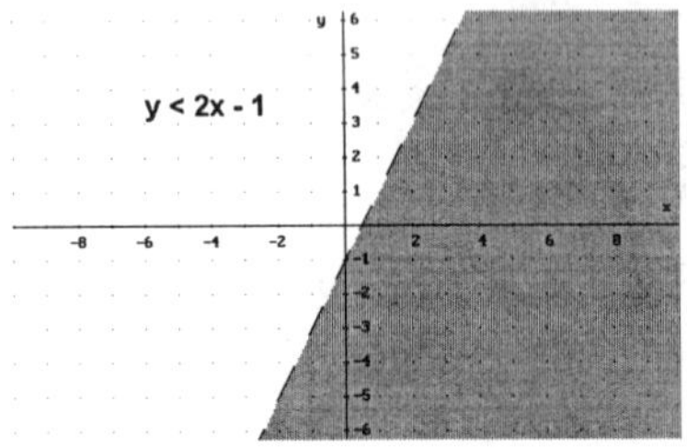

35. $P = x + (2x - 5) + (5x - 20)$

$P = (8x - 25)$ inches

37. $P = 2(x^2 + 3x + 1) + 2x^2$

$P = 2x^2 + 6x + 2 + 2x^2$

$P = (4x^2 + 6x + 2)$ meters

Exercise Set 10.7

1. $y < x^2$

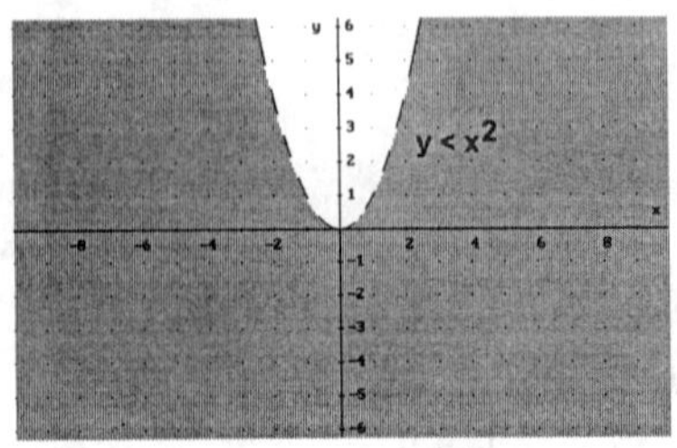

3. $x^2+y^2\geq 16$

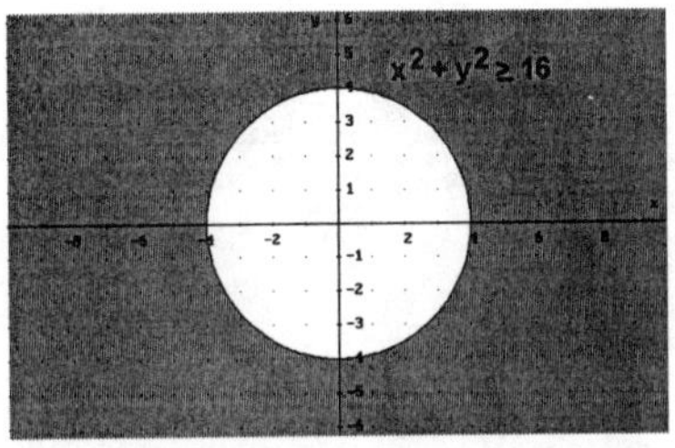

5. $\frac{x^2}{4}-y^2<1$

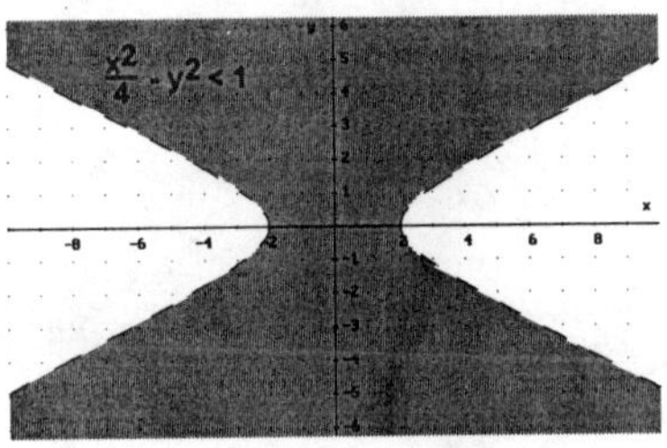

7. $\begin{cases}2x-y<2\\ y\leq -x\end{cases}$

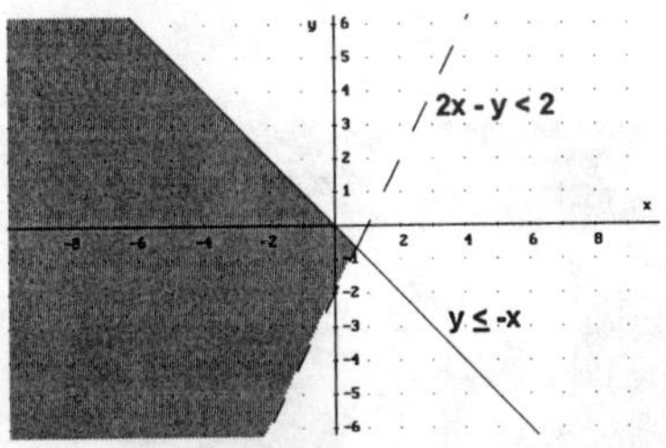

9. $\begin{cases}4x+3y\geq 12\\ x^2+y^2<16\end{cases}$

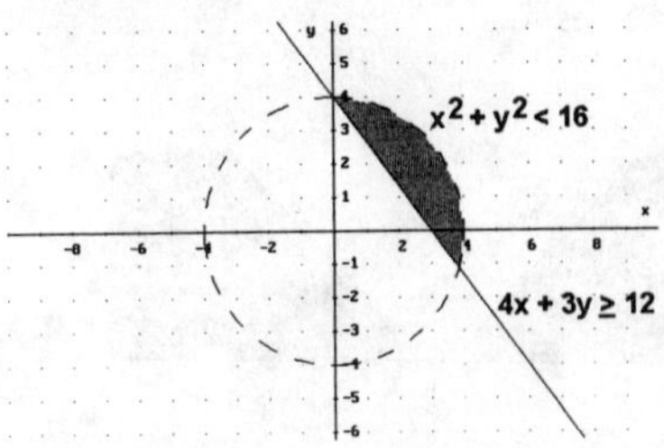

11. $\begin{cases}x^2+y^2\leq 9\\ x^2+y^2\geq 1\end{cases}$

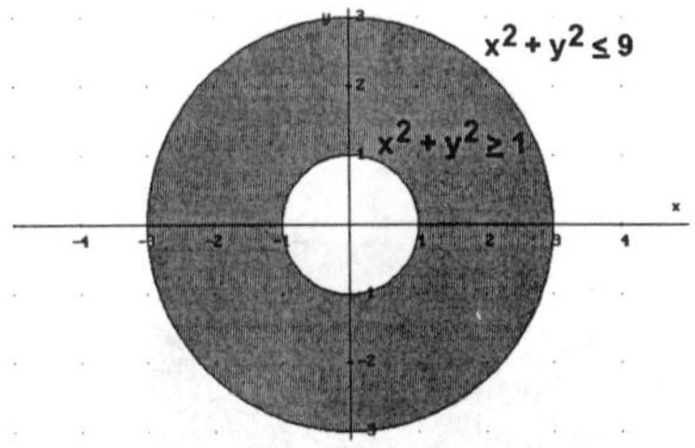

13. $y>(x-1)^2-3$

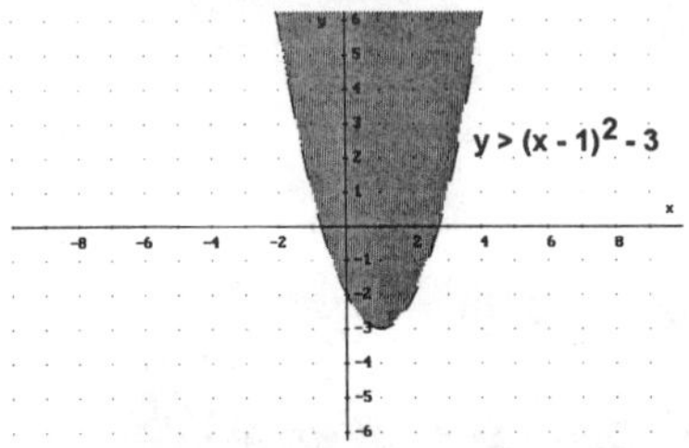

15. $x^2+y^2\leq 9$

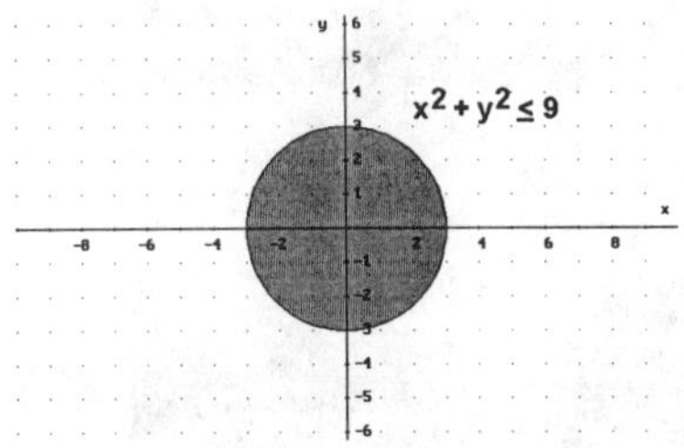

17. $y>-x^2+5$

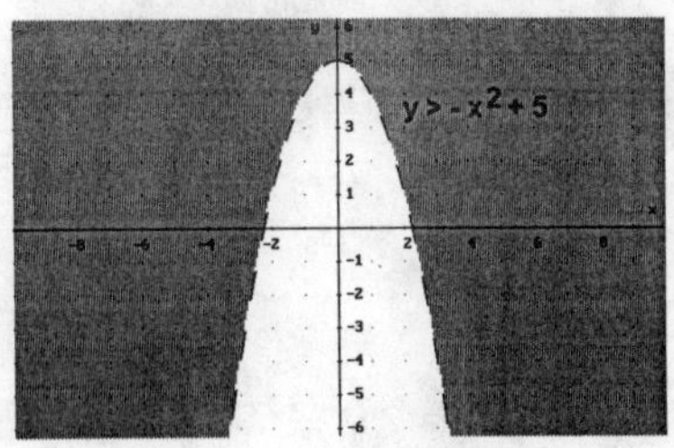

19. $\frac{x^2}{4}+\frac{y^2}{9}\leq 1$

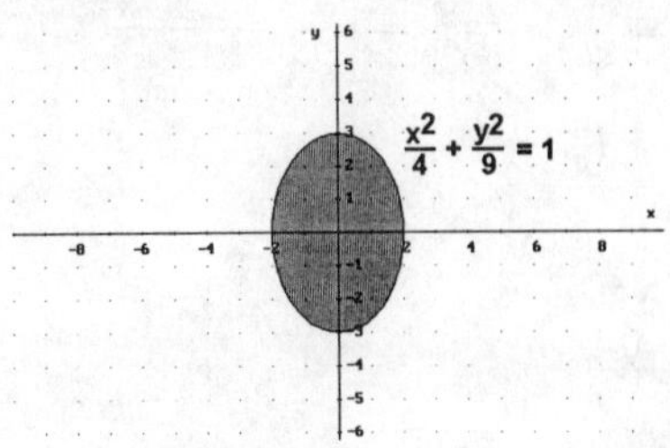

21. $\frac{y^2}{4} - x^2 \le 1$

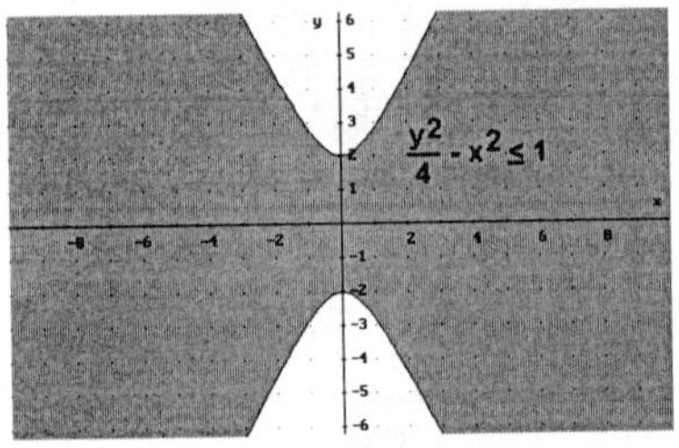

23. $y < (x-2)^2 + 1$

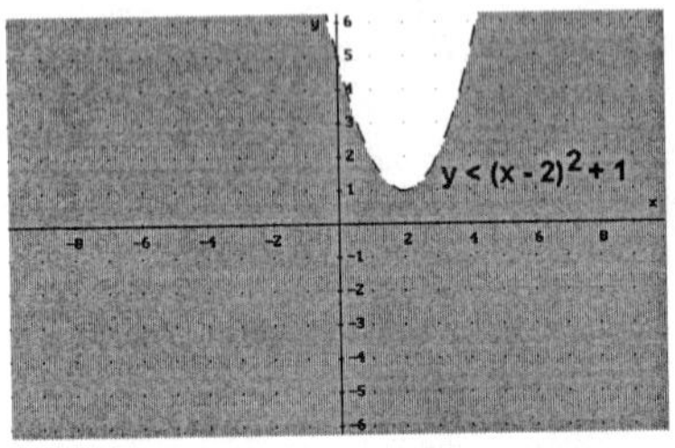

25. $y \le x^2 + x - 2$

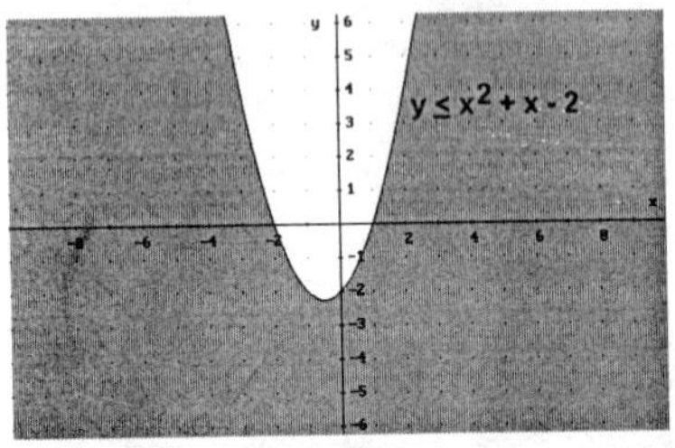

27. $\begin{cases} y > x^2 \\ y \ge 2x + 1 \end{cases}$

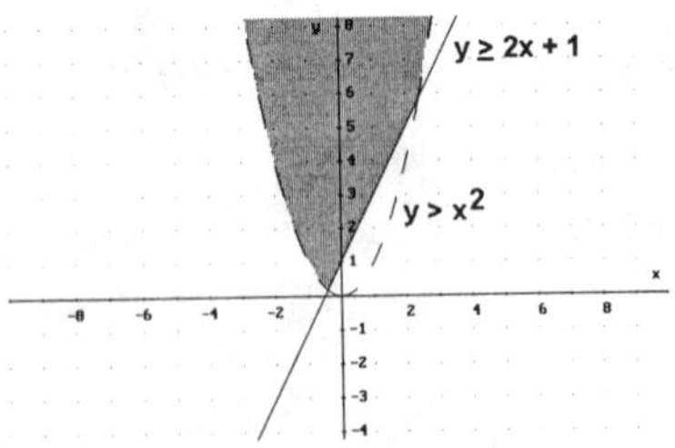

29. $\begin{cases} x > y^2 \\ y > 0 \end{cases}$

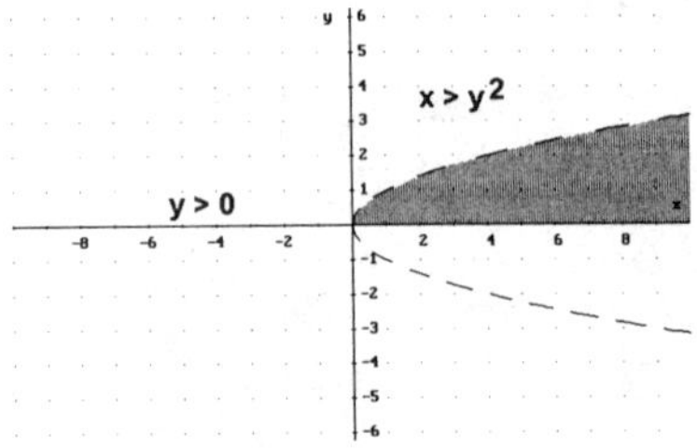

31. $\begin{cases} x^2 + y^2 > 9 \\ y > x^2 \end{cases}$

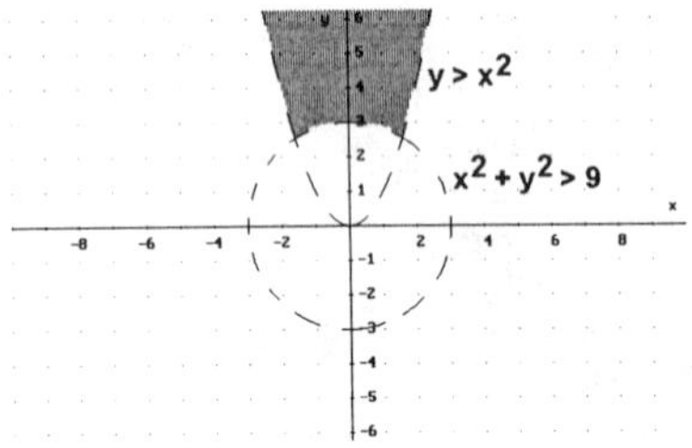

33. $\begin{cases} \frac{x^2}{4} + \frac{y^2}{9} \ge 1 \\ x^2 + y^2 \ge 4 \end{cases}$

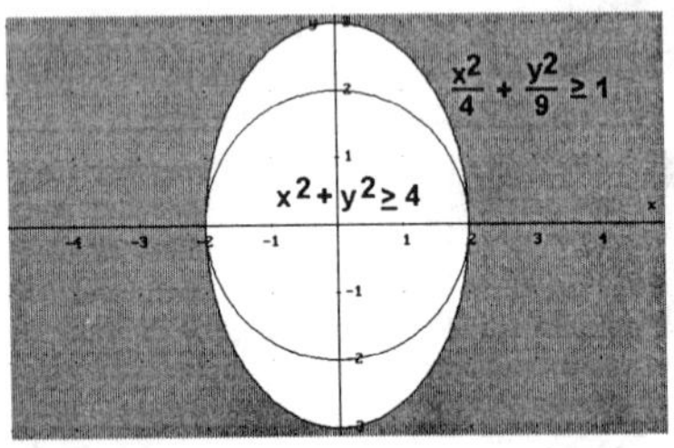

35. $\begin{cases} x^2 - y^2 \ge 1 \\ y \ge 0 \end{cases}$

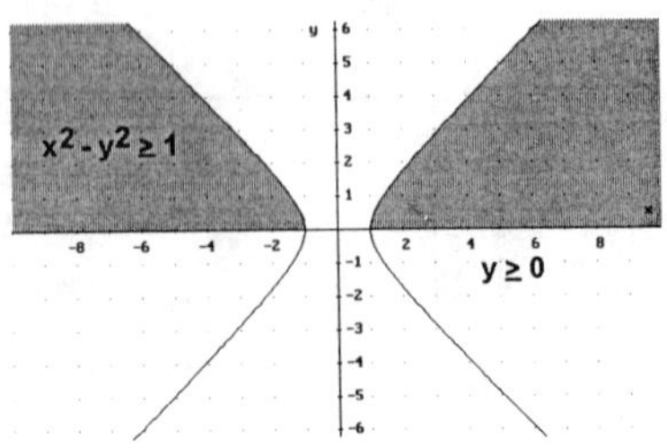

37. $\begin{cases} x+y \geq 1 \\ 2x+3y < 1 \\ x > -3 \end{cases}$

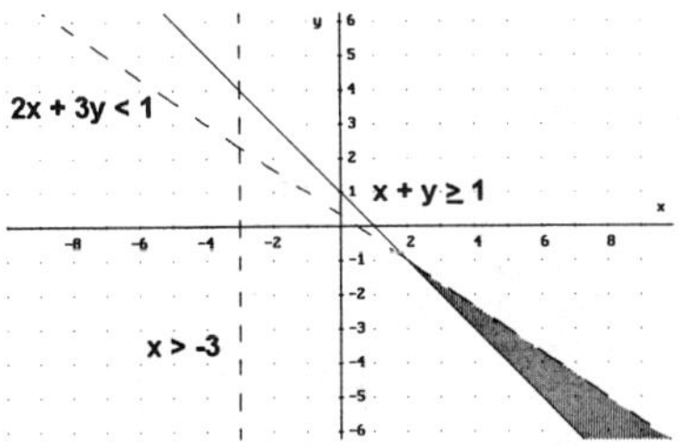

39. $\begin{cases} x^2-y^2 < 1 \\ \frac{x^2}{16}+y^2 \leq 1 \\ x \geq -2 \end{cases}$

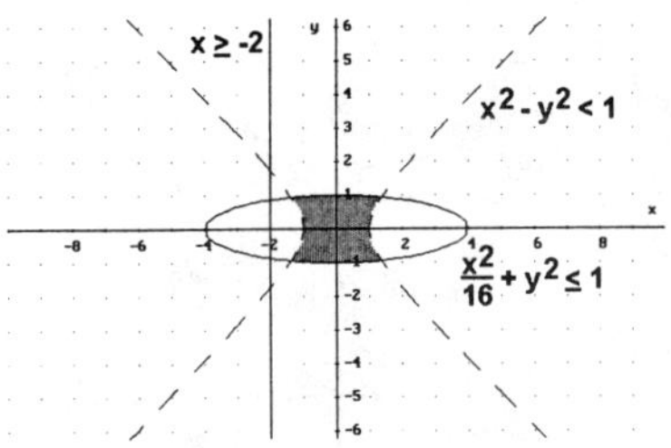

41. $x+3y = 5x$

$3y = 4x$

$y = \frac{4x}{3}$

43. $a-2y = c$

$a-c = 2y$

$y = \frac{a-c}{2}$

45. $(x-1)(x+2) > 0$

First solve:

$(x-1)(x+2) = 0$

$x-1 = 0$ or $x+2 = 0$

$x = 1$ or $x = -2$

Region	Interval	Test Point
A	$(-\infty, -2)$	-3
B	$(-2, 1)$	0
C	$(1, \infty)$	2

$x = -3$: $(-3-1)(-3+2) > 0$ True

$x = 0$: $(0-1)(0+2) > 0$ False

$x = 2$: $(2-1)(2+2) > 0$ True

The solution is $(-\infty, -2) \cup (1, \infty)$.

47. $\frac{x}{x-3} < 0$

First, solve both $x = 0$ and $x-3 = 0$.

$x = 3$

Region	Interval	Test Point
A	$(-\infty, 0)$	-1
B	$(0, 3)$	1
C	$(3, \infty)$	4

$x = -1$: $\frac{-1}{-1-3} < 0$ False

$x = 1$: $\frac{1}{1-3} < 0$ True

$x = 4$: $\frac{4}{4-3} < 0$ False

The solution is $(0, 3)$.

Chapter 10 Review

1. $\begin{cases} 3x+10y = 1 \\ x+2y = -1 \end{cases}$

a.

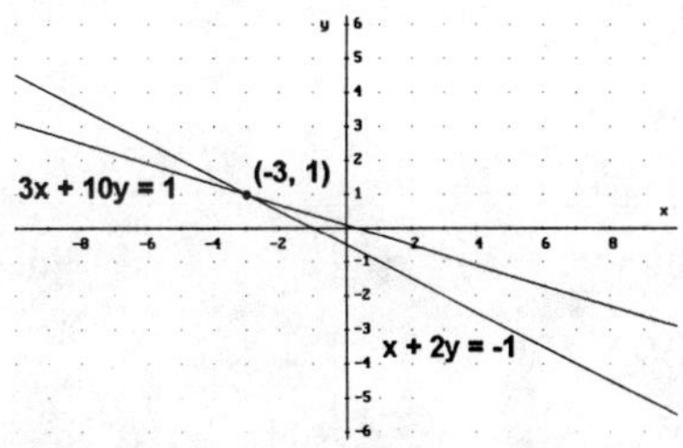

$\{(-3, 1)\}$

b. $x = -2y-1$

$3(-2y-1)+10y = 1$

$-6y-3+10y = 1$

$4y-3 = 1$

$4y = 4$

$y = 1$

Substitute back.

$x = -2(1)-1$

$x = -2 - 1 = -3$

$\{(-3,\ 1)\}$

c. $\begin{cases} 3x + 10y = 1 \\ 3x + 6y = -3 \end{cases}$

Subtract.

$4y = 4$

$y = 1$

Substitute back.

$x = -2(1) - 1$

$x = -2 - 1 = -3$

$\{(-3,\ 1)\}$

3. $\begin{cases} 2x - 4y = 22 \\ 5x - 10y = 16 \end{cases}$

a.

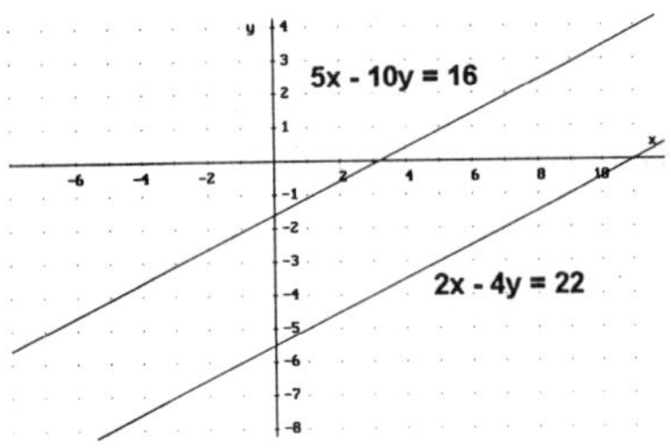

$\{\ \}$

b. $x - 2y = 11$

$x = 2y + 11$

Substitute.

$5(2y + 11) - 10y = 16$

$10y + 55 - 10y = 16$

$55 = 16$

Inconsistent system.
No solution.

$\{\ \}$

c. $\begin{cases} x - 2y = 11 \\ x - 2y = \frac{16}{5} \end{cases}$

$11 = \frac{16}{5}$

Inconsistent system.
No solution.

$\{\ \}$

5. $\begin{cases} \frac{1}{2}x - \frac{3}{4}y = -\frac{1}{2} \\ \frac{1}{8}x + \frac{3}{4}y = \frac{19}{8} \end{cases}$

a.

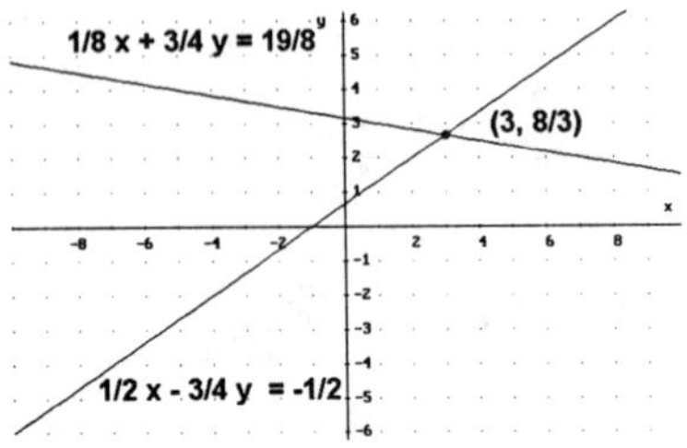

$\left\{\left(3,\ \frac{8}{3}\right)\right\}$

b. $\frac{3}{4}y = \frac{1}{2}x + \frac{1}{2}$

Substitute.

$\frac{1}{8}x + \frac{1}{2}x + \frac{1}{2} = \frac{19}{8}$

$x + 4x + 4 = 19$

$5x + 4 = 19$

$5x = 15$

$x = 3$

Substitute back.

$\frac{3}{4}y = \frac{1}{2}(3) + \frac{1}{2}$

$\frac{3}{4}y = 2$

$y = \frac{8}{3}$

$\left\{\left(3,\ \frac{8}{3}\right)\right\}$

c. Add.

$\frac{5}{8}x = \frac{15}{8}$

$5x = 15$

$x = 3$

Substitute back.

$\frac{1}{2}(3) - \frac{3}{4}y = -\frac{1}{2}$

$-\frac{3}{4}y = -2$

$-3y = -8$

$y = \frac{8}{3}$

$\left\{\left(3,\ \frac{8}{3}\right)\right\}$

7. $\begin{cases} 2x+5y=4 \\ x-5y+z=-1 \\ 4x-z=11 \end{cases}$

Add equations 2 and 3.

$5x-5y=10$

We now have the system:

$\begin{cases} 2x+5y=4 \\ 5x-5y=10 \end{cases}$

Add.

$7x=14$
$x=2$

$2(2)+5y=4$
$4+5y=4$
$5y=0$
$y=0$

$4(2)-z=11$
$8-z=11$
$8-11=z$
$z=-3$

$\{(2, 0, -3)\}$

9. $\begin{cases} 5x+7y=9 \\ 14y-z=28 \\ 4x+2z=-4 \end{cases}$

$2x+z=-2$
$z=-2x-2$

$14y-(-2x-2)=28$
$14y+2x+2=28$
$2x+14y=26$
$x+7y=13$

$\begin{cases} x+7y=13 \\ 5x+7y=9 \end{cases}$

Subtract.

$-4x=4$
$x=-1$

$-1+7y=13$
$7y=14$
$y=2$

$z=-2(-1)-2$
$z=2-2=0$

$\{(-1, 2, 0)\}$

11. $\begin{cases} x+2y+3z=11 \\ y+2z=3 \\ 2x-2z=10 \end{cases}$

$x-z=5$
$x=z+5$

Substitute.

$z+5+2y+3z=11$
$2y+4z+5=11$
$2y+4z=6$
$y+2z=3$
which is equation 2.
Dependent system.

$y=-2z+3$

$x+2(-2z+3)+3z=11$
$x-4z+6+3z=11$
$x-z+6=11$
$x=z+5$

$\{(z+5, -2z+3, z) | z \text{ is any real number}\}$

13. $\begin{cases} x-3y-5z=-5 \\ 4x-2y+3z=13 \\ 5x+3y+4z=22 \end{cases}$

Multiply equation 1 by -4 and add to equation 2.

$10y+23z=33$

Multiply equation 1 by -5 and add to equation 3.

$18y+29z=47$

We now have the system:

$\begin{cases} 10y+23z=33 \\ 18y+29z=47 \end{cases}$

$\begin{cases} 90y+207z=297 \\ 90y+145z=235 \end{cases}$

Subtract.

$62z=62$
$z=1$

$10y+23(1)=33$
$10y+23=33$
$10y=10$
$y=1$

$x-3(1)-5(1)=-5$
$x-3-5=-5$
$x-3=0$
$x=3$

$\{(3, 1, 1)\}$

15. Let p = the number of pennies, n = the number of nickels, and d = the number of dimes.

$$\begin{cases} p+n+d=95 \\ 0.01p+0.05n+0.10d=4.03 \\ p=2d \\ n=d-1 \end{cases}$$

Substitute into equation 1.

$$2d+d-1+d=95$$
$$4d-1=95$$
$$4d=96$$
$$d=24$$

$$p=2(24)=48$$
$$n=24-1=23$$

Check value
$0.01(48)+0.05(23)+0.10(24)$
$0.48+1.15+2.40$
4.03 as desired.

Alice has 48 pennies, 23 nickels, and 24 dimes.

17. Let p = Pat's age, and s = Sue's age.

$$\begin{cases} s=p+16 \\ s+15=2(p+15) \end{cases}$$

Substitute.

$$p+16+15=2(p+15)$$
$$p+31=2p+30$$
$$1=p$$

Substitute back.

$$s=1+16=17$$

Sue is 17 years old and Pat is 1 year old.

19. Let w = the width of the foundation and l = the length of the foundation.

$$\begin{cases} l=3w \\ 2w+21=296 \end{cases}$$

Substitute.

$$2w+2(3w)=296$$
$$2w+6w=296$$
$$8w=296$$
$$w=37$$

Substitute back.

$$l=3(37)=111.$$

The foundation is 37 feet wide and 111 feet long.

21. Let c = # of lbs. of chocolates used, n = # of lbs. of nuts used, and r = # of lbs. of raisins used.

$$\begin{cases} r=2n \\ c+n+r=45 \\ 3.00c+2.70n+2.25r=2.80(45) \end{cases}$$

Substitute equation 1 into equation 2.

$$c+n+2n=45$$
$$c+3n=45$$
$$c=-3n+45$$

Now substitute for c and r in equation 3.

$$3.00(-3n+45)+2.70n+2.25(2n)=126$$
$$-9n+135+2.7n+4.5n=126$$
$$-1.8n+135=126$$
$$-1.8n=-9$$
$$n=5$$

Substitute back.

$$r=2(5)=10$$
$$c=-3(5)+45$$
$$c=-15+45=30$$

She should use 30 lbs. of creme-filled chocolates, 5 lbs. of chocolate-covered nuts, and 10 lbs. of chocolate-covered raisins.

23. Let l = the rate of interest on the larger investment and s = the rate of interest on the smaller investment, both expressed as decimals.

$$\begin{cases} 10{,}000\,l+4000s=1250 \\ l=s+0.02 \end{cases}$$

Substitute.

$$10{,}000(s+0.02)+4000s=1250$$
$$10{,}000s+200+4000s=1250$$
$$14{,}000s+200=1250$$
$$14{,}000s=1050$$

$s=\dfrac{1050}{14{,}000}=0.075$ and

$l=0.075+0.02=0.095.$

The interest rate on the larger investment in 9.5% and is 7.5% on the smaller investment.

25. Let f = the first number, s = the second number, and t = the third number.

$$\begin{cases} f+s+t=295 \\ f=s+5 \\ f=2t \end{cases}$$

$$\begin{cases} f+s+t=295 \\ s=f-5 \\ t=\frac{f}{2} \end{cases}$$

Substitute.

$f+f-5+\frac{f}{2}=295$

$\frac{5}{2}f-5=295$

$\frac{5}{2}f=300$

$f=120$

Substitute back.

$s=120-5=115$

$t=\frac{120}{2}=60$

The first number is 120, the second is 115, and the third is 60.

27. $\begin{vmatrix} 3 & -1 \\ 2 & 5 \end{vmatrix} = 3(5)-(-1)2=15+2=17$

29. $\begin{vmatrix} -2 & 3 & 1 \\ 4 & 4 & 0 \\ 1 & -2 & 3 \end{vmatrix}$

$1\begin{vmatrix} 4 & 4 \\ 1 & -2 \end{vmatrix} - 0\begin{vmatrix} -2 & 3 \\ 1 & -2 \end{vmatrix} + 3\begin{vmatrix} -2 & 3 \\ 4 & 4 \end{vmatrix}$

$(-8-4)-0+3(-8-12)$

$-12+3(-20)=-12-60=-72$

31. $\begin{cases} 6x-6y=-5 \\ 10x-2y=1 \end{cases}$

$D=\begin{vmatrix} 6 & -6 \\ 10 & -2 \end{vmatrix}$

$D=6(-2)-(-6)(10)$

$D=-12+60=48$

$D_x=\begin{vmatrix} -5 & -6 \\ 1 & -2 \end{vmatrix}$

$D_x=(-5)(-2)-(-6)(1)$

$D_x=10+6=16$

$D_y=\begin{vmatrix} 6 & -5 \\ 10 & 1 \end{vmatrix}$

$D_y=6(1)-(-5)(10)$

$D_y=6+50=56$

$x=\frac{16}{48}=\frac{1}{3}$ and $y=\frac{56}{48}=\frac{7}{6}$

$\left\{\left(\frac{1}{3}, \frac{7}{6}\right)\right\}$

33. $\begin{cases} y=\frac{1}{2}x+\frac{2}{3} \\ 4x+6y=4 \end{cases}$

$\begin{cases} -\frac{1}{2}x+y=\frac{2}{3} \\ 4x+6y=4 \end{cases}$

$D=\begin{vmatrix} -\frac{1}{2} & 1 \\ 4 & 6 \end{vmatrix}$

$D=\left(-\frac{1}{2}\right)6-1(4)$

$D=-3-4=-7$

$D_x=\begin{vmatrix} \frac{2}{3} & 1 \\ 4 & 6 \end{vmatrix}$

$D_x=\left(\frac{2}{3}\right)6-1(4)=4-4=0$

$D_y=\begin{vmatrix} -\frac{1}{2} & \frac{2}{3} \\ 4 & 4 \end{vmatrix}=\left(-\frac{1}{2}\right)4-\left(\frac{2}{3}\right)4$

$D_y=-2-\frac{8}{3}=\frac{-14}{3}$

$$x = \frac{0}{-7} \text{ and } y = \frac{\frac{-14}{3}}{-7} = \frac{2}{3}$$

$\left\{\left(0,\ \frac{2}{3}\right)\right\}$

35. $\begin{cases} 3x - 6y = 12 \\ 2y = x - 4 \end{cases}$

$\begin{cases} 3x - 6y = 12 \\ -x + 2y = -4 \end{cases}$

$$D = \begin{vmatrix} 3 & -6 \\ -1 & 2 \end{vmatrix}$$

$D = 3(2) - (-6)(-1) = 6 - 6 = 0$

Therefore, Cramer's Rule cannot be used to solve this system. Since equation 1 is -3 times equation 2, the system is dependent.

$\{(x,\ y) \mid x - 2y = 4\}$

37. $\begin{cases} 2x + 5y = 4 \\ x - 5y + z = -1 \\ 4x - z = 11 \end{cases}$

$$D = \begin{vmatrix} 2 & 5 & 0 \\ 1 & -5 & 1 \\ 4 & 0 & -1 \end{vmatrix}$$

$$D = 0\begin{vmatrix} 1 & -5 \\ 4 & 0 \end{vmatrix} - 1\begin{vmatrix} 2 & 5 \\ 4 & 0 \end{vmatrix} - 1\begin{vmatrix} 2 & 5 \\ 1 & -5 \end{vmatrix}$$

$D = 0 - (0 - 20) - (-10 - 5)$

$D = 20 + 15 = 35$

$$D_x = \begin{vmatrix} 4 & 5 & 0 \\ -1 & -5 & 1 \\ 11 & 0 & -1 \end{vmatrix}$$

$$D_x = 0\begin{vmatrix} -1 & -5 \\ 11 & 0 \end{vmatrix} - 1\begin{vmatrix} 4 & 5 \\ 11 & 0 \end{vmatrix} - 1\begin{vmatrix} 4 & 5 \\ -1 & -5 \end{vmatrix}$$

$D_x = 0 - (0 - 55) - [-20 - (-5)]$

$D_x = 55 + 15 = 70$

$$D_y = \begin{vmatrix} 2 & 4 & 0 \\ 1 & -1 & 1 \\ 4 & 11 & -1 \end{vmatrix}$$

$$D_y = 0\begin{vmatrix} 1 & -1 \\ 4 & 11 \end{vmatrix} - 1\begin{vmatrix} 2 & 4 \\ 4 & 11 \end{vmatrix} - 1\begin{vmatrix} 2 & 4 \\ 1 & -1 \end{vmatrix}$$

$D_y = 0 - (22 - 16) - (-2 - 4)$

$D_y = -6 + 6 = 0$

$$D_z = \begin{vmatrix} 2 & 5 & 4 \\ 1 & -5 & -1 \\ 4 & 0 & 11 \end{vmatrix}$$

$$D_z = 4\begin{vmatrix} 1 & -5 \\ 4 & 0 \end{vmatrix} + 1\begin{vmatrix} 2 & 5 \\ 4 & 0 \end{vmatrix} + 11\begin{vmatrix} 2 & 5 \\ 1 & -5 \end{vmatrix}$$

$D_z = 4[0 - (-20)] + 1(0 - 20) + 11(-10 - 5)$

$D_z = 4(20) - 20 + 11(-15) = 60 - 165 = -105$

$x = \frac{70}{35} = 2$

$y = \frac{0}{35} = 0$

$z = \frac{-105}{35} = -3$

$\{(2,\ 0,\ -3)\}$

39. $\begin{cases} 2x - z = 1 \\ 3x - y + 2z = 3 \\ x + y + 3z = -2 \end{cases}$

$$D = \begin{vmatrix} 2 & 0 & -1 \\ 3 & -1 & 2 \\ 1 & 1 & 3 \end{vmatrix}$$

$$D = 2\begin{vmatrix} -1 & 2 \\ 1 & 3 \end{vmatrix} - 0\begin{vmatrix} 3 & 2 \\ 1 & 3 \end{vmatrix} - 1\begin{vmatrix} 3 & -1 \\ 1 & 1 \end{vmatrix}$$

$D = 2(-3 - 2) - 0 - [3 - (-1)]$

$D = 2(-5) - 4 = -10 - 4 = -14$

$$D_x = \begin{vmatrix} 1 & 0 & -1 \\ 3 & -1 & 2 \\ -2 & 1 & 3 \end{vmatrix}$$

$$D_x = 1\begin{vmatrix} -1 & 2 \\ 1 & 3 \end{vmatrix} - 0\begin{vmatrix} 3 & 2 \\ -2 & 3 \end{vmatrix} - 1\begin{vmatrix} 3 & -1 \\ -2 & 1 \end{vmatrix}$$

$D_x = (-3-2) - 0 - (3-2) = -5 - 1 = -6$

$$D_y = \begin{vmatrix} 2 & 1 & -1 \\ 3 & 3 & 2 \\ 1 & -2 & 3 \end{vmatrix}$$

$$D_y = 2\begin{vmatrix} 3 & 2 \\ -2 & 3 \end{vmatrix} - 1\begin{vmatrix} 3 & 2 \\ 1 & 3 \end{vmatrix} - 1\begin{vmatrix} 3 & 3 \\ 1 & -2 \end{vmatrix}$$

$D_y = 2[9-(-4)] - (9-2) - (-6-3)$

$D_y = 2(13) - 7 + 9 = 26 + 2 = 28$

$$D_z = \begin{vmatrix} 2 & 0 & 1 \\ 3 & -1 & 3 \\ 1 & 1 & -2 \end{vmatrix}$$

$$D_z = 2\begin{vmatrix} -1 & 3 \\ 1 & -2 \end{vmatrix} - 0\begin{vmatrix} 3 & 3 \\ 1 & -2 \end{vmatrix} + 1\begin{vmatrix} 3 & -1 \\ 1 & 1 \end{vmatrix}$$

$D_z = 2(2-3) - 0 + [3-(-1)]$

$D_z = 2(-1) + 4 = -2 + 4 = 2$

$x = \frac{-6}{-14} = \frac{3}{7}$

$y = \frac{28}{-14} = -2$

$z = \frac{2}{-14} = -\frac{1}{7}$

$\left\{\left(\frac{3}{7}, -2, -\frac{1}{7}\right)\right\}$

41. $\begin{cases} 5x + 7y = 9 \\ 14y - z = 28 \\ 4x + 2z = -4 \end{cases}$

$$D = \begin{vmatrix} 5 & 7 & 0 \\ 0 & 14 & -1 \\ 4 & 0 & 2 \end{vmatrix}$$

$$D = 5\begin{vmatrix} 14 & -1 \\ 0 & 2 \end{vmatrix} - 7\begin{vmatrix} 0 & -1 \\ 4 & 2 \end{vmatrix} + 0\begin{vmatrix} 0 & 14 \\ 4 & 0 \end{vmatrix}$$

$D = 5(28-0) - 7[0-(-4)] + 0$

$D = 140 - 28 = 112$

$$D_x = \begin{vmatrix} 9 & 7 & 0 \\ 28 & 14 & -1 \\ -4 & 0 & 2 \end{vmatrix}$$

$$D_x = 9\begin{vmatrix} 14 & -1 \\ 0 & 2 \end{vmatrix} - 7\begin{vmatrix} 28 & -1 \\ -4 & 2 \end{vmatrix} + 0\begin{vmatrix} 28 & 14 \\ -4 & 0 \end{vmatrix}$$

$D_x = 9(28-0) - 7(56-4) + 0 = 252 - 7(52)$

$D_x = 252 - 364 = -112$

$$D_y = \begin{vmatrix} 5 & 9 & 0 \\ 0 & 28 & -1 \\ 4 & -4 & 2 \end{vmatrix}$$

$$D_y = 5\begin{vmatrix} 28 & -1 \\ -4 & 2 \end{vmatrix} - 9\begin{vmatrix} 0 & -1 \\ 4 & 2 \end{vmatrix} + 0\begin{vmatrix} 0 & 28 \\ 4 & -4 \end{vmatrix}$$

$D_y = 5(56-4) - 9[0-(-4)] + 0$

$D_y = 5(52) - 9(4) = 260 - 36 = 224$

$$D_z = \begin{vmatrix} 5 & 7 & 9 \\ 0 & 14 & 28 \\ 4 & 0 & -4 \end{vmatrix}$$

$$D_z = 5\begin{vmatrix} 14 & 28 \\ 0 & -4 \end{vmatrix} - 0\begin{vmatrix} 7 & 9 \\ 0 & -4 \end{vmatrix} + 4\begin{vmatrix} 7 & 9 \\ 14 & 28 \end{vmatrix}$$

$D_z = 5(-56-0) - 0 + 4(196-126)$

$D_z = -280 + 4(70) = -280 + 280 = 0$

$x = \frac{-112}{112} = -1$

$y = \frac{224}{112} = 2$

$z = \frac{0}{112} = 0$

$\{(-1, 2, 0)\}$

43. $\begin{cases} 3x - 6y = 12 \\ 2y = x - 4 \end{cases}$

$$\begin{cases} 3x - 6y = 12 \\ -x + 2y = -4 \end{cases}$$

$$\left[\begin{array}{cc|c} 3 & -6 & 12 \\ -1 & 2 & -4 \end{array}\right]$$

$$\left[\begin{array}{cc|c} 1 & -2 & 4 \\ -1 & 2 & -4 \end{array}\right]$$

$$\left[\begin{array}{cc|c} 1 & -2 & 4 \\ 0 & 0 & 0 \end{array}\right]$$

Dependent system.
$\{(x, y) | x - 2y = 4\}$

45. $\begin{cases} 6x - 6y = -5 \\ 10x - 2y = 1 \end{cases}$

$$\left[\begin{array}{cc|c} 6 & -6 & -5 \\ 10 & -2 & 1 \end{array}\right]$$

$$\left[\begin{array}{cc|c} 1 & -1 & -\frac{5}{6} \\ 10 & -2 & 1 \end{array}\right]$$

$$\left[\begin{array}{cc|c} 1 & -1 & -\frac{5}{6} \\ 0 & 8 & \frac{28}{3} \end{array}\right]$$

$$\left[\begin{array}{cc|c} 1 & -1 & -\frac{5}{6} \\ 0 & 1 & \frac{7}{6} \end{array}\right]$$

$$\left[\begin{array}{cc|c} 1 & 0 & \frac{1}{3} \\ 0 & 1 & \frac{7}{6} \end{array}\right]$$

$\left\{\left(\frac{1}{3}, \frac{7}{6}\right)\right\}$

47. $\begin{cases} 5x - 3y = 10 \\ -2x + y = -1 \end{cases}$

$$\left[\begin{array}{cc|c} 5 & -3 & 10 \\ -2 & 1 & -1 \end{array}\right]$$

$$\left[\begin{array}{cc|c} 1 & -\frac{3}{5} & 2 \\ -2 & 1 & -1 \end{array}\right]$$

$$\left[\begin{array}{cc|c} 1 & -\frac{3}{5} & 2 \\ 0 & -\frac{1}{5} & 3 \end{array}\right]$$

$$\left[\begin{array}{cc|c} 1 & -\frac{3}{5} & 2 \\ 0 & 1 & -15 \end{array}\right]$$

$$\left[\begin{array}{cc|c} 1 & 0 & -7 \\ 0 & 1 & -15 \end{array}\right]$$

$\{(-7, -15)\}$

49. $\begin{cases} 3x + 2y = 8 \\ 3x - y = 5 \end{cases}$

$$\left[\begin{array}{cc|c} 3 & 2 & 8 \\ 3 & -1 & 5 \end{array}\right]$$

$$\left[\begin{array}{cc|c} 1 & \frac{2}{3} & \frac{8}{3} \\ 3 & -1 & 5 \end{array}\right]$$

$$\left[\begin{array}{cc|c} 1 & \frac{2}{3} & \frac{8}{3} \\ 0 & -3 & -3 \end{array}\right]$$

$$\left[\begin{array}{cc|c} 1 & \frac{2}{3} & \frac{8}{3} \\ 0 & 1 & 1 \end{array}\right]$$

$$\left[\begin{array}{cc|c} 1 & 0 & 2 \\ 0 & 1 & 1 \end{array}\right]$$

$\{(2, 1)\}$

51. $\begin{cases} 2x + 5y = 4 \\ x - 5y + z = -1 \\ 4x - z = 11 \end{cases}$

$$\left[\begin{array}{ccc|c} 2 & 5 & 0 & 4 \\ 1 & -5 & 1 & -1 \\ 4 & 0 & -1 & 11 \end{array}\right]$$

$$\left[\begin{array}{ccc|c} 1 & \frac{5}{2} & 0 & 2 \\ 1 & -5 & 1 & -1 \\ 4 & 0 & -1 & 11 \end{array}\right]$$

$$\left[\begin{array}{ccc|c} 1 & \frac{5}{2} & 0 & 2 \\ 0 & -\frac{15}{2} & 1 & -3 \\ 4 & 0 & -1 & 11 \end{array}\right]$$

$$\left[\begin{array}{ccc|c} 1 & \frac{5}{2} & 0 & 2 \\ 0 & -\frac{15}{2} & 1 & -3 \\ 0 & -10 & -1 & 3 \end{array}\right]$$

$$\left[\begin{array}{ccc|c} 1 & \frac{5}{2} & 0 & 2 \\ 0 & 1 & -\frac{2}{15} & \frac{2}{5} \\ 0 & -10 & -1 & 3 \end{array}\right]$$

$$\left[\begin{array}{ccc|c} 1 & 0 & \frac{1}{3} & 1 \\ 0 & 1 & -\frac{2}{15} & \frac{2}{5} \\ 0 & -10 & -1 & 3 \end{array}\right]$$

$$\left[\begin{array}{ccc|c} 1 & 0 & \frac{1}{3} & 1 \\ 0 & 1 & -\frac{2}{15} & \frac{2}{5} \\ 0 & 0 & -\frac{7}{3} & 7 \end{array}\right]$$

$$\left[\begin{array}{ccc|c} 1 & 0 & \frac{1}{3} & 1 \\ 0 & 1 & -\frac{2}{15} & \frac{2}{5} \\ 0 & 0 & 1 & -3 \end{array}\right]$$

$$\left[\begin{array}{ccc|c} 1 & 0 & 0 & 2 \\ 0 & 1 & -\frac{2}{15} & \frac{2}{5} \\ 0 & 0 & 1 & -3 \end{array}\right]$$

$$\left[\begin{array}{ccc|c} 1 & 0 & 0 & 2 \\ 0 & 1 & 0 & 0 \\ 0 & 0 & 1 & -3 \end{array}\right]$$

$\{(2,\ 0,\ -3)\}$

53. $\begin{cases} 5x + 7y + 3z = 9 \\ 14y - z = 28 \\ 4x + 2z = -4 \end{cases}$

$$\left[\begin{array}{ccc|c} 5 & 7 & 3 & 9 \\ 0 & 14 & -1 & 28 \\ 4 & 0 & 2 & -4 \end{array}\right]$$

$$\left[\begin{array}{ccc|c} 1 & \frac{7}{5} & \frac{3}{5} & \frac{9}{5} \\ 0 & 14 & -1 & 28 \\ 4 & 0 & 2 & -4 \end{array}\right]$$

$$\left[\begin{array}{ccc|c} 1 & \frac{7}{5} & \frac{3}{5} & \frac{9}{5} \\ 0 & 14 & -1 & 28 \\ 0 & -\frac{28}{5} & -\frac{2}{5} & -\frac{56}{5} \end{array}\right]$$

$$\left[\begin{array}{ccc|c} 1 & \frac{7}{5} & \frac{3}{5} & \frac{9}{5} \\ 0 & 1 & -\frac{1}{14} & 2 \\ 0 & -\frac{28}{5} & -\frac{2}{5} & -\frac{56}{5} \end{array}\right]$$

$$\left[\begin{array}{ccc|c} 1 & 0 & \frac{7}{10} & -1 \\ 0 & 1 & -\frac{1}{14} & 2 \\ 0 & 0 & -\frac{4}{5} & 0 \end{array}\right]$$

$$\left[\begin{array}{ccc|c} 1 & 0 & \frac{7}{10} & -1 \\ 0 & 1 & -\frac{1}{14} & 2 \\ 0 & 0 & 1 & 0 \end{array}\right]$$

$$\left[\begin{array}{ccc|c} 1 & 0 & 0 & -1 \\ 0 & 1 & -\frac{1}{14} & 2 \\ 0 & 0 & 1 & 0 \end{array}\right]$$

$$\left[\begin{array}{ccc|c} 1 & 0 & 0 & -1 \\ 0 & 1 & 0 & 2 \\ 0 & 0 & 1 & 0 \end{array}\right]$$

$\{(-1, 2, 0)\}$

55. $\begin{cases} x+2y+3z=14 \\ y+2z=3 \\ 2x-2z=10 \end{cases}$

$$\left[\begin{array}{ccc|c} 1 & 2 & 3 & 14 \\ 0 & 1 & 2 & 3 \\ 2 & 0 & -2 & 10 \end{array}\right]$$

$$\left[\begin{array}{ccc|c} 1 & 2 & 3 & 14 \\ 0 & 1 & 2 & 3 \\ 0 & -4 & -8 & -18 \end{array}\right]$$

$$\left[\begin{array}{ccc|c} 1 & 0 & -1 & 8 \\ 0 & 1 & 2 & 3 \\ 0 & -4 & -8 & -18 \end{array}\right]$$

$$\left[\begin{array}{ccc|c} 1 & 0 & -1 & 8 \\ 0 & 1 & 2 & 3 \\ 0 & 0 & 0 & -6 \end{array}\right]$$

No solution exists.

{ }

57. $\begin{cases} x^2+y^2=4 \\ x-y=4 \end{cases}$

$\begin{cases} x^2+y^2=4 \\ x=y+4 \end{cases}$

Substitute.

$(y+4)^2+y^2=4$

$y^2+8y+16+y^2=4$

$2y^2+8y+16=4$

$2y^2+8y+12=0$

$y^2+4y+6=0$

$b^2-4ac=4^2-4(1)(6)$

$b^2-4ac=16-24=-8$

Therefore, no real solutions exist.

{ }

59. $\begin{cases} y=x^2-5x+1 \\ y=-x+6 \end{cases}$

Substitute.

$-x+6=x^2-5x+1$

$0=x^2-4x-5$

$0=(x-5)(x+1)$

$x-5=0$ or $x+1=0$

$x=5$ or $x=-1$

$x=5$: $y=-5+6=1$

$x=-1$: $y=-(-1)+6=1+6=7$

$\{(5, 1), (-1, 7)\}$

61. $\begin{cases} x^2+4y^2=16 \\ x^2+y^2=4 \end{cases}$

Subtract.

$3y^2=12$

$y^2=4$

$y=\pm 2$

Substituting back.

$x^2+4=4$

$x^2=0$

$x=0$

$\{(0, 2), (0, -2)\}$

63. $\begin{cases} x^2+2y=9 \\ 5x-2y=5 \end{cases}$

Add.

$x^2+5x=14$

$x^2+5x-14=0$

$(x+7)(x-2)=0$

$x+7=0$ or $x-2=0$

$x=-7$ or $x=2$

Substituting back.

$x=-7$: $(-7)^2+2y=9$

$49+2y=9$

$2y=-40$

$y=-20$

$x=2$: $2^2+2y=9$

$4+2y=9$

$2y=5$

$y=\frac{5}{2}$

$\left\{(-7,-20),\ \left(2,\ \frac{5}{2}\right)\right\}$

65. $\begin{cases} x^2-3y^2=1 \\ 4x^2+5y^2=21 \end{cases}$

$\begin{cases} x^2=3y^2+1 \\ 4x^2+5y^2=21 \end{cases}$

Substitute.

$4(3y^2+1)+5y^2=21$

$12y^2+4+5y^2=21$

$17y^2+4=21$

$17y^2=17$

$y^2=1$

$y=\pm 1$

Substitute back.

$x^2-3(1)=1$

$x^2-3=1$

$x^2=4$

$x=\pm 2$

$\{(2,\ 1),\ (2,-1),\ (-2,\ 1),\ (-2,-1)\}$

67. $x^2+y^2<9$

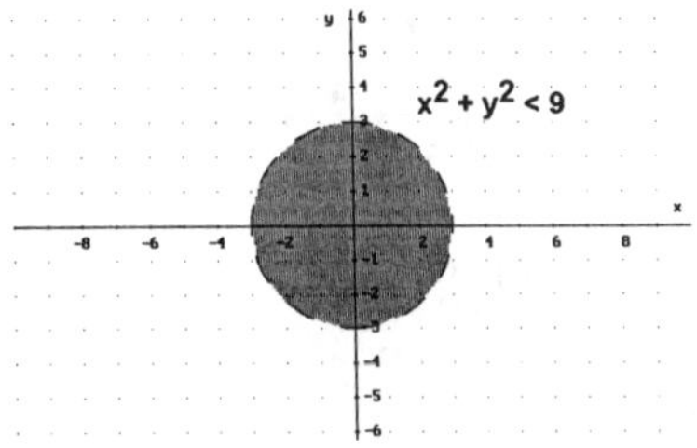

69. $\frac{x^2}{4}+\frac{y^2}{9}\geq 1$

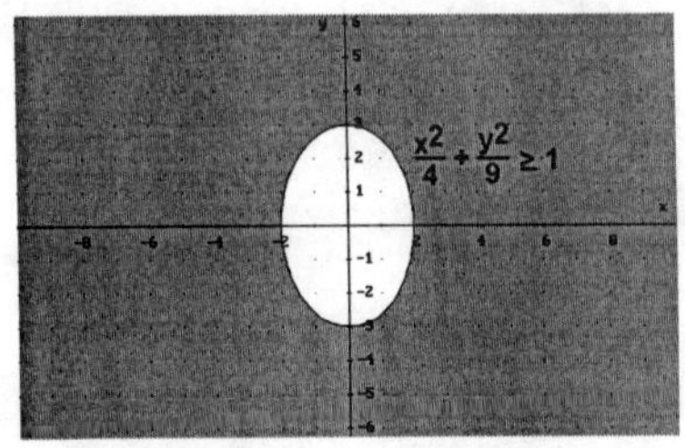

71. $\begin{cases} 3x+4y\leq 12 \\ x-2y>6 \end{cases}$

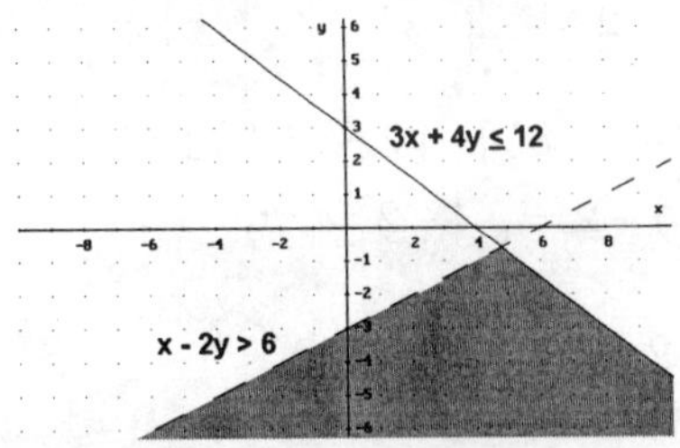

73. $\begin{cases} x^2+y^2\leq 16 \\ x^2+y^2\geq 4 \end{cases}$

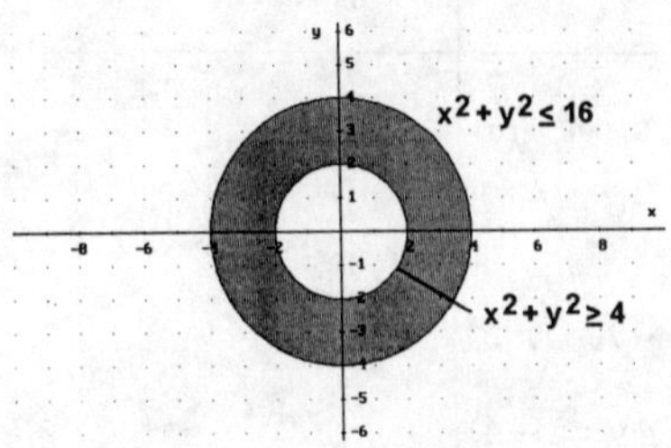

75. $\begin{cases} x^2+y^2<4 \\ y\geq x^2-1 \\ x\geq 0 \end{cases}$

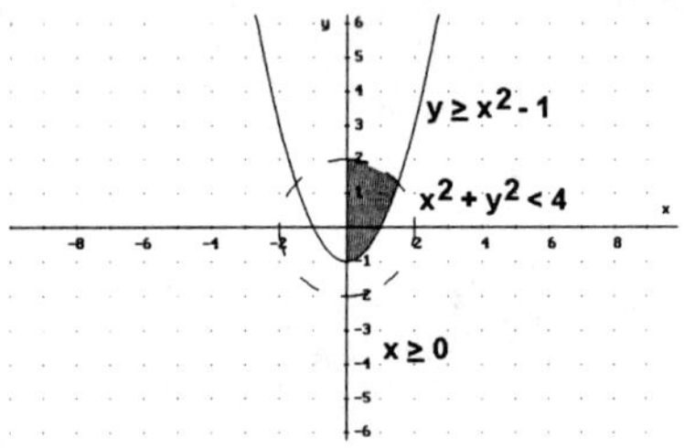

Chapter 10 Test

1. $\begin{vmatrix} 4 & -7 \\ 2 & 5 \end{vmatrix} = 4(5) - (-7)(2)$

$20 + 14 = 34$

2. $\begin{vmatrix} 4 & 0 & 2 \\ 1 & -3 & 5 \\ 0 & -1 & 2 \end{vmatrix}$

$4\begin{vmatrix} -3 & 5 \\ -1 & 2 \end{vmatrix} - 1\begin{vmatrix} 0 & 2 \\ -1 & 2 \end{vmatrix} + 0\begin{vmatrix} 0 & 2 \\ -3 & 5 \end{vmatrix}$

$4[-6-(-5)] - [0-(-2)] + 0$

$4(-1) - 2 = -4 - 2 = -6$

3. $\begin{cases} 2x - y = -1 \\ 5x + 4y = 17 \end{cases}$

a.

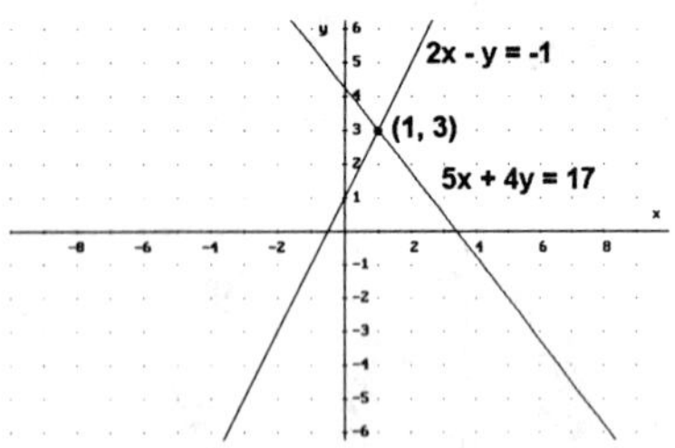

$\{(1,\ 3)\}$

b. $\begin{cases} 8x - 4y = -4 \\ 5x + 4y = 17 \end{cases}$

Add.

$13x = 13$
$x = 1$

$2(1) - y = -1$
$2 - y = -1$
$3 = y$
$y = 3$

$\{(1,\ 3)\}$

4. $\begin{cases} 7x - 14y = 5 \\ x = 2y \end{cases}$

Substitute.

$7(2y) - 14y = 5$
$14y - 14y = 5$
$0 = 5$

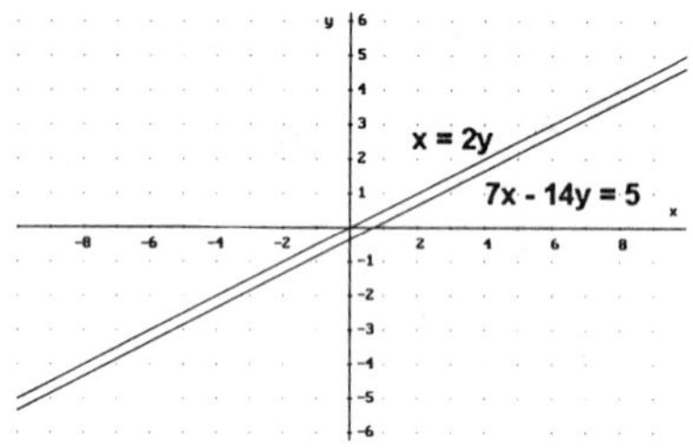

Inconsistent system.
No solution.

$\{\ \}$

5. $\begin{cases} 4x - 7y = 29 \\ 2x + 5y = -11 \end{cases}$

$\begin{cases} 4x - 7y = 29 \\ 4x + 10y = -22 \end{cases}$

Subtract.

$-17y = 51$
$y = -3$
$4x + 21 = 29$
$4x = 8$
$x = 2$

$\{(2, -3)\}$

6. $\begin{cases} 15x + 6y = 15 \\ 10x + 4y = 10 \end{cases}$

$\begin{cases} 5x + 2y = 5 \\ 5x + 2y = 5 \end{cases}$

The system is dependent.

$\{(x,\ y) \mid 5x + 2y = 5\}$

7. $\begin{cases} 2x - 3y = 4 \\ 3y + 2z = 2 \\ x - z = -5 \end{cases}$

Add equations 1 and 2.

$2x + 2z = 6$
$x + z = 3$

$\begin{cases} x + z = 3 \\ x - z = -5 \end{cases}$

Add.

$2x = -2$
$x = -1$

$-1 + z = 3$
$z = 4$

$2(-1) - 3y = 4$
$-2 - 3y = 4$
$-3y = 6$
$y = -2$

$\{(-1, -2, 4)\}$

8. $\begin{cases} 3x - 2y - z = -1 \\ 2x - 2y = 4 \\ 2x - 2z = -12 \end{cases}$

Subtract equation 2 from equation 1.

$x - z = -5$

Divide equation 3 by 2.

$x - z = -6$

Inconsistent system.
No solution.

$\{\ \}$

9. $\begin{cases} 3x - y = 7 \\ 2x + 5y = -1 \end{cases}$

$D = \begin{vmatrix} 3 & -1 \\ 2 & 5 \end{vmatrix}$

$D = 3(5) - (-1)(2)$

$D = 15 + 2 = 17$

$D_x = \begin{vmatrix} 7 & -1 \\ -1 & 5 \end{vmatrix}$

$D_x = 7(5) - (-1)(-1)$

$D_x = 35 - 1 = 34$

$D_y = \begin{vmatrix} 3 & 7 \\ 2 & -1 \end{vmatrix}$

$D_y = 3(-1) - 7(2)$

$D_y = -3 - 14 = -17$

$x = \frac{34}{17} = 2$ and $y = \frac{-17}{17} = -1$

$\{(2, -1)\}$

10. $\begin{cases} 4x - 3y = -6 \\ -2x + y = 0 \end{cases}$

$D = \begin{vmatrix} 4 & -3 \\ -2 & 1 \end{vmatrix}$

$D = 4(1) - (-3)(-2)$

$D = 4 - 6 = -2$

$D_x = \begin{vmatrix} -6 & -3 \\ 0 & 1 \end{vmatrix}$

$D_x = (-6)(1) - (-3)(0)$

$D_x = -6 - 0 = -6$

$D_y = \begin{vmatrix} 4 & -6 \\ -2 & 0 \end{vmatrix}$

$D_y = 4(0) - (-6)(-2)$

$D_y = 0 - 12 = -12$

$x = \frac{-6}{-2} = 3$ and $y = \frac{-12}{-2} = 6$

$\{(3, 6)\}$

11. $\begin{cases} x + y + z = 4 \\ 2x + 5y = 1 \\ x - y - 2z = 0 \end{cases}$

$D = \begin{vmatrix} 1 & 1 & 1 \\ 2 & 5 & 0 \\ 1 & -1 & -2 \end{vmatrix}$

$D = 1\begin{vmatrix} 2 & 5 \\ 1 & -1 \end{vmatrix} - 0\begin{vmatrix} 1 & 1 \\ 1 & -1 \end{vmatrix} - 2\begin{vmatrix} 1 & 1 \\ 2 & 5 \end{vmatrix}$

$D = (-2-5) - 0 - 2(5-2)$

$D = -7 - 2(3) = -7 - 6 = -13$

$$D_x = \begin{vmatrix} 4 & 1 & 1 \\ 1 & 5 & 0 \\ 0 & -1 & -2 \end{vmatrix}$$

$$D_x = 1\begin{vmatrix} 1 & 5 \\ 0 & -1 \end{vmatrix} - 0\begin{vmatrix} 4 & 1 \\ 0 & -1 \end{vmatrix} - 2\begin{vmatrix} 4 & 1 \\ 1 & 5 \end{vmatrix}$$

$D_x = (-1-0) - 0 - 2(20-1)$

$D_x = -1 - 2(19) = -1 - 38 = -39$

$$D_y = \begin{vmatrix} 1 & 4 & 1 \\ 2 & 1 & 0 \\ 1 & 0 & -2 \end{vmatrix}$$

$$D_y = 1\begin{vmatrix} 2 & 1 \\ 1 & 0 \end{vmatrix} - 0\begin{vmatrix} 1 & 4 \\ 1 & 0 \end{vmatrix} - 2\begin{vmatrix} 1 & 4 \\ 2 & 1 \end{vmatrix}$$

$D_y = (0-1) - 0 - 2(1-8)$

$D_y = -1 - 2(-7) = -1 + 14 = 13$

$$D_z = \begin{vmatrix} 1 & 1 & 4 \\ 2 & 5 & 1 \\ 1 & -1 & 0 \end{vmatrix}$$

$$D_z = 1\begin{vmatrix} 1 & 4 \\ 5 & 1 \end{vmatrix} + 1\begin{vmatrix} 1 & 4 \\ 2 & 1 \end{vmatrix} + 0\begin{vmatrix} 1 & 1 \\ 2 & 5 \end{vmatrix}$$

$D_z = (1-20) + 1(1-8) + 0 = -19 - 7 = -26$

$x = \dfrac{-39}{-13} = 3$

$y = \dfrac{13}{-13} = -1$

$z = \dfrac{-26}{-13} = 2$

$\{(3, -1, 2)\}$

12. $\begin{cases} 3x + 2y + 3z = 3 \\ x - z = 9 \\ 4y + z = -4 \end{cases}$

$$D = \begin{vmatrix} 3 & 2 & 3 \\ 1 & 0 & -1 \\ 0 & 4 & 1 \end{vmatrix}$$

$$D = -1\begin{vmatrix} 2 & 3 \\ 4 & 1 \end{vmatrix} + 0\begin{vmatrix} 3 & 3 \\ 0 & 1 \end{vmatrix} + 1\begin{vmatrix} 3 & 2 \\ 0 & 4 \end{vmatrix}$$

$D = -1(2-12) + 0 + 1(12-0)$

$D = -(-10) + 12 = 10 + 12 = 22$

$$D_x = \begin{vmatrix} 3 & 2 & 3 \\ 9 & 0 & -1 \\ -4 & 4 & 1 \end{vmatrix}$$

$$D_x = -9\begin{vmatrix} 2 & 3 \\ 4 & 1 \end{vmatrix} + 0\begin{vmatrix} 3 & 3 \\ -4 & 1 \end{vmatrix} + 1\begin{vmatrix} 3 & 2 \\ -4 & 4 \end{vmatrix}$$

$D_x = -9(2-12) + 0 + 1[12-(-8)]$

$D_x = -9(-10) + 12 + 8 = 90 + 20 = 110$

$$D_y = \begin{vmatrix} 3 & 3 & 3 \\ 1 & 9 & -1 \\ 0 & -4 & 1 \end{vmatrix}$$

$$D_y = 3\begin{vmatrix} 9 & -1 \\ -4 & 1 \end{vmatrix} - 1\begin{vmatrix} 3 & 3 \\ -4 & 1 \end{vmatrix} + 0\begin{vmatrix} 3 & 3 \\ 9 & -1 \end{vmatrix}$$

$D_y = 3(9-4) - [3-(-12)] + 0$

$D_y = 3(5) - (3+12) = 15 - 15 = 0$

$$D_z = \begin{vmatrix} 3 & 2 & 3 \\ 1 & 0 & 9 \\ 0 & 4 & -4 \end{vmatrix}$$

$$D_z = 3\begin{vmatrix} 0 & 9 \\ 4 & -4 \end{vmatrix} - 1\begin{vmatrix} 2 & 3 \\ 4 & -4 \end{vmatrix} + 0\begin{vmatrix} 2 & 3 \\ 0 & 9 \end{vmatrix}$$

$D_z = 3(0-36) - (-8-12) + 0$

$D_z = 3(-36) - (-20) = -108 + 20 = -88$

$x = \dfrac{110}{22} = 5$

$y = \dfrac{0}{22} = 0$

$z = \frac{-88}{22} = -4$

$\{(5, 0, -4)\}$

13. $\begin{cases} x - y = -2 \\ 3x - 3y = -6 \end{cases}$

$\left[\begin{array}{cc|c} 1 & -1 & -2 \\ 3 & -3 & -6 \end{array}\right]$

$\left[\begin{array}{cc|c} 1 & -1 & -2 \\ 0 & 0 & 0 \end{array}\right]$

Dependent system.
$\{(x, y) | x - y = -2\}$

14. $\begin{cases} x + 2y = -1 \\ 2x + 5y = -5 \end{cases}$

$\left[\begin{array}{cc|c} 1 & 2 & -1 \\ 2 & 5 & -5 \end{array}\right]$

$\left[\begin{array}{cc|c} 1 & 2 & -1 \\ 0 & 1 & -3 \end{array}\right]$

$\left[\begin{array}{cc|c} 1 & 0 & 5 \\ 0 & 1 & -3 \end{array}\right]$

$\{(5, -3)\}$

15. $\begin{cases} x - y - z = 0 \\ 3x - y - 5z = -2 \\ 2x + 3y = -5 \end{cases}$

$\left[\begin{array}{ccc|c} 1 & -1 & -1 & 0 \\ 3 & -1 & -5 & -2 \\ 2 & 3 & 0 & -5 \end{array}\right]$

$\left[\begin{array}{ccc|c} 1 & -1 & -1 & 0 \\ 0 & 2 & -2 & -2 \\ 2 & 3 & 0 & -5 \end{array}\right]$

$\left[\begin{array}{ccc|c} 1 & -1 & -1 & 0 \\ 0 & 2 & -2 & -2 \\ 0 & 5 & 2 & -5 \end{array}\right]$

$\left[\begin{array}{ccc|c} 1 & -1 & -1 & 0 \\ 0 & 1 & -1 & -1 \\ 0 & 5 & 2 & -5 \end{array}\right]$

$\left[\begin{array}{ccc|c} 1 & 0 & -2 & -1 \\ 0 & 1 & -1 & -1 \\ 0 & 5 & 2 & -5 \end{array}\right]$

$\left[\begin{array}{ccc|c} 1 & 0 & -2 & -1 \\ 0 & 1 & -1 & -1 \\ 0 & 0 & 7 & 0 \end{array}\right]$

$\left[\begin{array}{ccc|c} 1 & 0 & -2 & -1 \\ 0 & 1 & -1 & -1 \\ 0 & 0 & 1 & 0 \end{array}\right]$

$\left[\begin{array}{ccc|c} 1 & 0 & 0 & -1 \\ 0 & 1 & -1 & -1 \\ 0 & 0 & 1 & 0 \end{array}\right]$

$\left[\begin{array}{ccc|c} 1 & 0 & 0 & -1 \\ 0 & 1 & 0 & -1 \\ 0 & 0 & 1 & 0 \end{array}\right]$

$\{(-1, -1, 0)\}$

16. $\begin{cases} 2x - y + 3z = 4 \\ 3x - 3z = -2 \\ -5x + y = 0 \end{cases}$

$\left[\begin{array}{ccc|c} 2 & -1 & 3 & 4 \\ 3 & 0 & -3 & -2 \\ -5 & 1 & 0 & 0 \end{array}\right]$

$\left[\begin{array}{ccc|c} 1 & -\frac{1}{2} & \frac{3}{2} & 2 \\ 3 & 0 & -3 & -2 \\ -5 & 1 & 0 & 0 \end{array}\right]$

$$\left[\begin{array}{ccc|c} 1 & -\frac{1}{2} & \frac{3}{2} & 2 \\ 0 & \frac{3}{2} & -\frac{15}{2} & -8 \\ -5 & 1 & 0 & 0 \end{array}\right]$$

$$\left[\begin{array}{ccc|c} 1 & -\frac{1}{2} & \frac{3}{2} & 2 \\ 0 & \frac{3}{2} & -\frac{15}{2} & -8 \\ 0 & -\frac{3}{2} & \frac{15}{2} & 10 \end{array}\right]$$

$$\left[\begin{array}{ccc|c} 1 & -\frac{1}{2} & \frac{3}{2} & 2 \\ 0 & 1 & -5 & -\frac{16}{3} \\ 0 & -\frac{3}{2} & \frac{15}{2} & 10 \end{array}\right]$$

$$\left[\begin{array}{ccc|c} 1 & 0 & -1 & -\frac{2}{3} \\ 0 & 1 & -5 & -\frac{16}{3} \\ 0 & -\frac{3}{2} & \frac{15}{2} & 10 \end{array}\right]$$

$$\left[\begin{array}{ccc|c} 1 & 0 & -1 & -\frac{2}{3} \\ 0 & 1 & -5 & -\frac{16}{3} \\ 0 & 0 & 0 & 2 \end{array}\right]$$

Inconsistent system.
No solution.

{ }

17. $\begin{cases} x^2+y^2=169 \\ 5x+12y=0 \end{cases}$

$12y=-5x$

$y=-\frac{5x}{12}$

Substitute.

$x^2+\left(-\frac{5x}{12}\right)^2=169$

$x^2+\frac{25x^2}{144}=169$

$\frac{169x^2}{144}=169$

$x^2=144$

$x=\pm 12$

Substitute back.

$x=12$: $\quad y=\frac{-5}{12}(12)=-5$

$x=-12$: $\quad y=\frac{-5}{12}(-12)=5$

$\{(12,-5),\ (-12,\ 5)\}$

18. $\begin{cases} x^2+y^2=26 \\ x^2-y^2=24 \end{cases}$

Add.

$2x^2=50$

$x^2=25$

$x=\pm 5$

Substitute back.

$25+y^2=26$

$y^2=1$

$y=\pm 1$

$\{(5,\ 1),\ (5,-1),\ (-5,\ 1),\ (-5,-1)\}$

19. $\begin{cases} y=x^2-5x+6 \\ y=2x \end{cases}$

Substitute.

$2x=x^2-5x+6$

$0=x^2-7x+6$

$0=(x-1)(x-6)$

$x-1=0$ or $x-6=0$

$x=1$ or $x=6$

$x=1$: $\quad y=2(1)=2$

$x=6$: $\quad y=2(6)=12$

$\{(1,\ 2),\ (6,\ 12)\}$

20. $\begin{cases} x^2+4y^2=5 \\ y=x \end{cases}$

Substitute.

$x^2+4x^2=5$

$5x^2=5$

$x^2=1$

$x = \pm 1$

$x = 1: \quad y = 1$

$y = -1: \quad y = -1$

$\{(1,\ 1),\ (-1, -1)\}$

21. $\begin{cases} 2x + 5y \geq 10 \\ y \geq x^2 + 1 \end{cases}$

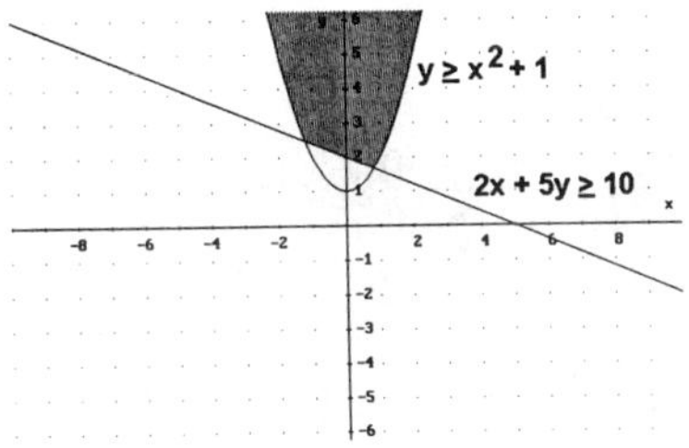

22. $\begin{cases} \frac{x^2}{4} + y^2 \leq 1 \\ x + y > 1 \end{cases}$

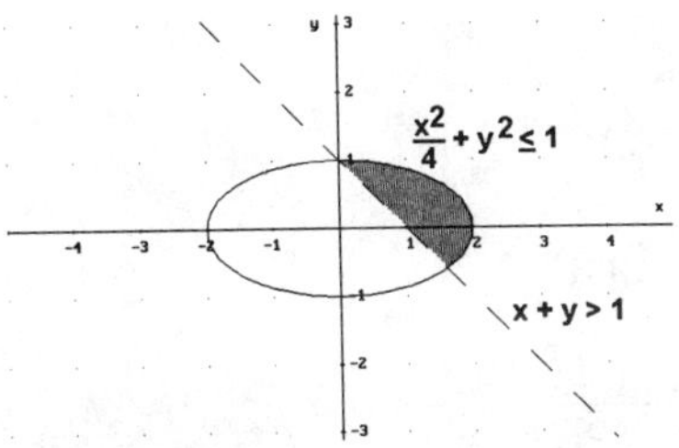

23. $\begin{cases} x^2 + y^2 > 1 \\ \frac{x^2}{4} - y^2 \geq 1 \end{cases}$

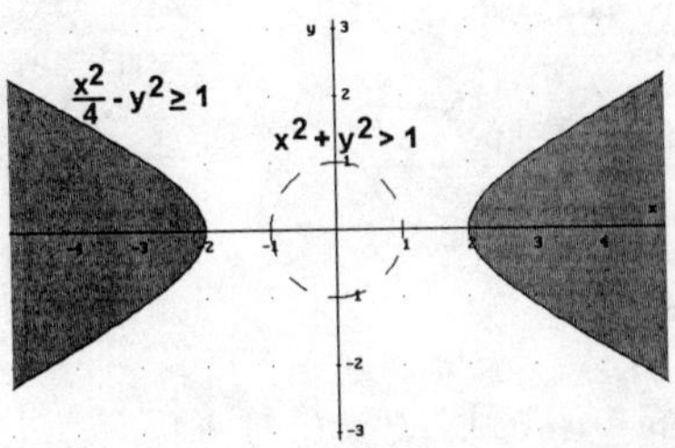

24. $\begin{cases} x^2 + y^2 \geq 4 \\ x^2 + y^2 < 16 \\ y \geq 0 \end{cases}$

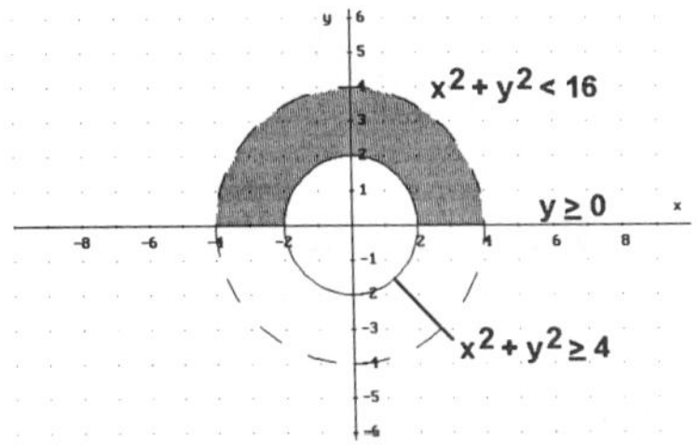

25. Let $d =$ Dean's rate and $t =$ Tom's rate, both in mph.

$\begin{cases} t = d + 10 \\ \frac{1}{6}d + \frac{1}{6}t = 4 \end{cases}$

where 10 minutes $= \frac{1}{6}$ hr.

$\begin{cases} t = d + 10 \\ d + t = 24 \end{cases}$

Substitute.

$d + d + 10 = 24$

$2d + 10 = 24$

$2d = 14$

$d = 7$

so $t = 7 + 10 = 17$ and also $7\left(\frac{1}{6}\right) = \frac{1}{6}$mi. thus, Dean's rate is 7 mph, Tom's rate is 17 mph. and Dean jogged $1\frac{1}{6}$ miles.

26. Let $s =$ the lowest score Jamie can get and still earn a C.

$70 \leq \frac{70 + 64 + 85 + 73 + s}{5} \leq 79$

$70 \leq \frac{292 + s}{5} \leq 79$

$350 \leq 292 + s \leq 395$

$58 \leq s \leq 103$

Thus, 58 is the lowest score Jamie can get on her fifth test and still earn a C.

Chapter 10 Cumulative Review

1. $2x + 7 \leq x - 11$

$2x - x + 7 \leq -11$

$x+7 \le -11$

$x \le -18$

$(-\infty, -18]$

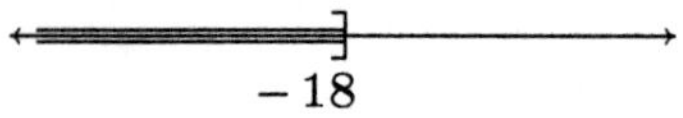

3. $2x+3y=-6$

$3y=-2x-6$

$y=-\frac{2}{3}x-2$

$m=-\frac{2}{3}$

$y-4=-\frac{2}{3}(x-4)$

$3(y-4)=-2(x-4)$

$3y-12=-2x+8$

$2x+3y-12=8$

$2x+3y=20$

5. $10x^3y^2-7x^2y^2-(4x^3y^2-3x^2y^2+2y^2)$

$10x^3y^2-7x^2y^2-4x^3y^2+3x^2y^2-2y^2$

$6x^3y^2-4x^2y^2-2y^2$

7a. $(f \circ g)(x)=(x+1)^2$

$(f \circ g)(x)=x^2+2x+1$

b. $(g \circ f)(x)=x^2+1$

$(g \circ f)(2)=2^2+1$

$(g \circ f)(2)=5$

9. $64x^3+1$

$(4x+1)(16x^2-4x+1)$

11a. $\frac{2+x}{x+2}=\frac{x+2}{x+2}=1$

b. $\frac{2-x}{x-2}=\frac{-1(-2+x)}{x-2}=\frac{-1(x-2)}{x-2}=-1$

c. $\frac{18-2x^2}{x^2-2x-3}=\frac{-2(-9+x^2)}{(x-3)(x+1)}$

$\frac{-2(x^2-9)}{(x-3)(x+1)}=\frac{-2(x+3)(x-3)}{(x-3)(x+1)}$

$\frac{-2(x+3)}{x+1}$

13. $\frac{\sqrt{x}+2}{5}=\frac{(\sqrt{x}+2)}{5}\bullet\frac{(\sqrt{x}-2)}{(\sqrt{x}-2)}$

$\frac{\sqrt{x^2}-2\sqrt{x}+2\sqrt{x}-4}{5(\sqrt{x}-2)}=\frac{x-4}{5(\sqrt{x}-2)}$

15. $3x^2-9x+8=0$

$3x^2-9x=-8$

$\frac{3x^2}{3}-\frac{9x}{3}=-\frac{8}{3}$

$x^2-3x=-\frac{8}{3}$

$x^2-3x+\left(\frac{3}{2}\right)^2=-\frac{8}{3}+\frac{9}{4}$

$\left(x-\frac{3}{2}\right)^2=-\frac{5}{12}$

$x-\frac{3}{2}=\pm\sqrt{\frac{-5}{12}}$

$x-\frac{3}{2}=\pm\frac{i\sqrt{5}}{\sqrt{12}}$

$x-\frac{3}{2}=\pm\frac{i\sqrt{5}}{2\sqrt{3}}$

$x-\frac{3}{2}=\pm\frac{i\sqrt{5}}{2\sqrt{3}}\bullet\frac{\sqrt{3}}{\sqrt{3}}$

$x-\frac{3}{2}=\pm\frac{i\sqrt{15}}{2(3)}$

$x-\frac{3}{2}=\pm\frac{i\sqrt{15}}{6}$

$x=\frac{3}{2}\pm\frac{i\sqrt{15}}{6}$

$x=\frac{9}{6}\pm\frac{i\sqrt{15}}{6}$

$x=\frac{9\pm i\sqrt{15}}{6}$

$\left\{\frac{9-i\sqrt{15}}{6}, \frac{9+i\sqrt{15}}{6}\right\}$

17. $\frac{x+2}{x-3}\le 0$

$x+2=0$ and $x-3=0$

$x=-2$ and $x=3$

Region	Interval	Test Point
A	$(-\infty, -2)$	-3

B	$(-2, 3)$	0
C	$(3, \infty)$	4

$x = -3$: $\frac{-3+2}{-3-3} \le 0$ False

$x = 0$: $\frac{0+2}{0-3} \le 0$ True

$x = 4$: $\frac{4+2}{4-3} \le 0$ False

The solution is $[-2, 3)$.

The interval is open at 3 since that is an undefined value for the expression.

19. $\frac{(x+3)^2}{25} + \frac{(y-2)^2}{36} = 1$

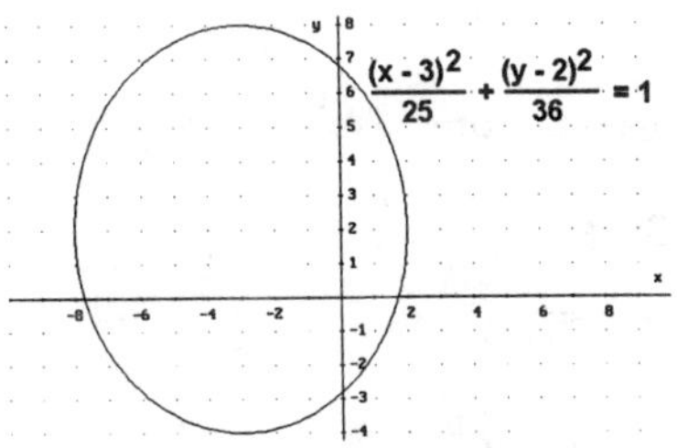

21.

	rate •	time =	distance
1st car	x	3	3x
2nd car	y	3	3y

$\begin{cases} 3x + 3y = 297 \\ x = y + 5 \end{cases}$

$x + y = 99$

$x - y = 5$

$2x = 104$

$x = 52$

$52 = y + 5$

$47 = y$

The rate of the 1st car is 52 mph and the rate of the 2nd car is 47 mph.

23. $4y^2 > x^2 + 16$

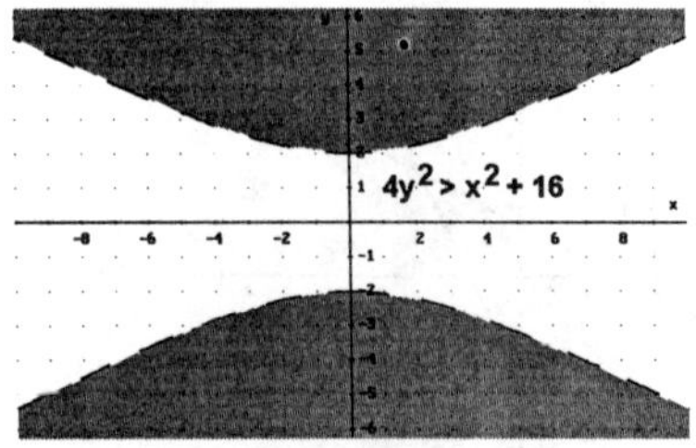

Exercise Set 11.1

1. $f = \{(-1, -1), (1, 1), (0, 2), (2, 0)\}$ is a one-to-one function.

3. $h = \{(10, 10)\}$ is a one-to-one function.

5. $f = \{(11, 12), (4, 3), (4, 3), (6, 6)\}$ is a one-to-one function.

7. The graph represents a one-to-one function.

9. The graph does not represent a one-to-one function.

11. The graph represents a one-to-one function.

13. The graph does not represent a one-to-one function.

15. $f(x) = x + 4$

$f^{-1}(x) = x - 4$

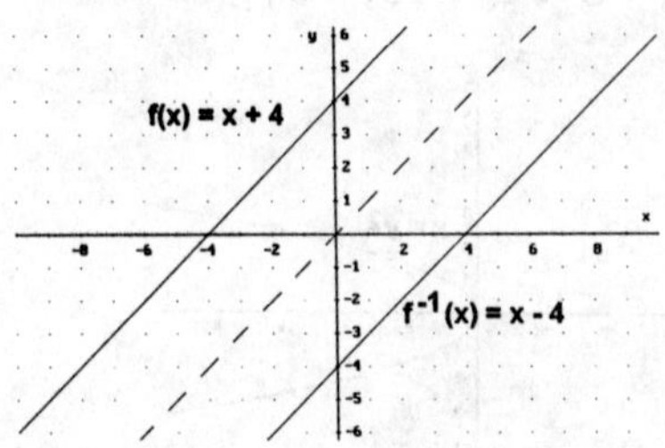

17. $f(x) = 2x - 3$

$f^{-1}(x) = \dfrac{x+3}{2}$

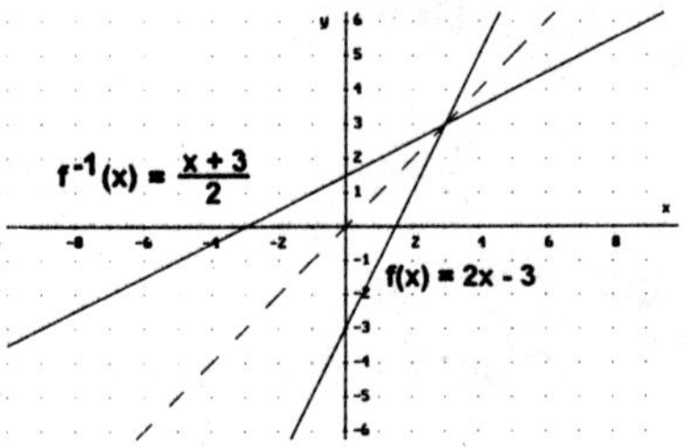

19. $f(x) = \dfrac{12x-4}{3}$

$f^{-1}(x) = \dfrac{3x+4}{12}$

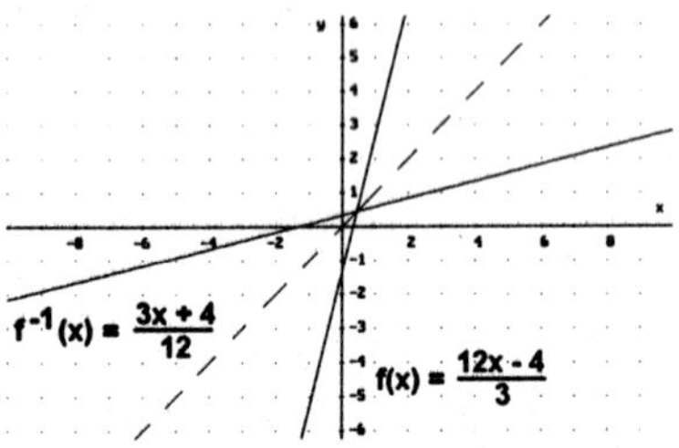

21. $h = \{(-3, 9), (-2, 4), (-1, 1), (0, 0), (1, 1)\}$ is not a one-to-one function due to the presence of both $(-1, 1)$ and $(1, 1)$.

23. $f = \{(1, 1), (2, 1), (3, 2), (4, 2)\}$ is not a one-to-one function due to the presence of both $(1, 1)$ and $(2, 1)$.

25. $f = \{(-4, -8), (-6, -12), (-8, -16), (-9, -18)\}$ is a one-to-one function.

$f^{-1} = \{(-8, -4), (-12, -6), (-16, -8), (-18, -9)\}$

27.

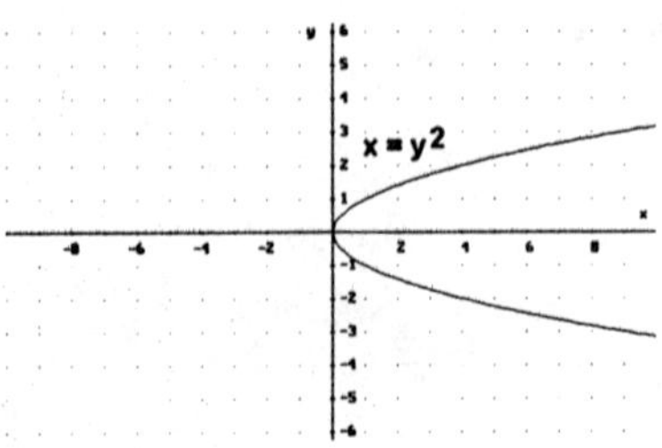

Not a one-to-one function.

29.

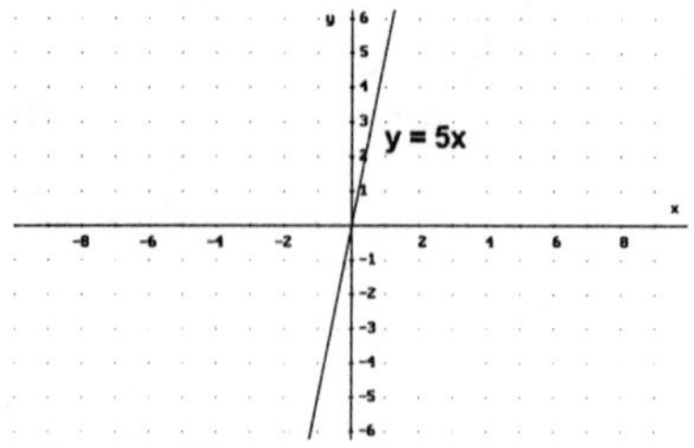

One-to-one function.

31.

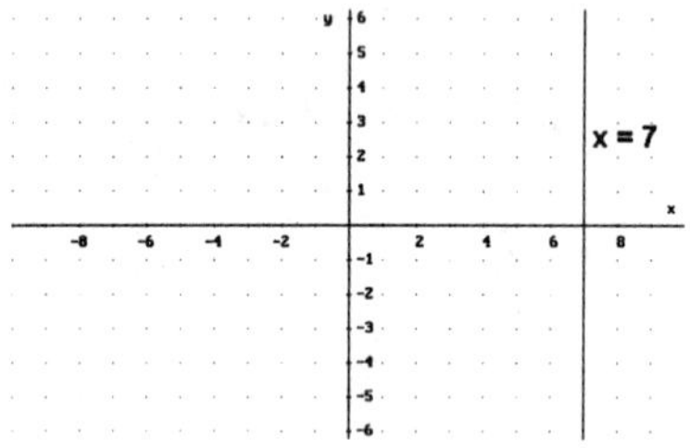

Not a one-to-one function.

33. $f(x) = 3x + 1$

$f^{-1}(x) = \dfrac{x-1}{3}$

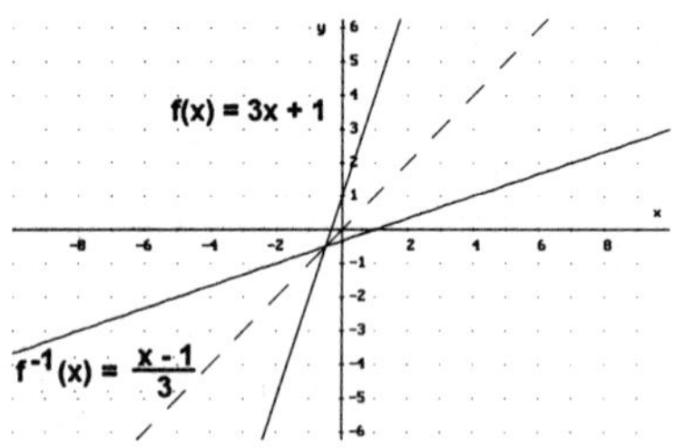

35. $f(x) = \dfrac{x-2}{5}$

$f^{-1}(x) = 5x + 2$

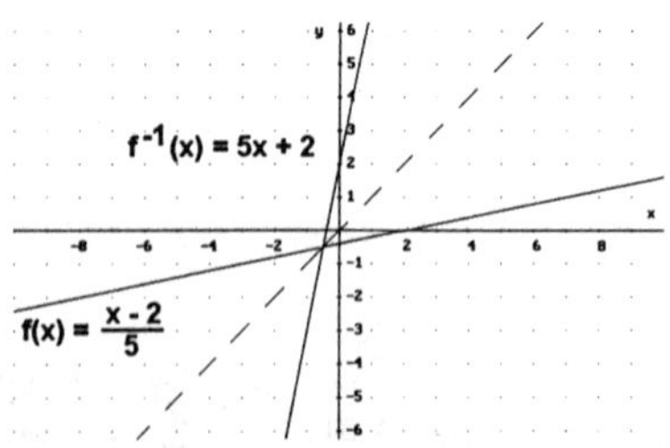

37. $g(x) = \frac{1}{2}x - 4$

$g^{-1}(x) = 2(x+4)$

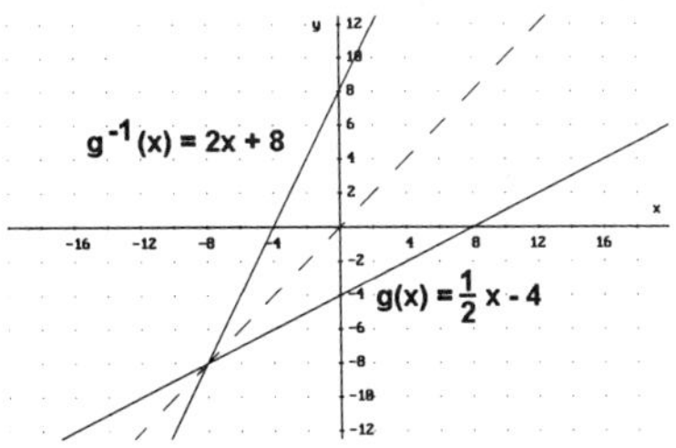

39. Let c = the hypotenuse of the right triangle shown. Then, by the Pythagorean theorem:

$c^2 = 4^2 + 5^2$

$c^2 = 16 + 25$

$c^2 = 41$

$c = \sqrt{41}$ miles

41. $5^0 = 1$

43. $3x^0 = 3(1) = 3$

45. $2^{-2} = \frac{1}{2^2} = \frac{1}{4}$

47. $2^3 = 8$

Exercise Set 11.2

1. $y = 4^x$

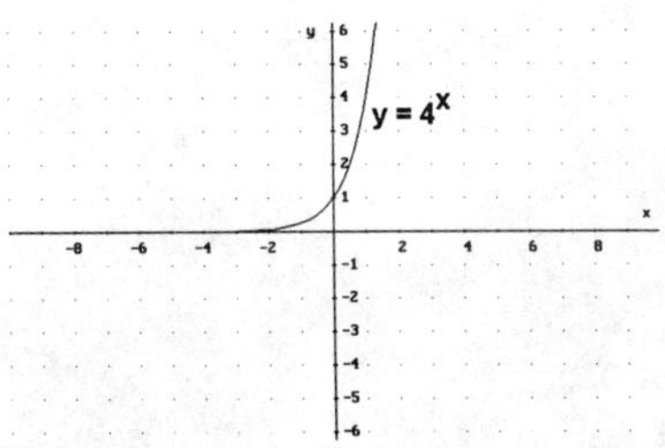

3. $y = 1 + 2^x$

$y = 2^x + 1$

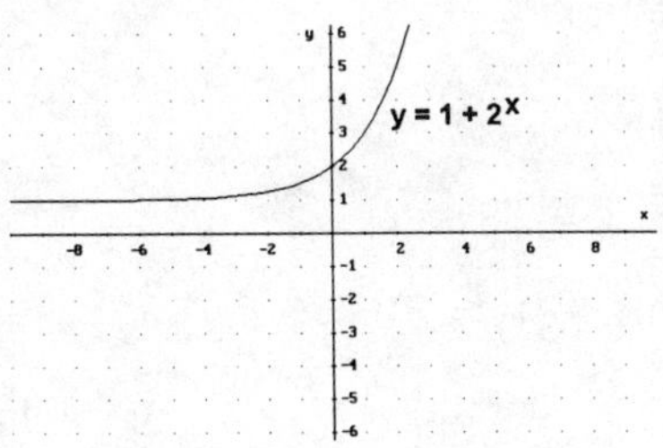

5. $y = \left(\frac{1}{4}\right)^x$

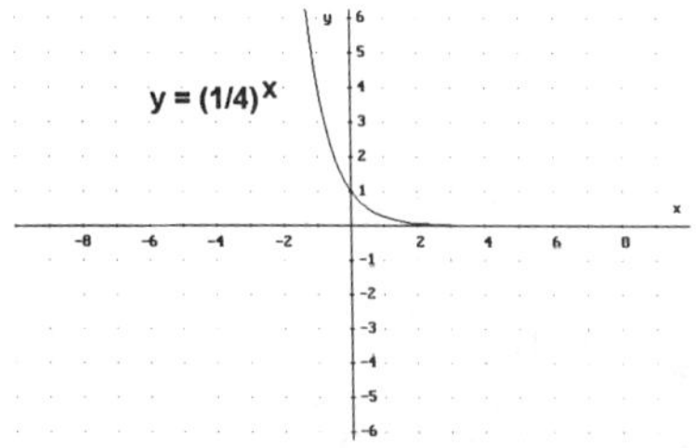

7. $y = \left(\frac{1}{2}\right)^x - 2$

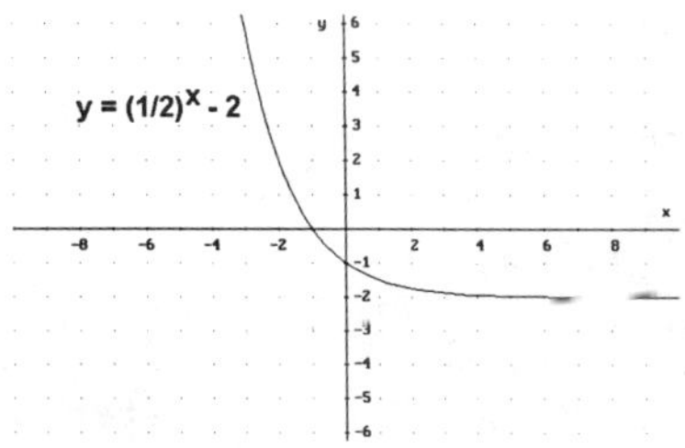

9. $3^x = 27$

$3^x = 3^3$

$x = 3$

$\{3\}$

11. $16^x = 8$

$(2^4)^x = 2^3$

$4x = 3$

$x = \frac{3}{4}$

$\left\{\frac{3}{4}\right\}$

13. $32^{2x-3} = 2$

$(2^5)^{2x-3} = 2$

$2^{10x-15} = 2^1$

$10x - 15 = 1$

$10x = 16$

$x = \frac{16}{10} = \frac{8}{5}$

$\left\{\frac{8}{5}\right\}$

15. $\frac{1}{4} = 2^{3x}$

$2^{-2} = 2^{3x}$

$3x = -2$

$x = -\frac{2}{3}$

$\left\{-\frac{2}{3}\right\}$

17. $y = 30(2.7)^{-0.004t}$

$y = 30(2.7)^{-(0.004)(50)}$

$y = 30(2.7)^{-0.2} \approx 24.6$

Therefore, approximately 24.6 lbs. of uranium will remain after 50 days.

19. $A = P\left(1 + \frac{r}{n}\right)^{nt}$

$A = 6000\left(1 + \frac{0.08}{12}\right)^{12(3)}$

$A = 6000(1.006)^{36}$

$A = 7621.42$

Erica would owe \$7621.42 after 3 years.

21. $y = -2^x$

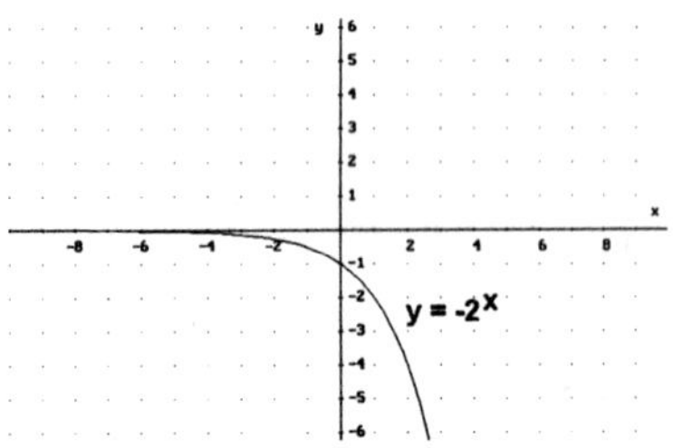

23. $y = 3^x - 2$

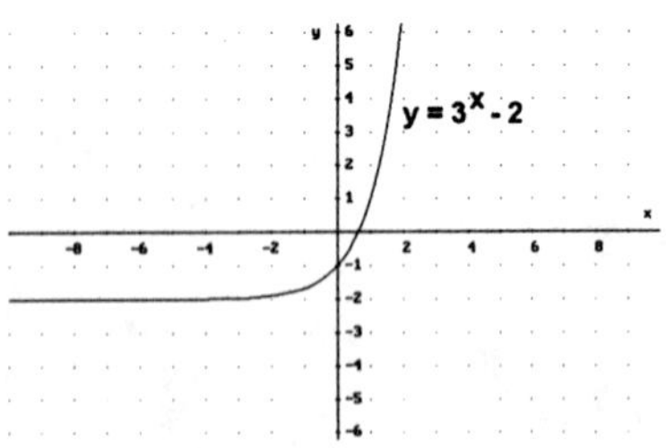

25. $y = -\left(\frac{1}{4}\right)^x$

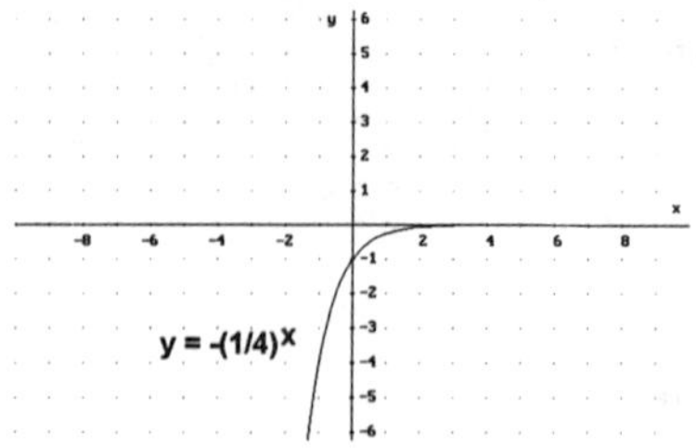

27. $y = \left(\frac{1}{3}\right)^x + 1$

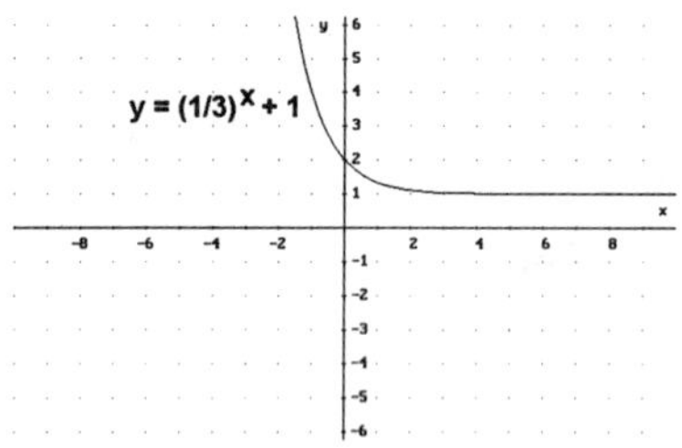

29. $5^x = 625$

$5^x = 5^4$

$x = 4$

$\{4\}$

31. $4^x = 8$

$(2^2)^x = 2^3$

$2^{2x} = 2^3$

$2x = 3$

$x = \frac{3}{2}$

$\left\{\frac{3}{2}\right\}$

33. $27^{x+1} = 9$

$(3^3)^{x+1} = 3^2$

$3^{3x+3} = 3^2$

$3x + 3 = 2$

$x = -\frac{1}{3}$

$\left\{-\frac{1}{3}\right\}$

35. $81^{x-1} = 27^{2x}$

$(3^4)^{x-1} = (3^3)^{2x}$

$3^{4x-4} = 3^{6x}$

$4x - 4 = 6x$

$-4 = 2x$

$x = -2$

$\{-2\}$

37. $f(x) = b^x, \ b > 1$

$f(1) = b^1 = 3$

$b = 3$

$f(x) = 3^x$

39. $f(x) = b^x, \ 0 < b < 1$

$f(1) = b^1 = \frac{1}{2}$

$b = \frac{1}{2}$

$f(x) = \left(\frac{1}{2}\right)^x$

41. $y = 200(2.7)^{0.08t}$

$y = 200(2.7)^{0.08(12)}$

$y = 200(2.7)^{0.96}$

$y \approx 519$

There should be approximately 519 rats by next January.

43. $y = 5(2.7)^{-0.15t}$

$y = 5(2.7)^{-0.15(10)}$

$y = 5(2.7)^{-1.5}$

$y \approx 1.127$ grams

$\frac{1.127}{5} = 0.225$

which is approximately 22.5% of the original 5 grams.

45. $y = 7,000,000(2.7)^{0.052t}$

$y = 7,000,000(2.7)^{0.052(5)}$

$y = 7,000,000(2.7)^{0.260}$

$y \approx 9,060,000$

Approximately 9,060,000 people will be living in Mexico City in 1995.

47. $A = P\left(1 + \frac{r}{n}\right)^{nt}$

$A = 2000\left(1 + \frac{0.06}{2}\right)^{2(12)}$

$A = 2000(1.03)^{24}$

$A \approx 4065.59$

Janina has approximately \$4065.59 in her savings account.

49. $5x - 2 = 18$

$5x = 20$

$x = 4$

$\{4\}$

51. $3x - 4 = 3(x + 1)$

$3x - 4 = 3x + 3$

$-4 = 3$

No solution.

$\{ \ \}$

53. $x^2 + 6 = 5x$

$x^2 - 5x + 6 = 0$

$(x - 3)(x - 2) = 0$

$x - 3 = 0 \quad \text{or} \quad x - 2 = 0$

$x = 3 \quad \text{or} \quad x = 2$

$\{2, \ 3\}$

55. $2^x = 8$

$2^x = 2^3$

$x = 3$

$\{3\}$

57. $5^x = \frac{1}{5}$

$5^x = 5^{-1}$

$x = -1$

$\{-1\}$

Exercise Set 11.3

1. $\log_2 8 = 3$

3. $\log_3 \frac{1}{9} = -2$

5. $\log_{25} 5 = \frac{1}{2}$

7. $\log_{1/2} 2 = -1$

9. $\log_3 9 = x$

$2 = x$

$\{2\}$

11. $\log_3 x = 4$

$x = 3^4 = 81$

$\{81\}$

13. $\log_x 49 = 2$

$x^2 = 49$

$x = \pm 7$

We discard the negative base.

$x = 7$

$\{7\}$

15. $\log_2 \frac{1}{8} = x$

$2^x = \frac{1}{8}$

$2^x = 2^{-3}$

$x = -3$

$\{-3\}$

17. $\log_5 5^3 = 3$

19. $2^{\log_2 3} = 3$

21. $\log_9 9 = 1$

23. $y = \log_3 x$

$y = 0$: $\log_3 x = 0$

$x = 3^0 = 1$

The x-intercept is 1.

$x = 0$: $y = \log_3 0$

undefined

No y-intercept exists.

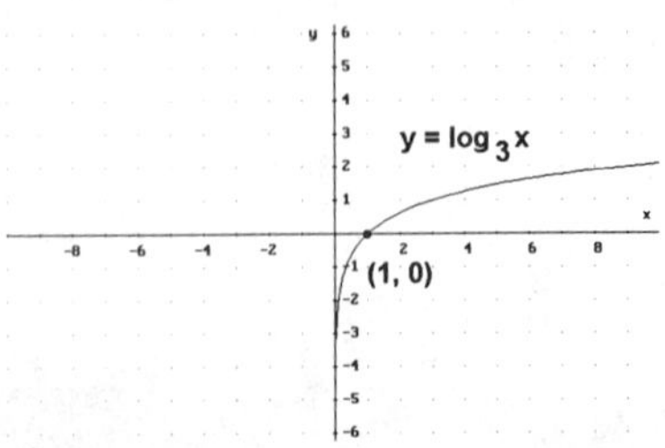

25. $f(x) = \log_{1/4} x$

$y = \log_{1/4} x$

$y = 0$: $0 = \log_{1/4} x$

$x = \left(\frac{1}{4}\right)^0 = 1$

$x = 0$: $y = \log_{1/4} 0$

undefined

No y-intercept exists.

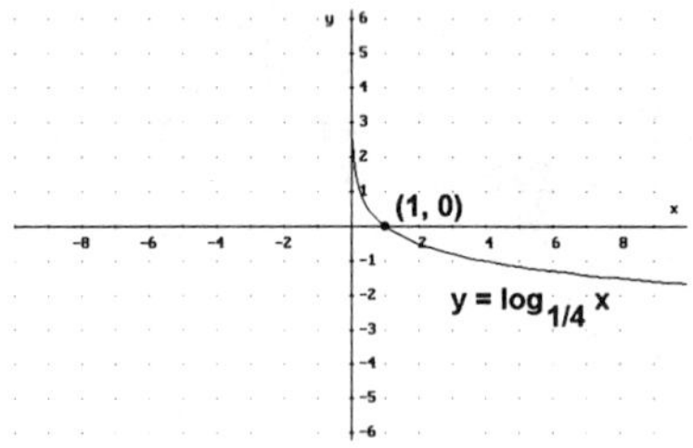

27. $y = 4^x$; $y = \log_4 x$

$x = 0$: $y = 4^0 = 1$

The y-intercept of $y = 4^x$ is 1 and hence is the x-intercept of $y = \log_4 x$.

$y = 0$: $4^x = 0$

undefined

No x-intercept for $y = 4^x$ and hence no y-intercept for $\log_4 x$.

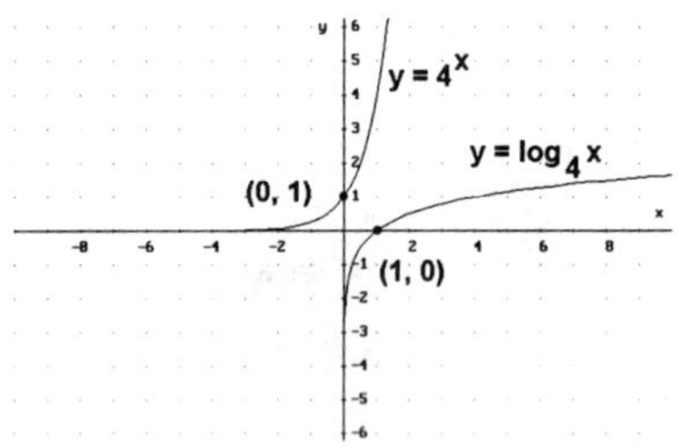

29. $y = \left(\frac{1}{3}\right)^x$; $y = \log_{1/3} x$

$x = 0$: $y = \left(\frac{1}{3}\right)^0 = 1$

The y-intercept for $y = \left(\frac{1}{3}\right)^x$ is 1 and hence is the x-intercept for $y = \log_{1/3} x$.

$y = 0$: $0 = \left(\frac{1}{3}\right)^x$

undefined

No x-intercept for $y=\left(\frac{1}{3}\right)^x$ and hence no y-intercept for $y=\log_{1/3}x$.

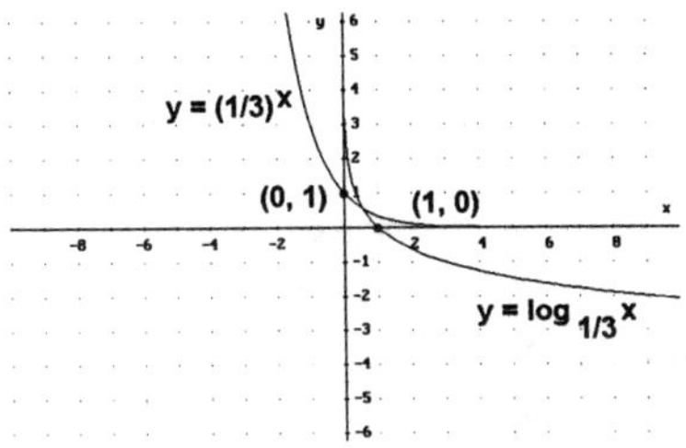

31. $\log_7 1=0$

33. $\log_2 2^4=4$

35. $\log_{10} 100=2$

37. $3^{\log_3 5}=5$

39. $\log_3 81=4$

41. $\log_4\left(\frac{1}{64}\right)=-3$

43. $\log_3\left(\frac{1}{27}\right)=x$

$\frac{1}{27}=3^x$

$3^{-3}=3^x$

$-3=x$

$\{-3\}$

45. $\log_8 x=\frac{1}{3}$

$x=8^{\frac{1}{3}}=2$

$\{2\}$

47. $\log_4 16=x$

$4^x=16$

$4^x=4^2$

$x=2$

$\{2\}$

49. $\log_{3/4}x=3$

$\left(\frac{3}{4}\right)^3=x$

$x=\frac{3^3}{4^3}=\frac{27}{64}$

$\left\{\frac{27}{64}\right\}$

51. $\log_x 100=2$

$x^2=100$

$x=\pm 10$

We discard the negative base.

$x=10$

$\{10\}$

53. $f(x)=\log_5 x$

$y=\log_5 x$

$x=0$: $y=\log_5 0$ undefined

No y-intercept exists.

$y=0$: $0=\log_5 x$

$x=5^0=1$

The x-intercept is 1.

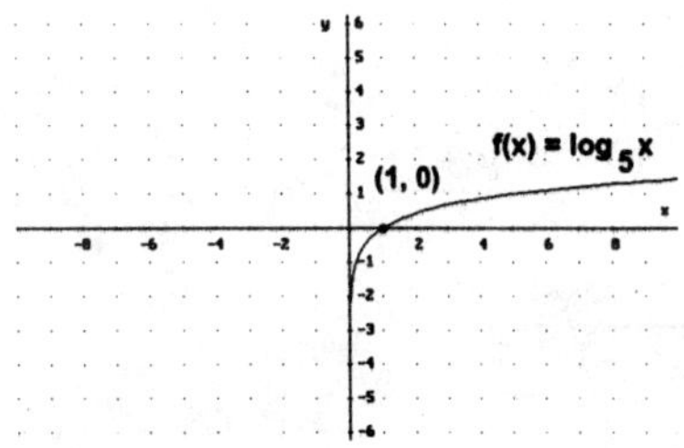

55. $f(x)=\log_{1/6}x$

$y=\log_{1/6}x$

$x=0$: $y=\log_{1/6}0$ undefined

No y-intercept exists.

$y=0$: $0=\log_{1/6}x$

$x=\left(\frac{1}{6}\right)^0=1$

The x-intercept is 1.

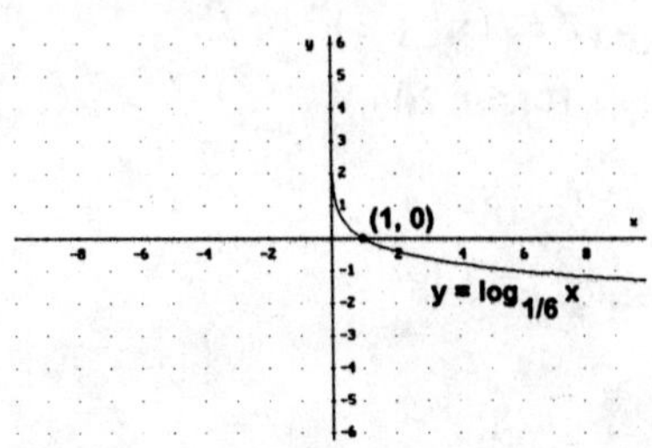

57. $\log_{10}(1-k) = \frac{-0.3}{H}$

$\log_{10}(1-k) = \frac{-0.3}{8}$

$\log_{10}(1-k) = -0.0375$

$1-k = 10^{-0.0375}$

$1-10^{-0.0375} = k$

$k \approx 0.0827$

59. $\frac{x-5}{5-x} = \frac{x-5}{-(x-5)} = \frac{1}{-1} = -1$

61. $\frac{x^2-3x-10}{2+x}$

$\frac{(x+2)(x-5)}{x+2}$

$x-5$

63. $\frac{3x}{x+3} + \frac{9}{x+3}$

$\frac{3x+9}{x+3} = \frac{3(x+3)}{x+3} = 3$

65. $\frac{5}{y+1} - \frac{4}{y-1}$

$\frac{5(y-1)-4(y+1)}{(y+1)(y-1)}$

$\frac{5y-5-4y-4}{y^2-1}$

$\frac{y-9}{y^2-1}$

Exercise Set 11.4

1. $\log_5 2 + \log_5 7$

$\log_5 (2 \bullet 7)$

$\log_5 14$

3. $\log_4 9 + \log_4 x = \log_4 (9x)$

5. $\log_{10} 5 + \log_{10} 2 + \log_{10}(x^2+2)$

$\log_{10}[5 \bullet 2(x^2+2)]$

$\log_{10}(10x^2+20)$

7. $\log_5 12 - \log_5 4$

$\log_5 \left(\frac{12}{4}\right) = \log_5 3$

9. $\log_2 x - \log_2 y = \log_2 \left(\frac{x}{y}\right)$

11. $\log_4 2 + \log_4 10 - \log_4 5$

$\log_4 2 \bullet 10 - \log_4 5 = \log_4 \left(\frac{20}{5}\right)$

$\log_4 4 = 1$

13. $2\log_2 5 = \log_2 5^2 = \log_2 25$

15. $3\log_5 x + 6\log_5 z$

$\log_5 x^3 + \log_5 z^6$

$\log_5 (x^3 z^6)$

17. $\log_{10} x - \log_{10}(x+1) + \log_{10}(x^2-2)$

$\log_{10} \frac{x}{x+1} + \log_{10}(x^2-2)$

$\log_{10} \frac{x(x^2-2)}{x+1} = \log_{10}\left(\frac{x^3-2x}{x+1}\right)$

19. $\log_3 \left(\frac{4y}{5}\right) = \log_3 4y - \log_3 5$

$\log_3 4 + \log_3 y - \log_3 5$

21. $\log_2 \left(\frac{x^3}{y}\right) = \log_2 x^3 - \log_2 y$

$3\log_2 x - \log_2 y$

23. $\log_b \sqrt{7x} = \log_b (7x)^{\frac{1}{2}}$

$\frac{1}{2}\log_b (7x) = \frac{1}{2}[\log_b 7 + \log_b x]$

$\frac{1}{2}\log_b 7 + \frac{1}{2}\log_b x$

25. $\log_b \left(\frac{5}{3}\right) = \log_b 5 - \log_b 3$

$\approx 0.7 - 0.5 = 0.2$

27. $\log_b 15 = \log_b (5 \bullet 3)$

$\log_b 5 + \log_b 3 \approx 0.7 + 0.5 = 1.2$

29. $\log_b \sqrt[3]{5} = \log_b 5^{\frac{1}{3}} = \frac{1}{3}\log_b 5$

$\approx \frac{1}{3}(0.7) = 0.23$

31. $\log_4 5 + \log_4 7 = \log_4 (5 \bullet 7)$

$\log_4 35$

33. $\log_3 8 - \log_3 2 = \log_3 \left(\frac{8}{2}\right) = \log_3 4$

35. $\log_7 6 + \log_7 3 - \log_7 4$

$\log_7 (6 \bullet 3) - \log_7 4$

$\log_7\left(\frac{18}{4}\right) = \log_7 \frac{9}{2}$

37. $3\log_4 2 + \log_4 6 = \log_4 2^3 + \log_4 6$

$\log_4 8 + \log_4 6 = \log_4 (8 \bullet 6)$

$\log_4 48$

39. $3\log_2 x + \frac{1}{2}\log_2 x - 2\log_2 (x+1)$

$\log_2 x^3 + \log_2 x^{\frac{1}{2}} - \log_2 (x+1)^2$

$\log_2 (x^3 \bullet x^{\frac{1}{2}}) - \log_2 (x+1)^2$

$\log_2 x^{\frac{7}{2}} - \log_2 (x+1)^2$

$\log_2\left[\frac{x^{\frac{7}{2}}}{(x+1)^2}\right]$

41. $2\log_8 x - \frac{2}{3}\log_8 x + 4\log_8 x$

$\left(2 - \frac{2}{3} + 4\right)\log_8 x = \frac{16}{3}\log_8 x$

$\log_8\left(x^{\frac{16}{3}}\right)$

43. $\log_7\left(\frac{5x}{4}\right) = \log_7 5x - \log_7 4$

$\log_7 5 + \log_7 x - \log_7 4$

45. $\log_5 x^3(x+1)$

$\log_5 x^3 + \log_5 (x+1)$

$3\log_5 x + \log_5 (x+1)$

47. $\log_6 \frac{x^2}{x+3} = \log_6 x^2 - \log_6 (x+3)$

$2\log_6 x - \log_6 (x+3)$

49. $\log_b 8 = \log_b 2^3 = 3\log_b 2$

$3(0.43) = 1.29$

51. $\log_b\left(\frac{3}{9}\right) = \log_b\left(\frac{1}{3}\right)$

$\log_b 3^{-1} = (-1)\log_b 3$

$-(0.68) = -0.68$

53. $\log_b \sqrt{\frac{2}{3}} = \log_b \left(\frac{2}{3}\right)^{\frac{1}{2}} = \frac{1}{2}\log_b \frac{2}{3}$

$\frac{1}{2}(\log_b 2 - \log_b 3)$

$\frac{1}{2}(0.43 - 0.68) = \frac{1}{2}(-0.25) = -0.125$

55. $y = 10^x$

$y = \log_{10} x$

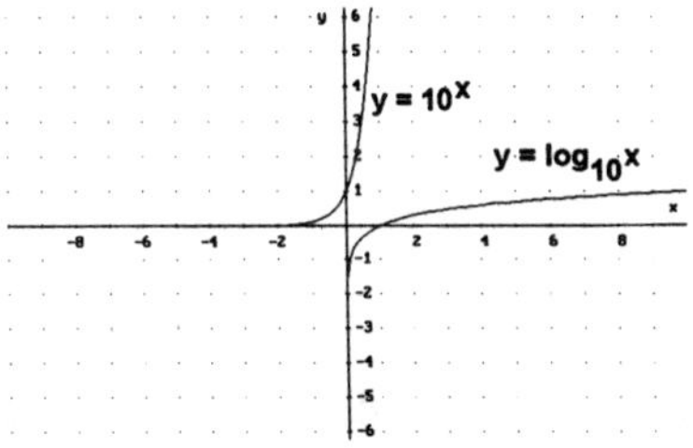

57. $\sqrt{2x-3} = 5$

$2x - 3 = 5^2$

$2x - 3 = 25$

$2x = 28$

$x = 14$

$\{14\}$

59. $\sqrt{x^2-2} = x - 2$

$x^2 - 2 = (x-2)^2$

$x^2 - 2 = x^2 - 4x + 4$

$-2 = -4x + 4$

$-6 = -4x$

$x = \frac{6}{4} = \frac{3}{2}$

which is extraneous.

No solution.

$\{\ \}$

61. $\log_{10} \frac{1}{10} = -1$

63. $\log_e \sqrt{e} = \frac{1}{2}$

Exercise Set 11.5

1. $\log 8 \approx 0.9031$

3. $\log 2.31 \approx 0.3636$

5. $\log 100 = \log 10^2 = 2$

7. $\log \frac{1}{1000} = \log 10^{-3} = -3$

9. $\log x = 1.3$

$x = 10^{1.3} \approx 19.9526$

11. $\log 2x = 1.1$

$2x = 10^{1.1}$

$x = \frac{1}{2}(10)^{1.1} \approx 6.2946$

13. $\ln 2 \approx 0.6931$

15. $\ln 0.0716 \approx -2.6367$

17. $\ln e^2 = 2$

19. $\ln \sqrt[4]{e} = \ln e^{\frac{1}{4}} = \frac{1}{4}$

21. $\ln x = 1.4$

$x = e^{1.4} \approx 4.0552$

23. $\ln(3x-4) = 2.3$

$3x - 4 = e^{2.3}$

$3x = 4 + e^{2.3}$

$x = \frac{4 + e^{2.3}}{3} \approx 4.6581$

25. $R = \log\left(\frac{a}{T}\right) + B$

$R = \log\left(\frac{200}{1.6}\right) + 2.1 \approx 4.2$

The earthquake measures 4.2 on the Richter scale.

27. $A = Pe^{rt}$

$A = 2000e^{(0.06)4}$

$A = 2000e^{0.24} \approx 2542.50$

Paul owes \$2542.50 at the end of 4 years.

29. $\log_2 3 = \frac{\ln 3}{\ln 2} \approx 1.5850$

31. $\log_{1/2} 5 = \frac{\ln 5}{\ln \frac{1}{2}} \approx -2.3219$

33. $\log 12.6 \approx 1.1004$

35. $\ln 5 \approx 1.6094$

37. $\log 41.5 \approx 1.6180$

39. $\log 10^3 = 3$

41. $\ln e^2 = 2$

43. $\log 0.0001 = \log 10^{-4} = -4$

45. $\ln \sqrt{e} = \ln e^{\frac{1}{2}} = \frac{1}{2}$

47. $\log x = 2.3$

$x = 10^{2.3} \approx 199.5262$

49. $\ln x = -2.3$

$x = e^{-2.3} \approx 0.1003$

51. $\log(2x+1) = -0.5$

$2x + 1 = 10^{-0.5}$

$2x = -1 + 10^{-0.5}$

$x = \frac{-1 + 10^{-0.5}}{2}$

$x \approx -0.3419$

53. $\ln 4x = 0.18$

$4x = e^{0.18}$

$x = \frac{e^{0.18}}{4} \approx 0.2993$

55. $\log_4 9 = \frac{\ln 9}{\ln 4} \approx 1.5850$

57. $\log_3\left(\frac{1}{6}\right) = \log_3 6^{-1} = (-1)\log_3 6$

$-\frac{\ln 6}{\ln 3} \approx -1.6309$

59. $\log_8 6 = \frac{\ln 6}{\ln 8} \approx 0.8617$

61. $R = \log\left(\frac{a}{T}\right) + B$

$R = \log\left(\frac{400}{2.6}\right) + 3.1 \approx 5.3$

The earthquake measures 5.3 on the Richter scale.

63. $A = Pe^{rt}$

$A = 1400e^{(0.08)12}$

$A = 1400e^{0.96}$

$A \approx 3656.38$

Dana has \$3656.38 after 12 years.

65. $t = \frac{1}{c}\ln\left(\frac{A}{A-N}\right)$

$A = \frac{1}{0.09}\ln\left(\frac{75}{75-50}\right)$

$A = \frac{\ln 3}{0.09} \approx 12.2$

It would take Norman 13 weeks to reach his goal.

67. $t = \frac{1}{c}\ln\left(\frac{A}{A-N}\right)$

$t = \frac{1}{0.03}\ln\left(\frac{65}{65-30}\right) \approx 20.6$

It would take the chimpanzee 21 weeks to achieve mastery of 30 signs.

69. $6x - 3(2-5x) = 6$

$6x - 6 + 15x = 6$

$21x - 6 = 6$

$21x = 12$

$x = \frac{12}{21} = \frac{4}{7}$

$\left\{\frac{4}{7}\right\}$

71. $2x + 3y = 6x$

$3y = 4x$

$x = \frac{3y}{4}$

73. $x^2 + 7x = -6$

$x^2 + 7x + 6 = 0$

$(x+6)(x+1) = 0$

$x + 6 = 0$ or $x + 1 = 0$

$x = -6$ or $x = -1$

$\{-6, -1\}$

75. $\begin{cases} x + 2y = -4 \\ 3x - y = 9 \end{cases}$

$\begin{cases} x + 2y = -4 \\ 6x - 2y = 18 \end{cases}$

Add.

$7x = 14$

$x = 2$

Substitute back.

$2 + 2y = -4$

$2y = -6$

$y = -3$

$\{(2, -3)\}$

Exercise Set 11.6

1. $3^x = 6$

$x = \log_3 6 = \frac{\ln 6}{\ln 3} \approx 1.6309$

$\left\{\frac{\ln 6}{\ln 3}\right\}$; $\{1.6309\}$

3. $3^{2x} = 3.8$

$2x = \log_3 3.8 = \frac{\ln 3.8}{\ln 3}$

$x = \frac{\ln 3.8}{2\ln 3} \approx 0.6076$

$\left\{\frac{\ln 3.8}{2\ln 3}\right\}$; $\{0.6076\}$

5. $2^{x-3} = 5$

$x - 3 = \log_2 5$

$x = 3 + \log_2 5$

$x = 3 + \frac{\ln 5}{\ln 2} \approx 5.3219$

$\left\{3 + \frac{\ln 5}{\ln 2}\right\}$; $\{5.3219\}$

7. $\log_2(x+5) = 4$

$x + 5 = 2^4$

$x + 5 = 16$

$x = 11$

$\{11\}$

9. $\log_3 x^2 = 4$

$x^2 = 3^4$

$x^2 = 81$

$x = \pm 9$

$\{-9, 9\}$

11. $\log_4 2 + \log_4 x = 0$

$\log_4(2x) = 0$

$2x = 4^0$

$2x = 1$

$x = \frac{1}{2}$

$\left\{\frac{1}{2}\right\}$

13. $\log_2 6 - \log_2 x = 3$

$\log_2\left(\frac{6}{x}\right) = 3$

$\frac{6}{x} = 2^3$

$\frac{6}{x} = 8$

$8x = 6$

$x = \frac{6}{8} = \frac{3}{4}$

$\left\{\frac{3}{4}\right\}$

15. $\log_4 x + \log_4 (x+6) = 2$

$\log_4 x(x+6) = 2$

$x(x+6) = 4^2$

$x^2 + 6x = 16$

$x^2 + 6x - 16 = 0$

$(x+8)(x-2) = 0$

$x+8 = 0 \quad \text{or} \quad x-2 = 0$

$x = -8 \quad \text{or} \quad x = 2$

We discard -8 as extraneous.

$x = 2$

$\{2\}$

17. $\log_5 (x+3) - \log_5 x = 2$

$\log_5\left(\frac{x+3}{x}\right) = 2$

$\frac{x+3}{x} = 5^2$

$\frac{x+3}{x} = 25$

$x + 3 = 25x$

$3 = 24x$

$x = \frac{3}{24} = \frac{1}{8}$

$\left\{\frac{1}{8}\right\}$

19. $y = y_0 e^{0.043t}$

$y = 83e^{0.043(5)}$

$y = 83e^{0.215}$

$y \approx 103$

There should be 103 wolves in 5 years.

21. $A = P\left(1 + \frac{r}{n}\right)^{nt}$

$2000 = 1000\left(1 + \frac{0.08}{2}\right)^{2t}$

$2 = (1.04)^{2t}$

$2t = \log_{1.04} 2 = \frac{\ln 2}{\ln 1.04}$

$t = \frac{1}{2} \bullet \frac{\ln 2}{\ln 1.04} \approx 8.8$

It would take approximately 8.8 years for the \$1000 to double.

23. $9^x = 5$

$x = \log_9 5 = \frac{\ln 5}{\ln 9} \approx 0.7325$

$\left\{\frac{\ln 5}{\ln 9}\right\}$; $\{0.7325\}$

25. $4^{x+7} = 3$

$x + 7 = \log_4 3$

$x = -7 + \log_4 3$

$x = -7 + \frac{\ln 3}{\ln 4} \approx -6.2075$

$\left\{-7 + \frac{\ln 3}{\ln 4}\right\}$; $\{-6.2075\}$

27. $7^{3x-4} = 11$

$3x - 4 = \log_7 11$

$3x = 4 + \log_7 11$

$x = \frac{4 + \log_7 11}{3}$

$x = \frac{4}{3} + \frac{\frac{\ln 11}{\ln 7}}{3} \approx 1.7441$

$\left\{\frac{4}{3} + \frac{\frac{\ln 11}{\ln 7}}{3}\right\}$; $\{1.7441\}$

29. $e^{6x} = 5$

$6x = \ln 5$

$x = \frac{1}{6}\ln 5 \approx 0.2682$

$\left\{\frac{1}{6}\ln 5\right\}$; $\{0.2682\}$

31. $\log_3 (x-2) = 2$

$x-2 = 3^2$

$x-2 = 9$

$x = 11$

$\{11\}$

33. $\log_4 (x^2-3x) = 1$

$x^2-3x = 4^1$

$x^2-3x = 4$

$x^2-3x-4 = 0$

$(x-4)(x+1) = 0$

$x-4 = 0$ or $x+1 = 0$

$x = 4$ or $x = -1$

$\{-1, 4\}$

35. $\log_3 5 + \log_3 x = 2$

$\log_3 (5x) = 2$

$5x = 3^2$

$5x = 9$

$x = \frac{9}{5}$

$\left\{\frac{9}{5}\right\}$

37. $3 \log_8 x - \log_8 x^2 = 2$

$3 \log_8 x - 2 \log_8 x = 2$

$\log_8 x = 2$

$x = 8^2$

$x = 64$

$\{64\}$

39. $\log_2 x + \log_2 (x+5) = 1$

$\log_2 x(x+5) = 1$

$x(x+5) = 2^1$

$x^2+5x = 2$

$x^2+5x-2 = 0$

$a = 1,\ b = 5,\ c = -2$

$$x = \frac{-5 \pm \sqrt{5^2-4(1)(-2)}}{2(1)}$$

$$x = \frac{-5 \pm \sqrt{25+8}}{2} = \frac{-5 \pm \sqrt{33}}{2}$$

$x = -\frac{5}{2} \pm \frac{\sqrt{33}}{2}$

Discard $-\frac{5}{2} - \frac{\sqrt{33}}{2}$.

$x = -\frac{5}{2} + \frac{\sqrt{33}}{2}$

$\left\{-\frac{5}{2} + \frac{\sqrt{33}}{2}\right\}$

41. $\log_4 x - \log_4 (2x-3) = 3$

$\log_4 \left(\frac{x}{2x-3}\right) = 3$

$\frac{x}{2x-3} = 4^3$

$\frac{x}{2x-3} = 64$

$x = 64(2x-3)$

$x = 128x - 192$

$192 = 127x$

$x = \frac{192}{127}$

$\left\{\frac{192}{127}\right\}$

43. $\log_2 x + \log_2 (3x+1) = 1$

$\log_2 x(3x+1) = 1$

$x(3x+1) = 2^1$

$3x^2+x = 2$

$3x^2+x-2 = 0$

$(3x-2)(x+1) = 0$

$3x-2 = 0$ or $x+1 = 0$

$3x = 2$ or $x = -1$

$x = \frac{2}{3}$

Discard -1 as extraneous.

$x = \frac{2}{3}$

$\left\{\frac{2}{3}\right\}$

45. $y = y_0 e^{0.026t}$

$y_0 = 7{,}000{,}000$

$t = 2000 - 1986$

$t = 14$

$y = 7,000,000e^{0.026(14)}$

$y = 7,000,000(1.43907)$

$y \approx 10,073,520$ people

47. $A = P(1 + \frac{r}{n})^{nt}$

$1200 = 600\left(1 + \frac{0.07}{12}\right)^{12t}$

$2 = (1.00583)^{12t}$

$12t = \log_{1.00583}(2)$

$t = \frac{1}{12}\log_{1.00583}(2)$

$t = \frac{1}{12} \bullet \frac{\ln 2}{\ln(1.00583)}$

$t = 10$

It would take approximately 10 years for the \$600 to double.

49. $A = P(1 + \frac{r}{n})^{nt}$

$1400 = 1200\left(1 + \frac{0.09}{4}\right)^{4t}$

$\frac{7}{6} = (1.0225)^{4t}$

$4t = \log_{1.0225}\left(\frac{7}{6}\right)$

$t = \frac{1}{4}\log_{1.0225}\left(\frac{7}{6}\right)$

$t = \frac{1}{4} \bullet \frac{\ln\left(\frac{7}{6}\right)}{\ln 1.0225}$

$t \approx 1.73$

It would take the investment approximately $1\frac{3}{4}$ years to earn \$200.

51. $w = 0.00185h^{2.67}$

$85 = 0.00185h^{2.67}$

$\frac{85}{0.00185} = h^{2.67}$

$h = \left(\frac{85}{0.00185}\right)^{\frac{1}{2.67}} \approx 55.7$

The expected height of the boy is approximately 56 inches.

53. $P = 14.7e^{-0.21x}$

$P = 14.7e^{-0.21(1)}$

$P = 14.7e^{-0.21} \approx 11.9$

The average atmospheric pressure of Denver is approximately 11.9 lbs./in^2.

55. $P = 14.7e^{-0.21x}$

$7.5 = 14.7e^{-0.21x}$

$\frac{7.5}{14.7} = e^{-0.21x}$

$-0.21x = \ln\left(\frac{7.5}{14.7}\right)$

$x = \frac{-\ln\left(\frac{7.5}{14.7}\right)}{0.21} \approx 3.2$

The elevation of the jet is approximately 3.2 miles.

57. $\frac{x^2 - y + 2z}{3x} = \frac{(-2)^2 - (0) + 2(3)}{3(-2)}$

$\frac{4+6}{-6} = \frac{-10}{6} = -\frac{5}{3}$

59. $\frac{3z - 4x + y}{x + 2z} = \frac{3(3) - 4(-2) + 0}{-2 + 2(3)}$

$\frac{9+8}{-2+6} = \frac{17}{4}$

61. $f(x) = 5x + 2$

$f^{-1}(x) = \frac{x-2}{5}$

Chapter 11 Review

1. $h = \{(-9, 14), (6, 8), (-11, 12), (15, 15)\}$ is a one-to-one function.

   $h^{-1} = \{(14, -9), (8, 6), (12, -11)$ $(15, 15)\}$

3. The graph does not represent a one-to-one function.

5. The graph does not represent a one-to-one function.

7. $f(x) = 6x + 11$

   $f^{-1}(x) = \frac{x-11}{6}$

9. $q(x) = mx + b$

   $q^{-1}(x) = \frac{x-b}{m}$

11. $r(x) = \frac{13}{2}x - 4$

$r^{-1}(x) = \frac{2}{13}(x+4)$

13. $h(x) = 5x - 5$

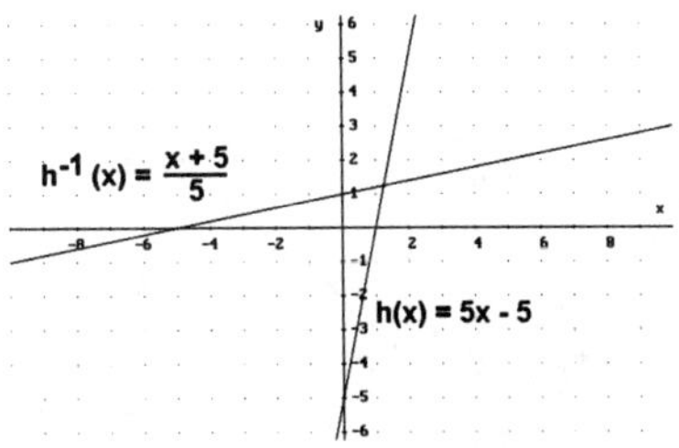

15. $3^x = \frac{1}{9}$

$3^x = 3^{-2}$

$x = -2$

$\{-2\}$

17. $5^{2x} = 125$

$5^{2x} = 5^3$

$2x = 3$

$x = \frac{3}{2}$

$\left\{\frac{3}{2}\right\}$

19. $8^{3x-2} = 4$

$(2^3)^{3x-2} = 2^2$

$2^{9x-6} = 2^2$

$9x - 6 = 2$

$9x = 8$

$x = \frac{8}{9}$

$\left\{\frac{8}{9}\right\}$

21. $y = \left(\frac{1}{3}\right)^x$

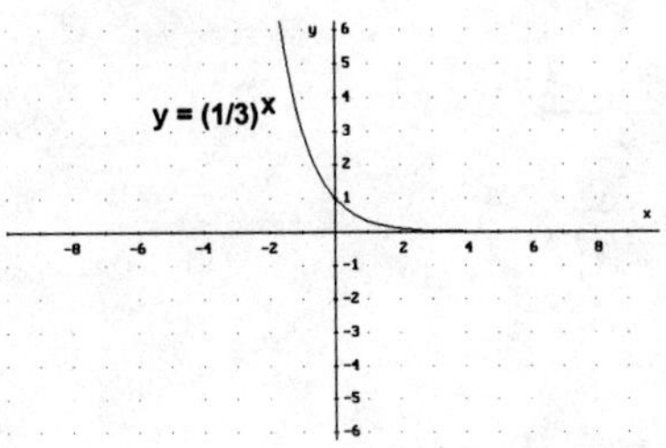

23. $y = 2^x + 4$

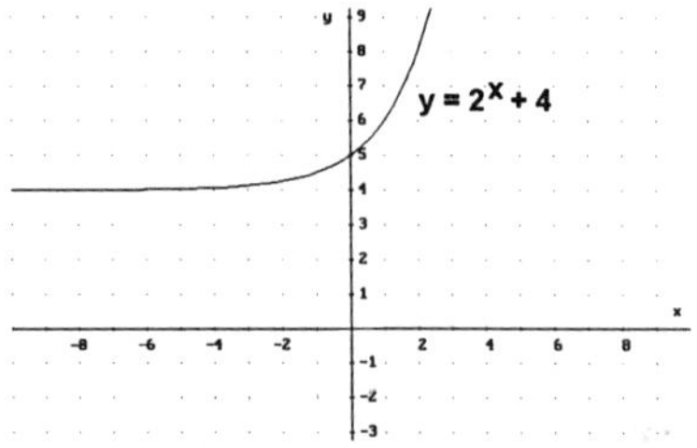

25. $A = P\left(1 + \frac{r}{n}\right)^{nt}$

$A = 800\left(1 + \frac{0.07}{4}\right)^{4(5)}$

$A = 800(1.0175)^{20}$

$A = 1131.82$

The certificate is worth $1131.82 at the end of 5 years.

27. $2^{-4} = \frac{1}{16}$

$-4 = \log_2\left(\frac{1}{16}\right)$

29. $\log_{0.4} 0.064 = 3$

$0.4^3 = 0.064$

31. $\log_3 x = 2$

$x = 3^2 = 9$

$\{9\}$

33. $\log_4 64 = x$

$3 = x$

$\{3\}$

35. $\log_x 81 = 4$

$x^4 = 81$

$x = \pm 3$

We discard the negative base -3.

$x = 3$

$\{3\}$

37. $\log_7 7^{-2} = x$

$-2 = x$

$\{-2\}$

39. $2^{\log_2 9} = x$

$9 = x$

$\{9\}$

41. $\log_3(2x+5) = 2$

$2x+5 = 3^2$

$2x+5 = 9$

$2x = 4$

$x = 2$

$\{2\}$

43. $\log_8(x^2+7x) = 1$

$x^2+7x = 8^1$

$x^2+7x = 8$

$x^2+7x-8 = 0$

$(x+8)(x-1) = 0$

$x+8 = 0$ or $x-1 = 0$

$x = -8$ or $x = 1$

$\{-8, 1\}$

45. $y = \left(\frac{1}{2}\right)^x$ and $y = \log_{1/2} x$

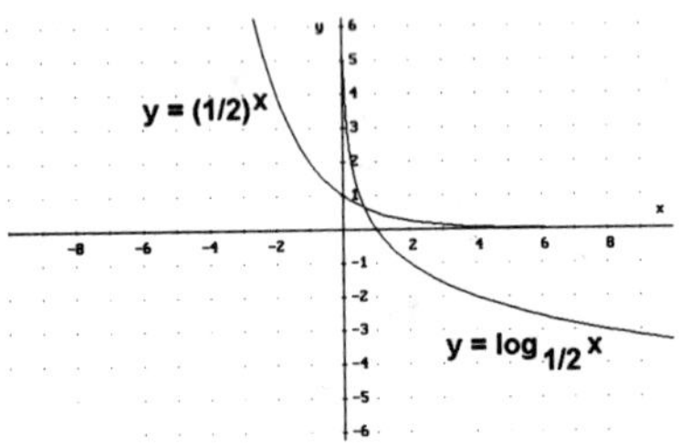

47. $\log_2 6 + \log_2 3 = \log_2(6 \bullet 3)$

$\log_2 18$

49. $\log 18 - \log 12 = \log \frac{18}{12}$

$\log\left(\frac{3}{2}\right)$

51. $\log_5 14 + \log_5 3 - \log_5 21$

$\log_5(14 \bullet 3) - \log_5 21$

$\log_5\left(\frac{42}{21}\right) = \log_5 2$

53. $4\log_3 x - \log_3 x + \log_3(x+2)$

$3\log_3 x + \log_3(x+2)$

$\log_3 x^3 + \log_3(x+2)$

$\log_3[x^3(x+2)]$

$\log_3(x^4+2x^3)$

55. $\log_4 \frac{x+5}{x^2} = \log_4(x+5) - \log_4 x^2$

$\log_4(x+5) - 2\log_4 x$

57. $\log_7 \frac{yz^3}{x} = \log_7(yz^3) - \log_7 x$

$\log_7 y + \log_7 z^3 - \log_7 x$

$\log_7 y + 3\log_7 z - \log_7 x$

59. $\log_b \frac{4}{5} = \log_b 4 - \log_b 5$

$\log_b 2^2 - \log_b 5$

$2\log_b 2 - \log_b 5$

$2(0.36) - 0.83$

$0.72 - 0.83 = -0.11$

61. $\log 0.15 \approx -0.8239$

63. $\ln 4.63 \approx 1.5326$

65. $\log \frac{1}{10} = \log 10^{-1} = -1$

67. $\ln(e^4) = 4$

69. $\ln(3x) = 1.6$

$3x = e^{1.6}$

$x = \frac{1}{3}e^{1.6}$

$\left\{\frac{e^{1.6}}{3}\right\}$

71. $\ln(3x+1) = 2$

$3x+1 = e^2$

$3x = -1+e^2$

$x = \frac{-1+e^2}{3}$

$\left\{\frac{-1+e^2}{3}\right\}$

73. $\ln\left(\frac{I}{I_0}\right) = -kx$

$I/I_0 = 0.02$

$\ln 0.02 = -3.2x$

$x = \frac{-\ln 0.02}{3.2} \approx 1.22$

2% of the original radioactivity will penetrate at a depth of approximately 1.22 mm.

75. $\log_3 4 = \frac{\log 4}{\log 3} \approx 1.2619$

77. $A = Pe^{rt}$

$A = 940e^{0.11(3)}$

$A = 940e^{0.33}$

$A \approx 1307.51$

The \$940 investment grows to \$1307.51 in 3 years.

79. $6^{3x} = 5$

$3x = \log_6 5$

$x = \frac{1}{3}\log_6 5$

$x = \frac{1}{3} \bullet \frac{\ln 5}{\ln 6}$

$x = \frac{\ln 5}{3\ln 6} \approx 0.2994$

$\left\{\frac{\ln 5}{3\ln 6}\right\}$; $\{0.2994\}$

81. $4^{3x+2} = 9$

$3x + 2 = \log_4 9$

$3x = \log_4 9 - 2$

$x = \frac{\log_4 9 - 2}{3}$

$x = \frac{\frac{\ln 9}{\ln 4} - 2}{3} \approx -0.1383$

$\left\{\frac{\ln 9}{3\ln 4} - \frac{2}{3}\right\}$; $\{-0.1383\}$

83. $8^{4x-2} = 3$

$4x - 2 = \log_8 3$

$4x = \log_8 3 + 2$

$x = \frac{\log_8 3 + 2}{4}$

$x = \frac{\frac{\ln 3}{\ln 8} + 2}{4} \approx 0.6321$

$\left\{\frac{\ln 3}{4\ln 8} + \frac{1}{2}\right\}$; $\{0.6321\}$

85. $3 \bullet 4^{x+5} = 2$

$4^{x+5} = \frac{2}{3}$

$x + 5 = \log_4\left(\frac{2}{3}\right)$

$x = \log_4\left(\frac{2}{3}\right) - 5$

$x = \frac{\ln\left(\frac{2}{3}\right)}{\ln 4} - 5 \approx -5.2925$

$\left\{\frac{\ln\left(\frac{2}{3}\right)}{\ln 4} - 5\right\}$; $\{-5.2925\}$

87. $\log_3 x + \log_3 10 = 2$

$\log_3 (10x) = 2$

$10x = 3^2$

$10x = 9$

$x = \frac{9}{10} = 0.9$

$\left\{\frac{9}{10}\right\}$

89. $\ln(3x) - \ln(x-3) = 2$

$\ln\left(\frac{3x}{x-3}\right) = 2$

$\frac{3x}{x-3} = e^2$

$3x = e^2(x-3)$

$3x = e^2x - 3e^2$

$3x - e^2x = -3e^2$

$(3 - e^2)x = -3e^2$

$x = \frac{-3e^2}{3 - e^2}$

$\left\{\frac{-3e^2}{3 - e^2}\right\}$

91. $-\log_6 (4x+7) + \log_6 x = 1$

$\log_6\left(\frac{x}{4x+7}\right) = 1$

$\frac{x}{4x+7} = 6^1$

$\frac{x}{4x+7} = 6$

$x = 6(4x+7)$

$x = 24x+42$

$-42 = 23x$

$x = -\frac{42}{23}$

We discard $x = -\frac{42}{23}$ as extraneous.

No solution.

{ }

93. $y = y_0e^{kt}$

$y = 176,800,000e^{0.017(14)}$

$y = 176,800,000e^{0.238}$

$y \approx 224,310,000$

The expected population of Indonesia by the year 2000 is approximately 224,310,000.

95. $y = y_0e^{kt}$

$700,000 = 650,000e^{0.0036t}$

$\frac{14}{13} = e^{0.0036t}$

$0.0036t = \ln\left(\frac{14}{13}\right)$

$t = \frac{\ln\left(\frac{14}{13}\right)}{0.0036} \approx 20.6$

It will take approximately 21 years for the population of Memphis to reach 700,000.

97. $y = y_0e^{kt}$

$3(16.9) = 16.9e^{0.034t}$

$3 = e^{0.034t}$

$0.034t = \ln 3$

$t = \frac{\ln 3}{0.034} \approx 32.3$

It will take Mexico City approximately 33 years to triple in population.

99. $A = P\left(1+\frac{r}{n}\right)^{nt}$

$10,000 = 6,000\left(1+\frac{0.06}{12}\right)^{12t}$

$\frac{5}{3} = (1.005)^{12t}$

$12t = \log_{1.005}\left(\frac{5}{3}\right)$

$t = \frac{1}{12} \bullet \log_{1.005}\left(\frac{5}{3}\right)$

$t = \frac{1}{12} \bullet \frac{\ln\left(\frac{5}{3}\right)}{\ln(1.005)} \approx 8.54$

It was invested for approximately 8.6 years.

Chapter 11 Test

1. $f(x) = 7x-14$

$f^{-1}(x) = \frac{x+14}{7}$

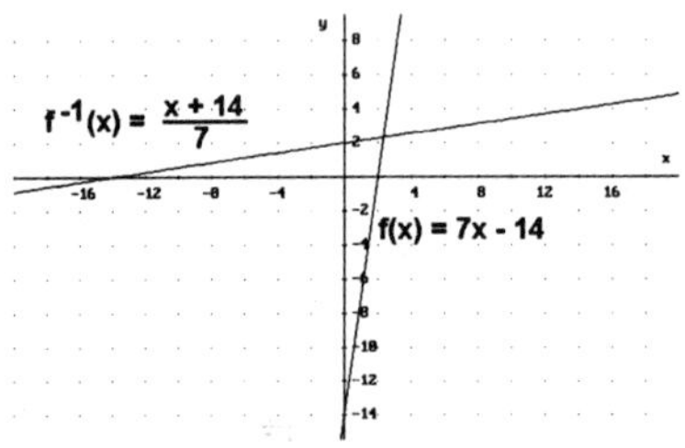

2. The graph does represent a one-to-one function.

3. The graph does not represent a one-to-one function.

4. $y = 6-2x$

$f(x) = -2x+6$

$f^{-1}(x) = \frac{x-6}{-2}$

$f^{-1}(x) = -\frac{x-6}{2}$

5. $f = \{(0, 0), (2, 3), (-1, 5)\}$

$f^{-1} = \{0, 0), (3, 2), (5, -1)\}$

6. $\log_3 6 + \log_3 4 = \log_3(6 \bullet 4)$

$\log_3(24)$

7. $\log_5 x + 3\log_5 x - \log_5 (x+1)$

$4\log_5 x - \log_5 (x+1)$

$\log_5 x^4 - \log_5 (x+1)$

$\log_5 \left(\frac{x^4}{x+1}\right)$

8. $\log_6 \frac{2x}{y^3} = \log_6 2x - \log_6 y^3$

$\log_6 2 + \log_6 x - 3\log_6 y$

9. $\log_b \left(\frac{3}{25}\right) = \log_b 3 - \log_b 25$

$\log_b 3 - \log_b 5^2$

$\log_b 3 - 2\log_b 5$

$0.79 - 2(1.16) = -1.53$

10. $\log_7 8 = \frac{\ln 8}{\ln 7} \approx 1.0686$

11. $8^{x-1} = \frac{1}{64}$

$8^{x-1} = 8^{-2}$

$x - 1 = -2$

$x = -1$

$\{-1\}$

12. $3^{2x+5} = 4$

$2x + 5 = \log_3 4$

$2x = \log_3 4 - 5$

$x = \frac{\log_3 4 - 5}{2}$

$x = \frac{\frac{\ln 4}{\ln 3} - 5}{2} \approx -1.8691$

$\left\{\frac{\ln 4}{2\ln 3} - \frac{5}{2}\right\}$; $\{-1.8691\}$

13. $\log_3 x = -2$

$x = 3^{-2} = \frac{1}{9}$

$\left\{\frac{1}{9}\right\}$

14. $\ln \sqrt{e} = x$

$\ln e^{\frac{1}{2}} = x$

$\frac{1}{2} = x$

$\left\{\frac{1}{2}\right\}$

15. $\log_8 (3x-2) = 2$

$3x - 2 = 8^2$

$3x - 2 = 64$

$3x = 66$

$x = 22$

$\{22\}$

16. $\log_5 x + \log_5 3 = 2$

$\log_5 (3x) = 2$

$3x = 5^2$

$x = \frac{25}{3}$

$\left\{\frac{25}{3}\right\}$

17. $\log_4 (x+1) - \log_4 (x-2) = 3$

$\log_4 \left(\frac{x+1}{x-2}\right) = 3$

$\frac{x+1}{x-2} = 4^3$

$x + 1 = 64(x-2)$

$x + 1 = 64x - 128$

$129 = 63x$

$x = \frac{43}{21}$

$\left\{\frac{43}{21}\right\}$

18. $\ln (3x+7) = 1.31$

$3x + 7 = e^{1.31}$

$3x = e^{1.31} - 7$

$x = \frac{e^{1.31} - 7}{3} \approx -1.0979$

$\{-1.0979\}$

19. $y=\left(\frac{1}{2}\right)^x+1$

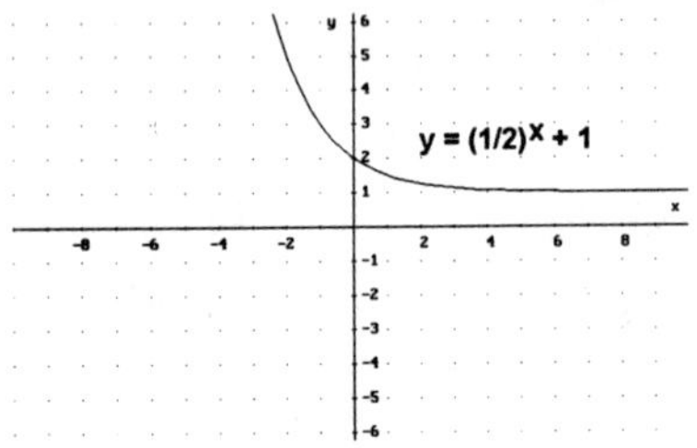

20. $y=3^x$

$y=\log_3 x$

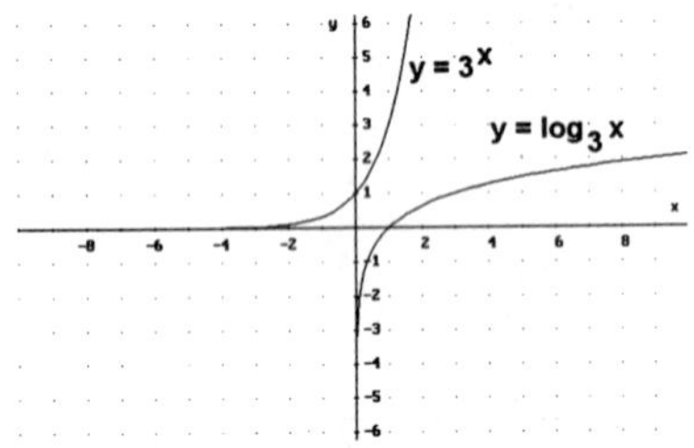

21. $A=P(1+\frac{r}{n})^{nt}$

$A=4000\left(1+\frac{0.09}{12}\right)^{12(3)}$

$A=4000(1.0075)^{36}\approx 5234.58$

\$5234.58 will be in the account.

22. $A=P(1+\frac{r}{n})^{nt}$

$3000=2000\left(1+\frac{0.07}{2}\right)^{2t}$

$1.5=(1.035)^{2t}$

$2t=\log_{1.035}1.5$

$t=\frac{\log_{1.035}1.5}{2}$

$t=\frac{1}{2}\bullet\frac{\ln 1.5}{\ln 1.035}\approx 5.9$

It would take 6 years for the investment to reach \$3000.

23. $y=y_0e^{kt}$

$y=57{,}000e^{0.026(5)}$

$y=57{,}000e^{0.13}\approx 64{,}913$

There will be approximately 64,913 prairie dogs 5 years from now.

24. $y=y_0e^{kt}$

$1000=400e^{0.062t}$

$2.5=e^{0.062t}$

$0.062t=\ln 2.5$

$t=\frac{\ln 2.5}{0.062}\approx 14.8$

It will take the naturalists approximately 15 years to reach their goal.

25. $\log(1+k)=\frac{0.3}{D}$

$\log(1+k)=\frac{0.3}{56}$

$1+k=10^{\frac{0.3}{56}}$

$k=10^{\frac{0.3}{56}}-1\approx 0.012$

The rate of population increase is approximately 1.2%.

Chapter 11 Cumulative Review

1. $|x|\le 3$

$-3\le x\le 3$

$[-3,\ 3]$

3. $x=5$ is a vertical line. The slope of a vertical line is undefined.

5.
$$\begin{array}{r|rrrr} 3 & 2 & -1 & -13 & 1 \\ & & 6 & 15 & 6 \\ \hline & 2 & 5 & 2 & 7 \end{array}$$

The quotient is

$2x^2+5x+2+\frac{7}{x-3}$

7a. $\frac{24x^6y^5}{8x^7y}=\frac{3y^4}{x}$

b. $\frac{2x^2}{10x^3-2x^2}$

$\frac{2x^2}{2x^2(5x-1)}$

$\frac{1}{5x-1}$

9a. $\frac{\sqrt{27}}{\sqrt{5}} = \frac{\sqrt{9}\sqrt{3}}{\sqrt{5}} = \frac{3\sqrt{3}}{\sqrt{5}}$

$\frac{3\sqrt{3}}{\sqrt{5}} \bullet \frac{\sqrt{5}}{\sqrt{5}} = \frac{3\sqrt{15}}{5}$

b. $\frac{2\sqrt{16}}{\sqrt{9x}} = \frac{2(4)}{\sqrt{9}\sqrt{x}} = \frac{8}{3\sqrt{x}}$

$\frac{8}{3\sqrt{x}} \bullet \frac{\sqrt{x}}{\sqrt{x}} = \frac{8\sqrt{x}}{3x}$

c. $\sqrt[3]{\frac{1}{2}} = \frac{\sqrt[3]{1}}{\sqrt[3]{2}} = \frac{1}{\sqrt[3]{2}} \bullet \frac{\sqrt[3]{4}}{\sqrt[3]{4}} = \frac{\sqrt[3]{4}}{\sqrt[3]{8}} = \frac{\sqrt[3]{4}}{2}$

11. $m^2 - 7m - 1 = 0$

$m^2 - 7m = 1$

$m^2 - 7m + \frac{49}{4} = 1 + \frac{49}{4}$

$\left(m - \frac{7}{2}\right)^2 = \frac{4}{4} + \frac{49}{4}$

$\left(m - \frac{7}{2}\right)^2 = \frac{53}{4}$

$m - \frac{7}{2} = \pm\sqrt{\frac{53}{4}}$

$m - \frac{7}{2} = \pm\frac{\sqrt{53}}{2}$

$m = \frac{7}{2} \pm \frac{\sqrt{53}}{2}$

$m = \frac{7 \pm \sqrt{53}}{2}$

$\left\{\frac{7 - \sqrt{53}}{2}, \frac{7 + \sqrt{53}}{2}\right\}$

13. $f(x) = -2x^2$

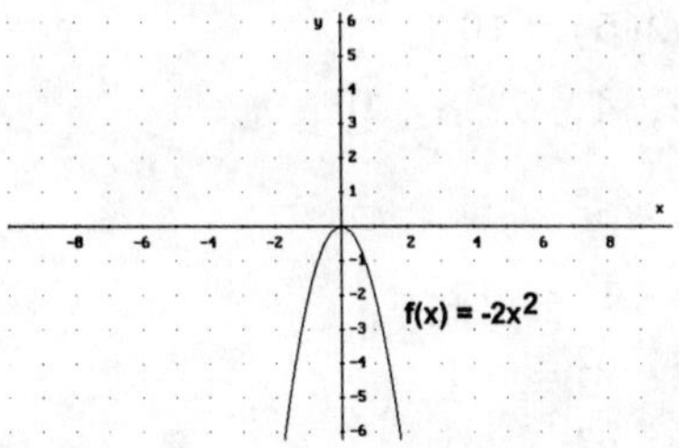

15. $\begin{cases} 3x - y + z = -15 \\ x + 2y - z = 1 \\ 2x + 3y - 2z = 0 \end{cases}$

Add first and second equations.
$4x + y = -14$

$2(3x - y + z) = -15(2)$
$6x - 2y + 2z = -30$

Add $2x + 3y - 2z = 0$.
$8x + y = -30$

$\begin{cases} 4x + y = -14 \\ 8x + y = -30 \end{cases}$

$-1(4x + y) = -14(-1)$
$-4x - y = 14$

Add $8x + y = -30$.
$4x = -16$
$x = -4$

Substitute.

$4(-4) + y = -14$
$-16 + y = -14$
$y = 2$

$-4 + 2(2) - z = 1$
$-4 + 4 - z = 1$
$-z = 1$
$z = -1$

$\{(-4, 2, -1)\}$

17. $\begin{cases} y = \sqrt{x} \\ x^2 + y^2 = 6 \end{cases}$

Substitute.

$x^2 + (\sqrt{x})^2 = 6$

$x^2 + x = 6$

$x^2 + x - 6 = 0$

$(x + 3)(x - 2) = 0$

$x + 3 = 0$ or $x - 2 = 0$

$x = -3$ or $x = 2$

$x = -3$: $y = \sqrt{-3} = i\sqrt{3}$

$i\sqrt{3}$ not real

$x = 2$: $y = \sqrt{2}$

$\{(2, \sqrt{2})\}$

19. $A = P\left(1 + \frac{r}{n}\right)^{nt}$

$A = 1600\left(1 + \frac{0.09}{12}\right)^{12(5)}$

$A = 1600(1+0.0075)^{60}$

$A = 1600(1.0075)^{60}$

$A = 1600(1.5657)$

$A = \$2505.09$

Exercise Set 12.1

1. $a_n = n+4$

   $a_1 = 1+5 = 5$

   $a_2 = 2+4 = 6$

   $a_3 = 3+4 = 7$

   $a_4 = 4+4 = 8$

   $a_5 = 5+4 = 9$

   or 5, 6, 7, 8, 9

3. $a_n = (-1)^n$

   $a_1 = (-1)^1 = -1$

   $a_2 = (-1)^2 = 1$

   $a_3 = (-1)^3 = -1$

   $a_4 = (-1)^4 = 1$

   $a_5 = (-1)^5 = -1$

   or $-1, 1, -1, 1, -1$

5. $a_n = \frac{1}{n+3}$

   $a_1 = \frac{1}{1+3} = \frac{1}{4}$

   $a_2 = \frac{1}{2+3} = \frac{1}{5}$

   $a_3 = \frac{1}{3+3} = \frac{1}{6}$

   $a_4 = \frac{1}{4+3} = \frac{1}{7}$

   $a_5 = \frac{1}{5+3} = \frac{1}{8}$

   or $\frac{1}{4}, \frac{1}{5}, \frac{1}{6}, \frac{1}{7}, \frac{1}{8}$

7. $a_n = 3n^2$

   $a_5 = 3(5)^2 = 3(25) = 75$

9. $a_n = 6n-2$

   $a_{20} = 6(20)-2 = 120-2 = 118$

11. $a_n = \frac{n+3}{n}$

    $a_{15} = \frac{15+3}{15} = \frac{18}{15} = \frac{6}{5}$

13. 3, 7, 11, 15 or

    $4(1)-1,\ 4(2)-1,\ 4(3)-1,\ 4(4)-1$

    In general, $a_n = 4n-1$

15. $-2, -4, -8, -16$ or

    $-2, -2^2, -2^3, -2^4$

    In general, $a_n = -2^n$

17. $\frac{1}{3}, \frac{1}{9}, \frac{1}{27}, \frac{1}{81}$ or

    $\frac{1}{3}, \frac{1}{3^2}, \frac{1}{3^3}, \frac{1}{3^4}$

    In general, $a_n = \frac{1}{3^n}$

19. $a_n = 32n-16$

    $a_2 = 32(2)-16 = 64-16 = 48$ ft.

    $a_3 = 32(3)-16 = 96-16 = 80$ ft.

    $a_4 = 32(4)-16 = 128-16 = 112$ ft.

21. 0.10, 0.20, 0.40 or

    $0.10,\ 0.10(2),\ 0.10(2^2)$

    In general, $a_n = 0.10(2^{n-1})$

    $a_{14} = 0.10(2^{13}) \approx \$819.20$

23. $a_n = 2n$

    $a_1 = 2(1) = 2$

    $a_2 = 2(2) = 4$

    $a_3 = 2(3) = 6$

    $a_4 = 2(4) = 8$

    $a_5 = 2(5) = 10$

    or 2, 4, 6, 8, 10

25. $a_n = -n^2$

    $a_1 = -1^2 = -1$

    $a_2 = -2^2 = -4$

    $a_3 = -3^2 = -9$

    $a_4 = -4^2 = -16$

    $a_5 = -5^2 = -25$

    or $-1, -4, -9, -16, -25$

27. $a_n = 2^n$

$a_1 = 2^1 = 2$

$a_2 = 2^2 = 4$

$a_3 = 2^3 = 8$

$a_4 = 2^4 = 16$

$a_5 = 2^5 = 32$

or 2, 4, 8, 16, 32

29. $a_n = 2n + 5$

$a_1 = 2(1) + 5 = 2 + 5 = 7$

$a_2 = 2(2) + 5 = 4 + 5 = 9$

$a_3 = 2(3) + 5 = 6 + 5 = 11$

$a_4 = 2(4) + 5 = 8 + 5 = 13$

$a_5 = 2(5) + 5 = 10 + 5 = 15$

or 7, 9, 11, 13, 15

31. $a_n = (-1)^n n^2$

$a_1 = (-1)^1(1^2) = -1(1) = -1$

$a_2 = (-1)^2(2^2) = 1(4) = 4$

$a_3 = (-1)^3(3^2) = -1(9) = -9$

$a_4 = (-1)^4(4^2) = 1(16) = 16$

$a_5 = (-1)^5(5^2) = -1(25) = -25$

or $-1, 4, -9, 16, -25$

33. $a_n = (-3)^n$

$a_6 = (-3)^6 = 729$

35. $a_n = \frac{n-2}{n+1}$

$a_6 = \frac{6-2}{6+1} = \frac{4}{7}$

37. $a_n = \frac{(-1)^n}{n}$

$a_8 = \frac{(-1)^8}{8} = \frac{1}{8}$

39. $a_n = -n^2 + 5$

$a_{10} = -10^2 + 5 = -100 + 5 = -95$

41. $a_n = \frac{(-1)^n}{n+6}$

$a_{19} = \frac{(-1)^{19}}{19+6} = -\frac{1}{25}$

43. $a_n = 75(2)^{n-1}$

$a_6 = 75(2)^5 = 75(32) = 2400$ cases

$a_1 = 75(2)^0 = 75(1) = 75$ cases

45. 800, 400, 200, 100, 50

The population estimate for 1998 is 50 sparrows. Continuing the sequence: 25, 12, 6, 3, 1, 0. We estimate the sparrows will be extinct in 2004.

47. $f(x) = (x-1)^2 + 3$

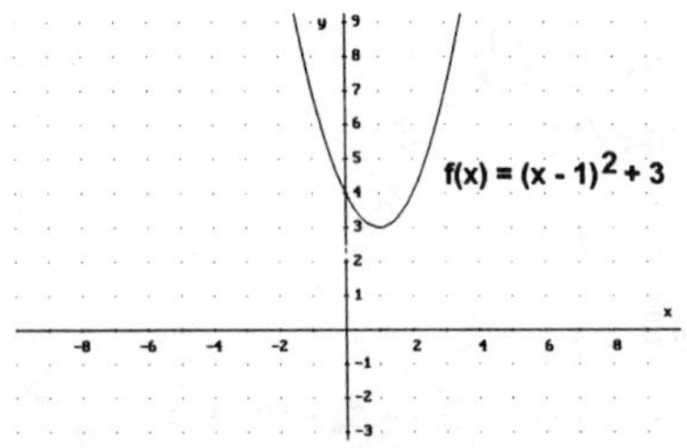

49. $f(x) = 2(x+4)^2 + 2$

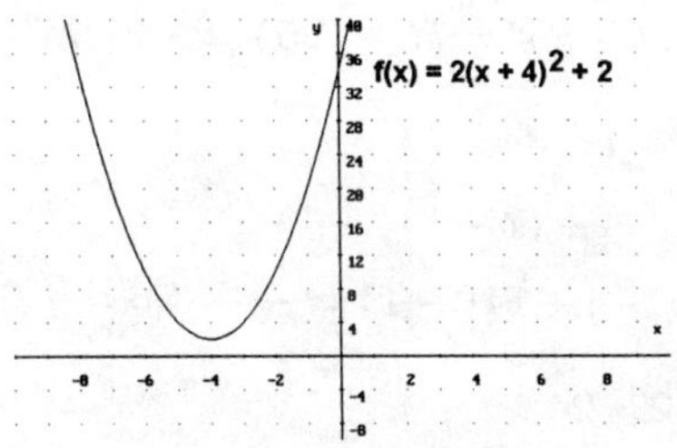

51. $d = \sqrt{[-7-(-4)]^2 + [-3-(-1)]^2}$

$d = \sqrt{(-7+4)^2 + (-3+1)^2}$

$d = \sqrt{(-3)^2 + (-2)^2}$

$d = \sqrt{9+4}$

$d = \sqrt{13}$

53. $d = \sqrt{(-3-2)^2 + [-3-(-7)]^2}$

$d = \sqrt{(-5)^2 + (-3+7)^2}$

$d = \sqrt{(-5)^2 + (4)^2}$
$d = \sqrt{25 + 16}$
$d = \sqrt{41}$

Exercise Set 12.2

1. $a_1 = 4;\ d = 2$
   4, 6, 8, 10, 12

3. $a_1 = 6,\ d = -2$
   6, 4, 2, 0, −2

5. $a_1 = 1,\ r = 3$
   1, 3, 9, 27, 81

7. $a_1 = 48,\ r = \frac{1}{2}$
   48, 24, 12, 6, 3

9. $a_1 = 12,\ d = 3$
   $a_n = 12 + (n-1)3$
   $a_8 = 12 + 7(3) = 12 + 21 = 33$

11. $a_1 = 7,\ r = -5$
   $a_n = a_1 r^{n-1}$
   $a_4 = 7(-5)^3 = 7(-125) = -875$

13. $a_1 = -4,\ d = -4$
   $a_n = -4 + (n-1)(-4)$
   $a_{15} = -4 + 14(-4) = -4 - 56 = -60$

15. 0, 12, 24
   $a_1 = 0$ and $d = 12$
   $a_n = 0 + (n-1)12$
   $a_9 = 8(12) = 96$

17. 20, 18, 16
   $a_1 = 20$ and $d = -2$
   $a_n = 20 + (n-1)(-2)$
   $a_{25} = 20 + 24(-2) = 20 - 48 = -28$

19. 2, −10, 50
   $a_1 = 2$ and $r = -5$
   $a_n = 2(-5)^{n-1}$
   $a_5 = 2(-5)^4 = 2(625) = 1250$

21. $a_4 = 19,\ a_{15} = 52$
   Use the relationship:
   $a_4 + 11d = a_{15}$
   $19 + 11d = 52$
   $11d = 33$
   $d = 3$
   Now use the relationship:
   $a_8 = a_4 + 4d$
   $a_8 = 19 + 4(3) = 19 + 12 = 31$

23. $a_2 = -1$ and $a_4 = 5$
   Use the relationship:
   $a_2 + 2d = a_4$
   $-1 + 2d = 5$
   $2d = 6$
   $d = 3$
   Now use the relationship:
   $a_9 = a_4 + 5d$
   $a_9 = 5 + 5(3)$
   $a_9 = 5 + 15 = 20$

25. $a_2 = \frac{-4}{3}$ and $a_3 = \frac{8}{3}$
   Use the relationship:
   $a_2 r = a_3$
   $-\frac{4}{3} r = \frac{8}{3}$
   $r = -2$
   Now use the relationship:
   $a_1 r = a^2$
   $a_1(-2) = \frac{-4}{3}$
   $a_1 = \frac{2}{3}$

27. 54, 58, 62
   $a_1 = 54$ and $d = 4$
   $a_n = 54 + (n-1)4$
   $a_{20} = 54 + 19(4) = 54 + 76 = 130$

There are 130 seats in the twentieth row.

29. $a_1 = 6$ and $r = 3$

$a_n = 6 \bullet 3^{n-1} = 2 \bullet 3 \bullet 3^{n-1} = 2 \bullet 3^n$

31. 2, 4, 6

$a_1 = 2$ and $d = 2$

33. 5, 10, 20

$a_1 = 5$ and $r = 2$

35. $\frac{1}{2}, \frac{1}{10}, \frac{1}{50}$

$a_1 = \frac{1}{2}$ and $r = \frac{1}{5}$

37. x, 5x, 25x

$a_1 = x$ and $r = 5$

39. p, p+4, p+8

$a_1 = p$ and $d = 4$

41. $a_1 = 14$ and $d = \frac{1}{4}$

$a_n = 14 + (n-1)\frac{1}{4}$

$a_{21} = 14 + 20\left(\frac{1}{4}\right) = 14 + 5 = 19$

43. $a_1 = 3$ and $r = -\frac{2}{3}$

$a_n = 3\left(-\frac{2}{3}\right)^{n-1}$

$a_4 = 3\left(-\frac{2}{3}\right)^3 = 3\left(\frac{-8}{27}\right) = -\frac{8}{9}$

45. $\frac{3}{2}, 2, \frac{5}{2}, \ldots$

$a_1 = \frac{3}{2}$ and $d = \frac{1}{2}$

$a_n = \frac{3}{2} + (n-1)\frac{1}{2}$

$a_{15} = \frac{3}{2} + 14\left(\frac{1}{2}\right) = \frac{17}{2}$

47. $24, 8, \frac{8}{3}, \ldots$

$a_1 = 24$ and $r = \frac{1}{3}$

$a_n = 24\left(\frac{1}{3}\right)^{n-1}$

$a_6 = 24\left(\frac{1}{3}\right)^5 = 24\left(\frac{1}{243}\right) = \frac{8}{81}$

49. $a_3 = 2$ and $a_{17} = -40$

Use the relationship:

$a_3 + 14d = a_{17}$

$2 + 14d = -40$

$14d = -42$

$d = -3$

Now use the relationship:

$a_{10} = a_3 + 7d$

$a_{10} = 2 + 7(-3) = 2 - 21 = -19$

51. 486, 162, 54, 18, 6

$a_1 = 486$ and $r = \frac{1}{3}$

$a_n = 486\left(\frac{1}{3}\right)^{n-1}$

Solve $486\left(\frac{1}{3}\right)^{n-1} = 1$

$\left(\frac{1}{3}\right)^{n-1} = \frac{1}{486}$

$\frac{1}{3^{n-1}} = \frac{1}{486}$

$3^{n-1} = 486$

$3^n = 1458$

$n = \log_3 1458$

$n = \frac{\ln 1458}{\ln 3} \approx 6.6$

The ball will rebound less than a foot on the 7th bounce.

53. $a_1 = 1000$ and $d = 125$

$a_n = 1000 + (n-1)125$

$a_{12} = 1000 + 11(125)$

$a_{12} = 1000 + 1375 = 2375$

His salary at the end of his training is $2375.

55. $a_1 = 400$ and $r = \frac{1}{2}$.

12 hrs = 4(3 hrs), so we seek the fourth term after a_1, namely a_5.

$a_n = a_1 r^{n-1}$

$a_5 = 400\left(\frac{1}{2}\right)^4 = \frac{400}{16} = 25$

25 grams of the radioactive material remains after 12 hours.

57. $\frac{1}{3(1)}+\frac{1}{3(2)}+\frac{1}{3(3)}$

$\frac{1}{3}\left(\frac{1}{1}+\frac{1}{2}+\frac{1}{3}\right)$

$\frac{1}{3}\left(\frac{6}{6}+\frac{3}{6}+\frac{2}{6}\right)$

$\frac{1}{3}\left(\frac{11}{6}\right)$

$\frac{11}{18}$

59. $3^0+3^1+3^2+3^3$

$1+3+9+27$

40

61. $\frac{8-1}{8+1}+\frac{8-2}{8+2}+\frac{8-3}{8+3}$

$\frac{7}{9}+\frac{6}{10}+\frac{5}{11}$

$\frac{770}{990}+\frac{594}{990}+\frac{450}{990}$

$\frac{1814}{990}=\frac{907}{495}$

Exercise Set 12.3

1. $\sum_{i=1}^{4}(i-3)$

$(1-3)+(2-3)+(3-3)+(4-3)$

$-2+(-1)+0+1=-2$

3. $\sum_{i=4}^{7}(2i+4)$

$[2(4)+4]+[2(5)+4]+[2(6)+4]+[2(7)+4]$

$12+14+16+18=60$

5. $\sum_{i=2}^{4}(i^2-3)$

$(2^2-3)+(3^2-3)+(4^2-3)$

$1+6+13=20$

7. $\sum_{i=1}^{3}\frac{1}{i+5}$

$\frac{1}{1+5}+\frac{1}{2+5}+\frac{1}{3+5}$

$\frac{1}{6}+\frac{1}{7}+\frac{1}{8}=\frac{28}{168}+\frac{24}{168}+\frac{21}{168}=\frac{73}{168}$

9. $1+3+5+7+9$

$[(2)-1]+[2(2)-1]+[2(3)-1]$
$+[2(4)-1]+[2(5)-1]$

$\sum_{i=1}^{5}(2i-1)$

11. $4+12+36+108$

$4+4(3)+4(3^2)+4(3^3)$

$\sum_{i=1}^{4}4\bullet 3^{i-1}$

13. $12+9+6+3+0+(-3)$

$[-3(1)+15]+[-3(2)+15]+[-3(3)+15]$
$+[-3(4)+15]+[-3(5)+15]+[-3(6)+15]$

$\sum_{i=1}^{6}(-3i+15)$

15. $a_n=-2n$

$\sum_{i=1}^{4}(-2i)$

$-2(1)+(-2)(2)+(-2)(3)+(-2)(4)$

$-2-4-6-8=-20$

17. $a_n=(n-1)^2$

$\sum_{i=1}^{5}(i-1)^2$

$(1-1)^2+(2-1)^2+(3-1)^2+(4-1)^2+(5-1)^2$

$0+1+4+9+16=30$

19. 1, 2, 3, ... , 10

$a_n=n$

$\sum_{i=1}^{10}=1+2+3+\ldots+10$

$\frac{10(11)}{2}=55$

A total of 55 trees were planted.

21. $a_1=6$ and $r=2$

$a_n=6\bullet 2^{n-1}$

$a_5=6\bullet 2^4=6\bullet 16=96$

There will be 96 fungus units at the beginning of the 5th day.

23. $\sum_{i=1}^{3} \frac{1}{6i} = \frac{1}{6(1)} + \frac{1}{6(2)} + \frac{1}{6(3)}$

$\frac{1}{6} + \frac{1}{12} + \frac{1}{18} = \frac{6+3+2}{36} = \frac{11}{36}$

25. $\sum_{i=2}^{6} 3i$

$3(2)+3(3)+3(4)+3(5)+3(6)$

$6+9+12+15+18=60$

27. $\sum_{i=3}^{5} i(i+2)$

$3(3+2)+4(4+2)+5(5+2)$

$15+24+35=74$

29. $\sum_{i=1}^{5} 2^i = 2^1+2^2+2^3+2^4+2^5$

$2+4+8+16+32=62$

31. $\sum_{i=1}^{4} \frac{4i}{i+3} = \frac{4(1)}{1+3} + \frac{4(2)}{2+3} + \frac{4(3)}{3+3} + \frac{4(4)}{4+3}$

$1+\frac{8}{5}+2+\frac{16}{7} = \frac{105}{35}+\frac{56}{35}+\frac{80}{35} = \frac{241}{35}$

33. $12+4+\frac{4}{3}+\frac{4}{9} = \frac{4}{3^{-1}}+\frac{4}{3^0}+\frac{4}{3^1}+\frac{4}{3^2}$

$\sum_{i=1}^{4} \frac{4}{3^{i-2}}$

35. $1+4+9+16+25+36+49$

$1^2+2^2+3^2+4^2+5^2+6^2+7^2$

$\sum_{i=1}^{7} i^2$

37. $a_n=(n+2)(n-5)$

$a_1=(1+2)(1-5)=3(-4)=-12$

$a_2=(2+2)(2-5)=4(-3)=-12$

$a_1+a_2=-12+(-12)=-24$

39. $a_n=(-1)^n$

$a_1=(-1)^1=-1$

$a_2=(-1)^2=1$

$a_3=(-1)^3=-1$

$a_4=(-1)^4=1$

$a_5=(-1)^5=-1$

$a_6=(-1)^6=1$

$\sum_{i=1}^{6} a_i = (-1)+1+(-1)+1+(-1)+1=0$

41. $a_n=(n+3)(n+1)$

$a_1=(1+3)(1+1)=4(2)=8$

$a_2=(2+3)(2+1)=5(3)=15$

$a_3=(3+3)(3+1)=6(4)=24$

$a_4=(4+3)(4+1)=7(5)=35$

$\sum_{i=1}^{4} a_i = 8+15+24+35=82$

43. $a_1=50$ and $r=2$

Since $48=4(12)$, we seek the fourth term after a_1, namely a_5.

$a_n=50(2)^{n-1}$

$a_5=50(2)^4=50(16)=800$

There are 800 bacteria after 48 hours.

45. $a_n=(n+1)(n+2)$

$a_4=(4+1)(4+2)=5(6)=30$ opossums

$a_1=(1+1)(1+2)=2(3)=6$

$a_2=(2+1)(2+2)=3(4)=12$

$a_3=(3+1)(3+2)=4(5)=20$

$\sum_{i=1}^{4} a_i = 6+12+20+30=68$ opossums

47. $a_n=100(0.5)^n$

$a_4=100(0.5)^4=6.25$ lbs. of decay.

$a_1=100(0.5)^1=50$

$a_2=100(0.5)^2=25$

$a_3=100(0.5)^3=12.5$

$\sum_{i=1}^{4} a_i = 50+25+12.5+6.25$

93.75 lbs. of decay.

49. $a_1 = 40$ and $r = \frac{4}{5}$

$a_5 = 40\left(\frac{4}{5}\right)^4 = 16.384$ or 16.4 in.

$a_2 = 40\left(\frac{4}{5}\right)^1 = 32$

$a_3 = 40\left(\frac{4}{5}\right)^2 = 25.6$

$a_4 = 40\left(\frac{4}{5}\right)^3 = 20.48$

$\sum_{i=1}^{5} a_i = 40 + 32 + 25.6 + 20.48 + 16.384$

134.464 or 134.5 in.

51. $\frac{-3}{1-\frac{1}{7}} = \frac{-3}{\frac{6}{7}} = -3 \bullet \frac{7}{6} = -\frac{21}{6} = -\frac{7}{2}$

53. $\frac{\frac{6}{11}}{1-\frac{1}{10}} = \frac{\frac{6}{11}}{\frac{9}{10}} = \frac{6}{11} \bullet \frac{10}{9} = \frac{60}{99} = \frac{20}{33}$

55. $\frac{2(1-5^3)}{1-5} = \frac{2(1-125)}{-4} = \frac{2(-124)}{-4}$

$\frac{-248}{-4} = 62$

57. $\frac{12}{2}(2+19) = 6(21) = 126$

Exercise Set 12.4

1. 1, 3, 5, 7, ...

$a_1 = 1,\ d = 2,\ n = 6$

$S_6 = \frac{6}{2}[2(1) + (6-1)2]$

$S_6 = 3[2 + 10] = 3(12) = 36$

3. 3, 6, 9, ...

$a_1 = 3,\ d = 3,\ n = 6$

$S_6 = \frac{6}{2}[2(3) + (6-1)(3)]$

$S_6 = 3[6 + 15] = 3(21) = 63$

5. 1, 2, 3, ... , 10

$a_1 = 1,\ d = 1,\ n = 10$

$S_{10} = \frac{10}{2}[2(1) + (10-1)(1)]$

$S_{10} = 5[2 + 9] = 5(11) = 55$

7. 1, 3, 5, 7

$a_1 = 1,\ d = 2,\ n = 4$

$S_4 = \frac{4}{2}[2(1) + (4-1)2]$

$S_4 = 2[2 + 6] = 2(8) = 16$

9. 4000, 3950, 3900, 3850, 3800

$a_1 = 4000,\ d = -50,\ n = 12$

$a_{12} = 4000 + 11(-50)$

$a_{12} = 4000 - 550$

$a_{12} = 3450$ cars sold in month 12.

$S_{12} = \frac{12}{2}[4000 + 3450]$

$S_{12} = 6(7450)$

$S_{12} = 44{,}700$ cars sold in the first 12 months.

11. Firm A:

$a_1 = 22{,}000,\ d = 1000,\ n = 10$

$S_{10} = \frac{10}{2}[2(22{,}000) + (10-1)1000]$

$S_{10} = 5[44{,}000 + 9000]$

$S_{10} = 5[53{,}000] = \$265{,}000$

Firm B:

$a_1 = 20{,}000,\ d = 1200,\ n = 10$

$S_{10} = \frac{10}{2}[2(20{,}000) + (10-1)1200]$

$S_{10} = 5[40{,}000 + 10{,}800]$

$S_{10} = 5[50{,}800] = \$254{,}000$

Thus, Firm A is making the more profitable offer.

13. 4, 12, 36, ...

$a_1 = 4,\ r = 3,\ n = 5$

$S_5 = \frac{4(1-3^5)}{1-3} = -2(1-243)$

$S_5 = -2(-242) = 484$

15. 2, $\frac{2}{5}$, $\frac{2}{25}$, ...

$a_1 = 2,\ r = \frac{1}{5},\ n = 4$

$S_4 = \frac{2\left[1-\left(\frac{1}{5}\right)^4\right]}{1-\frac{1}{5}} = \frac{5}{2}\left(1-\frac{1}{625}\right)$

$S_4 = \frac{5}{2}\left(\frac{624}{625}\right) = \frac{312}{125} = 2.496$

17. $a_1 = 30{,}000$, $r = 1.10$, $n = 4$

$a_4 = 30{,}000(1.10)^{4-1}$

$a_4 = \$39{,}930$ made during her fourth year of business.

$$S_4 = \frac{30{,}000(1 - 1.10^4)}{1 - 1.10}$$

$S_4 = \$139{,}230$ made during the first four years.

19. $a_1 = 30$, $r = 0.9$, $n = 5$

$a_5 = 30(0.9)^{5-1} = 19.683$ or

approximately 20 minutes to assemble the first computer.

$$S_5 = \frac{30(1 - 0.9^5)}{1 - 0.9} = 122.853$$

or approximately 123 minutes to assemble the first 5 computers.

21. 12, 6, 3, ...

$a_1 = 12$ and $r = \frac{1}{2}$

$$S_\infty = \frac{12}{1 - \frac{1}{2}} = \frac{12}{\frac{1}{2}} = 24$$

23. $\frac{1}{10}, \frac{1}{100}, \frac{1}{1000}, \ldots$

$a_1 = \frac{1}{10}$ and $r = \frac{1}{10}$

$$S_\infty = \frac{\frac{1}{10}}{1 - \frac{1}{10}} = \frac{\frac{1}{10}}{\frac{9}{10}} = \frac{1}{9}$$

25. $a_1 = 20$ and $r = \frac{4}{5}$

$$S_\infty = \frac{20}{1 - \frac{4}{5}} = \frac{20}{\frac{1}{5}} = 100$$

We double this number (to account for the flight up as well as down) and subtract 20 (since the first bounce was preceded by only a downward flight). Thus, the ball traveled a total distance of $2(100) - 20 = 180$ feet.

27. $-4, 1, 6, \ldots$

$a_1 = -4$, $d = 5$, and $n = 10$

$$S_{10} = \frac{10}{2}[2(-4) + (10 - 1)5]$$

$$S_{10} = 5[-8 + 45] = 5(37) = 185$$

29. $3, \frac{3}{2}, \frac{3}{4}, \ldots$

$a_1 = 3$, $r = \frac{1}{2}$, $n = 7$

$$S_7 = \frac{3\left[1 - \left(\frac{1}{2}\right)^7\right]}{1 - \frac{1}{2}} = 6\left(1 - \frac{1}{128}\right)$$

$$S_7 = 6\left(\frac{127}{128}\right) = \frac{381}{64}$$

31. $-12, 6, -3, \ldots$

$a_1 = -12$, $r = -\frac{1}{2}$, $n = 5$

$$S_5 = \frac{-12\left[1 - \left(-\frac{1}{2}\right)^5\right]}{1 - \left(-\frac{1}{2}\right)}$$

$$S_5 = -8\left(1 + \frac{1}{32}\right) = -8\left(\frac{33}{32}\right)$$

$S_5 = -\frac{33}{4}$ or -8.25

33. $\frac{1}{2}, \frac{1}{4}, 0, \ldots$

$a_1 = \frac{1}{2}$, $d = -\frac{1}{4}$, $n = 20$

$$S_{20} = \frac{20}{2}\left[2\left(\frac{1}{2}\right) + (20 - 1)\left(-\frac{1}{4}\right)\right]$$

$$S_{20} = 10\left(1 - \frac{19}{4}\right) = 10\left(\frac{-15}{4}\right) = -\frac{75}{2}$$

35. $a_1 = 8$, $r = -\frac{2}{3}$, $n = 3$

$$S_3 = \frac{8\left[1 - \left(-\frac{2}{3}\right)^3\right]}{1 - \left(-\frac{2}{3}\right)} = \frac{24}{5}\left(1 + \frac{8}{27}\right)$$

$$S_3 = \frac{24}{5}\left(\frac{35}{27}\right) = \frac{8}{1}\left(\frac{7}{9}\right) = \frac{56}{9}$$

37. $-10, -5, -\frac{5}{2}, \ldots$

$a_1 = -10$ and $r = \frac{1}{2}$

$$S_\infty = \frac{-10}{1 - \frac{1}{2}} = \frac{-10}{\frac{1}{2}} = -20$$

39. $2, -\frac{1}{4}, \frac{1}{32}, \ldots$

$a_1 = 2$ and $r = -\frac{1}{8}$

$$S_\infty = \frac{2}{1-\left(-\frac{1}{8}\right)} = \frac{2}{\frac{9}{8}} = \frac{16}{9}$$

41. $\frac{2}{3}, -\frac{1}{3}, \frac{1}{6}, \ldots$

$a_1 = \frac{2}{3}$ and $r = -\frac{1}{2}$

$$S_\infty = \frac{\frac{2}{3}}{1-\left(-\frac{1}{2}\right)} = \frac{\frac{2}{3}}{\frac{3}{2}} = \frac{4}{9}$$

43. Player A:

$a_1 = 1,\ d = 1,\ n = 9$

$S_9 = \frac{9}{2}[2(1) + (9-1)1]$

$S_9 = \frac{9}{2}[2+8] = \frac{9}{2}(10) = 45$ points

Player B:

$a_1 = 10,\ d = 1,$ and $n = 6$

$S_6 = \frac{6}{2}[2(10) + (6-1)1]$

$S_6 = 3[20+5] = 3(25) = 75$ points

45. $a_1 = 200,\ d = -5,\ n = 20$

$S_{20} = \frac{20}{2}[2(200) + (20-1)(-5)]$

$S_{20} = 10[400-95] = 10[305] = 3050$

Thus, \$3050 rent is paid for 20 days during the holiday rush.

47. $a_1 = 0.01,\ r = 2,\ n = 30$

$$S_{30} = \frac{0.01(1-2^{30})}{1-2} = 10{,}737{,}418.23$$

He would pay \$10,737,418.23 in room and board for the 30 days.

49. $0.88\overline{8} = 0.8 + 0.08 + 0.008 + \ldots$

$a_1 = 0.8$ and $r = 0.1$

$$S_\infty = \frac{0.8}{1-0.1} = \frac{0.8}{0.9} = \frac{8}{9}$$

51. $6 \bullet 5 \bullet 4 \bullet 3 \bullet 2 \bullet 1$

$(30)(12)(2) = 720$

53. $\frac{3 \bullet \cancel{2} \bullet \cancel{1}}{\cancel{2} \bullet \cancel{1}} = 3$

55. $(x+5)^2$

$x^2 + 2(5x) + 25$

$x^2 + 10x + 25$

57. $(2x-1)^3$

$(2x-1)(2x-1)^2$

$(2x-1)(4x^2-4x+1)$

$8x^3 - 8x^2 + 2x - 4x^2 + 4x - 1$

$8x^3 - 12x^2 + 6x - 1$

Exercise Set 12.5

1. $(m+n)^3$

$1 \bullet m^3 + 3 \bullet m^2n + 3 \bullet mn^2 + 1 \bullet n^3$

$m^3 + 3m^2n + 3mn^2 + n^3$

3. $(c+d)^5$

$1 \bullet c^5 + 5 \bullet c^4d + 10 \bullet c^3d^2 + 10 \bullet c^2d^3 + 5 \bullet cd^4 + 1 \bullet d^5$

$c^5 + 5c^4d + 10c^3d^2 + 10c^2d^3 + 5cd^4 + d^5$

5. $(y-x)^5 = [y + (-x)]^5$

$1y^5 + 5y^4(-x) + 10y^3(-x)^2 + 10y^2(-x)^3 + 5y(-x)^4 + (-x)^5$

$y^5 - 5y^4x + 10y^3x^2 - 10y^2x^3 + 5yx^4 - x^5$

7. $\frac{8!}{7!} = \frac{8 \bullet 7!}{7!} = 8$

9. $\frac{7!}{5!} = \frac{7 \bullet 6 \bullet 5!}{5!} = 7 \bullet 6 = 42$

11. $\frac{10!}{7!2!} = \frac{10 \bullet 9 \bullet 8 \bullet 7!}{7!2!} = \frac{10 \bullet 9 \bullet 8}{2 \bullet 1} = \frac{720}{2} = 360$

13. $\frac{8!}{6!0!} = \frac{8 \bullet 7 \bullet 6!}{6! \bullet 1} = 8 \bullet 7 = 56$

15. $(a+b)^7$

$a^7 + 7a^6b + \frac{7 \bullet 6}{2!}a^5b^2 + \frac{7 \bullet 6 \bullet 5}{3!}a^4b^3$

$+ \frac{7 \bullet 6 \bullet 5 \bullet 4}{4!}a^3b^4 + \frac{7 \bullet 6 \bullet 5 \bullet 4 \bullet 3}{5!}a^2b^5$

$+\frac{7\bullet 6\bullet 5\bullet 4\bullet 3\bullet 2}{6!}ab^6+b^7$

$a^7+7a^6b+21a^5b^2+35a^4b^3+35a^3b^4+21a^2b^5+7ab^6+b^7$

17. $(a+2b)^5$

$a^5+5a^4(2b)+\frac{5\bullet 4}{2!}a^3(2b)^2+\frac{5\bullet 4\bullet 3}{3!}a^2(2b)^3$

$+\frac{5\bullet 4\bullet 3\bullet 2}{4!}a(2b)^4+(2b)^5$

$a^5+10a^4b+40a^3b^2+80a^2b^3+80ab^4+32b^5$

19. $(2a-b)^5=[2a+(-b)]^5$

$(2a)^5+5(2a)^4(-b)+\frac{5\bullet 4}{2!}(2a)^3(-b)^2$

$+\frac{5\bullet 4\bullet 3}{3!}(2a)^2(-b)^3$

$+\frac{5\bullet 4\bullet 3\bullet 2}{4!}(2a)(-b)^4$

$+(-b)^5$

$32a^5-80a^4b+80a^3b^2-40a^2b^3+10ab^4-b^5$

21. $(c-2d)^6=[c+(-2d)]^6$

$c^6+6c^5(-2d)+\frac{6\bullet 5}{2!}c^4(-2d)^2$

$+\frac{6\bullet 5\bullet 4}{3!}c^3(-2d)^3+\frac{6\bullet 5\bullet 4\bullet 3}{4!}c^2(-2d)^4$

$+\frac{6\bullet 5\bullet 4\bullet 3\bullet 2}{5!}c(-2d)^5+(-2d)^6$

$c^6-12c^5d+60c^4d^2-160c^3d^3+240c^2d^4-192cd^5+64d^6$

23. 3rd term of $(x+y)^4$ corresponds to $r=2$.

$\frac{4!}{2!(4-2)!}x^{4-2}y^2=6x^2y^2$

25. 2nd term of $(a+3b)^{10}$ corresponds to $r=1$:

$\frac{10!}{1!(10-1)!}a^{10-1}(3b)^1=30a^9b$

27. $(q+r)^9$

$q^9+9q^8r+\frac{9\bullet 8}{2!}q^7r^2+\frac{9\bullet 8\bullet 7}{3!}q^6r^3$

$+\frac{9\bullet 8\bullet 7\bullet 6}{4!}q^5r^4+\frac{9\bullet 8\bullet 7\bullet 6\bullet 5}{5!}q^4r^5$

$+\frac{9\bullet 8\bullet 7\bullet 6\bullet 5\bullet 4}{6!}q^3r^6$

$+\frac{9\bullet 8\bullet 7\bullet 6\bullet 5\bullet 4\bullet 3}{7!}q^2r^7$

$+\frac{9\bullet 8\bullet 7\bullet 6\bullet 5\bullet 4\bullet 3\bullet 2}{8!}qr^8$

$+r^9$

$q^9+9q^8r+36q^7r^2+84q^6r^3+126q^5r^4$

$+126q^4r^5+84q^3r^6+36q^2r^7+9qr^8+r^9$

29. $(4a+b)^5$

$(4a)^5+5(4a)^4b+\frac{5\bullet 4}{2!}(4a)^3b^2+\frac{5\bullet 4\bullet 3}{3!}(4a)^2b^3$

$+\frac{5\bullet 4\bullet 3\bullet 2}{4!}(4a)b^4+b^5$

$1024a^5+1280a^4b+640a^3b^2+160a^2b^3+20ab^4+b^5$

31. $(5a-2b)^4$

$(5a)^4+4(5a)^3(-2b)+\frac{4\bullet 3}{2!}(5a)^2(-2b)^2$

$+\frac{4\bullet 3\bullet 2}{3!}(5a)(-2b)^3+(-2b)^4$

$625a^4-1000a^3b+600a^2b^2-160ab^3+16b^4$

33. $(2a+3b)^3$

$(2a)^3+3(2a)^2(3b)+\frac{3\bullet 2}{2!}(2a)(3b)^2+(3b)^3$

$8a^3+36a^2b+54ab^2+27b^3$

35. $(x+2)^5$

$x^5+5x^4(2)+\frac{5\bullet 4}{2!}x^3(2^2)+\frac{5\bullet 4\bullet 3}{3!}x^2(2^3)$

$+\frac{5\bullet 4\bullet 3\bullet 2}{4!}x(2^4)+2^5$

$x^5+10x^4+40x^3+80x^2+80x+32$

37. 5th term of $(c-d)^5$ corresponds to $r=4$:

$\frac{5!}{4!(5-4)!}c^{5-4}(-d)^4=5cd^4$

39. 8th term of $(2c+d)^7$ correspondes to $r=7$:

$\frac{7!}{7!(7-7)!}(2c)^{7-7}d^7=d^7$

41. 4th term of $(2r-s)^5$ corresponds to $r=3$:

$\frac{5!}{3!(5-3)!}(2r)^{5-3}(-s)^3=-40r^2s^3$

43. $f(x) = |x|$

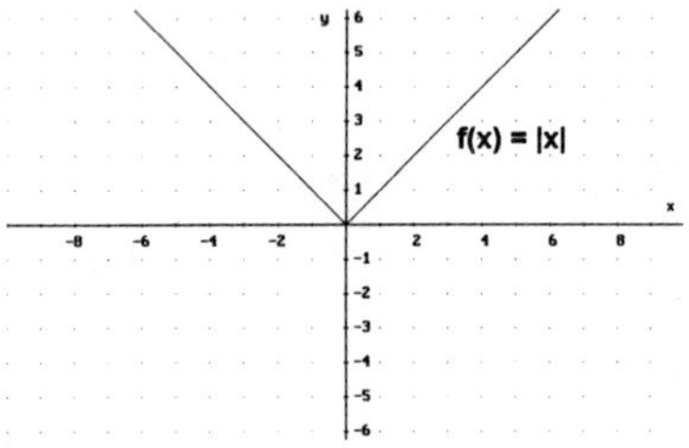

Not one-to-one.

45. $H(x) = 2x + 3$

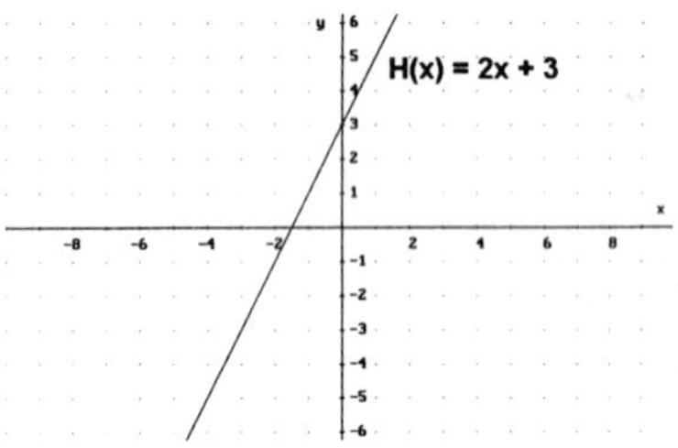

One-to-one

47. $f(x) = x^2 + 3$

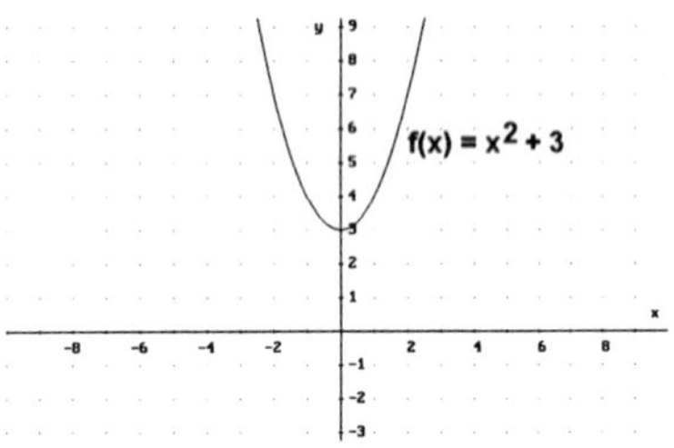

Not one-to-one

Chapter 12 Review

1. $a_n = -3n^2$

$a_1 = -3(1)^2 = -3$

$a_2 = -3(2)^2 = -12$

$a_3 = -3(3)^2 = -27$

$a_4 = -3(4)^2 = -48$

$a_5 = -3(5)^2 = -75$

or $-3, -12, -27, -48, -75$

3. $a_n = \dfrac{(-1)^n}{100}$

$a_{100} = \dfrac{(-1)^{100}}{100} = \dfrac{1}{100}$

5. $\dfrac{1}{6}, \dfrac{1}{12}, \dfrac{1}{18}, \ldots$

or $\dfrac{1}{6(1)}, \dfrac{1}{6(2)}, \dfrac{1}{6(3)}, \ldots$

In general, $a_n = \dfrac{1}{6n}$

7. $a_n = 32n - 16$

$a_5 = 32(5) - 16 = 160 - 16 = 144$ ft.

$a_6 = 32(6) - 16 = 192 - 16 = 176$ ft.

$a_7 = 32(7) - 16 = 224 - 16 = 208$ ft.

9. 450, 1350, 4050, 12150, 36450
We predict the number of infected people to be 36,450 in 1998.

11. $a_1 = -2$ and $r = \dfrac{2}{3}$

$-2, \dfrac{-4}{3}, \dfrac{-8}{9}, \dfrac{-16}{27}, \dfrac{-32}{81}$

13. $a_1 = -5,\ d = 4,\ n = 30$

$a_{30} = -5 + (30-1)4 = -5 + 116 = 111$

15. $12, 7, 2, \ldots$

$a_1 = 12,\ d = -5,\ n = 20$

$a_{20} = 12 + (20-1)(-5)$

$a_{20} = 12 - 95 = -83$

17. $a_4 = 18$ and $a_{20} = 98$

Use the relationship:

$a_4 + 16d = a_{20}$

$18 + 16d = 98$

$16d = 80$

$d = 5$

Now use the relationship:

$a_4 = a_1 + 3d$

$18 = a_1 + 3(5)$

$18 = a_1 + 15$

$a_1 = 3$

19. $\frac{3}{10}, \frac{3}{100}, \frac{3}{1000}, \ldots$

or $\frac{3}{10}, \frac{3}{10^2}, \frac{3}{10^3}, \ldots$

In general, $a_n = \frac{3}{10^n}$

21. $\frac{8}{3}, 4, 6, \ldots$

Geometric, since $\frac{4}{\frac{8}{3}} = \frac{6}{4} = \frac{3}{2}$

$a_1 = \frac{8}{3}$ and $r = \frac{3}{2}$

23. $7x, -14x, 28x$

Geometric, since

$\frac{-14x}{7x} = \frac{28x}{-14x} = -2$

$a_1 = 7x$ and $r = -2$

25. $a_1 = 8$ and $r = 0.75$

8, 6, 4.5, 3.4, 2.5, 1.9

Yes, a ball that rebounds to a height of 2.5 feet after the fifth bounce is good, since $2.5 \geq 1.9$.

27. $a_1 = 1$ and $r = 2$

$a_n = 1 \bullet 2^{n-1}$ or

$a_n = 2^{n-1}$

$a_{10} = 2^{10-1} = 2^9 = \$512$

$a_{30} = 2^{30-1} = 2^{29} = \$536,870,912$

29. $a_1 = 900$ and $d = 150$

$a_n = 900 + (n-1)150$

$a_6 = 900 + (6-1)150$

$a_6 = 900 + 750 = \$1650/\text{month}$

31. $\sum_{i=1}^{5} (2i-1)$

$[2(1)-1] + [2(2)-1] + [2(3)-1]$

$+ [2(4)-1] + [2(5)-1]$

$1 + 3 + 5 + 7 + 9 = 25$

33. $\sum_{i=2}^{4} \frac{(-1)^i}{2i} = \frac{(-1)^2}{2(2)} + \frac{(-1)^3}{2(3)} + \frac{(-1)^4}{2(4)}$

$\frac{1}{4} - \frac{1}{6} + \frac{1}{8} = \frac{6-4+3}{24} = \frac{5}{24}$

35. $a_n = (n-3)(n+2)$

$S_4 = (1-3)(1+2) + (2-3)(2+2)$
$+ (3-3)(3+2) + (4-3)(4+2)$

$S_4 = -6 - 4 + 0 + 6 = -4$

37. $a_n = -8 + (n-1)3$

$a_1 = -8 + (1-1)3 = -8 + 0 = -8$

$a_2 = -8 + (2-1)3 = -8 + 3 = -5$

$a_3 = -8 + (3-1)3 = -8 + 6 = -2$

$a_4 = -8 + (4-1)3 = -8 + 9 = 1$

$a_5 = -8 + (5-1)3 = -8 + 12 = 4$

$S_5 = -8 + (-5) + (-2) + 1 + 4 = -10$

39. $1 + 3 + 9 + 27 + 81 + 243$

$3^0 + 3^1 + 3^2 + 3^3 + 3^4 + 3^5$

$\sum_{i=1}^{6} 3^{i-1}$

41. $\frac{1}{4} + \frac{1}{16} + \frac{1}{64} + \frac{1}{256}$

$\frac{1}{4^1} + \frac{1}{4^2} + \frac{1}{4^3} + \frac{1}{4^4}$

$\sum_{i=1}^{4} \frac{1}{4^i}$

43. $a_1 = 20$ and $r = 2$

$a_n = 20(2)^n$ represents the number of yeast n 8-hour periods from the beginning.

$48 = n(8)$

$6 = n$

$a_6 = 20(2)^6 = 1280$

45. Job A:

$a_1 = 19,500, \; d = 1100, \; n = 5$

$a_5 = 19,500 + (5-1)1100$

$a_5 = 19,500 + 4400 = \$23,900$

Job B:

$a_1 = 21,000, \; d = 700, \; n = 5$

$a_5 = 21,000 + (5-1)700$

$a_5 = 21,000 + 2800 = \$23,800$

Thus, the Job A offer has a greater salary for the fifth year.

47. 15, 19, 23, ...

$a_1 = 15,\ d = 4,\ n = 6$

$S_6 = \frac{6}{2}[2(15) + (6-1)4]$

$S_6 = 3(30 + 20) = 3(50) = 150$

49. $a_1 = 1,\ d = 2,\ n = 30$

$S_{30} = \frac{30}{2}[2(1) + (30-1)2]$

$S_{30} = 15(2 + 58) = 15(60) = 900$

51. 8, 5, 2, ...

$a_1 = 8,\ d = -3,\ n = 20$

$S_{20} = \frac{20}{2}[2(8) + (20-1)(-3)]$

$S_{20} = 10[16 - 57] = 10(-41) = -410$

53. $a_1 = 6$ and $r = 5$

$S_4 = \frac{6(1-5^4)}{1-5} = \frac{-3}{2}(1-625)$

$S_4 = \frac{3}{2}(624) = 936$

55. $5, \frac{5}{2}, \frac{5}{4}, \ldots$

$a_1 = 5$ and $r = \frac{1}{2}$

$S_\infty = \frac{5}{1-\frac{1}{2}} = \frac{5}{\frac{1}{2}} = 10$

57. $-20, -4, -\frac{4}{5}, \ldots$

$a_1 = -20$ and $r = \frac{1}{5}$

$S_\infty = \frac{-20}{1-\frac{1}{5}} = \frac{-20}{\frac{4}{5}} = -25$

59. $a_1 = 20{,}000,\ r = 1.15,\ n = 4$

$a_4 = 20{,}000(1.15)^{4-1} = \$30{,}418$ earned in his fourth year.

$S_4 = \frac{20{,}000(1-1.15^4)}{1-1.15}$

$S_4 = \$99{,}868$ earned in his first four years.

61. $a_1 = 100,\ d = -7,\ n = 7$

$a_7 = 100 + (7-1)(-7)$

$a_7 = 100 - 42 = \$58$ rent paid for the seventh day.

$S_7 = \frac{7}{2}[2(100) + (7-1)(-7)]$

$S_7 = \frac{7}{2}[200 - 42] = \frac{7}{2}(158)$

$S_7 = \$553$ rent paid for the first seven days.

63. 1800, 600, 200, ...

$a_1 = 1800,\ r = \frac{1}{3},\ n = 6$

$S_6 = 1800\frac{\left[1-\left(\frac{1}{3}\right)^6\right]}{1-\frac{1}{3}} = 2700\left(1 - \frac{1}{729}\right)$

$S_6 = 2700\left(\frac{728}{729}\right) = \frac{72800}{27}$

$S_6 \approx 2696$ mosquitoes killed during the first six days after the spraying.

65. $0.55\overline{5} = 0.5 + 0.05 + 0.005 + \ldots$

$a_1 = 0.5$ and $r = 0.1$

$S_\infty = \frac{0.5}{1-0.1} = \frac{0.5}{0.9} = \frac{5}{9}$

Thus, $0.55\overline{5} = \frac{5}{9}$

67. $(x+z)^5$

$1 \bullet x^5 + 5 \bullet x^4z + 10 \bullet x^3z^2 + 10 \bullet x^2z^3 + 5 \bullet xz^4 + 1 \bullet z^5$

$x^5 + 5x^4z + 10x^3z^2 + 10x^2z^3 + 5xz^4 + z^5$

69. $(2x+y)^4$

$1 \bullet (2x)^4 + 4 \bullet (2x)^3y + 6 \bullet (2x)^2y^2 + 4 \bullet (2x)y^3 + 1 \bullet y^4$

$16x^4 + 32x^3y + 24x^2y^2 + 8xy^3 + y^4$

71. $(b+c)^8$

$b^8 + 8b^7c + \frac{8 \bullet 7}{2!}b^6c^2 + \frac{8 \bullet 7 \bullet 6}{3!}b^5c^3$

$+ \frac{8 \bullet 7 \bullet 6 \bullet 5}{4!}b^4c^4 + \frac{8 \bullet 7 \bullet 6 \bullet 5 \bullet 4}{5!}b^3c^5$

$+ \frac{8 \bullet 7 \bullet 6 \bullet 5 \bullet 4 \bullet 3}{6!}b^2c^6$

$+ \frac{8 \bullet 7 \bullet 6 \bullet 5 \bullet 4 \bullet 3 \bullet 2}{7!}bc^7 + c^8$

$b^8 + 8b^7c + 28b^6c^2 + 56b^5c^3 + 70b^4c^4$
$+ 56b^3c^5 + 28b^2c^6 + 8bc^7 + c^8$

73. $(4m-n)^4=[4m+(-n)]^4$

$(4m)^4+4(4m)^3(-n)+\frac{4\bullet 3}{2!}(4m)^2(-n)^2+\frac{4\bullet 3\bullet 2}{3!}(4m)(-n)^3+(-n)^4$

$256m^4-256m^3n+96m^2n^2-16mn^3+n^4$

75. 4th term of $(a+b)^7$ corresponds to $r=3$.

$\frac{7!}{3!(7-3)!}a^{7-3}b^3=35a^4b^3$

Chapter 12 Test

1. $a_n=\frac{(-1)^n}{n+4}$

$a_1=\frac{(-1)^1}{1+4}=\frac{-1}{5}$

$a_2=\frac{(-1)^2}{2+4}=\frac{1}{6}$

$a_3=\frac{(-1)^3}{3+4}=\frac{-1}{7}$

$a_4=\frac{(-1)^4}{4+4}=\frac{1}{8}$

$a_5=\frac{(-1)^5}{5+4}=\frac{-1}{9}$

or $\frac{-1}{5}, \frac{1}{6}, \frac{-1}{7}, \frac{1}{8}, \frac{-1}{9}$

2. $a_n=\frac{3}{(-1)^n}$

$a_1=\frac{3}{(-1)^1}=-3$

$a_2=\frac{3}{(-1)^2}=3$

$a_3=\frac{3}{(-1)^3}=-3$

$a_4=\frac{3}{(-1)^4}=3$

$a_5=\frac{3}{(-1)^5}=-3$

or $-3, 3, -3, 3, -3$

3. $a_n=10+3(n-1)$

$a_{80}=10+3(80-1)=10+237=247$

4. $a_n=(n+1)(n-1)(-1)^n$

$a_{200}=(200+1)(200-1)(-1)^{200}$

$a_{200}=200^2-1^2=40000-1=39{,}999$

5. $\frac{2}{5}, \frac{2}{25}, \frac{2}{125}, \ldots$

or $\frac{2}{5}, \frac{2}{5^2}, \frac{2}{5^3}, \ldots$

In general, $a_n=\frac{2}{5^n}$

or $\frac{2}{5}\left(\frac{1}{5}\right)^{n-1}$

6. $-9, 18, -27, 36, \ldots$

or $(-1)^1 9\bullet 1, (-1)^2 9\bullet 2, (-1)^3 9\bullet 3, (-1)^4 9\bullet 4, \ldots$

In general, $a_n=(-1)^n 9n$

7. $a_n=5(2)^{n-1}$

Geometric sequence with $a_1=5$ and $r=2$.

$S_5=\frac{5(1-2^5)}{1-2}=-5(1-32)$

$S_5=5(31)=155$

8. $a_n=18+(n-1)(-2)$

Arithmetic sequence with $a_1=18$ and $d=-2$

$S_{30}=\frac{30}{2}[2(18)+(30-1)(-2)]$

$S_{30}=15[36-58]=15(-22)=-330$

9. $a_1=24$ and $r=\frac{1}{6}$

$S_\infty=\frac{24}{1-\frac{1}{6}}=\frac{24}{\frac{5}{6}}=\frac{144}{5}$

10. $\frac{3}{2}, \frac{-3}{4}, \frac{3}{8}, \ldots$

$a_1=\frac{3}{2}$ and $r=\frac{-1}{2}$

$S_\infty=\frac{\frac{3}{2}}{1-\left(\frac{-1}{2}\right)}=\frac{\frac{3}{2}}{\frac{3}{2}}=1$

11. $\sum_{i=1}^{4} i(i-2)$

$1(1-2)+2(2-2)+3(3-2)+4(4-2)$

$-1+0+3+8=10$

12. $\sum_{i=2}^{4} 5(2)^{i}(-1)^{i-1}$

$5(2)^2(-1)^{2-1}+5(2)^3(-1)^{3-1}+5(2)^4(-1)^{4-1}$

$-20+40-80=-60$

13. $(a-b)^6=[a+(-b)]^6$

$1\bullet a^6+6\bullet a^5(-b)+15\bullet a^4(-b)^2+20\bullet a^3(-b)^3$

$+15\bullet a^2(-b)^4+6\bullet a(-b)^5+1\bullet(-b)^6$

$a^6-6a^5b+15a^4b^2-20a^3b^3+15a^2b^4-6ab^5+b^6$

14. $(2x+y)^5$

$1\bullet(2x)^5+5\bullet(2x)^4y+10\bullet(2x)^3y^2$

$+10\bullet(2x)^2y^3+5\bullet(2x)y^4+y^5$

$32x^5+80x^4y+80x^3y^2+40x^2y^3+10xy^4+y^5$

15. $(y+z)^8$

$y^8+8y^7z+\frac{8\bullet 7}{2!}y^6z^2+\frac{8\bullet 7\bullet 6}{3!}y^5z^3$

$+\frac{8\bullet 7\bullet 6\bullet 5}{4!}y^4z^4+\frac{8\bullet 7\bullet 6\bullet 5\bullet 4}{5!}y^3z^5$

$+\frac{8\bullet 7\bullet 6\bullet 5\bullet 4\bullet 3}{6!}y^2z^6$

$+\frac{8\bullet 7\bullet 6\bullet 5\bullet 4\bullet 3\bullet 2}{7!}yz^7$

$+z^8$

$y^8+8y^7z+28y^6z^2+56y^5z^3+70y^4z^4+56y^3z^5$

$+28y^2z^6+8yz^7+z^8$

16. $(2p+r)^7$

$(2p)^7+7(2p)^6r+\frac{7\bullet 6}{2!}(2p)^5r^2+\frac{7\bullet 6\bullet 5}{3!}(2p)^4r^3$

$+\frac{7\bullet 6\bullet 5\bullet 4}{4!}(2p)^3r^4$

$+\frac{7\bullet 6\bullet 5\bullet 4\bullet 3}{5!}(2p)^2r^5$

$+\frac{7\bullet 6\bullet 5\bullet 4\bullet 3\bullet 2}{6!}(2p)r^6$

$+r^7$

$128p^7+448p^6r+672p^5r^2+560p^4r^3$

$+280p^3r^4+84p^2r^5+14pr^6+r^7$

17. $a_n=250+75(n-1)$

$a_{10}=250+75(10-1)$

$a_{10}=250+675=925$ people in the town at the beginning of the tenth year.

$a_1=250+75(1-1)$

$a_1=250$ people in the town at the beginning of the first year.

18. 1, 3, 5, ...

$a_1=1,\ d=2,\ n=8$

$a_8=1+(8-1)2=1+14=15$

We want $1+3+5+\ldots+15$

$S_8=\frac{8}{2}(1+15)=4(16)=64$

shrubs planted in the 8 rows.

19. $a_1=80,\ r=\frac{3}{4},\ n=4$

$a_4=80\left(\frac{3}{4}\right)^{4-1}=80\left(\frac{27}{64}\right)=\frac{135}{4}$

or 33.75 cm. on the 4th swing.

$S_4=\frac{80\left[1-\left(\frac{3}{4}\right)^4\right]}{1-\frac{3}{4}}=320\left(1-\frac{81}{256}\right)$

$S_4=320\left(\frac{175}{256}\right)=\frac{875}{4}=218.75$ cm.

on the first 4 swings.

20. $a_1=80$ and $r=\frac{3}{4}$

$S_\infty=\frac{80}{1-\frac{3}{4}}=\frac{80}{\frac{1}{4}}=320$ cm.

before the pendulum comes to rest.

21. 16, 48, 80, ...

$a_1=16,\ d=32,\ n=10$

$a_{10}=16+(10-1)32$

$a_{10}=16+288=304$ feet fallen during the 10th second.

$S_{10}=\frac{10}{2}(16+304)=5(320)$

$S_{10}=1600$ ft. fallen during the first 10 seconds.

22. $0.42\overline{42}=0.42+0.0042+0.000042+\ldots$

$a_1=0.42$ and $r=0.01$

$S_\infty=\frac{0.42}{1-0.01}=\frac{0.42}{0.99}=\frac{42}{99}=\frac{14}{33}$

Thus, $0.42\overline{42}=\frac{14}{33}$

Chapter 12 Cumulative Review

1. $2(x+3) > 2x+1$

$2x+6 > 2x+1$

$6 > 1$

True statement. The solution set for the inequality is all real numbers.

$\{x|x \text{ is a real number}\}$

3a. $2x(5x-4)$

$10x^2-8x$

b. $-3x^2(4x^2-6x+1)$

$-12x^4+18x^3-3x^2$

c. $-xy(7x^2y+3xy-11)$

$-7x^3y^2-3x^2y^2+11xy$

5. Let $x=$ 1st leg.
$x+2=$ 2nd leg.
$x+4=$ hypotenuse.

$x^2+(x+2)^2=(x+4)^2$

$x^2+x^2+4x+4=x^2+8x+16$

$2x^2+4x+4=x^2+8x+16$

$x^2-4x-12=0$

$(x-6)(x+2)=0$

$x-6=0$ or $x+2=0$

$x=6$ or $x=-2$

Disregard $x=-2$, because length must be positive.

$x=6,\ x+2=8,\ x+4=10$

The sides are 6, 8, and 10 units.

7a. $\frac{\sqrt{45}}{4}-\frac{\sqrt{5}}{3}$

$\frac{\sqrt{9}\sqrt{5}}{4}-\frac{\sqrt{5}}{3}$

$\frac{3\sqrt{5}}{4}-\frac{\sqrt{5}}{3}$

$\frac{3}{3}\bullet\frac{3\sqrt{5}}{4}-\frac{4}{4}\bullet\frac{\sqrt{5}}{3}$

$\frac{9\sqrt{5}}{12}-\frac{4\sqrt{5}}{12}$

$\frac{5\sqrt{5}}{12}$

b. $\sqrt[3]{\frac{7x}{8}}+2\sqrt[3]{7x}$

$\frac{\sqrt[3]{7x}}{\sqrt[3]{8}}+2\sqrt[3]{7x}$

$\frac{\sqrt[3]{7x}}{2}+\frac{2}{2}\bullet 2\sqrt[3]{7x}$

$\frac{\sqrt[3]{7x}}{2}+\frac{4\sqrt[3]{7x}}{2}$

$\frac{5\sqrt[3]{7x}}{2}$

9. $p^4-3p^2-4=0$

$(p^2-4)(p^2+1)=0$

$p^2-4=0$ or $p^2+1=0$

$p^2=4$ or $p^2=-1$

$p=\pm\sqrt{4}$ or $p=\pm\sqrt{-1}$

$p=\pm 2$ or $p=\pm i$

$\{2, -2, i, -i\}$

11. $(x+1)^2+y^2=8$

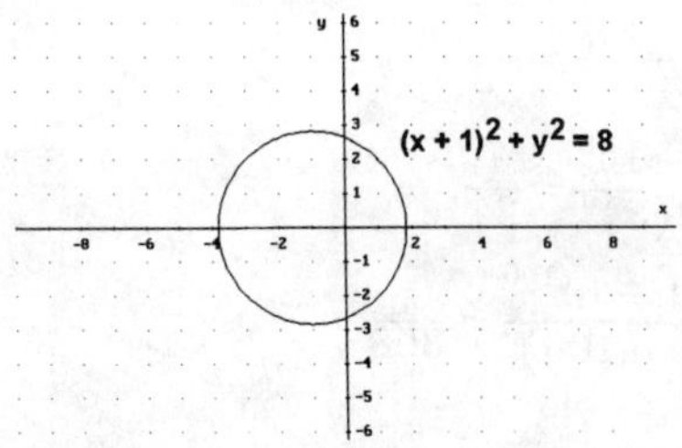

13a. $2^x=16$

$2^x=2^4$

$x=4$

$\{4\}$

b. $9^x=27$

$(3^2)^x=3^3$

$3^{2x}=3^3$

$2x=3$

$x = \frac{3}{2}$

$\left\{\frac{3}{2}\right\}$

c. $4^{x+3} = 8^x$

$(2^2)^{x+3} = (2^3)^x$

$2^{2x+6} = 2^{3x}$

$2x + 6 = 3x$

$6 = x$

$\{6\}$

15. $\log(x+2) - \log x = 2$

$\log\left(\frac{x+2}{x}\right) = 2$

$\frac{x+2}{x} = 10^2$

$\frac{x+2}{x} = 100$

$x + 2 = 100x$

$2 = 99x$

$\frac{2}{99} = x$

$\left\{\frac{2}{99}\right\}$

17. $a_n = \frac{(-1)^n}{3n}$

a. $a_1 = \frac{(-1)^1}{3(1)} = \frac{-1}{3}$

b. $a_8 = \frac{(-1)^8}{3(8)} = \frac{1}{24}$

c. $a_{100} = \frac{(-1)^{100}}{3(100)} = \frac{1}{300}$

d. $a_{15} = \frac{(-1)^{15}}{3(15)} = \frac{-1}{45}$

19a. $\sum_{i=0}^{6} \frac{i-2}{2} = \frac{1}{2}\sum_{i=0}^{6}(i-2)$

$\frac{1}{2}[-2 + (-1) + 0 + 1 + 2 + 3 + 4]$

$\frac{1}{2}(7) = \frac{7}{2}$

b. $\sum_{i=3}^{5} 2^i = 2^3 + 2^4 + 2^5 = 8 + 16 + 32 = 56$

21. $(x + 2y)^5$

$1x^5 + 5(x)^4(2y) + 10(x)^3(2y)^2 + 10(x)^2(2y)^3 + 5(x)(2y)^4 + (2y)^5$

$x^5 + 10x^4y + 40x^3y^2 + 80x^2y^3 + 80xy^4 + 32y^5$

Appendix A Exercise Set

1.
$$\begin{array}{r} 9.076 \\ +8.004 \\ \hline 17.080 \end{array}$$

3.
$$\begin{array}{r} 27.006 \\ -14.2 \\ \hline 12.806 \end{array}$$

5.
$$\begin{array}{r} 107.92 \\ +\quad 3.04 \\ \hline 110.96 \end{array}$$

7. $10 - 7.6$
$$\begin{array}{r} 10.0 \\ -\ 7.6 \\ \hline 2.4 \end{array}$$

9.
$$\begin{array}{r} 126.32 \\ -\ 97.89 \\ \hline 28.43 \end{array}$$

11.
$$\begin{array}{r} 3.25 \\ \times\quad 70 \\ \hline 000 \\ 2275 \\ \hline 227.50 \end{array}$$

13. $8.1 \div 3$
$$\begin{array}{r} 2.7 \\ 3\,\overline{)\,8.1} \\ \underline{6} \\ 21 \\ \underline{21} \\ 0 \end{array}$$

2.7

15. $55.405-6.1711$

$$\begin{array}{r} 55.4050 \\ -\ \ 6.1711 \\ \hline 49.2339 \end{array}$$

17. $60\div 0.75$

$$0.75.\overline{)60.00.0} \quad \text{quotient } 80.$$
$$\begin{array}{r} 60\ 0 \\ \hline 0 \end{array}$$

80

19. $7.612\div 100$

$$100\overline{)7.61200} \quad \text{quotient } 0.07612$$
$$\begin{array}{r} 7\ 00 \\ \hline 612 \\ 600 \\ \hline 120 \\ 100 \\ \hline 200 \\ 200 \\ \hline 0 \end{array}$$

0.07612

21. $12.312\div 2.7$

$$2.7.\overline{)12.3.12} \quad \text{quotient } 4.56$$
$$\begin{array}{r} 10\ 8 \\ \hline 1\ 5\ 1 \\ 1\ 3\ 5 \\ \hline 1\ 62 \\ 1\ 62 \\ \hline 0 \end{array}$$

4.56

23.
$$\begin{array}{r} 569.2 \\ 71.25 \\ +8.01 \\ \hline 648.46 \end{array}$$

25. $768-0.17$

$$\begin{array}{r} 768.00 \\ -\ \ \ 0.17 \\ \hline 767.83 \end{array}$$

27. $12+0.062$

$$\begin{array}{r} 12.000 \\ +\ 0.062 \\ \hline 12.062 \end{array}$$

29. $76-14.52$

$$\begin{array}{r} 76.00 \\ -14.52 \\ \hline 61.48 \end{array}$$

31. $3.311\div 0.43$

$$0.43.\overline{)3.31.1} \quad \text{quotient } 7.7$$
$$\begin{array}{r} 3\ 01 \\ \hline 30\ 1 \\ 30\ 1 \\ \hline 0 \end{array}$$

7.7

33.
$$\begin{array}{r} 762.12 \\ 89.7 \\ +\ 11.55 \\ \hline 863.37 \end{array}$$

35. $23.4-0.821$

$$\begin{array}{r} 23.400 \\ -\ 0.821 \\ \hline 22.579 \end{array}$$

37. $476.12-112.97$

$$\begin{array}{r} 476.12 \\ -112.97 \\ \hline 363.15 \end{array}$$

39. $0.007+7$

$$\begin{array}{r} 0.007 \\ +7.000 \\ \hline 7.007 \end{array}$$

Appendix B Exercise Set

1. Complement of 19°

   $90^\circ - 19^\circ$
   71°

3. Complement of 70.8°

   $90^\circ - 70.8^\circ$

   19.2°

5. Complement of $11\frac{1}{4}^\circ$

   $90^\circ - 11\frac{1}{4}^\circ$
   $78\frac{3}{4}^\circ$

7. Supplement of 150°

   $180^\circ - 150^\circ$

   30°

9. Supplement of 30.2°

   $180^\circ - 30.2^\circ$

   149.8°

11. Supplement of $79\frac{1}{2}^\circ$

    $180 - 79\frac{1}{2}^\circ$
    $100\frac{1}{2}^\circ$

13. $\angle 1 = 110^\circ$

    $\angle 2 = 180^\circ - 110^\circ = 70^\circ$

    $\angle 3 = 180^\circ - 110^\circ = 70^\circ$

    $\angle 4 = 70^\circ$

    $\angle 5 = 110^\circ$

    $\angle 6 = 70^\circ$

    $\angle 7 = 110^\circ$

15. $180^\circ - (11^\circ + 79^\circ)$

    $180^\circ - (90^\circ)$

    90°

17. $180^\circ - (25^\circ + 65^\circ)$

    $180^\circ - (90^\circ)$

    90°

19. $180^\circ - (30^\circ + 60^\circ)$

    $180^\circ - (90^\circ)$

    90°

21. $180^\circ - (45^\circ + 90^\circ)$

    $180^\circ - (135^\circ)$

    45°

    45°, 45°, 90°

23. $180^\circ - (17^\circ + 90^\circ)$

    $180^\circ - (107^\circ)$

    73°

    17°, 73°, 90°

25. $180^\circ - \left(39\frac{3}{4}^\circ + 90^\circ\right)$

    $180^\circ - \left(129\frac{3}{4}^\circ\right)$

    $50\frac{1}{4}^\circ$

    $39\frac{3}{4}^\circ$, $50\frac{1}{4}^\circ$, 90°

27. $\frac{x}{18} = \frac{4}{12}$

    $12 \bullet x = 18 \bullet 4$

    $12x = 72$

    $x = \frac{72}{12} = 6$

29. $\frac{x}{3} = \frac{9}{6}$

    $6 \bullet x = 3 \bullet 9$

    $6x = 27$

    $x = \frac{27}{6} = 4.5$

31. $a^2 + b^2 = c^2$

    $6^2 + 8^2 = c^2$

    $36 + 64 = c^2$

    $100 = c^2$

    $10 = c$

33. $a^2 + b^2 = c^2$

$5^2 + b^2 = 13^2$

$25 + b^2 = 169$

$b^2 = 169 - 25$

$b^2 = 144$

$b = 12$